Introduction to University Physics

Prototype model of Telstar, the Bell System's communication earth satellite. The dark squares on the surface are solar batteries that convert sunlight into electrical energy used to power the electronics contained in Telstar. The bands running around waist of the satellite are receiving and transmitting antennas. (By courtesy of Bell Telephone Laboratories.)

Introduction to UNIVERSITY

PHYSICS

Joseph Morgan

{TEXAS CHRISTIAN UNIVERSITY}

Volume One

BOSTON / *Allyn and Bacon, Inc.* / *1963*

To my wife and daughters

Preface

THIS TEXTBOOK IS INTENDED for an introductory course in college- or university-level physics for students of science and engineering. Its aim is to introduce, develop, discuss, and illustrate, with carefully chosen examples, the physical principles, incorporating the necessary mathematical formulations and disciplines essential to an understanding and eventual mastery of basic classical and present-day physical concepts.

The presentation is such as to make the book suitable for use by students who have a knowledge of algebra and the elements of trigonometry or by students who are concurrently taking or have had an introductory course in calculus. For either student there is continuity of treatment. This is accomplished by presenting throughout the text, where feasible and where it is significant and pedagogically advantageous, a noncalculus development on the left side of double-column pages and the parallel calculus development on the corresponding right side of the pages. This permits the student equipped with only algebra and trigonometry to study the material with no break in continuity, and affords the calculus student the benefit of both treatments. The author has even used this treatment successfully in classes in which some students had had no more than algebra and trigonometry while others were either concurrently taking or had had the calculus. Although the calculus invariably reflects a more direct and concise mathematical approach and obtains a result relatively quickly and often in a less cumbersome way, it frequently obscures or does not emphasize, for the beginning student, the physics involved. Some students can more easily comprehend a development physically while others can best see it mathematically. The parallel developments complement one another and the noncalculus treatment often not only tends to clarify the calculus treatment but also tends to keep the student aware of the basic physical principles involved. The bidevelopment therefore affords the student the benefits of both views. This method of treatment has met with success in the author's book *Introduction to Geometrical and Physical Optics*, McGraw-Hill Book Company, and it is at the kind suggestion of users of the optics text that the present book also incorporates this treatment.

This book is intended to satisfy the needs of a one-year (two-semester) course of three or four lecture hours and one laboratory session per week. In the interest of producing a book of such size as to make it possible for a student to master the material, digressions to topics which can be learned from collateral reading and related course work have been kept to a minimum without sacrificing coverage of the significant principles. Those departments which prefer to spend three semesters covering the material of general physics may do so by making appropriate divisions of the subject matter, covering the more significant sections in greater detail and augmenting some of the topics.

The aim throughout the text is to develop the classical and modern physical principles, emphasize the methods of analysis so characteristic of the fields of physics and applied and developmental engineering, and concentrate on stimulating and exercising individual thinking and reasoning. Experience has dictated that such disciplines may be most effectively accomplished by introducing adequate explanations and descriptions of laws and principles, supplementing this with carefully chosen illustrative worked examples, and then following this with carefully graded problems. With but few exceptions, where it was felt either unnecessary or more effective to introduce a deviation, the chapters terminate with a group of solved examples devised to illustrate the principles covered. Numerous problems are included at the end of each chapter. These are carefully devised and graded from the simpler variety, that enables the student to make an immediate and successful application of a principle, to the more difficult type, that requires a greater degree of analysis, insight, and mathematical skill. Included are numerical problems, exercises intended to augment the textual discussions, problems involving reasoning necessary to a derivation that parallels one given in the text or requires an alternative method of derivation, and problems requiring a solution in general symbolic form.

The symbols employed conform, for the most part, to those recommended by the agencies advocating uniformity, and the author has utilized the recommendations of the International Union of Pure and Applied Physics, the American Institute of Physics Committee on Physics in Engineering Education, and the Committee on Letter Symbols and Abbreviations of the American Standards Association. Although three absolute and three gravitational systems of units are explained and their interrelationships are described in the chapters on mechanics, only the following systems of units are primarily employed: the cgs and mks absolute and the English gravitational systems, in mechanics, and the rationalized mks units in the subjects of electricity and magnetism. In accordance with what the author has experienced as most effective and least confusing, deviations from some of the recommendations of symbols and abbreviations have been adopted. For example, we have found it most clarifying to employ the following units and abbreviations: pound mass (pm), pound force (pf), gram mass (gm), gram force (gf), kilogram mass (kgm), kilogram force (kgf).

The coverage of the material is divided into three parts: Part I treats of mechanics, heat, and wave motion and sound; Part II covers electricity, magnetism, and geometrical and physical optics; Part III takes up the elements of atomic and nuclear physics. Again, experience has revealed that this traditional order and treatment is the most effective in establishing a firm foundation for the interpretation of contemporary physical and engineering developments, and the integration of the generalized physical laws and principles may be successfully accomplished by the instructor who possesses the knowledge and experience to emphasize that the different phases of physics are not essentially compartmentalized sections but unified by generalizations. As an aid in the accomplishment of this unification there is incorporated and interwoven throughout the text integrating statements and concepts, and several chapters have been lengthened to preserve a unified, uninterrupted treatment of related classical and modern phenomena and concepts. Answers to the odd-numbered problems are given at the back of the text; the numerical examples and answers are worked out generally to three significant figures.

The author wishes to make the following grateful acknowledgments: to his colleagues Dr. H. M. Moseley and Dr. Leo L. Baggerly for various enlightening discussions; to his wife, Edith L. Morgan, for her constant encouragement and valuable advice throughout the entire writing of the manuscript; to his former colleague Dr. Newton Gaines for helpful suggestions in the early phases of the writing; to his student Sam Levine for preparing line drawings from manuscript originals, and to Mrs. Lois François and again to his wife for typing and preparing the manuscript and for aid in reading and checking.

Fort Worth, Texas   *Joseph Morgan*

Contents

Part One MECHANICS, HEAT,
WAVE MOTION AND SOUND

CONTENTS

The Greek Alphabet

Since many of the letters of the Greek Alphabet are employed as symbols to represent physical and geometrical quantities, there are given below the letters of the Greek alphabet with their names.

Alpha	A	α
Beta	B	β
Gamma	Γ	γ
Delta	Δ	δ or ∂
Epsilon	E	ϵ
Zeta	Z	ζ
Eta	H	η
Theta	Θ	θ
Iota	I	ι
Kappa	K	κ
Lambda	Λ	λ
Mu	M	μ
Nu	N	ν
Xi	Ξ	ξ
Omicron	O	o
Pi	Π	π
Rho	P	ρ
Sigma	Σ	σ
Tau	T	τ
Upsilon	Υ	υ
Phi	Φ	ϕ or φ
Chi	X	χ
Psi	Ψ	ψ
Omega	Ω	ω

Part One MECHANICS, HEAT, WAVE MOTION AND SOUND

Introduction

*I*T IS PERHAPS APPROPRIATE to start this book with the questions, What is physics? and With what does it deal? Various sources treating this subject will tell you that physics, whose name comes from the Greek word meaning nature, is an objective science and deals with bodies and events in nature, that it is a science of measurement, that it is the science of matter and energy, that it is the science in which the scientific method is exemplified to the highest degree, and that it is *the* most exact science. As you study the subject you will see that physics is all of the above and deals with the fields of mechanics, heat, sound, electricity, magnetism, and optics. Today we generally add another subdivision, atomic and nuclear physics. We shall devote a portion of this text to each of these fields in the order given above, starting with the fundamental subject of mechanics whose laws and principles are basic to all the other branches of physics.

In this chapter we shall consider some facts and concepts that apply to all the fields of physics, and then we shall pass on to the developments of the different subdivisions. The student should realize, however, from the start, that the various branches of physics have become unified; our choice of studying them separately not only is sound pedagogically but affords a type of presentation that has been most successful in the past. As we take up the developments in each portion the student will most certainly become aware of the significant veins that point to the interrelations and principles of unification.

1.1. The Scientific Method. The most effective way of acquiring knowledge in a science is by applying the principles of the scientific method. Although one learns best about the scientific method from experience its essential features may be revealed by the following outline of procedure.

(1) The scientist first must recognize that *there is a problem to be solved*—that is, one whose solution has not already been established, for otherwise an intelligent search of the proper literature would reveal the answers. If the field or area of study is new, in the sense that the investigator is pioneering, such as in the discovery of a new phenomenon, then the recognition of the presence of a problem is invariably easy. On the other hand, if the scientist

is working in some area of a well-established field, the recognition of a problem whose solution is unknown generally entails a rather thorough knowledge of what is known in the field. Of course, it is invaluable practice and helps to form a background of experience to apply the steps that follow to problems that previously have been solved, and that is what forms part of the training of the science student. The student will meet many such repeated applications during his studies not only in the field of physics, where the techniques of the scientific method have originated, but also in other fields of science.

(2) The next step is *accurate observation under controlled conditions.* This means taking precise measurements of the quantities which the experimenter arranges to vary in such a way that he knows at all times what change in conditions is responsible for an observed variation. To effect such a study may or may not involve the construction of elaborate apparatus, but the essential fact is the arrangement whereby the experiment is *controlled.* For instance, suppose we want to find out how the pressure of a confined gas changes when the volume is changed. The gas may be placed in a cylinder which is fitted with a gastight movable piston and is equipped with a pressure-measuring device. The gas may then be compressed to a series of known volumes by moving the piston inward, and the corresponding pressures exerted by the gas may be observed. However, such a procedure would not exemplify a controlled variation since the act of compressing the gas raises its temperature and we should not know what part of each observed pressure change is due to the temperature variation. To resolve the ambiguity the investigator would arrange after each new compression to cool the gas to the starting temperature before observing the pressure and volume values. In other words, by controlling the temperature so that it remains constant, we are certain that any observed change in pressure is due to the corresponding change in volume. The pressure, volume, and temperature of a gas are quantities that are interrelated, and the behavior of one of these when another is varied is best observed under the controlled condition of keeping the third quantity constant. All observations and measurements must be carefully recorded.

(3) The next step is the *analysis* of the data. This may involve studying data in the form of graphs, and usually entails a mathematical treatment. As a matter of fact, the more exact the science the more it is possible to analyze the observational data mathematically. Physics, being the most exact of the sciences, deals with phenomena that generally lend themselves to mathematical treatment. In this way it is possible to discover quantitative relationships between the measured quantities, and the extent to which this can be done depends on the particular problem at hand and, for the most part, on the analytical skill of the scientist. In any case, one goes as far as he can, reaching conclusions and generalizations which are always based on the experimentally observed facts. It takes scientific maturity, mastery of the subject matter, and a great amount of practice in the analysis of data to acquire those attributes that make it possible to exercise sound analytical

thinking, but these can all be acquired with sufficient study and perseverance and a thorough scientific development of one's subject matter.

(4) The fourth step is the formulation of a tentative explanation or description of the phenomenon or problem under investigation. When this is done we have what is called an *hypothesis*, whose formulation is based directly on the results and conclusions arrived at as a consequence of the analysis. Sometimes the analysis does not yield sufficient information to point directly to the hypothesis, or the information obtained from analysis points to two or more possible hypotheses. In the latter case all hypotheses must eventually be tested to see which best accords with the observed facts. Even when the analysis does not yield information that points to an hypothesis the investigator can sometimes call on his logical *intuition* or *feeling* about the problem and thus formulate an hypothesis that may prove to be fertile. The scientist who has given much thought to a problem and has worked up to this point is in a preferred position to make intelligent explanatory formulations.

(5) The fifth step in the scientific method is again *experimentation*, aimed at testing the hypotheses. The investigator now devises other controlled experiments designed to test what the hypothesis or the different hypotheses imply. Again observation, analysis, and mathematical treatment follow, until one of the hypotheses or a modified form of one appears the most favorable. The hypothesis which emerges as being best able to describe all the experimental facts is again tested in further experiments that will provide more substantiating evidence. Eventually the hypothesis, enriched with numerous tests in which it has been successful, becomes a *theory* that describes all of the known experimental facts qualitatively and quantitatively.

(6) The final step is the eventual formulation of a *law* or *principle*. This comes about in the following way. A worthwhile theory generally predicts certain as yet unobserved phenomena or qualitative and quantitative relationships. The extent to which such predictions are borne out by new experimentation indicates the merit of the theory. When these predictions are verified by experiment the theory becomes very strongly supported. Sometimes the new experiment fails to verify a prediction; this does not necessarily overthrow the theory but may cause the theory to be modified or amended in some fashion. When the final theory has been thoroughly tested not by one scientist but by other investigators working independently it may be universally adopted as the explanation of the phenomenon or problem. It then becomes a *law* or a *principle* which invariably is expressed mathematically in the form of an equation.

The student will notice that the three significant aspects of the scientific method are *experimentation*, *analysis*, and *mathematical formulation*, and it is generally agreed that a field of knowledge may be considered in the class of a science to the extent that its phenomena lend themselves to applications of these three techniques. We have already pointed out that almost all phenomena in the field of physics are subject to experimentation, analysis, and mathematical formulation. We urge the student to keep these aspects constantly in mind and attempt to visualize their application every time he meets with an hypothesis, a theory, a law, or a principle.

Some research investigations published in journals today go no further than step 2, most of them include step 3, a small number include step 4, and a relatively few ever get on to steps 5 and 6.

1.2. Definitions: Scientific Vocabulary. Physics makes use of many commonplace words but employs them with meanings which are often quite different from those of their everyday use. Many words, such as *work*, *power*, *intensity*, *temperature*, *weight*, and *velocity* carry a special connotation in a technical sense. In addition, physics employs many coined words which have specific and concrete scientific meaning. To build up a specialized scientific vocabulary it is therefore necessary to define carefully and painstakingly each term, and this we shall do as each word requiring such definition is introduced. It is well to point out here that the student must discipline himself to learn these definitions and thus obtain clear scientific concepts. Before long a scientific vocabulary will have been acquired and by its means it will be possible to give descriptions of natural phenomena in a most simple, clear, and thorough manner.

In the previous section we have used the terms "pressure" and "temperature" with no accompanying definitions since they were not needed for an understanding of the illustration we chose to employ. The strict definitions of these terms are given in the portions of the text dealing with these quantities. Concise definitions of the words "law," "principle," and "theory" are left as an exercise in the problems at the end of this chapter.

1.3. Measurement and Units. We have seen how experimental observation or measurement continually provides the data essential to analysis and mathematical treatment. We have already indicated that physics is the science of measurement and is principally concerned with the measurement of quantities. Lord Kelvin (1824–1907), an eminent English physicist, indicated the significance of quantitative measurement when he said, "When you can measure what you are talking about, and express it in numbers, you know what you are talking about; but when you cannot measure it, when you cannot express it in numbers, your knowledge is of a meagre and unsatisfactory kind; it may be the beginning of knowledge, but you have scarcely, in your thoughts, advanced to the stage of a Science."

To measure a physical quantity it is first necessary to choose a *unit* of that quantity; measuring the quantity then means comparing it with the unit or, stated another way, finding the ratio of the magnitude of the quantity to that of the unit. There are numerous physical quantities in mechanics but it proves to be true that if only three of these are chosen as fundamental then all other quantities may be expressed in terms of them, or as we say, derived from the fundamental quantities. The choice of these fundamental quantities is arbitrary and the three generally chosen in physics are *length, mass,* and *time,* while those selected in the field of engineering are *length, force,* and *time.* (Those quantities will be adequately studied and defined later.) It is now only necessary to choose a unit for each of the three fundamental quantities, for then the unit of any other quantity is obtained by combining the units of the fundamental quantities. For instance, we shall see that the ratio of the unit of length to the unit of time yields the unit of speed, and the product of the unit of force by the unit of length yields the unit of work, etc. Units that are formed by such combinations of fundamental units are called *derived units.*

A complete set of fundamental and derived units that is used to represent all quantities is called a *system* of units. Generally, the set of units is chosen so that many significant equations of physics are simplified. Any system of units is named in terms of the three fundamental units upon which it is based. Several different systems of units have been devised and we shall give a more thorough review of these in a later section. Here we wish to indicate the three systems of units that are in common use and which we shall employ in this book. These systems are:

(*1*) The system which is based upon the centimeter as the unit of length, the gram as the unit of mass, and the second as the unit of time. This is the metric cgs (centimeter-gram-second) system. As we shall see, this system employs decimals to express fractions and multiples of mass and of length. It is therefore very convenient and is the system that is used principally in scientific work everywhere. It suffers from the disadvantage that many of its derived units are inconveniently small.

(*2*) The system which is based upon the meter as the unit of length, the kilogram as the unit of mass, and the second as the unit of time. This is the metric mks (meter-kilogram-second) system. It, too, employs decimals for length and mass. The derived units here are of convenient size and especially useful in electricity. This system is used principally in scientific work and in electrical engineering.

(*3*) The system which is based upon the foot as the unit of length, the pound as the unit of force, and the second as the unit of time. This is called the English gravitational system and does not possess the decimal nature of the metric system. It is well adapted to most of the fields of engineering.

The fundamental units of physics are generally associated with arbitrarily selected standards of measurement. However, a multiple or submultiple of a fundamental unit may be of a more convenient size to employ as a unit. We take up the various standards and preliminary concepts of length, mass, and time in the next section. These concepts are elaborated upon in Chapter 4.

1.4. Standards. We shall here define the established standards of length, mass, and time.

Standards of Length. The original metric standard of length is the international *standard meter* which is a bar of platinum whose cross section is shown in Figure 1.1. The prototype meter is kept at the International Bureau of Weights and Measures at Sèvres, France. The meter is defined as the distance between two fine transverse lines engraved near the ends of the bar when it is at the temperature of melting ice. The meter was originally intended to be one ten-millionth of the distance between the earth's equator and the North Pole, measured along the meridian of Paris. Since the original surveys were somewhat inaccurate this relationship is not quite satisfied. Two accurate replicas of the prototype meter are kept in the National Bureau of Standards in Washington. These secondary standards are made of an alloy composed of 90 per cent platinum and 10 per cent iridium.

Figure 1.1.
Cross section of metric standard of length, the meter.

We have already indicated that the *meter* is the fundamental unit of length in the mks system, and the *centimeter*, which is one one-hundredth of the meter, is the fundamental unit of length in the cgs system. Other multiples and submultiples of the meter (m) are indicated by using the appropriate prefix as revealed in the following itemization (the letters appearing in the parentheses are the corresponding abbreviations):

dekameter (dkm)	= 10 m	centimeter (cm)	= 0.01 m
hectometer (hm)	= 100 m	millimeter (mm)	= 0.001 m
kilometer (km)	= 1000 m	micrometer	
megameter (Mm)	= 1,000,000 m	or micron (μ)	= 0.000001 m
decimeter (dm)	= 0.1 m	millimicron (mμ)	= 0.000000001 m

These prefixes for multiples and submultiples are also applied to other metric units. The prefixes deka, hecto, and deci are seldom used in scientific work.

In order to obtain a standard of length which not only is as permanent as can be expected but can be reproduced easily in any laboratory, Michelson (1852–1931) measured the length of the standard meter at 15 degrees centigrade in terms of the wavelength of the red color of light emitted by the cadmium vapor which is made luminous in an electric discharge. He found that one meter equals 1,553,163.5 wavelengths, and this was the standard of length until 1960 when the orange-red line of the krypton-86 isotope was found to be a more suitable standard. The existing international standard of length is the experimentally determined value 1 m = 1,650,763.73 wavelengths of the orange-red radiation of krypton-86 (see Section 34.5).

The English *standard yard* is the distance at 62 degrees Fahrenheit between two fine lines engraved on two gold plugs in a bronze bar kept at the Exchequer's office in London. However, in the United States the yard is legally defined in terms of the meter in order to avoid the necessity of maintaining more than one standard of length. By an act of Congress in 1866 the yard (yd) in the United States is defined exactly as 1 yard = 3600/3937 m. It is familiar that the yard is divided into 3 feet (ft) and each foot into 12 inches (in). The inch may further be divided into convenient parts. As we have seen, the *foot* is the fundamental unit of length in the English system. From our definition of the yard we have the simple approximate conversion factor

$$1 \text{ in} = 2.54 \text{ cm}$$

and this relationship enables one readily to pass over from the metric to the English length units or vice versa.

Standards of Mass. Before we concern ourselves with the standards of mass it is necessary to say a little about what is meant by mass. We shall not be able to say very much at this point, although there are rigorous definitions of mass, since we have not yet advanced sufficiently in our study of mechanics to give an adequate treatment. Nevertheless, we can present some of the fundamental concepts, and the meaning of the term will become clearer as we cover the principles of mechanics. This kind of treatment exemplifies the way one learns difficult and involved concepts in physics. He first meets, learns, and becomes thoroughly familiar with some aspects of a concept and then, along with repeated repetition distributed over some time, more aspects and illustrations are added until, by the time the student has met all the aspects, he has become thoroughly conversant with the concept.

One cannot get to first base, so to speak, in describing what is meant by the mass of a body without employing the word and concept of *inertia*. Inertia is a property that is possessed by all bodies and this means that bodies are inert mechanically. It takes a push or a pull or, more correctly, a force, as we shall later see, to set in motion a body which is initially at rest or to stop a body if it is initially in motion. In other words, a body offers resistance to any change in its state of motion. This property is measurable and the numerical measure of inertia is what we term the mass.

The metric standard of mass is the *standard kilogram* and the international prototype is a cylinder of platinum kept at the International Bureau of Weights and Measures at Sèvres, France. The United States possesses two accurate replicas made of platinum–iridium, forming our national secondary standard. As we have seen, the *kilogram mass* (kgm) is the fundamental unit of mass in the mks system, and the *gram mass* (gm), which is one one-thousandth as great as the standard kilogram, is the fundamental unit of mass in the cgs system. These units were originally chosen so as to make the gram equal to the mass of one cubic centimeter (1 cm³) of water at 4°C, the temperature at which water has its greatest density, but this equality is only approximately realized.

The English *standard pound* is the mass of a cylinder of platinum which is kept in the Standards Office, Westminster, London. To avoid maintaining more than one standard mass, the United States pound is defined in terms of the standard kilogram by the relation that the pound mass (pm) is equal to 0.4536 kilogram mass (kgm).

As defined above, the pound is a unit of mass in the English absolute system of units (see Section 1.6). We have already indicated that we shall employ the English gravitational system of units and, as we have seen, in this system there is no mass standard since the system is based on the three quantities length, force, and time. As will be explained later (Section 4.6), the unit of mass in the English gravitational system is a derived unit. The fundamental unit of force in the English gravitational system, as explained in Sections 1.6 and 4.6, is the *pound force* (pf), which is the force of the gravitational attraction that the earth exerts on the standard pound mass. This is also defined as the *weight* of the standard pound (see Section 4.6). Since the force with which an object is pulled vertically downward toward the earth varies somewhat over the earth's surface, the unit of force is stipulated to be equal to the weight of the standard pound at sea level and 45° latitude.

Standards of Time. To indicate the duration of an interval of time we may employ a periodic device such as a pendulum, an oscillating crystal of quartz, or the rotation of the earth on its axis. Both the metric and English systems use as the fundamental unit of time the *second* which is an arbitrarily chosen convenient fraction of the time it takes the earth on an average to make one complete revolution about its axis of rotation. If one observes the interval of time between successive transits of the sun across the earth's meridian at any place one obtains what is called the solar day. This is the time it takes the earth to make one complete revolution about its axis with respect to the sun. Since this solar day varies somewhat throughout the year we must use the more representative average of all solar days in a year and call it the *mean solar day*. This long interval of time is divided into 24 hours (hr), each hour being divided into 60 minutes (min) and each minute further subdivided into 60 seconds (sec). Multiplying these together yields 86,400 solar seconds in one mean solar day. The solar second is thus defined as 1/86,400 of the mean solar day. The solar second is the unit of time which is universally employed for physical or engineering work and for everyday purposes.

If one observes the interval of time between successive transits of a star across the earth's meridian, one obtains what is called a *sidereal day;* this represents the time required for the earth to rotate once about its axis according to astronomical measurements, and is about four minutes shorter than the mean solar day.

The earth's rotation about its axis is not an ideal standard of time measurement since the period of rotation is not constant. Observations indicate that the speed of rotation of the earth is decreasing at a very slow rate owing to various influences such as the action of tides, the effects of the motion of winds, and the slight changes in the shape of the earth occasioned by the shifting of earth masses, the occurrence of earthquakes, and the melting of polar ice caps. A clock that measures time as independent of the rotation of the earth is an atomic clock which makes use of the periodic vibration of a molecule as the basis of time measurement. In the "ammonia clock" the constant oscillations of the ammonia molecule (24×10^9 vibrations per second) synchronously control the oscillations of an electronic circuit which regulates the operation of a standard clock. Such frequency control can be maintained to about one part in ten billion or about one second in three hundred years, making the atomic clock an ideal time standard.

1.5. Manipulation of Units. The result of the measurement of a physical quantity consists of two parts, the numeric and the unit. To say that the length of a table measures 10 or 120 is certainly meaningless unless we express also the unit of measurement as 10 feet or 120 inches. Units are manipulated as ordinary algebraic factors and may therefore be multiplied or divided in a similar fashion. In carrying through a calculation involving physical quantities the student should discipline himself to include the units throughout. This not only makes it possible to see how and why the result comes out with a certain unit but it often reveals an omission made inadvertently or otherwise. We shall have frequent illustrations of such use of units. For the present, let us see how the units may be manipulated in carrying through a conversion computation. Suppose we wish to find how many kilometers are in one mile. We start with the identity expression

$$1 \text{ mi} = 1 \text{ mi}$$

We next want to convert the right-hand member of the equation to kilometers. Obviously, some elementary and easily remembered conversion factors will have to be employed. Since 5,280 feet equal 1 mile we have, by dividing both sides of this equality by 1 mile, 5,280 feet per one mile equals 1. Thus the conversion factor 5,280 feet/mile, as well as all other conversion factors, has the value unity and we may therefore multiply the right-hand member of the identity expression by this factor without altering its value. We may likewise use other conversion factors in the same way. Thus

$$1 \text{ mi} = 1 \text{ mi} \times \frac{5280 \text{ ft}}{1 \text{ mi}} \times \frac{12.0 \text{ in}}{1 \text{ ft}} \times \frac{2.54 \text{ cm}}{1 \text{ in}} \times \frac{1 \text{ m}}{100 \text{ cm}} \times \frac{1 \text{ km}}{1000 \text{ m}}$$

$$= \frac{5280 \times 12.0 \times 2.54}{100,000} \text{ km}$$

$$= 1.61 \text{ km}$$

As another example, we shall convert 1 ton mass (tm) to kilograms mass:

$$1 \text{ tm} = 1 \text{ tm} \times \frac{2.00 \times 10^3 \text{ pm}}{1 \text{ tm}} \times \frac{453.6 \text{ gm}}{1 \text{ pm}} \times \frac{1 \text{ kgm}}{1.00 \times 10^3 \text{ gm}}$$

$$= 907 \text{ kgm}$$

1.6.   Systems of Units.   There are six systems of units in mechanics. These are more or less generally employed and the student should have some knowledge of them.   Each system is consistent within itself and all are related to one another.

In three of these systems the fundamental quantities are length, mass, and time.   Since the mass of a body is independent of the place at which the measurement is made, a system of units based on these three fundamental quantities is called an *absolute* system.   The three absolute systems of units are as follows: the metric cgs system, in which the fundamental units are the centimeter, the gram mass, and the second; the metric mks system, in which the fundamental units are the meter, the kilogram mass, and the second; the English fps system, in which the fundamental units are the foot, the pound mass, and the second.

In the remaining three systems the fundamental quantities are length, force, and time.   Here the fundamental unit of force is generally defined in terms of the pull of the earth upon some standard mass.   Since the force unit is defined in terms of the gravitational pull at a specific place of observation, a system of units based on these three fundamental quantities is called a *gravitational* system.   The three gravitational systems are as follows: the metric gravitational system in which the fundamental units are the centimeter, the gram force (gf), and the second; the metric gravitational system in which the fundamental units are the meter, the kilogram force (kgf), and the second; the English gravitational system in which the fundamental units are the foot, the pound force (pf), and the second.   Definitions of the gram force, kilogram force, and pound force will be taken up in Chapter 4.

As we have pointed out in Section 1.3, in this text we shall employ principally the cgs absolute system, the mks absolute system, and the English gravitational system.   In this way we aim to avoid the confusion that invariably results when the same word is used to designate the unit of mass in one system and the unit of force in another system.   Nevertheless, we shall occasionally illustrate the use of the English absolute system and the metric gravitational systems in the solution of a problem wherever it appears that there is much to be gained pedagogically.   For instance, we have found that a student has a more thorough understanding of the manner in which the units work out in the equation for Newton's Second Law (Section 4.4) if he can apply the law with equal facility in each of the systems of units.

1.7.   Variables, Constants, and Variation.   In physics we are generally interested in observing the way in which some quantity varies when some other quantity is changed.   We then wish to express this mathematically and we formulate an equation which expresses the law of the relationship between the quantities.   Many of the laws of nature are amenable to rather simple mathematical formulations and we shall here present some of the simple mathematical principles that we will need in our study of the different phases of physics.

A symbol which may take on different values or which represents any one of a given set of values is called a *variable*. This symbol may stand for any measurable physical quantity such as force, mass, length, temperature, etc. A special case of a variable is a *constant*, which is a symbol that takes on only one value. For example, the area of any circle is given by the formula $A = \pi r^2$ wherein the area A and the radius r are variables and π is a constant since it represents the same approximate value, 3.1416, for all circles.

If two variables x and y are so related that to each value of one variable x there corresponds one or more values of the other variable y, then the second variable y is called a *function* of the first variable x. To say that y is a function of x is to say that the value of y depends on the value of x. Here x is called the *independent variable* and y is called the *dependent variable*.

If two variables x and y are so related that their ratio y/x is constant, then we say that y is *directly proportional* to x or, simply, that y is *proportional* to x, or that y *varies directly* as x. We then represent these facts by the symbolism

$$y \propto x$$

and form the equation

$$y = kx$$

where k, the constant ratio, is known as the *constant of proportionality* or the *constant of variation*.

If the two variables are so related that their product xy is constant, then we say that y *varies inversely* as x or that y is *inversely proportional* to x. We then have

$$y \propto 1/x$$

or

$$xy = k$$

where k is again the proportionality constant.

Another type of variation that we shall encounter is when a variable z varies directly as the product of two variables x and y; then

$$z \propto xy$$

and

$$z = kxy \qquad k = \text{constant}$$

Here we say that z *varies jointly* as x *and* y. The final expression implies also that, if z is proportional to x when y is constant and z is proportional to y when x is constant, then z is proportional to xy when both x and y are variable (see Problem 1.9).

Combined variations are also common in physics. For instance, if z varies directly as x and inversely as y, then

$$z \propto x/y$$

and

$$z = kx/y \qquad k = \text{constant}$$

1.8. Significant Figures. In physics we are always concerned with measured quantities. Now, any kind of measurement entails some uncertainty which may be due to the limitations inherent in the measuring instrument or to the error that attends a personal observation. Therefore, in expressing the result of a measurement, we must not write more digits than are probably correct. The number of figures that are used in expressing a numerical result indicates the *accuracy* of the measurement.

Those figures which we know to be trustworthy are called *significant figures*. The recorded result of a measurement should contain only one doubtful digit. Thus, if a measured distance is expressed as 25.1 cm it means that the measurement is correct to the nearest tenth of a centimeter, and we have a three-significant-figure accuracy. On the other hand, a measurement correct to the nearest hundredth of a centimeter would be expressed as 25.10 cm, a result with four-significant-figure accuracy. The true value of the distance represented by the approximate number 25.1 lies between 25.05 and 25.15, whereas the approximate number 25.10 means that the true value lies between 25.095 and 25.105. The number 25.10 is a closer approximation than the number 25.1; in general, the greater the number of significant figures the more accurate the indication.

A recorded number should be stated in such a way as to indicate clearly the number of figures that are significant. Zeros that are employed to place the decimal point are never significant. Thus the number 0.0121 has three significant figures and the number 864000 indicates six significant figures. On the other hand, if the 4 in the latter number is the last significant digit then the result should be expressed with a power of 10 as a factor, such as 864×10^3 or 8.64×10^5. In this way only the significant figures are retained.

In a computation involving measured quantities the result obtained is in general no more accurate than the least accurate number used. For example, suppose we measured the sides of a rectangle and found them to be 10.2 feet and 15.6 feet. To compute the area we multiply the two dimensions and obtain 10.2 feet $\times$ 15.6 feet = 159.12 square feet. However, not all of these figures are significant. Recalling the meanings of the approximate numbers 10.2 and 15.6 we see that the area lies between $10.15 \times 15.55 = 157.8325$ square feet and $10.25 \times 15.65 = 160.4125$ square feet. Hence it is incorrect to claim that the area has the accuracy indicated by five or even four significant figures. We must therefore round off the value 159.12 square feet to 159 square feet which contains the same number of significant figures as in each of the measured values. If one of the dimensions were measured to a smaller number of significant figures than the other, the result would have been rounded off so that it contained the same number of significant figures as appeared in the measured quantity having the smallest accuracy. In general, this is the way the result is stated in multiplication and division. In addition or subtraction, the result is rounded off to the digit in the first column containing a doubtful significant figure. Thus, after a computation it is often necessary to drop figures that are not significant.

In rounding off a result, the last significant figure that is retained remains unaltered if the following digit is less than 5 and it is increased by 1 if the following digit is 6 or greater. If the first digit dropped is 5, then the last significant figure retained should be increased by 1 if it is an odd number and should be left unchanged if it is an even number. For instance, rounded off to three significant figures, 2.648 becomes 2.65, 2.644 becomes 2.64, 2.645 becomes 2.64, and 2.675 becomes 2.68.

Numbers which are known to have an unlimited number of significant figures should be rounded off properly before being employed in a computation. For example, for the number $\pi = 3.14159265\ldots$, entering into a product with a measured quantity having three significant figures, we should use 3.14 in the computation. On the other hand, if we are working with six-significant-figure accuracy we should use 3.14159 for the value of π.

The student should realize that the concept of significant figures is most useful. Much time can be saved in a computation if the operations are carried out only as far as the data justify. Furthermore, the student learns to cogitate over a measured quantity in a critical fashion and to record it in an intelligent manner.

In this text we shall usually employ three-significant-figure accuracy in our computations and problems.

Problems

1.1. Formulate concise definitions of the terms law, principle, and theory.

1.2. After studying and digesting the material covered in Section 1.1, lay the text aside and write a few paragraphs on your own conception of the scientific method. Include your own illustration of a controlled experiment.

1.3. Convert 50.5 inches to kilometers.

1.4. Convert 5.34×10^5 mm to miles.

1.5. Convert 1 year to seconds (use $365\frac{1}{4}$ days in a year).

1.6. Convert 100.0 kgm to tons mass.

1.7. Convert 1 inch to millimicrons.

1.8. Make a table of the different systems of units showing the fundamental units for each system.

1.9. Show that, if $z \propto x$ when y is held constant and $z \propto y$ when x is held constant, then $z \propto xy$ when both x and y vary.

1.10. On a sheet of graph paper plot the equation $y = kx$, assigning arbitrary values to x. Plot y as ordinate (vertical) and x as abscissa (horizontal). What is the significance of the constant k on the graph?

1.11.   On a sheet of graph paper plot the equation $xy = k$ where k is a constant.   Can you identify the curve?

1.12.   Express the following numbers to three significant figures, using a power of 10 where necessary: 0.003025, 483000, 299.6, 0.00001005, 57748.

1.13.   In the following pairs of measured numbers, find their sum, their difference, their product, and their quotient (divide the first number of the pair by the second), retaining the correct number of significant figures in the results: 20.34 and 0.0152, 0.01742 and 1.54, 3.4 and 0.2143.

1.14.   The measured dimensions of a rectangle are 120.1 cm and 35.4 cm. Find the perimeter and the area of the rectangle, retaining the correct number of significant figures in the results.

1.15.   The measured radius of a circular track is 25.46 feet.   Find the area enclosed by the track, retaining the correct number of significant figures in the result.

1.16.   Find the volume of a right circular cylinder whose measured radius is 3.26 cm and whose measured height is 12.4 cm.   Retain the correct number of significant figures in the result.

Scalars, Vectors, and Vector Manipulations

*I*N THE STUDY OF PHYSICS we shall always be concerned with physical quantities such as displacement, velocity, speed, acceleration, force, mass, weight, energy, torque, and many others. We shall see that each quantity is a member of one of two general classes of quantities: either it is categorized as a *scalar* or its nature is such that it must be classed as a *vector*. The student is familiar with the manner in which scalars are handled. In fact, we do our daily arithmetic in a scalar fashion: one dollar plus one dollar equals two dollars, or x apples plus y apples equals $(x + y)$ apples. On the other hand, vector quantities do not add simply algebraically but combine in accordance with generalized vector methods. In physics and engineering we frequently must deal with vectors and it is important to become conversant with the methods of handling them. In this chapter we take up the distinction between scalars and vectors and develop the common methods of dealing with vectors. We shall then be in a position to handle any quantities that are vectors.

2.1. Scalar and Vector Quantities. Let us consider what must be stated in giving a complete specification of some quantity. Every quantity requires a statement of at least two things: first, a numerical specification, or a magnitude, and, second, the appropriate unit. For one class of quantities the statement of a numeral and a unit are all that are necessary for a complete specification. For example, the quantity volume is completely specified when we say 25 cubic feet. On the other hand, for another class of quantities one must state, in addition, a direction in order to afford a complete specification. For example, the quantity force is completely specified when we say "10 pounds acting vertically upward." A quantity that involves, other than the statement of a unit, only the idea of magnitude is called a *scalar*, while a quantity that needs for its complete specification a direction as well as magnitude is called a *vector*. Quantities such as displacement, velocity, acceleration, force, weight, and torque are vectors: each involves the idea of direction. Quantities such as speed, mass, and energy are scalars; none of these has associated with it a direction. (In physics the English word "speed" simply represents the magnitude of the vector velocity and it is entirely correct to state that a speed is 100 miles per hour. The vector it represents may be 100 miles per hour northeastward, but it would be incomplete to say that the velocity was 100 miles per hour.)

We shall be introducing many new quantities throughout our study and the student should categorize each quantity as he meets it.

2.2.   Vector Representation.   A vector quantity is represented by a directed straight line segment equipped with an arrowhead as illustrated by F in Figure 2.1.   The length of the vector is scaled to be proportional to its

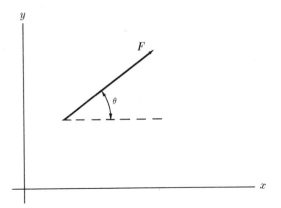

Figure 2.1.   *Vector representation.*

magnitude, and the direction is specified by giving the arrow the appropriate orientation.   We say the vector F here is directed so that it makes an angle $\theta°$ with the horizontal.   It is to be realized that if the arrow is started anywhere in the diagram and given the same length and direction it still represents the same vector F.

If we consider changing only the magnitude of the vector, say by a factor of 2, then the length of the arrow is doubled but its orientation remains the same; the vector is then represented by $2F$.   If we wish to reverse the direction of the vector F we place a negative sign before the vector symbol; thus $-F$ indicates a vector parallel to, and with the same magnitude as, F but with the opposite direction.

2.3.   Components of a Vector.   Consider that a body starts at O, Figure 2.2a, and moves 4 miles horizontally to point P.   This displacement is represented by the vector OP. Now let the body continue to move 3 miles vertically to point Q. This displacement is represented by the vector OQ, the starting point to the finishing point. Obviously, the resultant effect of the two displacements is the displacement vector OQ. Measurement of the scaled vector OQ shows that the body may reach the point Q by starting at O and moving 5 miles in the direction OQ. Notice that if the body first moves vertically upward 3 miles from O and then horizontally 4 miles to the right it arrives at the same point Q. The vector OQ is called the *resultant* of the two vectors OP and PQ. We see that the resultant is the single displacement that will produce the same result as the two displacements OP and PQ. In other words, the single vector OQ may be replaced by the two equivalent vectors OP and PQ. The vectors OP and PQ are called the *components* of the vector OQ. Figure 2.2b illustrates the resultant displacement vector OQ

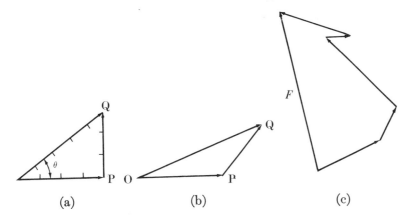

(a)   (b)   (c)

Figure 2.2. *Displacement vectors.*

and two component displacement vectors OP and PQ which are not at right angles to each other. Although we have employed displacement vectors in our discussion it is important to realize that the ideas presented hold just as well for any vector quantity.

It should be clear that a vector may have *any number* of components, as shown in Figure 2.2c which illustrates a vector F and five components. In physics and engineering it is usually more useful, however, to consider only the two rectangular components of a given vector, as in Figure 2.2a. The reasons for this will become clear as we make the necessary developments in the remaining sections of this chapter. In Figure 2.2a the horizontal component OP is the projection of OQ on a horizontal axis, or OP $=$ OQ cos θ, and the vertical component PQ is the projection of OQ on a vertical axis, or PQ $=$ OQ sin θ. If we refer to Figure 2.1 and call the horizontal component F_x and the vertical component F_y, then in the more usual symbolism we have

$$\left. \begin{aligned} F_x &= F \cos \theta \\ F_y &= F \sin \theta \end{aligned} \right\} \tag{2.1}$$

Since F_x, F_y, and F are vectors whose lengths are proportional to the magnitudes, Equations 2.1 are nothing more than the defining expressions for the cosine and sine functions.

2.4.   Addition of Vectors.   In Figure 2.2 we saw how by adding the vector PQ to the vector OP we obtained the equivalent vector OQ. In that case, adding the vector whose magnitude was 3 to the vector whose magnitude was 4 resulted in a vector whose magnitude was 5. Notice that each of these vectors has a different direction. If a vector whose magnitude is 3 has the same direction as a vector whose magnitude is 4 the total effect (sum) is a vector in the same direction but of magnitude 7. On the other hand, if a vector whose magnitude is 4 is directed to the right and a vector whose magnitude is 3 is directed to the left, the sum, or total effect, is a vector directed to the right with a magnitude of 1. Thus, depending on the direction of the vectors, the sum vector here may have any magnitude from 1 to 7. We see that, rather than being an arithmetic process, the addition of vectors is a geometric one.

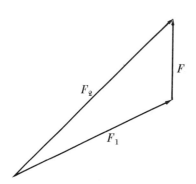

Figure 2.3.   *Subtraction of vectors.*

We shall now consider the generally useful ways in which vectors may be added, but first of all it must be realized that only vectors that represent the same kind of quantity may be added. Thus, we may add vector displacements to vector displacements, or vector forces to vector forces, or vector velocities to vector velocities, but never, for instance, a vector velocity to a vector force.

In Section 2.2 we saw that the negative of a vector is a vector parallel to, and with the same magnitude as, the vector, but with the opposite direction. By keeping this in mind it is clear that the addition of the negative of a vector, say F_1, to a given vector F_2 represents the subtraction of the vectors F_2 and F_1. If we consider the vector equation $F_2 - F_1 = F$ we see that the difference vector F is that vector which when added to F_1 yields the vector F_2. This is shown in Figure 2.3.

When two or more vectors are given, their vector sum is called their *resultant*, which is the single vector that substitutes for, or produces the same effect as, or is equivalent to, the system of vectors. The three common methods of finding the resultant are the *parallelogram method*, the *polygon method*, and the *method of components*. The first two are generally employed graphically but the method of components is invariably applied in an analytical fashion.

2.5.   Parallelogram Method.   By referring to Figure 2.2a it will be
recalled that the same point Q is reached if from O the vertical motion occurs
first and is then followed by the horizontal motion.   This is in accord with
the fact that vectors may be moved anywhere, provided their directions are
not changed.   The resultant vector OQ is then the diagonal of the parallelogram. Usually vectors F_1 and F_2 are drawn at a common origin O and then
a parallelogram as shown in Figure 2.4a is constructed.   The resultant, F_R,

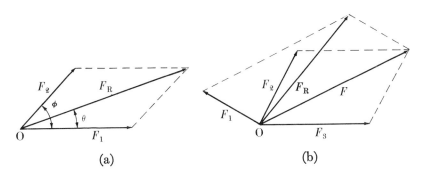

(a)   (b)

Figure 2.4.   *Parallelogram method of vector addition.*

is the diagonal of the parallelogram drawn from the origin O.   The magnitude
of F_R may be obtained graphically by measuring its scaled length, and its
direction θ determined by means of a protractor.   One may also use an
analytical method of computing F_R and θ.   Thus, applying the law of cosines
we have

$$F_R{}^2 = F_1{}^2 + F_2{}^2 - 2F_1F_2 \cos(180 - \phi)$$

or

$$F_R{}^2 = F_1{}^2 + F_2{}^2 + 2F_1F_2 \cos \phi \tag{2.2}$$

Since F_1, F_2, and ϕ are given, F_R is readily calculated.   Equation 2.2 gives
the magnitude of the resultant.   Knowing this, we can obtain the direction
of the resultant from

$$F_2{}^2 = F_1{}^2 + F_R{}^2 - 2F_1F_R \cos \theta$$

$$\cos \theta = \frac{F_1{}^2 + F_R{}^2 - F_2{}^2}{2F_1F_R} \tag{2.3}$$

If more than two vectors are given their resultant is obtained by dealing
with the vectors two at a time.   In Figure 2.4b is shown the addition of
three given vectors, F_1, F_2, and F_3.   Choosing any two of these first, say F_2
and F_3, their resultant is F which replaces them.   The system has now been
reduced by one vector and we have left only vector F_1 and F, whose resultant
is F_R.   Each application of the parallelogram method reduces the vector
system by one until the addition of the last two vectors yields the final
resultant.   It must be remembered that, in Figure 2.4a, not all three vectors
act simultaneously at O; either F_1 and F_2 are acting together or their resultant

F_R is acting alone.   Likewise, in Figure 2.4b F_1, F_2, and F_3 are acting simultaneously, or only F_2 and F are acting together, or simply F_R is acting alone.

2.6.   Polygon Method.   In Figure 2.2a,b the resultant vector OQ may be looked upon as having been obtained by laying the *tail* of vector PQ to the head of the starting vector OP and then closing the polygon (in this case a triangle) with the resultant vector whose tail is made to coincide with the tail of the starting vector.   Observe that the resultant F_R in Figure 2.4b forms the closing vector of the quadrilateral whose other three vectors are F_3, F_2, and F_1, laid out in that order.   By studying the figure closely the student should convince himself that the vectors can be laid out in any order whatsoever.   This is illustrated in Figure 2.5 which shows the addition of

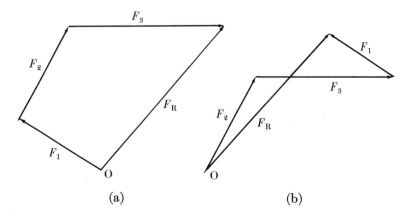

(a)   (b)

Figure 2.5.   *Polygon method of vector addition.*

the vectors F_1, F_2, and F_3 of Figure 2.4b.   In Figure 2.5a the order of the vectors is F_1, F_2, F_3, while in Figure 2.5b the order of the vectors is F_2, F_3, F_1. The polygon method is the one most often employed in graphical solutions. The accuracy of all graphical solutions is of course limited to the accuracy with which the drawings can be made and measured.   By dividing the polygon into triangles one may obtain an analytical solution with successive applications of Equations 2.2 and 2.3.

2.7.   Method of Components.   When there are more than two vectors and it is desired to obtain an analytical solution for the resultant, the most useful method is the *method of components.*
Let us consider adding the four vectors shown in Figure 2.6a by the analytical method of rectangular components.   First we pass x and y axes

through the intersection point of the four vectors, and let us assume that the directions of the vectors are known so that the acute angle that each makes with the x axis may be indicated as in Figure 2.6b. Next, each of the vectors is resolved into its equivalent horizontal and vertical components in accordance with Equations 2.1. This converts Figure 2.6b into Figure 2.6c. Al-

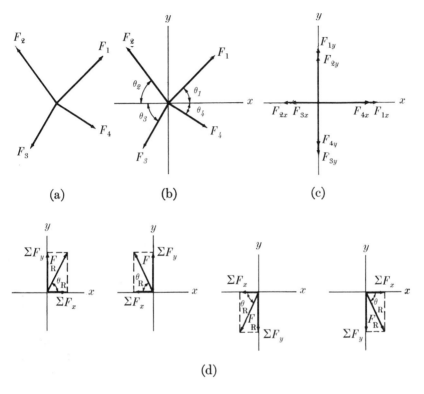

(a)   (b)   (c)

(d)

Figure 2.6. *Vector addition by the method of components.*

though the number of vectors has thus been doubled, all the vectors point parallel to the x axis or parallel to the y axis. All the components along the x axis may now be added algebraically, those pointing to the right, or in the positive x direction, considered plus $(+)$ and those pointing to the left, or in the negative x direction, considered minus $(-)$. The algebraic sum of all the components along the y axis may likewise be obtained. Thus in Figure 2.6c the x components of F_1 and F_4 are $F_{1x} = F_1 \cos \theta_1$ and $F_{4x} = F_4 \cos \theta_4$ respectively. The x components of F_2 and F_3 are $F_{2x} = -F_2 \cos \theta_2$ and $F_{3x} = -F_3 \cos \theta_3$ respectively. The y components of F_1 and F_2 are $F_{1y} = F_1 \sin \theta_1$ and $F_{2y} = F_2 \sin \theta_2$ respectively. The y components of F_3 and F_4 are $F_{3y} = -F_3 \sin \theta_3$ and $F_{4y} = -F_4 \sin \theta_4$. By calling the sum of all the x components $\sum F_x$ and the sum of all the y components $\sum F_y$, Figure 2.6c is finally converted into one of the four possible diagrams in Figure 2.6d. These four possibilities are a consequence of the fact that $\sum F_x$ and $\sum F_y$ may each come out plus or minus. In each case we end up with two rectangular components, and their resultant F_R, which is the resultant of the original system of vectors, is given by the diagonal of the rectangle as shown. In actual practice we generally employ only (b) and the appropriate diagram in (d) of Figure 2.6, but we keep in mind (c) when forming the sums.

Then, after having a figure such as Figure 2.6b before us, we proceed as follows:

$$\sum F_x = F_1 \cos \theta_1 - F_2 \cos \theta_2 - F_3 \cos \theta_3 + F_4 \cos \theta_4$$
$$\sum F_y = F_1 \sin \theta_1 + F_2 \sin \theta_2 - F_3 \sin \theta_3 - F_4 \sin \theta_4 \qquad (2.4)$$

At this point, having the values of $\sum F_x$ and $\sum F_y$ before us we construct whichever diagram of Figure 2.6d corresponds to the problem at hand. Then the magnitude of the resultant vector F_R is given by

$$F_R^2 = (\sum F_x)^2 + (\sum F_y)^2 \qquad (2.5)$$

and its direction, making an acute angle θ_R with the x axis, is obtained from

$$\tan \theta_R = \frac{|\sum F_y|}{|\sum F_x|} \qquad (2.6)$$

where we have used the symbol $|\quad|$ to indicate the absolute value. Often the direction of the resultant is stated in terms of the angle it makes, measured counterclockwise, with the positive extension of the x axis. This can be easily obtained, for resultant vectors falling in the second quadrant, by using $180° - \theta_R$; for those falling in the third quadrant, by using $180° + \theta_R$; and for those falling in the fourth quadrant, by using $360° - \theta_R$. The student should realize that if the absolute value symbols were dispensed with in Equation 2.6 the sign of the tangent function would indicate the correct quadrant in which the resultant falls. However, experience dictates that the student acquires a much more *physical* feeling of the problem by using Equation 2.6 and Figure 2.6d. In practice one generally simplifies the computation involved by orienting the system of vectors in Figure 2.6a with respect to the rectangular axes in Figure 2.6b so that one of the vectors (and more if possible) lies along the x or y axis. This vector then has no component in a direction perpendicular to itself.

It is to be noticed that Equation 2.2 with $\phi = 90°$ (see Figure 2.4) is nothing more than Equation 2.5.

2.8. The *i-j* Rōt Method of Analysis.*
In this method we designate the horizontal axis the i axis and the vertical axis the j axis. We then represent a vector or directed quantity by the symbol $i/\underline{\theta}N$, which is read i-rōt-θ-N,

---

*This method was first conceived and used in the manner outlined by Dr. Newton Gaines, former Chairman of the Physics Department, Texas Christian University. Rōt is pronounced "rote," for "rotation."

where i is a unit vector directed along the positive extension of the i axis, $\underline{/\theta}$
indicates that the unit vector is rotated counterclockwise by an amount θ,
and N stands for some number which is the magnitude of the vector.   To
illustrate, consider the rotating vector of magnitude 100 units shown in positions I to VI in Figure 2.7.   In position I the vector is designated $i100$.   In
position II the vector is designated $i\underline{/30°}100$.   In position III we have
$i\underline{/150°}100$ which may be rewritten as $-i\underline{/-30°}100$.   In position IV the
designation is $-i100$.   In position V we have $i\underline{/210°}100$ or $-i\underline{/30°}100$.   In
position VI we have $i\underline{/330°}100$ or $i\underline{/-30°}100$.

Since $i\underline{/\theta}$ is a unit vector oriented
in the i-j plane it may be resolved
into an i component and into a j
component where j is a unit vector
in the j direction.   Thus we have

$$i\underline{/\theta} = i\cos\theta + j\sin\theta \quad (2.7a)$$

where the rotor $\underline{/\theta}$ operating on i
causes the unit vector to make the
angle θ with the positive extension of
the i axis.   Likewise,

$$i\underline{/-\theta} = i\cos\theta - j\sin\theta \quad (2.7b)$$

since $\cos(-\theta) = \cos\theta$ and $\sin(-\theta)$
$= -\sin\theta$.   By means of the expansion expressions, Equations 2.7a,b,
we obtain the horizontal and vertical

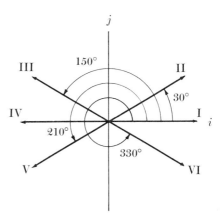

Figure 2.7.

components of the resultant vector.   The procedure from then on is similar
to that employed in the analytical method of components.   An illustration
of the application of the method is given in Example 2.2.

Example 2.1.   Three vectors of 10.0, 30.0, and 50.0 units act through a
point and make 120.0° with each other.   Find their resultant by the method
of components.

Solution.   The three vectors are shown oriented as in Figure 2.8a; one of
the vectors is conveniently made to point along the x axis.   Notice that we
have indicated the acute angle that each of the vectors makes with the x axis.
Applying Equations 2.4 we have

$$\sum F_x = 10.0 - 30.0\cos 60.0° - 50.0\cos 60.0°$$
$$= 10.0 - 30.0(0.500) - 50.0(0.500)$$
$$= -30.0 \text{ units}$$
$$\sum F_y = 30.0\sin 60.0° - 50.0\sin 60.0°$$
$$= 30.0(0.866) - 50.0(0.866)$$
$$= -17.3 \text{ units}$$
$$F_R^2 = (-30.0)^2 + (-17.3)^2$$
$$F_R = 34.6 \text{ units}$$

The acute angle that this resultant makes with the x axis is indicated in Figure 2.8b and given by

$$\tan \theta_R = \frac{17.3}{30.0} = 0.5766$$

$$\theta_R = 30.0°$$

The angle that the resultant makes with the positive extension of the x axis is $\theta_R + 180° = 210.0°$.

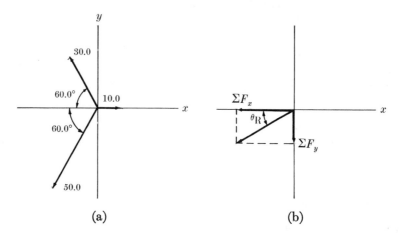

(a)   (b)

Figure 2.8. *Resultant by method of components.*

Example 2.2. Solve the problem given in Example 2.1 by the i-j rōt method.

Solution. The resultant F_R is given by the vector sum of F_1, F_2, and F_3, or

$$F_R = F_1 + F_2 + F_3$$

where F_1, F_2, and F_3 are separately the 10.0-unit, 30.0-unit, and 50.0-unit vectors. It must be remembered that these F's must be added vectorially. In the symbolism given in Section 2.8 we have

$$F_R = i10.0 - i\underline{/-60.0°}30.0 - i\underline{/60.0°}50.0$$

and, expanding the directed quantities in accordance with Equations 2.7a,b, we have

$$F_R = i10.0 - (i \cos 60.0° - j \sin 60.0°)30.0 - (i \cos 60.0° + j \sin 60.0°)50.0$$
$$= i(10.0 - 15.0 - 25.0) + j(26.0 - 43.3)$$
$$= -i30.0 - j17.3$$
$$= -i \left/ \tan^{-1} \frac{17.3}{30.0} \right. \sqrt{(30.0)^2 + (17.3)^2}$$
$$= -i\underline{/30.0°}34.6 \text{ units}$$

which, as can be seen in Figure 2.8b, is the result we obtained in Example 2.1.

Problems

2.1. A vector displacement has a magnitude of 10.0 cm and points in a direction making an angle of 160.0° with the x axis. What are the vector's rectangular components?

2.2. A vector displacement has a magnitude of 8.00 feet and makes an angle of 300.0° with the x axis. Find the rectangular components of the vector.

2.3. A vector displacement has a horizontal component of -5.00 feet and a vertical component of 12.0 feet. Find the magnitude and the direction of the vector.

2.4. Two vectors of 10.0 units and 15.0 units make an angle of 120.0° with each other. Find their sum (**a**) graphically, (**b**) analytically using Equations 2.2 and 2.3, and (**c**) analytically by the method of rectangular components.

2.5. Three vectors whose magnitudes are 100, 200, and 300 units are concurrent (pass through one point) and make angles of 30.0°, 225.0°, and 350.0°, respectively, with the positive extension of the horizontal axis. Find the resultant vector (**a**) graphically by the parallelogram method, (**b**) graphically by the polygon method, (**c**) analytically by the method of rectangular components, (**d**) analytically by the *i-j* rōt method.

2.6. A vector of 30.0 units is directed toward the east and a vector of 40.0 units is directed 35.0° west of south. What must be the magnitude and direction of a third vector if the system of three vectors is to have a zero resultant?

2.7. Figure 2.9 shows a vector drawn at O through which the rectangular *x-y* axes and oblique *ʓ-η* axes pass. By graphical means resolve the vector into two components directed along the oblique axes, then verify that these are the true components by employing the rectangular axes.

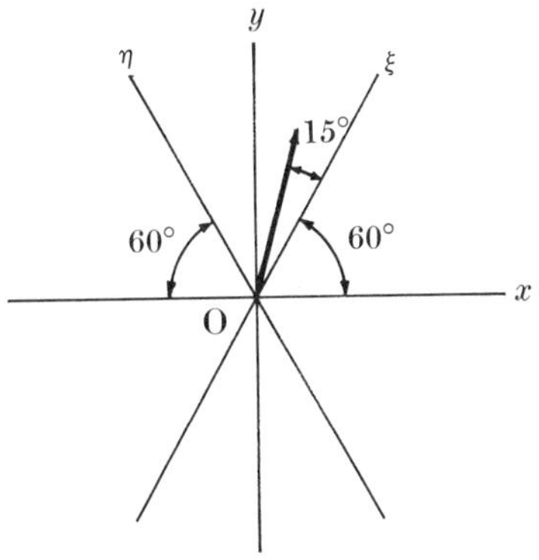

Figure 2.9. *Problem 2.7.*

2.8. Find the sum of four concurrent vectors oriented as follows: 300 units directed eastward, 500 units directed 25.0° west of north, 200 units directed at 210.0° with the positive extension of the horizontal axis, 400 units directed southeast. Solve in the four ways specified in Problem 2.5.

2.9. Find the angle between two vectors whose magnitudes are F and $3F$ and the magnitude of whose resultant is $3F$.

2.10. A box is moved on rough horizontal ground by applying two aiding vector forces, a force of 25.5 units directed downward at an angle of 70.0° with the vertical and a force of 50.0 units directed upward at an angle of 40.0°

with the horizontal. Find the resultant horizontal and resultant vertical components of these forces.

2.11. In what direction must a pilot head his plane, which has a vector air velocity of 300 units, in order to travel due north when there is a wind blowing with a vector velocity of 50.0 units toward the west?

2.12. Find the sum of the following displacement vectors (**a**) graphically by the method of the polygon and (**b**) analytically by the method of components: 2.55 feet acting toward the east, 5.50 feet acting 30.0° west of north, 10.5 feet acting 70.5° south of west, and 1.75 feet acting 25.5° south of east.

2.13. Using the *i-j* rōt method find the resultant of three concurrent vectors as follows: 38.5 units, 50.8 units, and 135 units making angles of 20.5°, 185.0°, and 301.0°, respectively, with the positive extension of the *x* axis.

2.14. Find the sum of the vectors given in Problem 2.13 graphically by the parallelogram and polygon methods.

2.15. Find the resultant of the following vector displacements: $i/35.5°100$, $i/112.0°50.7$, $i/210.0°78.5$, and $i/320.0°200$. The magnitude of each displacement is in meters.

Kinematics of Translation

NOW THAT WE KNOW HOW to deal with any system of vectors we are ready to study the various phases of mechanics. The field of mechanics is subdivided into the studies of *kinematics* and *dynamics*. Kinematics is that branch of physics that deals with the description of the motion of bodies without regard to the forces acting and causing the motion. Dynamics, on the other hand, includes a treatment of the causes of the changes in motion. One further subdivides the field of dynamics into the study of *statics*, which deals with bodies in a state of equilibrium (i.e., bodies under the action of balanced forces), and the study of *kinetics*, which deals with changes in motion in relation to the action of unbalanced forces or non-zero resultant forces.

In general, in dealing with motion we must consider both *translation* and *rotation*. Translational motion is linear motion in which any line in a body moves so that it remains at all times parallel to itself, i.e., motion which is nonrotatory. In this chapter we shall be dealing with the kinematics of translation. We shall study the principles of rotation in a later chapter.

A body in motion is continuously changing its position and what we do in kinematics is to describe the position of an arbitrary point on the body as a function of the time. In order that we may do this it is first necessary that we take up in working detail the concepts of *speed, velocity,* and *acceleration*.

3.1. Speed and Velocity. In Section 2.1 we pointed out the distinction between speed and velocity in connection with scalar and vector quantities. We now want to know more than just that speed is a scalar possessing magnitude only while velocity is a vector possessing also direction. We are interested in descriptions of motion which are labeled by the terms *uniform speed* or *velocity, average speed* or *velocity,* and *instantaneous speed* or *velocity.* In general, by *speed* we mean *distance traversed in a unit of time.*

An object that is moving with uniform speed covers equal distances in equal time intervals. The distance covered per unit time, or the time rate of change of distance, is here the same for each succeeding arbitrarily chosen unit of time.

On the other hand, if a body has a variable speed, so that it slows down at some places and speeds up at others, we define the average speed as the ratio of the entire distance traversed to the corresponding total time which has elapsed. Thus, if s is the total distance traversed and t is the time elapsed, then the average speed v_{av} is given by

$$v_{\mathrm{av}} = s/t \qquad\qquad (3.1)$$

If a body were to travel with a uniform speed equal to its average speed it would cover the same total distance in the same total time. For example, suppose a body covers 20 miles in the first hour and 30 miles in the next hour. The average speed is 25 miles per hour. If the body traveled with a uniform speed of 25 miles per hour for 2 hours it would cover the same distance of 50 miles.

We now come to the meaning of instantaneous speed or speed at a point. When we start our car from rest and soon acquire a speed of, say, 20 miles per hour as indicated by the speedometer, we have the feeling that the car has a definite and different speed at each point of its path. As another example, we may be saying that the baseball passed the batter with a speed of so many feet per second. Obviously, the scheme of dividing the distance traversed by the time to obtain the instantaneous speed does not have any definite meaning here, for, since we are dealing with a mathematical point, the distance shrinks to zero and the corresponding time also approaches the value zero, or the ratio s/t is $0/0$. Each year we ask of our classes, How much is $0/0$? We invariably receive the answer zero from some, infinity from others, and unity from still others. They are all, of course, incorrect. The student with a knowledge of some calculus says it is an indeterminate form. Let us now see what this means. First consider keeping the numerator constant at the value s. Then, as the denominator goes through the values 1, 10^{-1}, 10^{-2}, 10^{-3}, . . . , 10^{-6}, . . . , the ratio has the corresponding values s, $10s$, $100s$, $1{,}000s$, $1{,}000{,}000s$, ... What value does the ratio have when the denominator has the smallest value, zero? The answer is a value greater than the greatest conceivable one, and this we call infinity. Next, consider keeping the denominator constant at the value t. Then, as the numerator goes through the values 1, 10^{-1}, 10^{-2}, 10^{-3}, . . . , 10^{-6}, . . . , the ratio assumes the corresponding values $1/t$, $1/10t$, $1/100t$, $1/1{,}000t$, $1/1{,}000{,}000t$, ... When the numerator has the smallest value, zero, the ratio has the value zero. We see then that the value of the ratio s/t, as both s and t approach zero, depends on the manner in which the numerator and denominator approach zero. If the numerator approaches zero faster than the denominator the ratio approaches zero. If the denominator approaches the value zero faster than the numerator, the ratio approaches the value infinity. Hence, in general, the limiting value of s/t, as both s and t approach zero in some arbitrary fashion, is anything between zero and infinity. In other words, the ratio $0/0$ could be any value!

The meaning of instantaneous speed can now be more profitably presented with the aid of Figure 3.1. Suppose we have a particle that is moving along a straight line with a variable speed and we concern ourselves with the instantaneous speed at some point P along its path. We can consider an interval

AB containing the midpoint P and determine the average speed over this interval. The value of this average speed depends on the size of the interval AB but, as the interval is chosen to be progressively smaller, we shall find that the average speed approaches a constant value, and for a constant speed the average speed and the instantaneous speed are the same. Thus, using the symbol Δ to represent an infinitesimal increment and choosing the infinitesimal interval Δs and corresponding time increment Δt, we see that the value of the average speed Δs/Δt when the time interval approaches zero is the instantaneous speed at P. We thus describe the speed v_P at the point P as

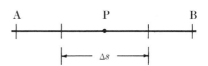

Figure 3.1. *Illustrating instantaneous speed.*

$$v_\mathrm{P} = \lim_{\Delta t \to 0} \frac{\Delta s}{\Delta t} \tag{3.2}$$

where the right-hand member is read "the limit of Δs/Δt as Δt approaches zero." Of course, as Δt approaches 0 so does Δs approach 0, but the ratio approaches a definite limiting value which is the instantaneous speed at P.

The vector velocity has for its magnitude the speed, so that the above descriptions, when considered additionally with respect to direction, hold for velocity. *Velocity* is defined as *the time rate of change of displacement.* Thus uniform or constant velocity means not only that the distance traversed per unit time is constant but that the direction as well does not change; the average velocity is given by Equation 3.1 where *s* is the vector displacement or the distance traversed in a given direction; the instantaneous velocity, or the velocity at a point, is given by Equation 3.2 where Δs is the incremental displacement vector. The units used to express the magnitude of the velocity are the same as those used for speed, but of course a direction must also be stated for velocity. Hereafter, when we use the terms speed or velocity we shall mean the instantaneous speed or velocity.

3.2. Accelerated Motion. When the motion is such that the velocity changes from point to point we have what is known as *accelerated motion.* The velocity may be increasing from point to point, in which case we have a positive acceleration. On the other hand, if the velocity decreases from point to point the acceleration is negative and we designate it a *deceleration* or *retardation.* Acceleration is defined as *the time rate of change of velocity.* Thus, since velocity is a vector quantity and time is a scalar, acceleration is a vector quantity. Furthermore, since a change in velocity of a body may be due to a change in magnitude, a change in direction, or a change in both magnitude and direction, the acceleration of a particle may be due to a change in speed, a change in direction, or a change in both speed and direction. For example, a body accelerated along a straight line would have its speed changing but not its direction, a body rotating with constant speed in a circle is accelerated because of a continuously changing direction, and a body rotating with variable speed in a circle is accelerated because of changes in both magnitude and direction.

As in the case of velocity, we have *uniform acceleration, average acceleration*, and *instantaneous acceleration*.

In uniformly accelerated motion, say motion along a straight line, the velocity of the body changes by equal amounts in equal intervals of time. If we let v_0 be the initial velocity at time t_0 and v be the velocity at time t_1, then the acceleration a is given by

$$a = \frac{v - v_0}{t_1 - t_0} = \frac{v - v_0}{t} \tag{3.3}$$

where we have set t for the time interval $t_1 - t_0$.   During this time interval t the velocity has changed from the value v_0 to the value v.

The acceleration in Equation 3.3 is constant if the velocity is changing at a uniform rate.   However, if the velocity does not change by equal amounts in equal intervals of time, then Equation 3.3 defines the average acceleration.

The instantaneous acceleration, or acceleration at a point, is described in a manner analogous to the way in which the instantaneous velocity was described.   Thus, if Δv is the increment in velocity corresponding to the time increment Δt, then the instantaneous acceleration a_P at the point P which is situated in the time interval is

$$a_P = \lim_{\Delta t \to 0} \frac{\Delta v}{\Delta t} \tag{3.4}$$

The student should draw a figure illustrating what Equation 3.4 states.

If v is greater than v_0 in Equation 3.3 the acceleration is positive and is in the sense in which the particle is moving.   If v is less than v_0 the acceleration is negative and the sense of the acceleration is opposite to that in which the particle is moving; there is then present a deceleration.

3.3.   Units of Velocity and Acceleration.

Referring to Equation 3.1 we see that since the fundamental units for s and t are respectively centimeters and seconds in the metric cgs system, and feet and seconds in the English system, the *derived* unit for speed or velocity is the centimeter per second (cm/sec) or the foot per second (ft/sec).   Any other combination of units for distance and time may be employed, such as miles per minute, miles per hour, meters per second, kilometers per second.   As an illustration of the manipulation of the velocity units, let us indicate the conversion of the velocity unit miles per hour to feet per second:

$$\frac{1 \text{ mi}}{\text{hr}} = \frac{1 \cancel{\text{ mi}}}{\cancel{\text{hr}}} \times \frac{5280 \text{ ft}}{\cancel{\text{mi}}} \times \frac{\cancel{\text{hr}}}{60 \cancel{\text{ min}}} \times \frac{\cancel{\text{min}}}{60 \text{ sec}} = \frac{44 \text{ ft}}{30 \text{ sec}}$$

It is very convenient to remember and use when necessary the fact that 30 miles/hour is equal to 44 ft/sec.

From Equation 3.3 it is clear that the derived unit of acceleration is the ratio of the unit of velocity to the unit of time. In the metric cgs system the unit of acceleration is the centimeter per second, per second (cm/sec/sec) or

$$\frac{cm}{sec \cdot sec}$$

which is usually written cm/sec². Any other combination of metric units may be employed such as:

$$\frac{cm}{min \cdot sec} \qquad \frac{m}{hr \cdot min} \qquad \frac{km}{sec^2} \qquad \frac{m}{hr^2}$$

In the English system acceleration may be stated as

$$\frac{ft}{sec^2} \qquad \frac{mi}{hr \cdot sec} \qquad \frac{mi}{hr^2} \qquad etc.$$

No special name has been generally adopted for the unit of acceleration. However, in the field of geophysics the name "gal," in honor of Galileo, is employed to represent the centimeter per square second. As a second illustration of the use of units we shall indicate the conversion of the acceleration unit miles per hour, per hour, to centimeters per second, per second:

$$1\frac{mi}{hr^2} = 1\frac{\cancel{mi}}{\cancel{hr^2}} \times \frac{5280\,\cancel{ft}}{\cancel{mi}} \times \frac{\cancel{hr^2}}{(3600)^2\,sec^2} \times \frac{12.0\,\cancel{in}}{\cancel{ft}} \times \frac{2.54\,cm}{\cancel{in}} = 124 \times 10^{-3}\frac{cm}{sec^2}$$

3.4. Equations of Motion for a Uniform or Constant Acceleration.

One does not often encounter uniformly accelerated motions. The one prime example of nearly constant accelerated motion in nature is the freely falling body occurring in a vacuum under the action of gravity. We shall treat this case in detail in a later section. Nevertheless, the linear motion of a body with constant acceleration is the simplest type of accelerated motion and we shall here develop the expressions that are employed in dealing with it.

Equation 3.3 may be restated as

$$v = v_0 + at \qquad (3.5)$$

We recall that v_0 is the velocity at the time $t = 0$ and v is the velocity after an interval of time t. It is useful to keep in mind the graph of v as a function of t, considering the acceleration a constant. Figure 3.2 shows the graph to be a straight line having a vertical intercept v_0 and a slope equal to the constant acceleration.

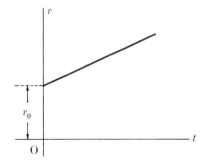

Figure 3.2. *Graph of velocity as a function of time for constant accelerated motion.*

In the analysis of constant accelerated motion we are interested in knowing not only what the velocity of the body is at any time t but also where the body is at any time. It is thus advantageous to derive two other expressions involving the displacement s. This we do in two ways, by a noncalculus development on the left side of the page and a calculus one on the right.

From Equation 3.1:

$$s = v_{av}t$$

Since the graph in Figure 3.2 is linear, the average velocity is given by

$$v_{av} = \frac{v_0 + v}{2}$$

and we have, using $v_0 + at$ for v,

$$s = v_0t + \tfrac{1}{2}at^2 \qquad (3.6a)$$

Now using for t its equal $(v - v_0)/a$ we have

$$s = \frac{v + v_0}{2} \cdot \frac{v - v_0}{a}$$

or:

$$v^2 = v_0^2 + 2as \qquad (3.6b)$$

Expressing Equation 3.5 in calculus notation we have

$$\frac{ds}{dt} = v_0 + at$$

Since v_0 and a are constants we have, integrating,

$$s = v_0t + \tfrac{1}{2}at^2 + s_0$$

where s_0, the constant of integration, is the value of s at $t = 0$. Choosing the origin so that $s_0 = 0$ when $t = 0$ we have

$$s = v_0t + \tfrac{1}{2}at^2 \qquad (3.6a)$$

Differentiating with respect to t the equation for ds/dt,

$$\frac{d^2s}{dt^2} = a$$

Now multiply both sides by $2(ds/dt)$:

$$\frac{d}{dt}\left(\frac{ds}{dt}\right)^2 = 2a\frac{ds}{dt}$$

Integrating and using v for ds/dt we have

$$v^2 = v_0^2 + 2as \qquad (3.6b)$$

where v_0, the constant of integration, is the value of v at $s = 0$.

Let us now examine more closely the derived equations of linear motion with constant acceleration. These are:

$$\left.\begin{array}{l} v = v_0 + at \\ s = v_0t + \tfrac{1}{2}at^2 \\ v^2 = v_0^2 + 2as \end{array}\right\} \qquad (3.7)$$

Each of Equations 3.7 expresses a relationship between four of the five quantities v, v_0, a, t, s. The first of the equations is simply the definition of acceleration and enables one to find the velocity v at any time t if the initial velocity v_0 and the constant acceleration a are known. The second of the equations gives the position s of the body at any time t when v_0 and a are known. This equation is also used to obtain t when s, v_0, and a are known. The last equation relates the velocity v and position s of a body having an initial velocity v_0 and moving with constant acceleration a. The equation may be employed to yield v when s is known or s when v is known.

In employing the kinematic equations 3.7 it must be realized that the quantities v, v_0, a, and s are vectors and that t is the only scalar. Hence it is more than just advisable—it is imperative—that the scheme below be followed in applying the equations to the solution of a problem.

(*1*) First, to facilitate acquiring a physical picture of what is occurring, a sketch or simplified drawing should be made.

(*2*) The application of each of the equations must be made with respect to a chosen origin. This origin need not remain fixed but may be changed for successive applications of the equations.

(*3*) A positive and negative direction must be specified with respect to the chosen origin.

(*4*) When a known value is substituted for a vector quantity, its associated sign must be consistent with the chosen positive and negative directions. On the other hand, for an unknown quantity the sign in its solution indicates its physical direction.

Examples illustrating the applications of Equations 3.7 in accordance with the above scheme will be found at the end of this chapter. Much time will be saved and greater facility in handling problems will be acquired if the student makes a sincere effort to learn Equations 3.7 well enough so that he can readily choose that equation which most directly determines the unknown quantity.

3.5.   Gravitational Acceleration: Freely Falling Bodies.   A freely falling body is defined as a body that is under the influence of the earth's gravitational pull only. It takes no more than common observation to realize that a freely falling body, starting from rest, acquires a progressively increasing velocity as it falls. But it was Galileo Galilei (1564–1642) who showed that a heavy body and a light object released simultaneously from the same height in vacuum keep abreast of each other in the course of their fall. By experiment Galileo arrived at the conclusion that, in the absence of air resistance, the velocity acquired at any instant by any object falling freely from rest is directly proportional to the time that has elapsed. He thus proved that all objects are uniformly accelerated by the same amount. This gravitational acceleration is customarily denoted by the symbol g.

The value of g varies somewhat over the surface of the earth, depending upon latitude and upon height above sea level. The variation with latitude is due (*1*) to the fact that the earth is not a perfect sphere but is an oblate spheroid, being slightly flattened at the poles, and (*2*) to the rotation of the earth about its spinning axis. Since the earth has a polar radius some 14 miles shorter than its equatorial radius, the value of g at the poles is greater than its value at the equator; the gravitational force exerted on a body depends on its distance from the earth's center, increasing as this distance decreases. The rotation of the earth, as we shall see later (Section 9.4), sets up a centripetal force which, again, has the effect of making the value of g at the equator less than its value at the poles. At sea level the numerical value of g at 0° latitude is 32.0878 feet/sec² or 9.78039 m/sec², and at 90° latitude it is 32.2577 feet/sec² or 9.83217 m/sec². Thus the entire latitude variation from the poles to the equator is 0.17 feet/sec² or 0.052 m/sec². At sea level and 45° latitude g has the value 32.2 feet/sec² or 9.81 m/sec²; to three significant figures this is the standard value adopted by the International Committee on Weights and Measures. The correction for h meters above sea level is obtained by subtracting from the sea level value of g, given in meters per second, per second, the amount 0.000003086h m/sec².

It is clear that Equations 3.7 apply to the motion of freely falling bodies, the acceleration a being replaced by the value of g. The direction of g is always downward, irrespective of the motion of the body; therefore, if "upward" is taken as positive, g must have a minus sign preceding it.

In our discussions we have assumed the absence of any air resistance. A dense 1-inch-diameter steel ball falling through the air from a moderate height follows the laws developed above. On the other hand, if a body is very small, a water or oil droplet, the frictional resistance of the air cannot be neglected and the kinematic equations of free fall must be modified so that they are true descriptions of the physical situation. The frictional drag of the air depends on the speed of the falling object and as the object gains speed the resistance, being in an upward direction, becomes greater, until it equals the downward accelerating effect of gravity. From then on the body falls with uniform speed, having reached its *terminal velocity*, that velocity which the body, falling from rest, can never exceed. (A treatment of the effects of air resistance is beyond the scope of this book.)

3.6.   Projectile Motion.   The study of the motion of projectiles is known by the name of *ballistics* and the path followed by a projectile is called the *trajectory*. This path, in actuality, may be rather complex because of the effects of air resistance. In our studies we shall neglect those effects and assume that the motion takes place under the action of gravity alone; once this simplified treatment is mastered the student is in a position to study more advanced treatments on ballistics which deal with the effects of air resistance.

First, let us consider the motion of a body projected horizontally at the origin O with a velocity v_0 as shown in Figure 3.3. The path of the projectile, starting at a height h above the ground level AB, is indicated by the curve OB. It is best to analyze the motion of the projectile in terms of its component horizontal and vertical motions, keeping in mind at all times that the resultant motion at every instant may be obtained by the vector addition of the component motions.

From the time that the body leaves the projection mechanism at O it possesses two velocity components: a horizontal component $v_x = v_0$ and a vertical component v_y. The horizontal velocity component v_0 is the horizontal projection velocity which remains constant while the body is in flight, since in the absence of air resistance there is no other influence acting horizontally to change that state of motion. The vertical component v_y, acting down,

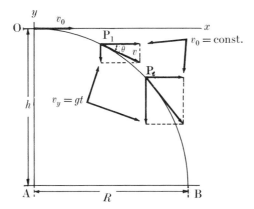

Figure 3.3. *Trajectory of projectile fired horizontally.*

starts out at O with a value zero and increases in accordance with the vertical constant acceleration, Equations 3.7. Taking the upward direction as $(+)$ and the downward direction as $(-)$ we have, for the horizontal displacement x at time t,

$$x = v_0 t$$

and for the vertical displacement y at time t,

$$y = -\tfrac{1}{2}gt^2$$

Now, eliminating the parameter t from the last two equations yields

$$y = -\left(\frac{g}{2v_0^2}\right) x^2 \qquad (3.8)$$

and, since g and v_0 are constants, the equation is of the form $y = -kx^2$ where k is a constant. The trajectory is then a parabola with vertex at the origin. At each point on the trajectory the resultant velocity of the body is tangent to the curve and is given by

$$v = \sqrt{v_x^2 + v_y^2}$$
$$= \sqrt{v_0^2 + g^2 t^2}$$

where t is the time corresponding to the successive positions of the body along the path. Thus the horizontal component velocity remains the same but the vertical component velocity vector increases downward with increase in t, as illustrated by the vector constructions at the points P_1 and P_2 in Figure 3.3. The direction θ of the resultant velocity is given in the usual manner by

$$\tan \theta = v_y / v_x = -gt / v_0$$

In projectile problems one is usually interested in solving for the *time of flight*, which is the total time the body is in flight, and the *range R* which is the total horizontal distance traversed by the projectile. The time of flight t_f is obtained from the expression above for the vertical displacement. Thus, when $y = -h$, $t = t_f$ and we have

$$-h = -\tfrac{1}{2}gt_f^2$$

or:
$$t_f = \sqrt{2h/g} \qquad\qquad (3.9)$$

The range is obtained from Equation 3.8. Thus, when $y = -h$, $x = R$ and we have

$$-h = -\left(\frac{g}{2v_0{}^2}\right)R^2$$

or:
$$R = v_0\sqrt{2h/g} \qquad\qquad (3.10)$$

The student should realize that the components of vertical and horizontal velocities act independently of each other, as they should. Also, the time it takes the body to cover the distance OB along the path of the trajectory is the same as the time it would have taken the body to cover the distance OA falling from rest, and these are the same as the time it would have taken the body to cover the distance AB when traveling with the constant velocity v_0 in the absence of gravity.

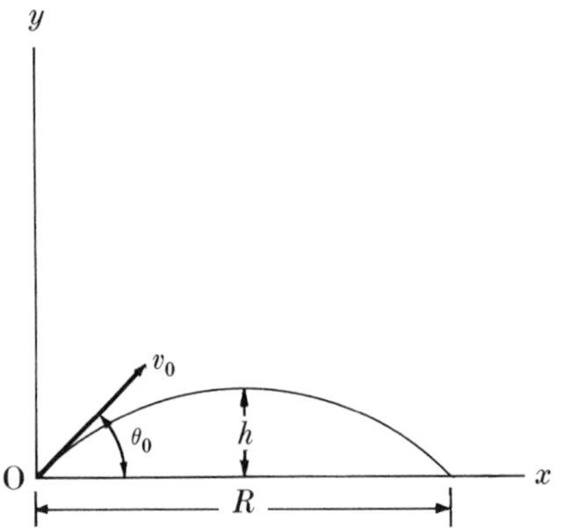

Figure 3.4.   *Trajectory of projectile fired at an angle θ_0 with the horizontal.*

Let us now consider the more general development of a projectile that is given an initial velocity v_0 at some angle θ_0 with the horizontal. The trajectory is indicated in Figure 3.4. As before, the analysis is made by considering the independent effects of the horizontal and vertical motions. The initial velocity v_0 has a horizontal velocity component v_{0x} and a vertical component v_{0y} given by

$$v_{0x} = v_0 \cos\theta_0 \qquad \text{and} \qquad v_{0y} = v_0 \sin\theta_0$$

Taking the upward direction as $(+)$ the horizontal displacement x at time t is

$$x = (v_0 \cos\theta_0)t \qquad\qquad (3.11)$$

and the vertical displacement y at time t is

$$y = (v_0 \sin\theta_0)t - \tfrac{1}{2}gt^2 \qquad\qquad (3.12)$$

Eliminating the parameter t from Equations 3.11 and 3.12 yields

$$y = -\frac{g}{2v_0{}^2 \cos^2\theta_0}\left(x^2 - \frac{2v_0{}^2 \cos^2\theta_0 \tan\theta_0}{g}x\right)$$

Now, completing the square inside the parentheses (this is done by adding and subtracting the square of one half of the coefficient of the x term) yields

$$y - \frac{v_0^2 \sin^2 \theta_0}{2g} = -\frac{g}{2v_0^2 \cos^2 \theta_0}\left(x - \frac{v_0^2 \sin \theta_0 \cos \theta_0}{g}\right)^2 \tag{3.13}$$

Equation 3.13 is that of a parabola with vertex displaced or translated to the right by the amount $(v_0^2 \cos^2 \theta_0 \tan \theta_0)/g$ and upward by the amount $(v_0^2 \sin^2 \theta_0)/2g$. Therefore the maximum height h is given by

$$h = \frac{v_0^2 \sin^2 \theta_0}{2g} \tag{3.14}$$

and the range R is

$$R = \frac{2v_0^2 \sin \theta_0 \cos \theta_0}{g} = \frac{v_0^2 \sin 2\theta_0}{g} \tag{3.15}$$

The time of flight t_f is obtained from Equation 3.11. Thus

$$t_f = \frac{R}{v_0 \cos \theta_0} = \frac{2v_0 \sin \theta_0}{g} \tag{3.16}$$

By proceeding in a manner similar to the case of Figure 3.3, Equations 3.14, 3.15, and 3.16 may alternatively be derived. We leave this as an exercise in the Problems. The student should realize that the vertical velocity is zero at the vertex of the parabola and the time it takes the body to travel from O to the vertex is one-half the time of flight.

Equation 3.15 shows that the range of the projectile is a function of the angle θ_0. That there is an angle of elevation for which the horizontal range is a maximum is shown as follows. On the left side of the page is the non-calculus proof and on the right the calculus proof.

$$R_{\max} = \frac{v_0^2}{g}(\sin 2\theta_0)_{\max}$$

and since the maximum value of the sine of an angle is unity,

$$\sin 2\theta_0 = 1$$
$$2\theta_0 = 90°$$
$$\theta_0 = 45°$$

Differentiating Equation 3.15 with respect to θ_0 gives

$$\frac{dR}{d\theta_0} = \frac{2v_0^2}{g}\cos 2\theta_0$$

and equating this to zero for an extreme, we have

$$\cos 2\theta_0 = 0$$
$$2\theta_0 = 90°$$
$$\theta_0 = 45°$$

The second derivative with respect to θ_0 is

$$\frac{d^2R}{d\theta_0} = \frac{-4v_0^2}{g}\sin 2\theta_0$$

which is negative for $\theta_0 = 45°$. Therefore $\theta_0 = 45°$ is the condition for a maximum.

Hence the maximum horizontal range, when air resistance is neglected, occurs when the angle of elevation is 45°.

Although the equations developed in this section are general for projectile motion in the absence of air resistance, the student is asked not to use the equations as formulas in the solution of problems. The best procedure for the student to follow is to provide himself with a diagram for each problem and obtain a solution by working with the horizontal and vertical components of displacement and velocity and apply Equations 3.7 which are general for motion which has a constant acceleration.

3.7. Relative Velocity. Velocities, or motions in general, are relative so that it is necessary for us to decide upon a frame of reference or a set of axes with respect to which the motion is specified. No object in the universe is stationary, so there are no really fixed axes, but we usually make our specifications with respect to axes on the earth which we consider at rest even though the earth is in motion through space. We therefore let the earth be our reference body and when we speak of the velocity of a body we mean the velocity relative to the earth.

Consider two bodies A and B having velocities v_A and v_B with respect to a frame of reference that is assumed fixed. Then the *velocity of one body relative to the other is the vector difference between the velocities of the bodies.* Thus, if v_{AB} is the velocity of A relative to B, and v_{BA} is the velocity of B relative to A, then

$$v_{AB} = v_A - v_B \quad \text{(vector difference)}$$
$$\text{and} \quad v_{BA} = v_B - v_A \quad \text{(vector difference)} \quad (3.17)$$

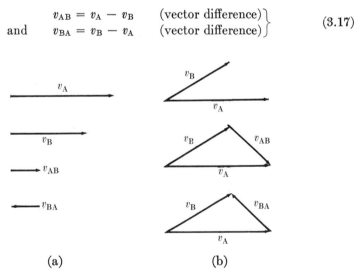

(a)   (b)

Figure 3.5. *Illustrating the velocity of one body relative to another.*

These statements of fact are illustrated in Figure 3.5. In (a) are shown A and B moving in the same direction, and their relative velocities. In (b)

A and B are moving in different directions and their relative velocities are also indicated. It is to be observed by studying these diagrams that the velocity of A relative to B is what it would be if we considered that B were at rest and A had added to it another velocity equal to that of B but opposite in direction.

The student may prefer to think of Equations 3.17 in the following way: The velocity of A is equal to the velocity of B plus the velocity of A relative to the velocity of B, the addition being performed vectorially.

Example 3.1. An automobile traveling at 45.0 miles/hour in a straight line slows down at a constant rate to 15.0 miles/hour in 10.0 sec. Find (a) the acceleration, (b) how far the automobile moves in the 10.0 sec, and (c) how much longer before the car comes to rest.

Solution. (a) Applying the first of Equations 3.7 we have

$$a = \frac{v - v_0}{t} \qquad\qquad \begin{aligned} v &= 15.0 \text{ mi/hr} \\ v_0 &= 45.0 \text{ mi/hr} \\ t &= 10.0 \text{ sec} \end{aligned}$$

$$= \frac{15.0 \text{ mi/hr} - 45.0 \text{ mi/hr}}{10.0 \text{ sec}}$$

$$= -\frac{3.00 \text{ mi}}{\text{hr} \cdot \text{sec}}$$

$$= -\frac{3.00 \,\cancel{\text{mi}}}{\cancel{\text{hr}} \cdot \text{sec}} \times \frac{44.0}{30.0} \times \frac{\text{ft}}{\text{sec}} \times \frac{\cancel{\text{hr}}}{\cancel{\text{mi}}}$$

$$= -4.40 \text{ ft/sec}^2$$

Thus the velocity decreases by 4.40 feet/sec during each second, the accelera-

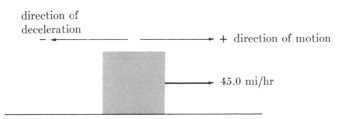

direction of
deceleration

+ direction of motion

45.0 mi/hr

Figure 3.6.

tion being in a direction opposite to the direction of motion (see Figure 3.6).
(b) Applying the last of Equations 3.7 gives

$$v^2 = v_0^2 + 2as \qquad\qquad \begin{aligned} v &= 15.0 \text{ mi/hr} = 22.0 \text{ ft/sec} \\ v_0 &= 45.0 \text{ mi/hr} = 66.0 \text{ ft/sec} \\ a &= -3.00 \text{ ft/sec}^2 \end{aligned}$$

$$(22.0)^2 \frac{\text{ft}^2}{\text{sec}^2} = (66.0)^2 \frac{\text{ft}^2}{\text{sec}^2} - 2(4.40) \frac{\text{ft}}{\text{sec}^2} s$$

$$s = \frac{3872 \text{ ft}^2/\text{sec}^2}{8.80 \text{ ft/sec}^2}$$

$$= 440 \text{ ft}$$

Notice that this result may be obtained by using the average velocity. Thus

$$v_{av} = \frac{45.0\,\frac{mi}{hr} + 15.0\,\frac{mi}{hr}}{2}$$

$$= 30.0 \text{ mi/hr}$$
$$= 44.0 \text{ ft/sec}$$
$$s = v_{av}t$$

$$= 44.0\,\frac{ft}{sec} \times 10.0 \text{ sec}$$

$$= 440 \text{ ft}$$

(c) Here we apply:

$$t = \frac{v - v_0}{a}$$

$$v = 0$$
$$v_0 = 15.0 \text{ mi/hr} = 22.0 \text{ ft/sec}$$
$$a = -4.40 \text{ ft/sec}^2$$

$$t = \frac{0 - 22.0 \text{ ft/sec}}{-4.40 \text{ ft/sec}^2}$$

$$t = 5.00 \text{ sec}$$

Example 3.2. A body moves along a straight line so that its displacement s cm from the origin is given by $s = 5.00t^2$, where t is the time in seconds. Find the instantaneous velocity after 2.00 sec.

Solution. Corresponding to an increment in displacement, Δs, there is an increment of time, Δt. Thus:

$$s + \Delta s = 5.00(t + \Delta t)^2$$
$$= 5.00[t^2 + 2t\Delta t + (\Delta t)^2]$$
$$\Delta s = 10.0t\Delta t + 5.00(\Delta t)^2$$

$$\frac{\Delta s}{\Delta t} = 10.0t + 5.00\Delta t$$

The instantaneous velocity v is given by Equation 3.2. Thus

$$v = \lim_{\Delta t \to 0} \frac{\Delta s}{\Delta t} = 10.0t$$

and for $t = 2.00$ sec, $v = 20.0$ cm/sec.

The student with a knowledge of the calculus will see that by differentiation the same result is readily obtained:

$$v = \frac{ds}{dt} = 10.0t = 20.0 \text{ cm/sec}$$

Example 3.3. A body is projected vertically upward from the top of a 160-foot tower with a velocity of 80.0 feet/sec. On the way down the body misses the tower and continues downward. Find (a) the greatest height obtained by the body, (**b**) the time it takes the body to return to the level of its starting point, (**c**) where the body is 6.00 sec after it is projected, (**d**) the total elapsed time before the body strikes the ground, and (**e**) the speed with which the body strikes the ground. Use the value $g = 32.0$ feet/sec². Neglect air resistance.

Solution. Figure 3.7 shows the tower and path of the body, the upward and downward portions being separated for convenience. We shall indicate the choice of origin by the appropriate letter from the diagram and the positive direction by an arrow.

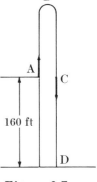

Figure 3.7.

(**a**) A ↑ +: to find the maximum height reached we choose the origin at A and the upward direction as positive (+). The velocity at B is zero. Hence:

$$v^2 = v_0{}^2 + 2as \qquad v = 0$$
$$\qquad\qquad\qquad v_0 = 80.0 \text{ ft/sec}$$
$$0 = (80.0)^2 \frac{\text{ft}^2}{\text{sec}^2} - 64.0 \frac{\text{ft}}{\text{sec}^2} s \qquad a = -g = -32.0 \text{ ft/sec}^2$$

$$s = 100 \text{ ft}$$

Thus the body rises 100 feet before starting on its downward journey.

(**b**) A ↑ +: the time it takes the body to go from A to B is obtained by applying

$$v = v_0 + at \qquad\qquad v = 0$$
$$\qquad\qquad\qquad v_0 = 80.0 \text{ ft/sec}$$
$$0 = 80.0 \frac{\text{ft}}{\text{sec}} - 32.0t \qquad a = -g = -32.0 \text{ ft/sec}^2$$

$$t = 2.50 \text{ sec}$$

The time it takes the body to fall from B to C will also be 2.50 sec passing the point C with a downward speed of 80.0 feet/sec. (The student should verify this.) Hence the total time to go from A to C is 5.00 sec.

(**c**) C ↓ +: we may solve this by taking the origin at C and the downward direction as positive. Thus:

$$s = v_0 t + \tfrac{1}{2}at^2 \qquad\qquad v_0 = 80.0 \text{ ft/sec}$$
$$\qquad\qquad\qquad t = 1.00 \text{ sec}$$
$$s = 80.0 \frac{\text{ft}}{\text{sec}} \times 1.00 \text{ sec} + 16.0 \frac{\text{ft}}{\text{sec}^2} \times (1.00)^2 \text{ sec}^2 \qquad a = g = 32.0 \text{ ft/sec}^2$$

$$s = 96.0 \text{ ft}$$

The body is 96.0 feet below the starting point.

This result may also be obtained by choosing the origin at A. Thus, using A ↑ +, we have:

$$s = v_0 t + \tfrac{1}{2}at^2 \qquad\qquad v_0 = 80.0 \text{ ft/sec}$$
$$\qquad\qquad\qquad t = 6.00 \text{ sec}$$
$$s = 80.0 \frac{\text{ft}}{\text{sec}} \times 6.00 \text{ sec} - 16.0 \frac{\text{ft}}{\text{sec}^2} \times (6.00)^2 \text{ sec}^2 \qquad a = -g = -32 \text{ ft/sec}^2$$

$$s = 480 \text{ ft} - 576 \text{ ft}$$
$$ = -96.0 \text{ ft}$$

which again signifies 96.0 feet below the starting point.

(d) C ↓ +: for this we choose the origin at C and the downward direction as positive.

$$s = v_0 t + \tfrac{1}{2}at^2$$

$$160 \text{ ft} = 80.0t \frac{\text{ft}}{\text{sec}} + 16.0t^2 \frac{\text{ft}}{\text{sec}^2}$$

$v_0 = 80.0 \text{ ft/sec}$
$s = 160 \text{ ft}$
$a = g = 32 \text{ ft/sec}^2$

$$t = \frac{-5.00 \pm \sqrt{25.0 + 40.0}}{2}$$

$$t = 1.53 \text{ sec or } -6.53 \text{ sec}$$

Only the positive solution meets the physical conditions of the problem so the total elapsed time is $1.53 + 5.00 = 6.53$ sec. What does the negative answer for t tell us?

(e) Taking the same choice of origin as in (d) we have:

$$v = v_0 + at$$

$$v = 80.0 \frac{\text{ft}}{\text{sec}} + 32.0 \frac{\text{ft}}{\text{sec}^2} \times 1.53 \text{ sec}$$

$v_0 = 80.0 \text{ ft/sec}$
$a = g = 32.0 \text{ ft/sec}^2$
$t = 1.53 \text{ sec}$

$$v = 129 \text{ ft/sec}$$

and the body strikes the ground with a speed of 129 feet/sec.

Example 3.4. If the body in Example 3.3 is projected horizontally with the same speed from the top of the tower find (a) the time of flight, (b) the range, and (c) the velocity with which the body strikes the ground. Neglect air resistance. Use 32.0 ft/sec² for g.

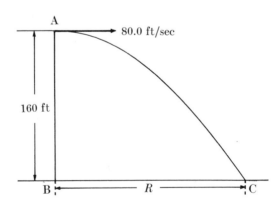

A

80.0 ft/sec

160 ft

B   R   C

Figure 3.8.

(a) A ↓ +: the time of flight is the time it takes the body to travel from A to C (see Figure 3.8) or, what is equivalent, the time it would have taken the body to cover the distance AB, falling from rest. Choosing the origin at A and positive direction downward we apply:

$$s = v_0 t + \tfrac{1}{2}at^2 \qquad s = 160 \text{ ft}$$

$$v_0 = 0$$

$$160 \text{ ft} = 16.0 \frac{\text{ft}}{\text{sec}^2} t_f^2 \qquad a = g = 32.0 \text{ ft/sec}^2$$

$$t_f = 3.16 \text{ sec}$$

where we have retained the positive solution as the one which fits the situation physically.

(b) A→+: the range is given by the product of the constant horizontal velocity and the time of flight. Thus, with the origin and choice of direction shown:

$$R = 80.0 \frac{\text{ft}}{\text{sec}} \times 3.16 \text{ sec}$$

$$= 253 \text{ ft}$$

(c) A $_{+\downarrow}$→+: to find the velocity at C we shall first find the horizontal and vertical components of velocity at C. Choosing A as the origin and positive for the horizontal and vertical directions as indicated we have, for the horizontal velocity v_x,

$$v_x = 80.0 \frac{\text{ft}}{\text{sec}}$$

and for the vertical component of velocity v_y,

$$v_y = v_0 + at \qquad v_0 = 0$$

$$a = g = 32.0 \text{ ft/sec}^2$$

$$= 32.0 \frac{\text{ft}}{\text{sec}^2} \times 3.16 \text{ sec} \qquad t = 3.16 \text{ sec}$$

$$= 101 \frac{\text{ft}}{\text{sec}}$$

The magnitude of the resultant velocity is

$$v = \sqrt{(80.0)^2 + (101)^2}$$

$$= 129 \text{ ft/sec}$$

and the direction θ (see Figure 3.9) is given by:

$$\tan \theta = 101/80.0$$

$$= 1.2625$$

$$\theta = 51.6°$$

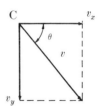

Figure 3.9.

Example 3.5. If the body in Example 3.3 is projected upward at an angle of 30.0° with the same speed from the top of the tower find (a) the maximum height attained, (b) the time of flight, and (c) the range. Neglect air resistance and use 32.0 feet/sec² for *g*.

Solution. The path of the projectile is indicated in Figure 3.10.

(a) A ↑ +: using the choice of origin and positive direction as shown we have for the path AB:

$$v^2 = v_{0y}^2 + 2as \qquad\qquad v = 0$$

$$0 = (40.0)^2 \frac{\text{ft}^2}{\text{sec}^2} - 64.0 \frac{\text{ft}}{\text{sec}^2} h \qquad v_{0y} = 80.0 \sin 30.0° \frac{\text{ft}}{\text{sec}} = 40.0 \frac{\text{ft}}{\text{sec}}$$

$$h = 25.0 \text{ ft} \qquad\qquad\qquad a = -g = -32.0 \text{ ft/sec}^2$$
$$s = h$$

The body attains a maximum height of $160 + 25 = 185$ feet.

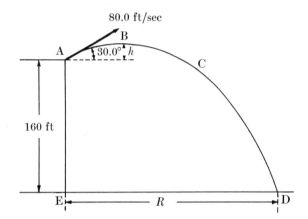

Figure 3.10.

(b) B ↓ +: the time t_{BD} it takes the body to cover the path BCD is, with B the origin and downward direction positive,

$$s = v_{0y}t + \tfrac{1}{2}at^2 \qquad v_{0y} = 0$$
$$\qquad\qquad\qquad s = 185 \text{ ft}$$
$$185 \text{ ft} = 16.0 \frac{\text{ft}}{\text{sec}^2} t_{BD}^2 \qquad a = g = 32.0 \text{ ft/sec}^2$$

$$t_{BD} = 3.40 \text{ sec}$$

where we have retained the positive solution as the physical one. To this must be added the time t_{AB} it takes the body to traverse the path AB. Using the same origin and direction as in (a) we have

$$v = v_{0y} + at \qquad\qquad v = 0$$
$$\qquad\qquad\qquad\qquad v_{0y} = 40.0 \text{ ft/sec}$$
$$0 = 40.0 \frac{\text{ft}}{\text{sec}} - 32.0 \frac{\text{ft}}{\text{sec}^2} t_{AB} \qquad a = -g = -32.0 \text{ ft/sec}^2$$

$$t_{AB} = 1.25 \text{ sec}$$

The time of flight t_f is
$$t_f = t_{AB} + t_{BD}$$
$$= 4.65 \text{ sec}$$

(c) A→+: The horizontal range is:

$$R = (80.0 \cos 30.0°) \frac{\text{ft}}{\text{sec}} \times 4.65 \text{ sec}$$
$$R = 322 \text{ ft}$$

Example 3.6. From a car which has a velocity of 60.0 miles/hour northward with respect to the earth a man
projects a small package whose velocity
is 44.0 feet/sec in a direction 30.0° north
of east relative to the car. What is the
velocity of the package with respect to
the earth?

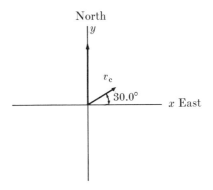

Solution. Let v_c = velocity of the
car, v_p = velocity of the package, and
v_{pc} = velocity of the package relative to
the car. Then

$$v_p = v_c + v_{pc}$$

From Figure 3.11 we see that the vector
v_p is the resultant between v_c and v_{pc}.
Thus

Figure 3.11.

$$v_p = \sqrt{(v_{pc} \cos 30.0°)^2 + (v_c + v_{pc} \sin 30.0°)^2} \qquad v_c = 60.0 \text{ mi/hr} = 88.0 \text{ ft/sec}$$
$$= \sqrt{(38.1)^2 + (110)^2} = 116 \text{ ft/sec} \qquad v_{pc} = 44.0 \text{ ft/sec}$$

and the direction of projection is

$$\tan \theta = 110/38.1$$
$$= 2.8871$$
$$\theta = 70.9° \text{ with the } x \text{ axis, or } 19.1° \text{ east of north.}$$

Problems

In all the problems involving g use the value 32.0 feet/sec² or 9.80 m/sec².
Neglect air resistance.

3.1. A ship is steaming 30.0° east of north at 30.0 miles/hour in still
water. What are its velocity components toward the east and toward the
north?

3.2. If the water in Problem 3.1 is moving with a velocity of 5.00
miles/hour in a westward direction, what is the resultant velocity of the
steamship?

3.3. A boat is directed with a velocity of 10.0 knots in a direction 60.0°
north of east in water which has a current of 5.00 miles/hour east; 1 knot =
1.15 miles/hour. What is the resultant velocity of the boat?

3.4. A train covers a distance of 250 miles in 8.00 hours. Find the average speed in miles per hour. Convert the result to feet per second, meters per second, and centimeters per second.

3.5. An automobile covers the distance of 50.0 miles from city A to city B in 1.00 hour and 10.0 minutes and then covers the distance of 75.0 miles from city B to city C in 2.00 hours. (a) Find the average speed from A to B in feet per second. (b) Find the average speed from B to C in feet per second. (c) Find the average speed from A to C in feet per second.

3.6. A body moves along a straight line so that its displacement s cm from the origin is given by $s = 10t$ where t is the time in seconds. Find the instantaneous speed at any time.

3.7. The displacement in Problem 3.6 is given by $s = 10.0t^3$; find the instantaneous speed at the end of 2.00 sec. (see Example 3.2).

3.8. The velocity of a body in centimeters per second changes with distance in centimeters according to the law $v = 20.0s$. What is the acceleration at a distance of 8.00 cm? *Hint:* observe that

$$\frac{dv}{dt} = \frac{dv}{ds}\frac{ds}{dt} = v\frac{dv}{ds}$$

3.9. Show that for constant accelerated motion the average speed over a time interval is the same as the instantaneous speed at the midpoint of the time interval. (*Hint:* Use the second equation of Equations 3.7 and form the ratio $(s_{n+1} - s_n)/(t_{n+1} - t_n)$.) Interpret the result.

3.10. A car moving northward with a velocity of 60.0 miles/hour is brought to rest in 45.0 sec. Find the average acceleration during this time interval.

3.11. An automobile is moving eastward with a velocity of 30.0 miles/hour. To avoid a head-on collision the brakes are applied and the car is brought to rest in 10.0 sec. Find the average acceleration.

3.12. A car with an initial velocity of 3.00 m/sec southward acquires a velocity of 15.0 m/sec in the same direction in 6.00 sec. Find the average acceleration of the car.

3.13. The following data represent the velocity v of a train as a function of the time t. Plot v as ordinate and t as abscissa:

v, mi/hr	0	20	40	52.5	57	60	60	60
t, sec	0	10	20	30	40	50	60	70

Then indicate the regions that correspond to (a) uniform acceleration, (b) variable acceleration, and (c) zero acceleration.

3.14. A body with an initial speed of 50.0 feet/sec is accelerating 2.00 feet/sec². Find (a) the speed after the body has traversed a distance of 500 feet and (b) the time taken to traverse this distance.

3.15. A body is projected horizontally on an ice skating floor with a speed of 100 feet/sec. It then decelerates at 10.0 feet/sec². After 5.00 sec what are (a) the speed of the body and (b) the distance traversed?

3.16. Plot the second of Equations 3.7 with v as ordinate and t as abscissa. Can you identify the resulting curve?

3.17. Referring to the last of Equations 3.7 and having at hand data giving v as a function of s, show how by plotting these data one can determine both the initial speed v_0 and the acceleration a.

3.18. Eliminate the parameter t between the first two of Equations 3.7 and thereby obtain the third equation.

3.19. As a man drives his car into a 20.0-foot garage with a velocity of 20.0 miles/hour he applies the brakes, producing a constant deceleration. Find (**a**) the smallest deceleration necessary to avoid striking the back wall of the garage and (**b**) how long it takes the car to come to rest.

3.20. A train starts from rest and travels with a constant acceleration a distance of 200 m in 20.0 sec. Find (**a**) the acceleration, (**b**) the average speed, and (**c**) the final speed.

3.21. Two bodies A and B, traveling in opposite directions, pass a given point. Body A traveling eastward passes the point with a velocity of 10.0 miles/hour and thereafter accelerates uniformly at 10.0 feet/sec². Body B traveling westward passes the point with a velocity of 20.0 miles/hour and thereafter accelerates uniformly at 6.00 feet/sec². When are A and B one tenth of a mile apart?

3.22. (**a**) The variation of g with latitude ϕ at sea level is given by $g = 978.1 + 5.17 \sin^2 \phi$. Plot g as a function of ϕ from the equator ($\phi = 0°$) to the poles ($\phi = 90°$). (**b**) The variation of g at a given latitude with altitude h above sea level is given by $g = g_0 - 0.000309h$, where g_0 is the value of g at sea level and a given latitude. If h is in meters, g is in centimeters per second, per second. Plot g as a function of h. Make any significant observations possible from the graphs.

3.23. A body is projected vertically upward from the top of a 400-foot building with a velocity of 80.0 feet/sec. Assuming that it just misses the building on the way down find (**a**) how high above the building the body rises, (**b**) the time it takes the body to return to its starting level, (**c**) where the body is 7.00 sec after projection, (**d**) the velocity with which the body strikes the ground, and (**e**) how long it takes the body to return to the bottom of the building.

3.24. A body is projected vertically upward from a point 100 feet above the ground with a velocity of 64.0 feet/sec. After 2.00 sec another body is projected vertically downward from a point 200 feet above the ground with a velocity of 64.0 feet/sec. (**a**) Find where the second body overtakes the first body. (**b**) How much sooner does the second body strike the ground?

3.25. From the three equations 3.7 prove that a body projected vertically upward with an initial speed v_0 has the same speed when it returns to its starting point.

3.26. From the three equations 3.7 prove that a body projected vertically upward with an initial speed v_0 takes the same time to reach the top of its flight as it does to return from the top to its starting point.

3.27. Prove that the average speed, as defined in Section 3.1, is the time average of the instantaneous speed. *Hint:* The time average of the instantaneous speed v_P between the times t_1 and t_2 is

$$\frac{1}{t_2 - t_1} \int_{t_1}^{t_2} v_P dt$$

3.28. A ball is projected upward from the top of a 300-foot building with a velocity of 64.0 feet/sec. (a) Find the position and the velocity of the ball at successive one-second intervals from the time it is projected to the time it strikes the ground. (b) Find also the time of flight.

3.29. A ball is thrown vertically upward and reaches a height of 15.0 m. Find (a) the projection velocity, (b) the time of flight, and (c) the speed with which the ball passes the starting point.

3.30. Two seconds after body A is projected downward from a tall building with a velocity of 100 feet/sec, a second body B is projected downward from the same point with a velocity of 200 feet/sec. Find where the bodies are abreast of each other.

3.31. Two bodies are projected vertically upward, one with a speed of 100 feet/sec and the other, 2.00 sec later, with a speed of 80.0 feet/sec. Where will the bodies meet?

3.32. An elevator with occupants is accelerating upward at 6.00 feet/sec². When the elevator has an upward speed of 10.0 feet/sec the hotel key drops from one of the occupant's hand a distance of 4.00 feet from the elevator floor. Find (a) how long before the key strikes the floor and (b) the position of the key, relative to its starting point, at the instant it strikes the floor.

3.33. A gun, located 32.0 feet above the horizontal, fires a shell horizontally with a muzzle velocity of 900 feet/sec. Find (a) the time of flight and (b) the range.

3.34. A ball is thrown horizontally from the top of a building with a speed of 20.0 m/sec. What is the velocity of the ball after 5.00 sec?

3.35. The range of a projectile fired horizontally with a speed of 600 feet/sec is 2.00×10^3 feet. Assuming the ground level, how high above it is the gun?

3.36. An airplane traveling horizontally at 8.00×10^3 feet above ground drops a bomb. Find (a) the time of flight and (b) the range of the bomb. For successive time intervals, show by diagram the position of the airplane in relation to that of the bomb, assuming that the airplane does not change its course and continues with the same speed.

3.37. A bomb is dropped from an airplane 6.00×10^3 feet above ground and traveling horizontally with a speed of 200 miles/hour. To score a hit on a mountain top 1.00×10^3 feet above ground, where should the plane be with respect to the target when the bomb is released?

3.38. A bomb, dropped from an airplane moving horizontally at constant speed 5.00×10^3 feet above ground, strikes a target on ground horizontally distant 2.60×10^3 feet. With what speed is the airplane traveling?

3.39. A projectile is fired at ground level with a speed of 500 m/sec at an angle of 30.0° above the horizontal. Find (**a**) the maximum height attained, (**b**) the time of flight, and (**c**) the range.

3.40. A baseball is thrown upward at an angle of 20.0° with the horizontal from the top of a building 44.0 feet high. The ball leaves the thrower's hand 6.00 feet above the rooftop with a velocity of 100 feet/sec. Find (**a**) the maximum height attained, (**b**) the time of flight, (**c**) the range, and (**d**) the velocity with which the ball strikes the ground.

3.41. Obtain Equations 3.14, 3.15, and 3.16 directly from the individual Equations 3.11 and 3.12.

3.42. Solve Problem 3.40 for the case of an angle of projection of 45.0° above the horizontal.

3.43. The distance s in feet covered by a body as a function of the time t in seconds follows the law $s = kt^3$ where k is a constant. Find the speed of the body after 3.00 sec. The value of k is 10.0.

3.44. The acceleration of a particle moving horizontally is given by $a = 12t - 2.0$, where t is in seconds and a is in feet per second, per second. When $t = 1.0$ sec the particle is at the origin and its acceleration is toward the left. When $t = 3.0$ sec the particle is 8.0 feet to the right of the origin. Find the velocity of the particle at $t = 3.0$ sec.

✓ **3.45.** A ship in still water is moving in a direction northeast with a velocity of 10.0 miles/hour. A man walks on deck in a direction east with a velocity of 2.50 miles/hour. What is the man's velocity relative to the earth?

Force, Mass, and the Dynamics of Translation

IN THIS CHAPTER WE SHALL study the concepts of force and mass and we shall see that their true significance is best obtained by a study of Newton's laws of motion which form the basis of the science of dynamics. It was pointed out in the previous chapter that dynamics deals with the effects of forces on the motions of bodies and we shall here confine our study to the kinetics of translation, leaving the study of statics, which is a special case of kinetics, to a later chapter. Newton's laws of motion form the basic framework for an adequate understanding of all branches of physics and engineering and the student is urged to devote a great deal of energy in learning these laws and their applications to the solution of problems of motion.

4.1. Force. Perhaps the first thing that comes to the mind of a student who meets the word *force* in a general course in physics is that it represents a *push* or a *pull* exerted upon a body. This idea is usually accompanied by the muscular effort that one must exert in doing things. In fact, some forces may be measured by the muscular effort involved, although it is a very inexact method. A much more scientific concept of force is obtained when we observe the effect of a push or a pull on a body. For example, when you exert an upward pull on a heavy box which is resting on the ground you are exerting a force which tends to lift the body. If you are strong enough you move the box upward, but if you are not, the force exerted only *tends* to change the state of motion of the body. Likewise, if you get behind the box and push, the force exerted has the effect of tending to change the state of motion of the body. In either case, if the box does not move under the application of this force there is a balancing force acting on the body in the opposite direction; in the first case the opposing force is the earth's gravitational attraction, pulling the box downward, and in the second case the opposing force is friction acting on the body in a direction that opposes the tendency to motion. When the applied force is great enough to produce an unbalanced force, a nonzero resultant force, the box moves and its state changes from one of rest to one of motion, i.e., there is produced a change in velocity, an acceleration.   These facts exemplify our common experience that a large enough force applied to a body resting on the ground is needed to set it in motion, and that, if a body is moving in a straight line with uniform motion, again a force, applied parallel to the direction of motion, is needed to slow it down or speed it up or, if applied sidewise, to deviate the body from its straight-line path.

We are now in a position to define force in a technical fashion.   *A force is a push or a pull, that is, an action, exerted by one body on another body; the effect is to tend to change the state of motion of the body on which the force acts.*   When we study Newton's laws of motion later in the chapter we shall see more clearly that an unbalanced force acting on a body produces an acceleration, and whenever a body is accelerating there is an unbalanced force acting.   In our study we shall be meeting various kinds of forces—gravitational force, frictional force, magnetic force, electric force, force of elasticity, nuclear force, etc.   Besides affecting the state of motion of a body, the application of a force may also change the size or shape of a body, as we shall see in the chapter on elasticity and strength of materials.

These effects of a force, the change in shape or physical dimensions of a body, or the acceleration of a body, are employed in comparing magnitudes of forces quantitatively.   We shall here describe as an example an instrument based on the first-mentioned effect, and the one having to do with accelerations will become evident after we have discussed Newton's laws of motion. The spring balance is a very convenient device for measuring forces.   It consists of a coil spring enclosed in a metal case; one end of the spring is attached to the case while the other end, attached to a pointer, is free to move so that the pointer traverses scale markings on the case.   The balance is most frequently used in its normal position with the free end hanging vertically down.   When the free end is subjected to a downward pull the spring stretches and the pointer always registers the same displacement for the same force. The balance must first be calibrated such that the scale markings indicate force units.   When the metric system is used a standard kilogram mass (see Section 1.4) is suspended from the balance and that scale marking opposite which the pointer comes to rest is marked "1 kg."   This designation represents the force with which the standard kilogram is pulled vertically downward toward the earth and is taken to mean the kilogram force, which is also defined (later in this chapter) as the weight of the kilogram mass.   Submultiples and multiples of the standard kilogram mass are in turn suspended from the balance to provide corresponding force unit markings.   After the balance has been calibrated it may be used to measure unknown forces.   When the English system is used the calibration is made with the standard pound and then the markings represent pound force.

4.2.   The Concept of Mass.   In Section 1.4 we stated that it takes a force to set in motion a body which is initially at rest or to stop a body initially in motion, and that this resistance which a body offers to any change in its state of rest or motion is due to the inertial property of the body. We also indicated that the numerical measure of inertia is what is termed the mass. We are now in a position to develop more clearly the meaning of mass.

Suppose we consider an experiment performed as illustrated in Figure 4.1. In (a) is shown a spring S in its normal (unstretched and uncompressed) state. In (b) the same spring is compressed, a body marked 1 and resting on a frictionless level platform is attached, and the system is released. The body moves to the right and its initial acceleration is observed to be a_1. In (c) the same spring has been compressed by the same amount as in (b), a different body marked 2 is attached, and the system is released. The observed initial acceleration here is a_2. When the experiment with bodies 1 and 2 is repeated with the use of a different compression value of the spring it is observed that the magnitudes of both a_1 and a_2 change, but in such a way that their ratio remains constant, or

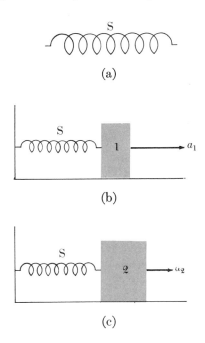

$$a_2/a_1 = \text{constant}$$

This ratio has a definite constant value for a given pair of bodies 1 and 2. If

Figure 4.1. *Illustrating the meaning of mass.*

another body marked 3, differing from either 1 or 2, is used in place of 2 and the experiment in (c) is repeated, the ratio of the observed initial acceleration a_3 to a_1 is again a constant whose value is different from the constant ratio value a_2/a_1. The constant is then a property of the two bodies involved. Furthermore, if, in particular, two bodies identical with body 1 are joined together, attached to the spring in (b), and the experiment is repeated, the observed initial acceleration is $a_1/2$. Again, if body 1 is cut in half so that two similar bodies are thus produced and the experiment is repeated with either of these smaller bodies, the observed initial acceleration is $2a_1$. In general, then, the initial acceleration is observed to be inversely proportional to the numerical measure of a property of the body. Hence, as a numerical measure of this property a constant number m_1 may be assigned to body 1 and a constant number m_2 may be assigned to body 2, and then the constant acceleration ratio is set equal to m_1/m_2, or

$$a_2/a_1 = m_1/m_2 \qquad (4.1)$$

The constant m_1 is now defined as the mass of body 1 and the constant m_2

is defined as the mass of body 2. This "operational" definition of mass, a definition based on experimental operation and observation, enables us to determine the mass of a body quantitatively. For, if m_1 is the mass of the standard kilogram, then the mass m_2 of any other body may be determined from Equation 4.1, since the ratio of the accelerations is obtainable from experiment.

Equation 4.1 states that under the action of a given force, acceleration is inversely proportional to mass; the smaller the mass the larger the acceleration, and the larger the mass the smaller the acceleration. Mass, then, is the numerical measure of that property of a body that resists being linearly accelerated and this property, as we have stated, is called *inertia*. An automobile with a mass of the order of 10^3 kgm possesses a great deal of inertia and it takes a correspondingly large effort to accelerate it. On the other hand, an electron with a mass of the order of 10^{-30} kgm possesses very little inertia. In a later section we shall describe the manner in which masses may be compared more conveniently by the process of weighing.

Mass is a scalar quantity and was considered a constant, since it is a measure of inertia, which was assumed to be an invariant property of a body, independent of the position and speed of the body. However, Einstein has shown theoretically in his theory of relativity that the mass of a body is actually a function of its speed, the relationship being

$$m = \frac{m_0}{\sqrt{1 - \left(\dfrac{v}{c}\right)^2}} \tag{4.2}$$

where m_0 is the mass of the body when at rest, v is the speed of the body, and c is the speed of light. This equation states that the mass of a body increases as its speed increases, becoming very large when v approaches c. When a body travels at high speed its inertia is greater, in accordance with Equation 4.2, and it therefore has a greater resistance to any change in its state of motion. The increase in m does not become appreciable until v approaches c, so that for ordinary bodies, moving with speeds small compared with c, the increase in m is negligible and undetectable. The equation has been demonstrated to be valid in experiments on very rapidly moving electrons and other atomic and nuclear particles, which may acquire speeds that are comparable to the speed of light and thus undergo a measurable increase in mass over their rest mass. Einstein's investigations in relativity theory led him to redefine mass in accordance with Equation 4.2 (see Section 34.5). We shall continue to employ the classical concept of mass and make the approximation that the mass is independent of the speed except in developments where the particles involved may attain speeds that demand the use of Equation 4.2. The student should keep in mind that whenever v is a significant fraction of c the relativistic mass as given by Equation 4.2 must be employed, and we shall call attention to this when necessary.

4.3. Linear Momentum. The product of the mass m of a body and its linear velocity v is called the *linear momentum*. Symbolically we write it as

$$\text{linear momentum} = mv \tag{4.3}$$

which is a vector quantity and has the same direction as the vector velocity. In the metric cgs and mks absolute systems the units of linear momentum are respectively the gram-centimeter per second (gm·cm/sec) and the kilogram-meter per second (kgm·m/sec). The English gravitational unit of linear momentum is the product of an English gravitational unit of mass, the slug (Section 4.6), and the foot per second, or the slug-foot per second (slug·ft/sec). In the following section we take up the mechanical laws of motion and we shall see how the linear momentum enters into the equation governing the laws of motion of bodies.

4.4. Newton's Laws of Motion: Translation. The complex science of mechanics has been simplified and unified by three natural laws of motion which are based principally on the observations of the great English physicist and mathematician Sir Isaac Newton (1642–1727). It was Newton who first formulated the laws most completely and accurately and they have become known as Newton's first law of motion, Newton's second law of motion, and Newton's third law of motion. We shall here study the statements, meanings, and applications of these laws in motions of translation only; Newton's laws as applied to motions of rotation are taken up in a later chapter. We shall first give statements of the laws (which should be committed to memory by the student), then follow with discussion, development, and applications.

NEWTON'S FIRST LAW: *A body at rest remains at rest, and a body in motion continues to move with a constant velocity in a straight line, unless, in either case, it is acted upon by an unbalanced force or a nonzero resultant force.*

NEWTON'S SECOND LAW: *The time rate of change of the linear momentum of a body is equal to the resultant force acting upon the body, and has the same direction as the resultant force.*

NEWTON'S THIRD LAW: *To every action (force) there is an equal and opposite reaction (force).*

Discussion of Newton's First Law. The first part of this law states that it takes an unbalanced force or a nonzero resultant force to change the state of rest of a body. Any body at rest certainly has forces acting upon it but analysis will reveal that the resultant of these forces is zero. For example, a book lying on a table is at rest simply because the forces acting on the book are balanced. Gravity exerts a downward force on the book but the table exerts an equal and opposite upward force, so that the resultant vertical force is zero and the book remains at rest. To effect a motion of the book, let us say an upward one, there would have to be applied an upward force greater in magnitude than the downward gravitational force. Then this net, or non-zero resultant, force acting upward would cause the body to change its state from one of rest to one of motion. Again, if we should desire to start the body moving in a horizontal direction we should have to provide a horizontal force of sufficient magnitude that it would be greater than the opposing maximum frictional force existing between the book and the table. Then the nonzero resultant force acting horizontally would impart motion to the book in the direction of the unbalanced force.

The second part of the first law says that a body which is set in motion and left to itself will maintain a motion of translation with constant velocity unless there is an unbalanced or nonzero resultant force acting on the body. We can illustrate the meaning of this when we consider what happens when a wooden block is projected horizontally on the living room rug. Experience tells us that the block quickly comes to rest since a large unbalanced force, due to friction and acting opposite to the direction of motion, decelerates the body and brings it to rest. If the block is projected on a horizontal polished floor, the unbalanced force due to friction is less and the body travels a longer distance before being brought to rest. Once again, if the block is projected on an ice skating floor it will travel a much longer distance before coming to rest. In none of the above illustrations has the body been left to itself, although the degree to which this is true is greatest in the case of the ice floor. However, if friction could be entirely eliminated, the block of wood once set in motion would continue to move forever with no deceleration, that is, with constant velocity. Let us now consider that there is maintained just enough constant horizontal push on the block to keep the body moving in a straight line on any horizontal surface with constant velocity. In this case there is no unbalanced force, the force of push being balanced by the force of friction. The body under these conditions will move with uniform velocity indefinitely unless an unbalanced force is acting such as by decreasing the pushing force—in which case the body would decelerate along the line of motion and eventually come to rest—or by increasing the pushing force—in which case the body would accelerate along the line of motion—or by introducing a force sidewise to the line of motion—in which case the body would change its *direction* of motion. Thus, the presence of an unbalanced force may change the magnitude or the direction of the velocity (or both); in Section 9.1 we shall see that a change in direction of velocity also is a type of acceleration.

The student will recognize that the above ideas are precisely those employed in our development of the concepts of mass. In fact, Newton's first law is often referred to as the law of inertia. If friction could be completely eliminated in our example above, the inertia of the body would keep it moving forever with constant velocity, and an unbalanced force or nonzero resultant force would be required to change the state of the motion. The first law in effect gives a qualitative relationship between the action of an unbalanced force and the resulting acceleration. The quantitative relationship between the resultant force and the acceleration is embodied in the second law of Newton. In fact, as will soon become evident, the first law is simply a special case of the second law.

Mathematical Formulation and Discussion of Newton's Second Law. In expressing mathematically the experimental observation that the measurable resultant force is equal to the measurable time rate of change in linear momentum the significant thing to realize is that a change in linear momentum can arise from a change in velocity only, a change in mass only, or a change in both mass and velocity. The formulation most often employed is the one in which the mass remains unchanged. Situations in which the mass varies, although more complex, are rather infrequently met with in most of the elementary applications of physics and engineering. We shall therefore proceed in the usual manner in which the mass is considered constant. In what follows we give a noncalculus development on the left side of the page and a calculus one on the right.

Let $\sum F$ represent the resultant force acting on a body whose mass is m. Let v_0 be the velocity of the body at the time t_0 and v its velocity at the time t_1. The change in linear momentum during the time interval $t = t_1 - t_0$ is $mv - mv_0$ and, by Newton's second law, we have

$$\sum F = \frac{m(v - v_0)}{t} \qquad (4.4\text{a})$$

where the right-hand member is the time rate of change of linear momentum. Since $(v - v_0)/t$ represents the acceleration a we have

$$\sum F = ma \qquad (4.5)$$

Let $\sum F$ represent the resultant force acting on a body whose mass is m and whose velocity at any time t is v. Then, by Newton's second law, we have

$$\sum F = \frac{\mathrm{d}(mv)}{\mathrm{d}t} \qquad (4.4\text{b})$$

where mv is the linear momentum. Performing the indicated differentiation:

$$\sum F = m\frac{\mathrm{d}v}{\mathrm{d}t} + v\frac{\mathrm{d}m}{\mathrm{d}t}$$

where the first term on the right represents a change in linear momentum due to a change in velocity, and the second term a change in linear momentum due to a change in mass. Taking the mass as constant and observing that $\mathrm{d}v/\mathrm{d}t$ is the acceleration a we have

$$\sum F = ma \qquad (4.5)$$

Equation 4.5 is the mathematical formulation of Newton's second law of motion for translation, as it is ordinarily stated, and it must be borne in mind that it is valid under the condition that the mass is constant. In accordance with the equation Newton's second law may be expressed as: *The acceleration of a body is directly proportional to the resultant force acting on the body and is in the same direction as the resultant force.* The equation states that it takes an unbalanced force to impart an acceleration to a body, and if the resultant force is zero there is no acceleration, the body being either at rest or in uniform motion in a straight line. Also, the larger the inertia of the body the larger the value of m and the smaller the acceleration or, to state it more generally, under the action of a constant resultant force, mass and acceleration are inversely proportional to each other. This leads again to Equation 4.1 which we obtained in our development of the classical concept of mass.

Equation 4.5 is undoubtedly the most significant equation in all of classical mechanics. Being a vector equation it expresses, first, an equality in magnitude—that is, the magnitude of $\sum F$ must be equal to the magnitude of ma, second, an equality in direction—that is, the resultant acceleration a is in the same direction as the resultant force $\sum F$ and, third, an equality in units— that is, the units used to express $\sum F$ must be the same as those used to express ma.

Although Equation 4.5 does not apply to bodies whose speed v is a significant fraction of the speed of light, c, it proves to be true that Newton's second law in the form given by Equation 4.4b, involving the time rate of change of momentum, holds in relativistic mechanics if the momentum is defined as $m_0 v / \sqrt{1 - (v/c)^2}$ (see also Section 34.5).

Discussion of Newton's Third Law. Experience has shown that a very effective way of exhibiting the meaning of the third law is by discussing some well-chosen examples which illustrate the principle of action and reaction.

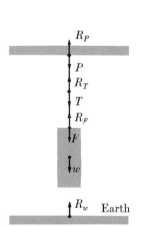

Figure 4.2. *Illustrating Newton's third law of motion: body at rest.*

As a first illustration consider a mass m supported by a cord above the earth's surface, as shown in Figure 4.2. One pair of action and reaction forces is the weight of the body, a downward force that is exerted by the earth on the body, and the equal and opposite upward force exerted by the body on the earth. Either of these being termed the action, the other is termed the reaction. If the weight of the body is taken to be the action w, then the reaction R_w is the force exerted by the body on the earth. Another pair of action and reaction forces is the downward pull F of the body on the cord and the equal and opposite upward pull R_F of the cord on the body. A third pair of action and reaction forces is the downward force P exerted by the cord on the support and the equal and opposite upward force R_P exerted by the support on the cord. In each of these cases it is to be especially noted that forces always occur in pairs as action and reaction forces, and these never act on the same body but always on different bodies. Action and reaction may also act on different parts of the same body as, for example, the downward action force T exerted by the lower portion of the cord on the upward portion and the upward reaction force R_T exerted by the upward portion of the cord on the lower portion. In general, if there is an interaction between two bodies A and B the force exerted by A on B is equal in magnitude but opposite in direction to the force exerted by B on A. When you exert an action force with your hand against the wall the wall exerts the equal and opposite reaction force on you. In the case of a bat striking a ball, during impact the bat exerts a force on the ball and the ball exerts an equal and opposite force on the bat.

Let us now consider another illustration, in which there is motion. The equality of action and reaction holds here as well. Consider the application of a horizontal force F to a mass m situated on a horizontal surface, as in Figure 4.3. Let the friction force between the body and the surface be f.

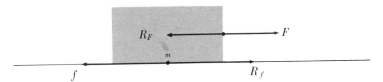

Figure 4.3. *Illustrating Newton's third law of motion: body in motion.*

We shall see in our study of friction that the magnitude of the friction force f for a given body at rest and in contact with a surface is equal to the magnitude of the applied force F, as shown, and varies from a value zero to some maximum value f_{max} which occurs when the body is in impending motion. With $F < f_{max}$ the body remains at rest, and we have the following pairs of action and reaction forces: the action F exerted on m and the reaction R_F exerted by m on the agent (say a rope) through which F is applied; the action f exerted by the surface on m and the reaction R_f exerted by m on the surface. If we apply Newton's second law to the body with respect to the forces acting horizontally on the body we have $F - f = ma = 0$ since $a = 0$. Hence the magnitude of the applied force F is equal to that of the frictional force f. As F increases, R_F increases by the same amount, and when F exceeds f_{max} the body accelerates in the direction of F. Under these conditions the reaction force R_F is still equal and opposite to the action force F. We may here ask how it is that the body ever attains a state of motion if it exerts as much in one direction as F exerts on it in the other. The answer is that only those forces that act *on* the body tend to change the state of motion of the body. The reaction forces R_F and R_f are exerted by m on other bodies and hence have no effect on the state of motion of m. When the body is accelerating, the amount by which the applied force F is in excess of the friction force overcomes the inertia of the body and imparts an acceleration to m. The reaction R_F then equals the resistance due to both friction and the inertia of m. When the force F is reduced to the value that maintains the body in uniform motion, then $a = 0$, F is just enough to overcome friction, and R_F equals the resistance due to friction alone.

4.5. Distinction between Mass and Weight. We have already stated that the mass of a body is the measure of the property known as inertia and is independent of the location of the body, the degree to which the body resists a change in its state of rest or motion being the same anywhere and wherever we make our measurement. We have also seen that by its nature mass is a scalar quantity.

Weight, on the other hand, we briefly defined as the force with which the earth attracts a body on its surface. This force is always directed vertically downward in the direction of a plumb line and is due to the phenomenon of gravitation. Since weight is a force, it is a vector quantity. If a body could be completely isolated it would have no weight but would still possess mass. Now it is an experimental fact, first demonstrated by Galileo, that all objects irrespective of their masses fall in a vacuum, under the action of gravity, with a constant acceleration g at any given place (see Section 3.5). When a mass m is permitted to fall freely, it is the constant downward unbalanced gravitational force acting on the body that is responsible for the constant acceleration g. Let us apply Newton's second law, Equation 4.5, to the motion of a freely falling body of mass m. Here $\sum F$ is the weight of the body w and we have

$$w = mg \tag{4.6}$$

which shows that the weight of a body at a particular place on the earth's surface is directly proportional to its mass. The proportionality holds only for some particular location since the value of g varies from the equator to the poles (see Section 3.5). Thus, although the scalar m is invariant with respect to location, the vector w is not. Equation 4.6 gives the relationship between m and w and is quite general; one may substitute mg for w or w/g for m whenever one wishes to make these substitutions. The units employed in this equation follow the general scheme of units for $\sum F$, m, and a in Equation 4.5, and we shall discuss these systems of units in the next section.

In view of the form of Equation 4.6 it is possible to compare the masses of bodies by comparing their weights. For this purpose an equal-arm balance is employed. An unknown mass is placed in one scale pan and standard or known masses are placed in the other scale pan until a balance is obtained. Using the subscripts x for unknown and s for standard we have

$$w_x = m_x g \quad \text{and} \quad w_s = m_s g$$

or $(w_x/w_s = m_x/m_s)$.

Since enough standard masses were used to effect a balance, the two scale pans and contents are equal: $w_x = w_s$ and $m_x = m_s$. This method of measuring the mass of a body is both convenient and accurate.

4.6. Systems of Units. Newton's second law affords the relationship that is basic in setting up the consistent systems of units. In Section 1.6 we pointed out that there were three absolute systems of units and three gravitational systems of units. We shall now see how these systems of units are derived.

Absolute Systems of Units. In an absolute system of units the fundamental quantities chosen are length, mass, and time. Let us now substitute the units of m and a in $\sum F = ma$ to obtain the derived absolute units of force in the cgs, mks, and fps absolute systems.

In the cgs absolute system, the unit of mass is the gram, the unit of acceleration is the centimeter per second, per second. Hence the derived unit of force in this system must be of such magnitude that, when acting alone, it imparts to a mass of one gram an acceleration of one centimeter per second, per second. This force is called one *dyne* and is rigorously defined as follows: *A dyne is that resultant force which imparts to a one-gram mass an acceleration of one centimeter per second, per second (1 cm/sec²).*

In the mks absolute system, the unit of mass is the kilogram, the unit of acceleration is the meter per second, per second. Hence the derived unit of force in this system must be of such magnitude that, when acting alone, it imparts to a mass of one kilogram an acceleration of one meter per second, per second. This force is called one *newton* (nt) and is rigorously defined as follows: *A newton is that resultant force which imparts to a one-kilogram mass an acceleration of one meter per second, per second (1 m/sec²).*

In the fps absolute system, the unit of mass is the pound, the unit of acceleration is the foot per second, per second. Hence the derived unit of force in this system must be of such magnitude that, when acting alone, it imparts to a mass of one pound an acceleration of one foot per second, per second. This force is called one *poundal* and is rigorously defined as follows: *A poundal is that resultant force which imparts to a one-pound mass an acceleration of one foot per second, per second (1 ft/sec²).*

The relationships between the dyne, the newton, and the poundal are obtained by the following conversions:

$$1 \text{ newton} = \frac{1 \text{ k\hspace{-0.5em}\rule[0.35em]{0.7em}{0.4pt}\hspace{-0.8em}gm} \cdot 1 \text{ \rule[0.35em]{0.5em}{0.4pt}\hspace{-0.65em}m}}{\text{sec}^2} \times \frac{1000 \text{ gm}}{\text{k\hspace{-0.5em}\rule[0.35em]{0.7em}{0.4pt}\hspace{-0.8em}gm}} \times \frac{100 \text{ cm}}{\text{\rule[0.35em]{0.5em}{0.4pt}\hspace{-0.65em}m}} = \frac{10^5 \text{ gm} \cdot \text{cm}}{\text{sec}^2}$$

$$= 10^5 \text{ dynes}$$

$$1 \text{ poundal} = \frac{1 \text{ p\hspace{-0.5em}\rule[0.35em]{0.6em}{0.4pt}\hspace{-0.7em}m} \cdot 1 \text{ f\hspace{-0.45em}\rule[0.35em]{0.5em}{0.4pt}\hspace{-0.6em}t}}{\text{sec}^2} \times \frac{453.6 \text{ gm}}{\text{p\hspace{-0.5em}\rule[0.35em]{0.6em}{0.4pt}\hspace{-0.7em}m}} \times \frac{30.48 \text{ cm}}{\text{f\hspace{-0.45em}\rule[0.35em]{0.5em}{0.4pt}\hspace{-0.6em}t}}$$

$$= 1.38 \times 10^4 \frac{\text{gm} \cdot \text{cm}}{\text{sec}^2}$$

$$= 1.38 \times 10^4 \text{ dynes}$$

Gravitational Systems of Units. In a gravitational system of units the fundamental quantities are length, force, and time. It will be recalled (Section 1.6) that their units are called gravitational units because they depend upon the gravitational force, the fundamental unit of force being the gravitational pull on (weight of) a standard or unit mass. Since the gravitational pull on a body varies from place to place over the earth's surface the unit of force is taken to be the weight of a standard mass at sea level and 45° latitude, where the acceleration due to gravity has the arbitrarily chosen standard value 9.80665 m/sec² or 32.174 feet/sec².

When the unit of mass is taken as one gram mass (1 gm) the unit of force is the gram force (1 gf). This is defined as follows. *The gram force is the gravitational pull on, or the weight of, a one-gram mass where the acceleration due to gravity is 980.665 cm/sec².*

When the unit of mass is taken as one kilogram mass (1 kgm) the unit of force is the kilogram force (1 kgf). This is defined as follows: *The kilogram force is the gravitational pull on, or the weight of, a one-kilogram mass where the acceleration due to gravity is 9.80665 m/sec².*

When the unit of mass is taken as one pound mass (1 pm) the unit of force is the pound force (1 pf). This is defined as follows: *The pound force is the gravitational pull on, or the weight of, a one-pound mass where the acceleration due to gravity is 32.174 feet/sec².*

With our units of force defined as above we are now in a position to express the units for $\sum F$ and a in Newton's second law and proceed to obtain the derived gravitational units of mass in the cgs, mks, and English gravitational systems.

We shall first consider the English gravitational system. Here the unit of force is the pound force and the unit of acceleration is the foot per second, per second. Hence the derived unit of mass in this system must be of such magnitude that when acted on by a resultant force of one pound force its acceleration is one foot per second, per second. This mass is called one *slug* and is rigorously defined as follows: *One slug is the mass of a body that accelerates one foot per second, per second (1 ft/sec²) when acted upon by a resultant force of one pound force (1 pf).*

In the cgs gravitational system the unit of force is the gram force and the unit of acceleration is the centimeter per second, per second. Hence the derived unit of mass in this system must be of such magnitude that when acted on by a resultant force of one gram force its acceleration is one centimeter per second, per second. No name has been assigned to this cgs gravitational mass but it is rigorously defined as *the mass of a body that accelerates one centimeter per second, per second (1 cm/sec²) when acted upon by a resultant force of one gram force (1 gf).*

In the mks gravitational system the unit of force is the kilogram force and the unit of acceleration is the meter per second, per second. Hence the derived unit of mass in this system must be of such magnitude that when acted on by a resultant force of one kilogram force its acceleration is one meter per second, per second. Here also no name has been assigned to this mks gravitational mass, but it is rigorously defined as *the mass of a body that accelerates one meter per second, per second (1 m/sec²) when acted upon by a resultant force of one kilogram force (1 kgf).*

In accordance with the definitions above, a one-pound force (1 pf) imparts an acceleration of 32.2 feet/sec² to a one-pound mass (1 pm) and an acceleration of one foot per second, per second (1 ft/sec²) to a mass of one slug. Thus:

$$1 \text{ pf} = 1 \text{ pm} \times 32.2 \text{ ft/sec}^2 \qquad (4.7)$$
$$1 \text{ pf} = 1 \text{ slug} \times 1 \text{ ft/sec}^2 \qquad (4.8)$$

From Equations 4.7 and 4.8 we see that the slug is 32.2 times as massive as the pound mass, or

$$1 \text{ slug} = 32.2 \text{ pm} \qquad (4.9)$$

Since the weight of 32.2 pounds mass is 32.2 pounds force, the mass of a body in slugs is obtained by dividing its weight in pounds force by 32.2 feet/sec². This is shown by the general relation between mass and weight, Equation 4.6, which for this purpose is better expressed as $m = w/g$. If w is in pounds force and g is the gravitational acceleration in feet per second, per second, then m is in slugs.

Similarly we have the relations

$$1 \text{ gf} = 1 \text{ gm} \times 981 \text{ cm/sec}^2 \qquad (4.10)$$
$$1 \text{ kgf} = 1 \text{ kgm} \times 9.81 \text{ m/sec}^2 \qquad (4.11)$$

Since $1 \text{ pm} \times 1 \text{ ft/sec}^2 = 1 \text{ poundal}$, $1 \text{ gm} \times 1 \text{ cm/sec}^2 = 1 \text{ dyne}$, and $1 \text{ kgm} \times 1 \text{ m/sec}^2 = 1 \text{ newton}$, we see from Equations 4.7, 4.10, and 4.11 that

$$1 \text{ pf} = 32.2 \text{ poundals} \qquad (4.12)$$
$$1 \text{ gf} = 981 \text{ dynes} \qquad (4.13)$$
$$1 \text{ kgf} = 9.81 \text{ newtons} \qquad (4.14)$$

In Table 4.1 are summarized these systems of units. Of the six systems

Table 4.1. *Systems of Units.*

	Absolute systems (fundamental quantities: length, mass, time)			Gravitational systems (fundamental quantities: length, force, time)		
	cgs	mks	English (fps)	cgs	mks	English
Mass	gm	kgm	pm	(*)	(*)	slug
Force	dyne	newton	poundal	gf	kgf	pf
Acceleration	cm/sec²	m/sec²	ft/sec²	cm/sec²	m/sec²	ft/sec²

* No name assigned.

of units, the English fps absolute, the cgs gravitational, and the mks gravitational are rarely employed. The cgs absolute and the mks absolute systems are used by physicists and engineers and the English gravitational system is widely used in engineering applications. As we have pointed out, we shall primarily employ these last three. However, we shall not avoid using the gram force and the kilogram force as purely force or weight units. Occasionally, we shall include in our illustrations and problems the English fps absolute system so that the student can acquire a more thorough working knowledge of the manipulation of diversified systems of units. When the pound is to be used as a force unit we shall indicate it as a pound force (pf) and when it is used as a mass unit we shall indicate it as a pound mass (pm). We shall similarly use the gram force (gf) and the gram mass (gm), also the kilogram force (kgf) and the kilogram mass (kgm). Often the way a statement is made leaves no doubt as to whether force or mass is meant; for example, if we say a force or weight of 10 pounds we mean 10 pounds force, or if we say a mass of 10 pounds we mean 10 pounds mass, etc.

Problems

4.1. The pointer of a spring balance used in a vertical position registers vertical displacements corresponding to masses hung on its lower end as follows:

Mass, gm	15.0	20.0	35.0	50.0	70.0	100
Displacement, cm	1.20	1.60	2.78	4.00	5.62	8.05

(a) Plot the force in dynes as a function of the displacement in centimeters. (b) Are the force and displacement proportional? Why? (c) How many dynes are necessary to stretch the spring 1 cm?

4.2. Two bodies B_1 and B_2 are attached to the ends of a spring as shown in Figure 4.4 and are made to interact by stretching and then releasing the spring. The masses B_1 and B_2 are 100 kgm and 6.00 kgm respectively. If the initial acceleration of B_1 is 3.25 m/sec² find the initial acceleration of B_2.

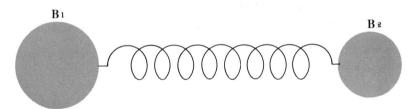

B_1 B_2

Figure 4.4. *Problem 4.2.*

4.3. The spring in Figure 4.4 of Problem 4.2 is compressed and the bodies are released simultaneously. The initial accelerations of B_1 and B_2 are −5.50 feet/sec² and 7.75 feet/sec² respectively. If the mass of B_1 is 0.125 slug find the mass of B_2. Express the answer in slugs and in pounds mass.

4.4. The rest mass of an electron is 9.11×10^{-28} gm. What is its mass when traveling at a speed which is 0.950 times that of light? What percentage increase in inertia does this represent?

4.5. Plot m/m_0 in Equation 4.2 as a function of the following values of v/c: 0.1, 0.2, 0.3, 0.4, 0.5, 0.6, 0.7, 0.8, 0.9, 0.95, 0.98. What significance do you attach to this graph?

4.6. An automobile with a mass of 4.00×10^3 pm is moving with a constant velocity of 30.0 miles/hour northward. Express the momentum of the car in the following systems of units: (**a**) cgs absolute, (**b**) mks absolute, (**c**) English fps absolute, (**d**) English gravitational.

4.7. A bullet with a mass of 3.00×10^{-2} kgm is fired from a gun whose mass is 5.00 kgm with a velocity of 610 m/sec, eastward. Find the velocity of recoil of the gun. (*Hint:* The forward momentum of the bullet is equal in magnitude to the backward momentum of the gun. This follows the principle of the conservation of momentum which is developed in Chapter 13.)

4.8. A 10.5 pm projectile is fired from a gun whose mass is 3.50×10^3 pm. The muzzle velocity of the projectile is 1.50×10^3 feet/sec, northward. What is the initial recoil velocity of the gun? See the hint, Problem 4.7.

4.9. Show that the time rate of change of linear momentum, when the mass m is variable in accordance with Equation 4.2, is given by $m^3 a / m_0^2$ where m_0 is the rest mass and a is the linear acceleration.

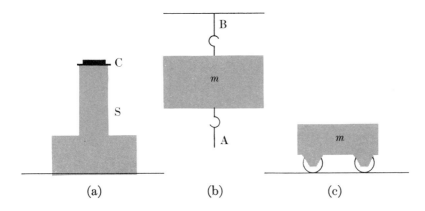

Figure 4.5. *Problem 4.10.*

4.10. In Figure 4.5a a card C rests on a stand S and a coin is positioned upon the card. The card can be snapped from under the coin without disturbing the coin. In (b) is shown a mass m suspended by a fine thread B, and a similar fine thread, A, is suspended from the mass. By applying a slowly acting downward force on A it is found that the thread B invariably breaks. However, if the downward applied force is in the form of a rapid jerk the thread A always breaks. In (c) is shown a car of mass m on a short section of a smooth track. When the track is rapidly moved to the right or the left the wheels of the car turn but the car remains at rest. Write out an explanation of each of the above.

4.11. Given the second and third laws of Newton, is it necessary to have the first law as a separate statement? Explain.

4.12. What is the relationship between the newton and the poundal?

4.13. What is the weight in pounds force of a 1-slug mass?

4.14. What is the relationship between the slug mass and the kilogram mass?

4.15. A body whose mass is 100 kgm is falling toward the earth with an acceleration of 9.80 m/sec². Taking the mass of the earth as 5.96×10^{24} kgm, find its reaction acceleration.

Applications of Newton's Second Law for Translation

$W_{E\ SHALL\ NOW\ CONSIDER}$ some examples which typify the application of Newton's second law to the solution of problems in dynamics. It is of value to realize that the equation $\sum F = ma$ may be applied to an entire system which is in motion or it may be applied to any individual part of that system. When applied to an entire system, $\sum F$ is the resultant force acting on the whole system, m is the mass of the system, and a is the acceleration of the system. When applied to an individual part of the system, $\sum F$ is the resultant force acting on that part, m is the mass of that part, and a is the acceleration of that part. This is illustrated by the Atwood machine, which is considered in this chapter.

5.1. Recommended Procedure. It is best to follow a definite procedure in applying Newton's second law to the solution of problems in dynamics. Often the student is unable to see through to a solution after reading the statement of a problem. By exercising a systematic approach it is possible not only to bite into the problem, so to speak, but also to effect a satisfactory solution. The steps that are generally employed are as follows:

(1) Read the statement of the problem carefully two or three times.

(2) Make a fair-sized neat diagram depicting the general idea involved in the problem. The values of length and angles and other data should be clearly indicated.

(3) Study the diagram in relation to the statement of the problem and decide on the choice of the body to which Newton's law is to be applied. Most often it is very easy to make the best choice, sometimes it is more difficult. Experience, obtained by working many problems, will make it possible to make the most judicious choice.

(4) Consider the body as being at the origin of a set of rectangular axes. Sometimes it is more convenient and advisable to draw the diagram through the body. At other times it is best to draw the axes separately and place the body at the origin. Next indicate the concurrent vectors which represent all the forces that act *on* the body. Label these vectors as to magnitude and

direction, using the numerical values given in the problem for the knowns and symbols for the unknowns.

(5) From this vector diagram find the resultant force $\sum F$ acting on the body.

(6) Apply Newton's second law, which is usually employed to determine an unknown acceleration.

5.2. Examples of Applications of Newton's Second Law. In the following examples the more convenient approximate values 980 cm/sec² = 9.80 m/sec² = 32.0 feet/sec² will be used.

Example 5.1. What unbalanced force acting on a mass of 200 gm will produce an acceleration of 3.25 cm/sec²? Solve the problem in the three absolute systems and in the English gravitational system.

Solution. In the cgs absolute system:

$$\sum F = ma$$
$$= 200 \text{ gm} \times 3.25 \text{ cm/sec}^2$$
$$= 650 \text{ dynes}$$

In the mks absolute system:

$$\sum F = ma$$
$$= 0.200 \text{ kgm} \times 0.0325 \text{ m/sec}^2$$
$$= 650 \times 10^{-5} \text{ nt}$$

In the English absolute system:

$$\sum F = ma$$
$$= 0.442 \text{ pm} \times 0.106 \text{ ft/sec}^2$$
$$= 4.68 \times 10^{-2} \text{ poundal}$$

$$m = 200 \text{ gm} \times \frac{\text{pm}}{454 \text{ gm}} = 0.442 \text{ pm}$$

$$a = \frac{3.25 \text{ cm}}{\text{sec}^2} \times \frac{\text{ft}}{30.5 \text{ cm}} = \frac{0.106 \text{ ft}}{\text{sec}^2}$$

In the English gravitational system:

$$\sum F = ma$$
$$= 1.38 \times 10^{-2} \text{ slug} \times 0.106 \text{ ft/sec}^2$$
$$= 1.47 \times 10^{-3} \text{ pf}$$

$$m = 0.442 \text{ pm} \times \frac{\text{slug}}{32.0 \text{ pm}}$$
$$= 1.38 \times 10^{-2} \text{ slug}$$

Example 5.2. An unbalanced force of 2.00 gf (4.42×10^{-3} pound force) acts on a mass of 300 gm (0.662 pound mass). Find the acceleration in the cgs and English absolute systems.

Solution. In the cgs absolute system:

$$a = \frac{\sum F}{m}$$

$$= \frac{1.96 \times 10^3 \text{ dynes}}{300 \text{ gm}}$$

$$= 6.53 \text{ cm/sec}^2$$

$$\sum F = 2.00 \text{ gf} \times \frac{980 \text{ dynes}}{\text{gf}}$$

$$= 1.96 \times 10^3 \text{ dynes}$$

In the English absolute system:

$$a = \frac{\Sigma F}{m} \qquad\qquad \Sigma F = 4.42 \times 10^{-3} \, \text{pf} \times \frac{32.0 \text{ poundals}}{\text{pf}}$$

$$= \frac{0.141 \text{ poundals}}{0.662 \text{ pm}} \qquad\qquad = 0.141 \text{ poundals}$$

$$= 0.213 \text{ ft/sec}^2$$

Example 5.3. An automobile of mass 3.50×10^3 pounds mass is moving at a velocity of 30.0 miles/hour toward the north. When the brakes are applied the automobile comes to rest in 22.0 sec. What is the unbalanced force, assuming a constant braking force? Express the answer in pounds force and in poundals.

Solution.

$$\Sigma F = ma \qquad\qquad m = 3.50 \times 10^3 \, \text{pm} \times \frac{\text{slug}}{32.0 \, \text{pm}}$$
$$= 109 \text{ slugs} \times 2.00 \text{ ft/sec}^2 \qquad\qquad = 109 \text{ slugs}$$
$$= 218 \text{ pf toward the south}$$

$$\Sigma F = 218 \, \text{pf} \times \frac{32.0 \text{ poundals}}{\text{pf}} \qquad a = \frac{(44.0 - 0) \text{ ft/sec}}{22.0 \text{ sec}} = 2.00 \text{ ft/sec}^2$$

$$= 6.98 \times 10^3 \text{ poundals toward the south}$$

Example 5.4. A block whose mass is 15.0 kgm rests on a rough horizontal surface. A constant horizontal force of 48.0 nt is applied to the block and accelerates it against a frictional force of 3.00 nt. Find how far the body moves in 2.50 sec.

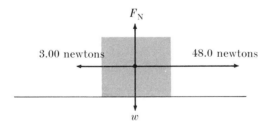

F_N

3.00 newtons   48.0 newtons

w

Figure 5.1.

Solution. The forces acting on the block are shown in Figure 5.1: w is the weight of the block and F_N, the force normal (meaning perpendicular) to the horizontal surface, is the reaction to w exerted on the block by the surface. Applying Newton's second law in the horizontal direction,

$$\Sigma F = ma$$

$$a = \frac{\Sigma F}{m}$$

$$= \frac{(48.0 - 3.00) \text{ nt}}{15.0 \text{ kgm}}$$

$$= 3.00 \text{ m/sec}^2$$

Now applying the kinematic equation:

$$s = v_0t + \tfrac{1}{2}at^2$$

$$= 0 + \frac{1}{2} \times \frac{3.00 \text{ m}}{\cancel{\text{sec}^2}} \times (2.50)^2 \cancel{\text{sec}^2}$$

$$= 9.38 \text{ m}$$

Example 5.5.   An elevator having a mass of 5.00 tons accelerates upward at the rate of 6.00 feet/sec². Find the tension in the supporting cable. Solve the problem in the English gravitational and English absolute systems.

Solution.   When a cord or cable is under the action of simultaneous pulls at both its ends, the cord or cable is said to be in *tension*. The force exerted by or on any element or length of the cord or cable is called the tension of that element. When a length of cord supports a weight the tension of the cord at its upper end is greater than that at its lower end. However, if the weight of the cord is relatively negligible, as we shall assume, the cord is considered to be under the same tension all along its length. In Figure 5.2 are shown in (a) the elevator E and the supporting cable C and in (b) the tension force T exerted by the cable and the elevator weight w, both acting on the elevator which is considered to be at the origin of coordinates.

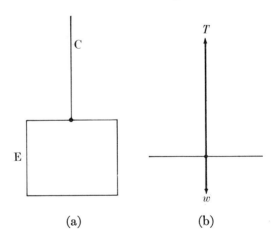

(a)   (b)

Figure 5.2.   (a) *An elevator* E *and support-ing cable* C.   (b) *Forces acting on an elevator.*

Since the system is being accelerated upward, the unbalanced force acts upward and is given by $T - w$. Applying Newton's second law to the elevator:

$$\Sigma F = ma$$
$$T - w = ma$$

In the English gravitational system, T and w are in pounds force, m is in slugs, and a is in feet per second, per second. Since 5.00 tons mass is 1.00×10^4 pounds mass,

$$m = 1.00 \times 10^4 \, \cancel{pm} \times \frac{\text{slug}}{32.0 \, \cancel{pm}}$$
$$= 312.5 \text{ slugs}$$
$$w = 1.00 \times 10^4 \text{ pf}$$

and

$$T - 1.00 \times 10^4 \text{ pf} = 312.5 \text{ slugs} \times 6.00 \text{ ft/sec}^2$$
$$T = 11,875 \text{ pf}$$
$$= 5.94 \text{ tf}$$

In the English absolute system, T and w are in poundals, m is in pounds mass, and a is in feet per second, per second. Hence

$$T - 3.20 \times 10^5 \, \cancel{\text{poundals}} = 1.00 \times 10^4 \text{ pm} \times 6.00 \text{ ft/sec}^2$$
$$T = 3.80 \times 10^5 \, \cancel{\text{poundals}}$$

This is the same as obtained above:

$$3.80 \times 10^5 \text{ poundals} \times \frac{\text{pf}}{32.0 \text{ poundals}} = 11,875 \text{ pf} = 5.94 \text{ tf}$$

Example 5.6. If a man of 144 pounds force is in the elevator of Example 5.5, what is the force exerted on him by the floor of the elevator as it accelerates upward?

Solution. It is here best to apply Newton's second law to the man standing on the elevator floor. Figure 5.3 shows the forces acting on the man at the origin. The downward force of 144 pounds force is the weight of the man and the upward force P represents the push of the elevator floor on the man. The unbalanced force is $P - 144$ pounds force; application of Newton's second law yields

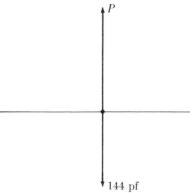

$$\Sigma F = ma$$
$$P - 144 \text{ pf} = 4.50 \text{ slugs} \times 6.00 \text{ ft/sec}^2$$
$$P = 171 \text{ pf}$$

Figure 5.3. *Forces acting on a man in elevator.*

Example 5.7. A block slides down an inclined frictionless plane. The angle of the plane is θ with the horizontal; find the acceleration of the block.

Solution. A diagram of block and plane is depicted in Figure 5.4. As shown, only two forces act on the block: the body's weight which we have represented by mg, where m is the mass and g is the gravitational acceleration, and the reaction of the plane on the block. This reaction may be considered to have two components, one parallel and one normal to the inclined plane. Since we are assuming a frictionless plane, the parallel component, which would be the frictional drag exerted by the plane on the block, is absent, and the only remaining component is the one normal to the plane, indicated as F_N. It is wise to choose a set of axes parallel and perpendicular to the inclined plane, as is done here. Since the block is accelerating downward along the negative x direction, the resultant force between F_N and mg is along this same direction. Since F_N acts perpendicularly to the x direction, the unbalanced force acting to accelerate the body is $mg \sin \theta$. An equivalent way of obtain-

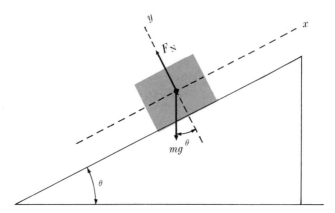

Figure 5.4. *Forces acting on a block situated on an inclined plane.*

ing this result for the unbalanced force is to consider that mg is resolved into a component $mg \cos \theta$ acting in the negative y direction and a component $mg \sin \theta$ acting in the negative x direction. The component $mg \cos \theta$ balances the force F_N, and the component $mg \sin \theta$ is unbalanced in the negative x direction. Now applying Newton's second law to the block,

$$\Sigma F = ma$$
$$mg \sin \theta = ma$$
$$a = g \sin \theta$$

We observe from this result that the acceleration is independent of the mass of the block and all bodies would slide down with the same acceleration $g \sin \theta$. If the body were free to fall vertically its acceleration would be g, but constrained to fall along the plane it acquires that component of the vertical acceleration which is parallel to the inclined plane.

Example 5.8.   The block in Figure 5.4 starts from rest at the top of the plane which is inclined at 30.0° with the horizontal.   Find the speed of the block after it has slid 150 cm.

Solution.   Using the expression for acceleration obtained in the previous example,

$$a = 980 \frac{\text{cm}}{\text{sec}^2} \times \sin 30.0°$$

$$= 490 \text{ cm/sec}^2$$

Now applying the kinematic equation:

$$v^2 = v_0^2 + 2as$$

$$= 2 \times 490 \ \frac{\text{cm}}{\text{sec}^2} \times 150 \ \text{cm}$$

$$= 147{,}000 \ \text{cm}^2/\text{sec}^2$$

$$v = 383 \ \text{cm/sec}$$

Example 5.9. In this example we shall illustrate the *free-body principle.* Let us take a system in motion that is composed of two or more parts or bodies which exert forces on each other. In such a case Newton's second law is applicable to any part of the system, and that part is considered isolated from the rest of the system. The motion of the isolated part, considered as a "free body," is then governed by its mass and the resultant of all the forces that act on it. When this is done it is helpful to indicate the isolated body by drawing a dotted closed loop around it and to show in a separate force diagram all of the forces acting on that part of the system. Then in succession, if necessary, other parts of the system may be considered free bodies and analyzed by the application of Newton's second law. The resulting expressions for all isolated bodies are mathematically simultaneous and can be combined to yield the desired result.

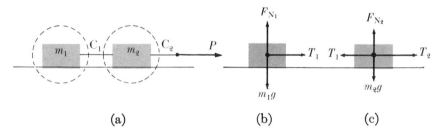

(a) (b) (c)

Figure 5.5. *Illustrating the application of Newton's second law to two bodies.*

As an illustration, consider the system in Figure 5.5a. Two bodies with masses m_1 and m_2 are on a horizontal frictionless surface and connected by a cord C_1. A horizontal force P applied to cord C_2 imparts an acceleration to the system. Find expressions for the tensions T_1 in cord C_1 and T_2 in cord C_2.

Solution. In (b) are shown the forces acting on m_1, considered as a free body, and in (c) are shown the forces acting on m_2 considered as a free body. On body m_1 there are three forces acting: a force m_1g due to its weight, the normal force F_{N_1} exerted by the surface, and the tension T_1. On body m_2 there are four forces acting: a force m_2g due to its weight, the normal force F_{N_2} exerted by the surface, and the tensions T_1 and T_2. Notice that T_1 acts to the right with respect to m_1, and acts to the left with respect to m_2. These represent an action-and-reaction pair between both bodies. Both bodies experience the same horizontal acceleration a. Applying Newton's second law in the horizontal direction to each of the bodies (the vertical forces are balanced on each body) we have

in (b): $\qquad T_1 = m_1 a$ $\hfill$ (5.1)

in (c): $\qquad T_2 - T_1 = m_2 a$ $\hfill$ (5.2)

The sum of these equations yields

$$T_2 = (m_1 + m_2)a \qquad\qquad (5.3)$$

which is simply the result when Newton's second law is applied to the entire system. Thus the unbalanced force is T_2, and the total mass is the sum of both masses. It is to be noticed that the tension in C_2 is greater than that in C_1.

Example 5.10. In this example we shall illustrate the laboratory device known as the Atwood machine, shown in Figure 5.6a. It consists of a cord passing over a pulley and masses m_1 and m_2 attached to the ends of the cord. The larger of the masses, say m_2, accelerates downward and the smaller mass accelerates upward. We shall here consider the more simplified version in accordance with which it is assumed that the influences of friction and the masses of the cord and pulley are negligible. It is then true that the cord, assumed inextensible, has the same tension T throughout and the accelerations of m_1 and m_2 are numerically the same. We wish to find an expression for the acceleration a, and this may be done by isolating the masses m_1 and m_2 as free bodies and applying Newton's second law to the bodies separately.

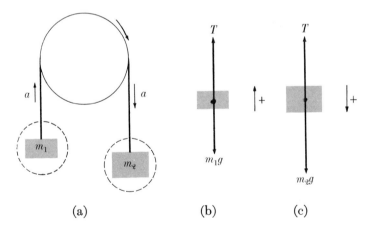

(a) $\qquad\qquad\qquad$ (b) $\qquad\qquad\qquad$ (c)

Figure 5.6. *The Atwood machine.*

In Figure 5.6b are shown the forces acting on m_1 considered as a free body and in Figure 5.6c are shown the forces acting on m_2 considered as a free body. Applying Newton's second law $\Sigma F = ma$, we have in (b), taking the upward direction as positive:

$$T - m_1 g = m_1 a \qquad\qquad (5.4)$$

and in (c), taking the downward direction as positive:

$$m_2 g - T = m_2 a \tag{5.5}$$

Adding Equations 5.4 and 5.5 we have

$$(m_2 - m_1)g = (m_1 + m_2)a \tag{5.6}$$

and

$$a = \frac{m_2 - m_1}{m_1 + m_2} g \tag{5.7}$$

which is the required expression. By applying Newton's second law to the whole system we observe that the unbalanced force is $(m_2 - m_1)g$ and the entire mass is $m_1 + m_2$. Hence $\sum F = ma$ leads directly to Equation 5.6. The advantage in using the method of isolating each body in turn is that it leads to expressions which make it possible to calculate the tension in the cord. From Equation 5.7 we see that the acceleration of the masses is always less than the acceleration due to gravity. By using two masses that are nearly equal the acceleration of the system can be made quite small and thus precisely measurable. In this way Equation 5.6 may be used to measure g accurately. When the Atwood machine is employed to measure g accurately one must correct for pulley friction and for the pulley motion.

From Equation 5.4 we see that the tension is greater than $m_1 g$ by an amount $m_1 a$, where $m_1 g$ is the amount that the tension would be if the cord simply supported the mass m_1. From Equation 5.5 we see that the tension is less than $m_2 g$ by an amount $m_2 a$, where $m_2 g$ is the amount that the tension would be if the cord simply supported the mass m_2. The student should have no difficulty in explaining these facts.

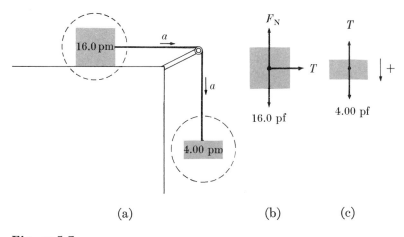

(a)   (b)   (c)

Figure 5.7.

Example 5.11. In Figure 5.7a a 4.00-pound-mass block hanging freely over the pulley is attached by a cord to the 16.0-pound-mass block which is on a frictionless horizontal table. When released the system accelerates. Find the acceleration and the tension in the cord. Neglect the friction and the motion of the pulley.

Solution.   Isolating each body as indicated we have the free-body force diagrams in (b) for the 16.0-pound mass and in (c) for the 4.00-pound mass. Now applying Newton's second law $\sum F = ma$ to each we obtain, using the English gravitational system, for (b):

$$T = \frac{16.0}{32.0}\, a$$

and for (c):

$$4.00 - T = \frac{4.00}{32.0}\, a$$

Therefore,

$$4.00 = \frac{20.0}{32.0}\, a$$

or

$$a = 6.40 \text{ ft/sec}^2$$

and

$$T = 3.20 \text{ pf}$$

Problems

In the following, use the convenient and approximate values $g = 980 \text{ cm/sec}^2 = 9.80 \text{ m/sec}^2 = 32.0 \text{ feet/sec}^2$.

5.1.   A body of 2.50 pounds mass experiences an acceleration of 3.64×10^{-2} feet/sec². Find the unbalanced force. Solve the problem in the three absolute systems and the English gravitational system.

5.2.   An unbalanced force of 5.50 nt acts on a body whose mass is 10.4 kgm. If the body is initially at rest, **(a)** how far does the body move in 3.00 sec and **(b)** what is the velocity attained by the body at the end of this time?

5.3.   An automobile of 3.60×10^3 pounds mass enters a 20.0-foot garage with a speed of 6.00 miles/hour. How much must the car decelerate, after

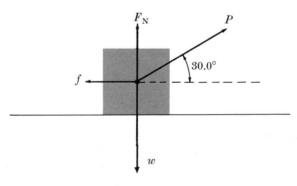

Figure 5.8.   *Problem 5.4.*

the driver applies the brakes upon entering the garage, to avoid striking the back end of the garage? Also, find the force acting, assuming it is constant.

5.4. Figure 5.8 shows a 4.50 kgm block on a horizontal surface. The applied force P is 25.0 nt and the frictional force f is 5.00 nt. Find (**a**) the horizontal acceleration and (**b**) the value of F_N.

5.5. Find the difference in the tension existing in the supporting cable of an elevator (mass 4.00 tons) when it accelerates upward and downward, at 8.00 feet/sec².

5.6. A man of 160 pounds mass stands in an elevator which descends with an acceleration of 5.52 feet/sec². Find the apparent weight of the man in motion.

5.7. A child weighing 64.0 pounds force stands on a spring scale which is on the floor of an elevator. What is the scale reading (**a**) when the elevator ascends with an acceleration of 3.50 feet/sec², (**b**) when the elevator descends with the same acceleration, and (**c**) when the elevator descends with an acceleration of 32.0 feet/sec²?

5.8. What is the tension in the supporting cable of a 980 kgf elevator when (**a**) the elevator has an upward acceleration of 0.600 m/sec², (**b**) it has a downward acceleration of 0.600 m/sec², and (**c**) it moves with constant velocity upward or downward?

5.9. An elevator of 960 pounds mass is descending with a speed of 20.0 feet/sec. Find the shortest distance at which the elevator can be stopped if the greatest load the cable can support is 0.500 ton force.

5.10. A man weighing 200 pounds force has an apparent weight of 180 pounds force when he stands in an accelerating elevator. Find the acceleration.

5.11. A man can lift a maximum load of 130 pounds force. What must be the acceleration of an elevator that will enable the man to lift a load of 150 pounds force in the moving elevator?

5.12. Figure 5.9 shows a 10.0-pound mass on a frictionless inclined plane joined to an 8.00-pound mass by a cord stretched over a pulley. Neglecting

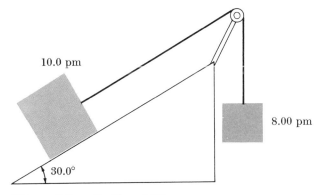

Figure 5.9. *Problem 5.12.*

the friction and motion of the pulley, find the acceleration and tension in the cord.

5.13. Figure 5.10 shows two inclined planes supporting two masses which are joined by a cord passing over a pulley. If m_2 is greater than m_1, under what condition (**a**) will the system accelerate with m_2 moving downward and (**b**) will the system not accelerate? Neglect friction and the motion of the pulley.

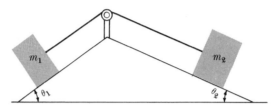

Figure 5.10. *Problem 5.13.*

5.14. In an experiment with an Atwood machine the mass m_1 in Figure 5.6 was 3.65 kgm and its acceleration was 30.5 cm/sec² downward. Find the mass m_2 and the tension in the string. Neglect friction and the motion of the pulley.

5.15. In an experiment with an Atwood machine the masses on opposite sides of the pulley were 4.00 and 4.25 pounds mass. Find the acceleration and tension in the string. Neglect the friction and motion of the pulley.

5.16. A shell of 8.00 pounds mass is fired from a gun. The barrel of the gun is 6.00 feet in length and the muzzle velocity of the shell is 1.80×10^3 feet/sec. What is the unbalanced force acting on the shell while it is in the barrel? Assume a constant acceleration.

5.17. A crate weighing 100 pounds force falls from a delivery truck traveling at 30.0 miles/hour. The crate slides a distance of 2.5 feet before coming to rest. Find the unbalanced force, assuming a constant deceleration.

5.18. A circus performer weighing 150 pounds force slides down a rope with an acceleration of 1.55 feet/sec². Find the tension in the rope.

5.19. In Example 5.11, call the mass of the block on the table m_1, and that of the hanging block m_2. Show that the tension is given by $T = m_1 m_2 g/(m_1 + m_2)$. Interpret the result.

5.20. A spring balance whose mass is 100 gm hangs from a cord which is attached to the ceiling of an elevator cage. When a mass of 500 gm is suspended from the balance and the elevator accelerates upward at 40.0 cm/sec² what are (**a**) the reading on the balance and (**b**) the tension in the cord?

5.21. Find, Figure 5.11, (**a**) the acceleration of the system and (**b**) the tensions in the cords. Neglect friction and the motion of the pulley.

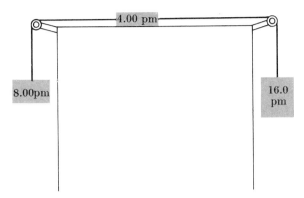

Figure 5.11. *Problem 5.21.*

5.22. Figure 5.12 shows two blocks on frictionless planes. Show that (**a**) the acceleration of the system is given by $m_2g \sin \theta/(m_1 + m_2)$ and (**b**) the tension in the connecting cord is given by $m_1m_2g \sin \theta/(m_1 + m_2)$. Neglect friction and the motion of the pulley.

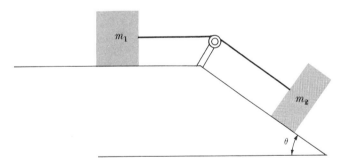

Figure 5.12. *Problem 5.22.*

5.23. A car of 4.80×10^3 pounds mass is traveling with a velocity of 15.0 feet/sec when the driver accelerates at such a rate that his velocity after a time t is given by $v = 15.0 + 0.100t^3$ where v is in feet per second and t is in seconds. Find (**a**) the velocity, (**b**) the acceleration, and (**c**) the unbalanced force acting on the car 4.00 sec after acceleration sets in. Note that the car accelerates nonuniformly.

5.24. A body whose mass is 490 gm is at rest when a variable force, given by $F = 75.0 - 2.00t$ where F is in grams force and t is in seconds, acts on it. Find (**a**) the acceleration at time $t = 0$, (**b**) the acceleration at time $t = 5.00$ sec, (**c**) the velocity at $t = 5.00$ sec, and (**d**) the distance traversed after 5.00 sec.

5.25. Find the accelerations of body A and body B, in Figure 5.13, neglecting friction and the masses of the pulleys. (*Hint:* The displacement of B upward is one-half the displacement of A downward. Let T be the tension in the cord supporting B; then $2T$ is the tension throughout the cord supporting A.)

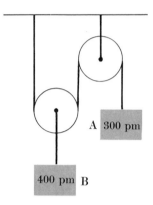

Figure 5.13.   *Problem 5.25.*

5.26. In Figure 5.14 what are the accelerations of bodies A and B and the tension in the cord supporting B? Neglect friction and the masses of the pulleys. (*Hint:* The displacement of B downward is twice the displacement of A upward. Let T be the tension in the cord supporting B, then $2T$ is the tension in the cord supporting A.)

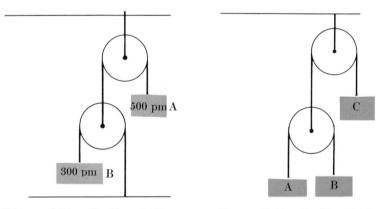

Figure 5.14.   *Problem 5.26.*   **Figure 5.15.**   *Problem 5.27.*

5.27. In Figure 5.15 find the accelerations of the masses A, B, and C when (**a**) A = 100 gm, B = 200 gm, C = 160 gm, and (**b**) A = 100 gm, B = 200 gm, C = 300 gm. Neglect friction and the masses of the pulleys.

Friction

WE SAW THAT IT IS NECESSARY, in order to ascertain the state of motion of a body, to consider the combined effects of *all* the forces that act upon the body. In the preceding chapters on mechanics we neglected the effects of friction simply because we wished to concentrate on the laws, principles, and manipulations which were there developed. Whenever an object moves or tends to move while in contact with another object or medium, there is always present a frictional force which opposes the motion or tendency of motion. We must now see how to take friction into account, and study the friction laws which make it possible to express quantitatively the force of friction.

We shall see that there are three kinds of friction: *sliding* (static and kinetic) *friction*, *rolling friction*, and *viscous friction*. Sliding and rolling friction apply to the relative motion, or tendency of motion, of one solid body in contact with another solid body. Viscous friction comes into play when a body moves through a fluid (i.e., a liquid or a gas).

The effects of friction are at times desirable and at other times undesirable. Without friction we could not walk, or stop and start an automobile or train or airplane, or expect nails to hold boards in place. On the other hand, whenever friction is present the cost of operating machinery increases, since work must be done to overcome friction. Friction causes wear between contact surfaces and it generates much heat. The engineer must minimize these effects by the use of bearings, rollers, and lubricants.

6.1. Coefficients of Static and Kinetic Friction. Consider a block on a table top (Figure 6.1) under the action of an applied force F. The weight of the block is w, the normal (perpendicular) reaction of the table on the block is F_N, and the friction force is f, which actually acts tangent to the contact surfaces of block and table but which has been placed for simplicity as shown, since its effect is to oppose the tendency of motion of the block.

First consider the conditions under which the block remains at rest. The applied force F could then have any value from zero to some critical value beyond which the block would cease to be in a static state. As F increases from zero to this critical value the friction force f, at all times equal to F when the body is at rest, increases in like manner from zero to a maximum

limiting value f_s. When the maximum value of friction is acting, the body
is in *impending* motion, and an increase of F beyond the corresponding critical value would accelerate the body in the direction of F. The value of f_s
may be determined by measuring—for example, with a spring balance—the
critical value of the force F. In the case of the block shown in Figure 6.1,

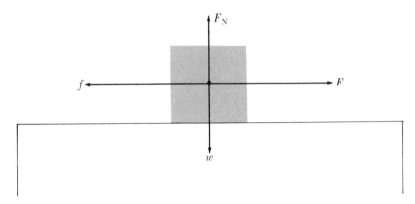

Figure 6.1.   *Illustrating the force of friction.*

and again when different weights are placed on top of the block so that the
determinations are made for varying values of F_N, it is found that the value
of the maximum static friction is directly proportional to the normal reaction, or

$$f_s \propto F_N$$

Forming an equation in the usual manner:

$$f_s = \mu_s F_N \tag{6.1}$$

where μ_s, the constant of proportionality, is called the *coefficient of static friction* and is defined, for a pair of surfaces, as the ratio of the maximum static
friction to the normal force pressing the surfaces together. Since the limiting friction between a pair of surfaces depends only upon the normal (perpendicular) force, the value of f_s should be the same when the block (Figure 6.1)
is on edge: the area of contact is then different but F_N remains unaltered.
This, in fact, is roughly true, and illustrates the empirical observation that
*the force of friction between a pair of surfaces is roughly independent of the area
of contact of their surfaces.* Some representative values of μ_s are listed in
Table 6.1. It is a rather simple task, with a more extensive table, to compute f_s for any given situation.

Let us now see what is the state of affairs when the block in Figure 6.1 is
set in sliding motion. To do so requires a momentary applied force F which
is just larger than the critical value. However, experiment shows that while
it takes an applied force larger than the critical value to set a body in motion,
once the body is in motion it takes an applied force less than the critical value

Table 6.1. *Some coefficients of static friction μ_s and kinetic friction μ_k.*

Surfaces	μ_s	μ_k
Steel on ice	0.02	0.01
Brass on steel	0.51	0.44
Oak on oak (perpendicular to grain)	0.54	0.32
Oak on oak (parallel to grain)	0.62	0.48
Leather on oak (parallel to grain)	0.61	0.52
Copper on glass	0.68	0.53
Rubber tire on dry concrete road	0.90	0.70

to keep it at constant velocity. When the velocity is constant there is no acceleration, and the applied force is equal to the friction force on the sliding body. It is this force of sliding friction, also called *kinetic friction, f_k*, which also is proportional to the force F_N, so that

$$f_k = \mu_k F_N \tag{6.2}$$

where μ_k is called the *coefficient of kinetic friction* and is defined, for a pair of surfaces, as the ratio of the force of kinetic friction to the normal force pressing the surfaces together. As in the case of static friction, f_k is roughly independent of the area of contact of the surfaces. Furthermore, f_k is nearly independent of the relative velocity of the sliding surfaces. Some representative values of μ_k are listed in Table 6.1 where it is to be noted that $\mu_k < \mu_s$.

6.2. Laws of Friction. The facts that we have covered in the preceding section are ordinarily stated as follows and known as the laws of friction.

(1) The frictional force (static or kinetic) is proportional to the normal force pressing the surfaces together.

(2) The frictional force (static or kinetic) is independent (approximately) of the area of the contact surfaces.

(3) Static friction is greater than kinetic friction.

(4) The frictional force (kinetic) is independent (approximately) of the relative velocity of the sliding surfaces.

When we look at a greatly magnified view of a pair of flat surfaces in contact we see a condition similar to that depicted in Figure 6.2. The sur-

Figure 6.2. *Magnified view of two flat surfaces in contact.*

faces are not even approximately flat, exhibiting a myriad of irregularities which are mutually interlocked. To undo such intermeshing requires a force.

Furthermore, at the contact areas there are interatomic and intermolecular forces that also contribute to the frictional forces. When the surfaces are metallic the force acting on each small area of contact brings about an actual welding together of the materials.

Although the "laws" of friction entail approximations they serve quite adequately in physics and engineering applications. One must be certain, however, that he does not step out of the range of validity of the law when it is applied. For instance, the coefficient of kinetic friction is substantially independent of the velocity for speeds of less than about 250 cm/sec except very slow speeds, of the order of 5×10^{-4} cm/sec. For such slow speeds the kinetic coefficient approaches the static coefficient, while for very large ones the coefficient decreases with increasing speed.

In general, the amount of friction present depends on the nature of the surfaces in contact and on their condition, i.e., whether the surfaces are smooth, rough, polished, wet, dry, etc. Liquid lubricants are often employed to reduce friction but then the resulting smaller friction is due to the sliding of one film of lubricant over another. This really alters the character of the friction and we shall deal with this kind of friction in Section 6.4.

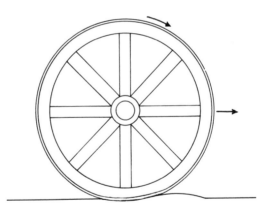

Figure 6.3. *Illustrating rolling friction.*

6.3. Rolling Friction. Figure 6.3 shows the condition of contact surfaces when a wheel (or cylinder) rolls over a horizontal surface. Both the wheel and the surface may be distorted, the amount of distortion depending on the hardness of the surfaces. As the wheel moves forward it must continually come out of depressions and overcome humps in front of it. This creates a resistance to motion which gives rise to *rolling friction*. Rolling friction is much less than sliding friction for equal contact surfaces. If the horizontal surface is hard and the spherical surface is soft, as an automobile tire on a hard road, the tire experiences the greater amount of depression. In the case of two hard surfaces, a train wheel rolling on a track, the depressions are very slight and the rolling friction is considerably smaller.

The sliding friction present when a shaft rotates in a sleeve may be very much reduced by the use of a lubricant, so that the axle rides on a thin film of oil, involving a relatively small amount of friction. To simplify the problem of lubrication and wear between contact surfaces, sliding friction is replaced by rolling friction with the use of ball or roller bearings.

Rolling friction is treated quantitatively in the same way as sliding friction, and the force of rolling friction is proportional to the normal reaction. However, as already stated, the coefficients for rolling friction are very small—for instance, of the order of a few thousandths for ball bearing on steel.

6.4. Viscous Friction. When a body moves through a fluid (liquid or gas), its motion is opposed by a force called *viscous friction*, which is a type of friction that acts between the fluid particles. The laws of viscous friction are entirely different from those of sliding and rolling friction, viscous friction force depending on the relative speed and the contact area of fluid and body.

To see on what quantities this internal friction in fluids depends let us consider a layer of liquid such as glycerin between two flat solid surfaces U and L, as depicted in cross section in Figure 6.4. Let there be applied to the

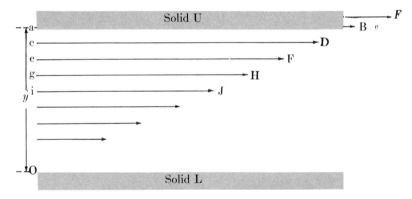

Figure 6.4. *Liquid friction.*

upper solid a constant force F of sufficient magnitude to set the solid in motion. It will be found that U accelerates in the direction of F for a short time, after which it moves with a constant limiting velocity v, represented by the vector AB. Now suppose the layer of liquid between AB and CD removed, and consider the lower surface of U in contact with the new top of the liquid CD. Under the action of the same constant force F the solid U will acquire a limiting velocity represented by the vector CD. Proceeding in like manner with respect to the levels EF, GH, IJ, etc., in the liquid, we should find that the limiting velocities, under the action of the same constant force F, are represented respectively by the vectors EF, GH, IJ, etc. It will be observed that the terminating points of the vectors B, D, F, H, J, etc., fall along a straight line which passes through the point O on the upper surface of solid L. A vertical line through O passes through the points A, C, E, G, I, etc. We thus have the experimental result that

$$v \propto y \qquad (6.3a)$$

where y, as indicated in the figure, is the vertical distance between the restraining surfaces of U and L measured upward from L. The proportionality given by the expression 6.3a holds under the controlled conditions that F is constant and that the contact area A of solid U is constant. For any given value of y and A, it is found that the limiting velocity is proportional to the applied force:

$$v \propto F \qquad (6.3b)$$

Finally, if F and y are maintained constant, then

$$v \propto 1/A \qquad (6.3c)$$

When all the quantities are permitted to vary, then

$$v \propto Fy/A \qquad \text{or} \qquad F \propto Av/y$$

and, forming an equation, we have

$$F = \eta Av/y \qquad (6.4)$$

where the constant of proportionality, η, is known as the *coefficient of viscosity* and is characteristic of a given liquid at a given temperature. Since the action of the applied force is that of maintaining uniform motion, there is no acceleration and the frictional force is equal and opposite to the applied force. Hence the right-hand expression of Equation 6.4 represents in magnitude the viscous friction.

Before discussing the law expressed by Equation 6.4 let us say something of the nature of this viscous friction. On the lower surface of U and on the upper surface of L there is a layer of liquid that adheres to, and has zero velocity with respect to, the solid. When U moves with uniform speed v, the force necessary to maintain this motion is what is required to overcome the friction between these adhering liquid films and the intervening layers of liquid. The nature of this friction is such that one layer of intervening liquid slides past the adjacent one below it. It is as if an upper layer drags a lower layer of liquid, but the lower layer moves along at a reduced speed. The layer of liquid that is directly above the zero-velocity layer adhering to L moves with a small velocity, the succeeding layers above that with velocities in accordance with the expression 6.3a. Thus, a cubic portion of liquid, before there is relative motion between U and L, deforms into a rhomboidal shape while U moves with respect to L. This type of flow, characterized by the fact that adjacent thin sheets (laminae) of fluid slide over one another, is called laminar flow.

Equation 6.4 shows that the coefficient of viscosity, often called simply the viscosity, has the dimensions of a force times a distance divided by area times velocity. In the cgs absolute system this leads to the unit dyne-second per centimeter, per centimeter (dyne·sec/cm²); in the mks absolute system the unit is the newton-second per meter, per meter (nt·sec/m²). A coefficient of viscosity of 1 dyne·sec/cm² is called a *poise*, which may be defined from the physical concept of the coefficient of viscosity. Thus, suppose we consider a layer of fluid 1 cm thick between two plane surfaces. The force, applied tangent to one surface, per unit area of the surface, in dynes per square centimeter, that is necessary to move the surface with a speed of 1 cm/sec is numerically equal to the coefficient of viscosity of the fluid. If the magnitude of this force per unit area is 1 dyne/cm² the magnitude of the viscosity is 1 poise. Viscosities are also expressed in centipoises (1 cp = 10^{-2} poise) or in micropoises (1 μp = 10^{-6} poise). Table 6.2 gives some typical values of coefficients of viscosity.

Table 6.2. *Some coefficients of viscosity.*

Liquids	Temp., °C	η, cp	Gases	Temp., °C	η, μp
Acetone	15	0.34	Air	0	171
Benzene	20	0.65	,,	20	181
Glycerin	20	830	,,	80	209
Mercury	20	1.55	Carbon dioxide	20	148
Oil			Chlorine	20	133
Light machine	15	114	Helium	20	194
Heavy machine	15	660	Hydrogen	20	88
Paraffin	18	1018	Neon	20	311
Water	0	1.79	Nitrogen	15	174
,,	20.20	1.0000	Oxygen	19	201
,,	100	0.28			

Since the cohesive forces between the atoms or molecules of a liquid decrease with increasing temperature we should expect the viscosity of liquids to decrease likewise. They do, as is illustrated for water in Table 6.2. On the other hand, for gases the viscosity increases with increasing temperature, as may be seen from the values for air. In a gas the atoms or molecules are relatively far apart, exerting comparatively little interatomic or intermolecular influence. The manifestation of viscosity in the laminar flow of a gas is attributed to the drag of one sheet on another due to the diffusion of molecules from one layer to neighboring layers. The phenomenon is one of momentum transfer. When the molecules in one layer cross over into an adjacent layer having a lower velocity, the momentum transfer is greater than that occurring when molecules move to a layer having higher velocity. Thus a drag occurs: the high-velocity layer tends to slow down and the low-velocity layer tends to speed up. Increasing the temperature of a gas increases the molecular speeds, and theory shows that the viscosity should increase.

The laws of viscous friction embodied in Equation 6.4 hold for low veloc-

ities and flow that is laminar in character.   When the velocity exceeds a certain critical value the fluid resistance is no longer proportional to the first
power of the velocity, and the character of the flow changes from the laminar
type to a *turbulent flow*.   Turbulent flow, as well as methods of measuring
viscosity coefficients, are taken up in Section 18.5.

Example 6.1.   How much force applied parallel to a horizontal plane will
cause a box of 100 pounds mass, in contact with the plane, to be in impending
motion?   The coefficient of static friction is 0.250.

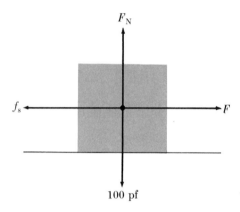

Figure 6.5.

Solution.   Figure 6.5 shows the forces acting on the box.   Since there is
no motion horizontally, the horizontal forces are balanced,

$$F = f_s$$

and from the law of friction, $f_s = \mu_s F_N = 0.250 F_N$.   Therefore,

$$F = 0.250 F_N$$

The vertical forces are also balanced.   Hence,

$$F_N = 100 \text{ pf}$$

and this leads to

$$F = 0.250 \times 100$$
$$F = 25.0 \text{ pf}$$

Example 6.2.   How much force is required, in Example 6.1, if F is applied
upward at an angle of 30.0° with the horizontal?
    Solution.   The forces acting on the box are shown in Figure 6.6.   Consider
F replaced by its horizontal and vertical components; we then have

$$F \cos 30.0° = f_s = 0.250 \, F_N$$

and

$$F_N + F \sin 30.0° = 100$$

where it is seen that the normal force here is not the weight of the box but less than this value by the amount $F \sin 30.0°$. From these equations

$$F \cos 30 = 0.250(100 - F \sin 30.0°)$$

from which

$$F = 25.2 \text{ pf}$$

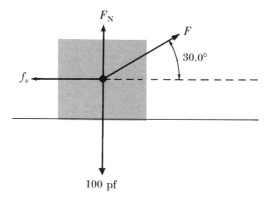

Figure 6.6.

Example 6.3. A body is projected with an initial horizontal speed of 3.00 m/sec on a level surface. It comes to rest at 15.0 m. Find the coefficient of kinetic friction. Take $g = 9.80$ m/sec².

Solution. The frictional force is the unbalanced force acting on the body of mass m. Thus,

$$\sum F = ma$$
$$f_k = ma = \mu_k mg$$

and

$$\mu_k = a/g$$

The acceleration is obtained by applying the kinematic equation

$$v^2 = v_0^2 + 2as$$
$$0 = (3.00)^2 + 2a \times 15.0$$
$$a = -0.300 \text{ m/sec}^2$$

where the minus sign indicates a deceleration. Thus,

$$\mu_k = 0.300/9.80 = 0.0306$$

Example 6.4. In this example we shall illustrate the determination of the coefficients of static and kinetic friction by the use of an inclined plane. A body rests on an adjustable inclined plane. When the angle of the plane is increased from zero to some critical value θ the body is on the point of sliding downward. Find an expression for the coefficient of static friction as a function of the angle.

Solution.   The forces acting on the body of mass m are shown in Figure 6.7.   As in Examples 6.1 and 6.2, the forces in a direction parallel to the in-

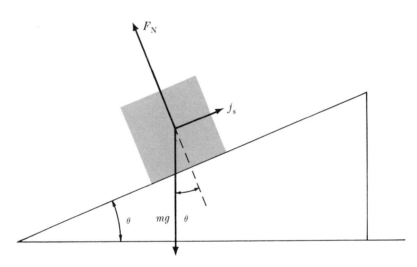

Figure 6.7.

cline are balanced, as well as those in a direction perpendicular to the incline. Thus,

$$f_s = mg \sin \theta$$

and

$$F_N = mg \cos \theta$$

Dividing the first equation by the second and using $\mu_s = f_s/F_N$ we have

$$\mu_s = \tan \theta \tag{6.5}$$

In Equation 6.5, θ is known as the *angle of repose*, which can readily be determined, yielding the coefficient of static friction.

The coefficient of kinetic friction is measured in a similar way, by adjusting the angle of the plane to the value that permits the body to slide down the incline with uniform speed.   Then the coefficient of kinetic friction is given by the tangent of this angle of uniform slip.   The angle of uniform slip is always less than the angle of repose.

Example 6.5.   A box weighing 100 pounds force is just supported on a 30.0° inclined plane by two external forces, one of 10.0 pounds force applied upward and parallel to the incline and the other a force applied parallel to the base of the incline and in such a direction as to increase the normal reaction on the box. What is the magnitude of this latter force if the coefficient of static friction is 0.350?

Solution. Figure 6.8 is a diagram of box, inclined plane, and forces acting. Since the body is just supported, the friction force is acting upward, opposite

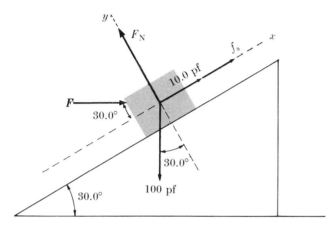

Figure 6.8.

to the direction of tendency of motion. Using the x and y axes as shown, the sum of the forces acting upward along the $+x$ direction and opposing the tendency of motion is

$$10.0 + f_s + F \cos 30.0°$$

The force tending to move the box in the $-x$ direction is

$$100 \sin 30.0°$$

These must be equal since there is no motion. Hence,

$$10.0 + f_s + F \cos 30.0° = 100 \sin 30.0°$$
$$f_s = 40.0 - F \cos 30.0°$$

Likewise, equating the force acting in the $+y$ direction to the sum of the forces acting in the $-y$ direction:

$$F_N = 100 \cos 30.0° + F \sin 30.0°$$

Since here $\mu_s = f_s/F_N = 0.350$, we have, from the last two equations,

$$0.350 = \frac{40.0 - F \cos 30.0°}{100 \cos 30.0° + F \sin 30.0°}$$

an equation in F which leads to the solution $F = 9.38$ pounds force.

Problems

Unless otherwise stated use $g = 32.0 \text{ ft/sec}^2 = 980 \text{ cm/sec}^2 = 9.80 \text{ m/sec}^2$ when necessary.

6.1. A horizontal force of 5.50 pounds is required to start a sled weighing 20.0 pounds force on which there is a child weighing 40.0 pounds force. Find the coefficient of static friction.

6.2. After the sled (and child) are started, Problem 6.1, it takes a force of 5.75 pounds force to cause an acceleration of 2.00 feet/sec². Find the coefficient of kinetic friction.

6.3. A 1.00 kgm body is projected on a level surface with a horizontal speed of 1.35 m/sec. The coefficient of sliding friction is 0.200; find (**a**) how long it takes the body to come to rest and (**b**) how far the body travels.

6.4. A car with a mass of 1.80×10^3 kgm is traveling with a speed of 54.0 km/hour when the brakes are suddenly applied. Assuming a constant frictional force find the coefficient of sliding friction if the car comes to rest at 16.5 m.

6.5. Find the coefficient of kinetic friction in Problem 5.17.

6.6. Solve Problem 5.21, assuming that there is friction between the 4-pound mass and the table, the coefficient of kinetic friction being 0.500.

6.7. A trunk weighing 300 pounds force is pushed along a horizontal floor by a force applied downward at an angle of 30.0° with the horizontal. The coefficient of static friction is 0.440. Find (**a**) the magnitude of the force necessary to set the trunk in motion, (**b**) the total reaction of the floor on the trunk when it is on the point of moving, and (**c**) the magnitude of the force required to maintain the body in motion at a moderate speed if the coefficient of kinetic friction is 0.300.

6.8. A block of 30.0 pounds mass is on a plane that is inclined at an angle of 25.0° with the horizontal. The coefficient of static friction is 0.230. What force applied parallel to the incline will cause the body to be in impending motion (**a**) up the incline and (**b**) down the incline?

6.9. What value of F in Figure 6.9 will just keep the body from sliding down the incline? Take θ as 30.0°, ϕ as 15.0°, μ_s as 0.300, and m as 100 pounds mass.

6.10. The coefficient of kinetic friction between a box of 80.0 pounds mass and the surface of a plane inclined at 28.5° with the horizontal is 0.200. What force applied parallel to the plane is necessary to move the box upward (**a**) with uniform speed and (**b**) with an acceleration of 3.55 feet/sec²?

6.11. A body slides down a 30.0° inclined plane with an acceleration of 1.22 m/sec². What is the coefficient of kinetic friction?

6.12. A sled weighing 75.0 pounds force starts from rest at the top of a 20.0° snow-covered hill, travels a distance of 45.0 feet to the bottom of the hill, and then continues for some distance on the horizontal snow-covered ground. If the coefficient of kinetic friction is 0.0300, what are (**a**) the speed of the sled at the foot of the hill and (**b**) the distance from the foot of the hill the sled comes to rest?

6.13. One end of a meter stick is raised 30.0 cm above the other. How long will it take a coin whose mass is 2.50 gm to slide down the length of the incline, starting from rest at the top, if the coefficient of kinetic friction is 0.280?

6.14. A block weighing 5.00 nt is pushed up a vertical wall by a force applied at an angle of 10.0° with the wall. The coefficient of kinetic friction is 0.500 and the block moves vertically at uniform speed. Find the magnitude of the force.

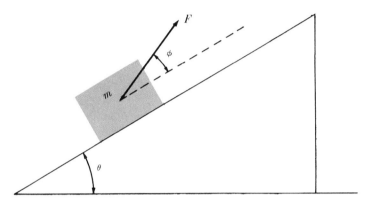

Figure 6.9. *Problem 6.9.*

6.15. The angle of repose for a metal block weighing 10.0 pounds force on an incline is 15.0°. What force applied to the block at an angle of 30.0° with the horizontal will cause the body to be in impending motion up the incline?

6.16. A body of weight w, on a level floor, is on the point of moving under the action of a force F applied upward at an angle θ with the horizontal. (**a**) Show that $F = \mu_s w/(\cos \theta + \mu_s \sin \theta)$ where μ_s is the coefficient of static friction. (**b**) Show that the condition that F is an extreme with respect to θ is $\mu_s = \tan \theta$. Interpret this in terms of whether F is a maximum or a minimum.

6.17. A roller skate is projected with a speed of 12.0 miles/hour on a polished floor and comes to rest after traveling 300 feet. Find the coefficient of rolling friction.

6.18. An automobile traveling at 6.00 miles/hour is permitted to coast. The coefficient of rolling friction is 0.0300. Find (**a**) how far the car rolls before coming to rest and (**b**) how long before the car comes to rest.

6.19.   An automobile starts from rest at the top of a hill making an angle of 5.00° with the horizontal.   It coasts for one-half minute.   Find (**a**) how far down the hill the car has come and (**b**) the speed of the car at the end of this time.   The coefficient of rolling friction is 0.0250.

6.20.   A layer of glycerin at 20°C is contained between two horizontal flat glass plates 0.850 mm apart.   The plates are rectangular, of dimensions 3.00 cm by 5.00 cm.   What horizontal force must be applied to the top plate so that it moves with a speed of 2.50 cm/sec?   Express the answer in dynes and in newtons.

6.21.   A convenient method of measuring the viscosity of a liquid is to force the liquid through a tube of small bore.   The flow of liquid is dependent on its viscosity and, for laminar flow (here, annular layers), Poiseuille's law states that

$$V = \frac{\pi R^4 t \Delta p}{8L\eta}$$

where V is the volume of liquid discharging in time t, L is the length, R the inner radius of the bore, and Δp the difference in pressure between the ends of the tube.   In the cgs system V is in cubic centimeters, r and L are in centimeters, t is in seconds, and Δp is in dynes per square centimeter.   Calculate the viscosity of a liquid which flows at a rate of 1.80 cm³/minute through a tube whose length is 25.0 cm and whose inner radius is 0.100 mm, the pressure difference being 3.00×10^6 dynes/cm².

Statics

*W*HEN *A BODY OR STRUCTURE* is under the action of a system of forces we may want to know the conditions under which the body or structure is in equilibrium. Mechanical and civil engineers, having to do with structures, building, and bridge design, are constantly applying the principles that govern the balance or equilibrium of forces. The phase of physics that deals with the conditions of equilibrium is *statics* which, as we have earlier stated, is a branch of mechanics. If a body is in equilibrium it means there is no acceleration, so it is rather simple to arrive at the conditions of equilibrium by considering statics as a special case of dynamics. We shall adhere to this in developing the laws of equilibrium.

Since an extended body, under the action of a system of forces, may experience changes in translational and rotational motion, we shall deal with the conditions of translational equilibrium and rotational equilibrium. We shall see that these conditions invariably lead to a system of algebraic simultaneous equations by which unknown force quantities may be determined. When the system is composed of forces that are *concurrent*, i.e., which all act through one point, it tends to produce translation only and equilibrium results when there is satisfied what is known as the first condition of equilibrium. On the other hand, when the forces are not all concurrent, and act at different points of an extended body, there is a tendency not only toward translation but also toward rotation. For total equilibrium an additional condition of equilibrium, known as the second condition of equilibrium, must be satisfied.

In order to present these conditions of equilibrium it becomes necessary to deal also with the concepts of moment or torque and center of gravity.

7.1. First Condition of Equilibrium. Let us consider the translational effect of a system of concurrent forces acting on a particle. For the particle to be in translational equilibrium there must be no linear acceleration. The mathematical formulation of Newton's second law for translation then yields the equation

$$\sum F = 0 \qquad\qquad (7.1)$$

This equation states that the vector sum or resultant of the system of forces equals zero. Considering that all the forces are resolved into x and y components, we have as the first condition of equilibrium

$$\left.\begin{array}{c} \sum F_x = 0 \\ \sum F_y = 0 \end{array}\right\} \tag{7.2}$$

a pair of simultaneous equations in which $\sum F_x$ and $\sum F_y$ are, respectively, the sum of the x and the sum of the y components of the forces. Equation 7.1 in general leads to the condition that the sum of the components of force in any two orthogonal directions be zero, and the choice of the x and y directions is made in the interest of simplicity. When all the forces are coplanar, Equations 7.2 are both necessary and sufficient for translational equilibrium. Application of Equations 7.2 then makes it possible to determine the values of two unknowns. When the forces are not all in one plane, then we consider that each force is resolved into the three components F_x, F_y, and F_z along the x, y, and z axes, respectively, and the first condition of equilibrium leads to three equations: $\sum F_x = 0$, $\sum F_y = 0$, and $\sum F_z = 0$. When the forces acting on a body are not concurrent the first condition of equilibrium must still be fulfilled to insure translational equilibrium. The student should be aware of the significant fact that no acceleration means either the body is at rest or it is in motion with constant velocity. Thus constant-velocity motion means that the forces are balanced and the system is in translational equilibrium. We have already had some examples of constant-velocity motion.

We shall now give some examples of the application of the first condition of equilibrium. For best results it is advisable that a procedure of discipline be adopted in working the problems, and we shall precede the examples with one that should be followed in the analytical solutions.

(1) Make a sketch depicting the facts stated in the problem.

(2) Make a corresponding vector diagram showing all the forces that act on the body which you have chosen as being in equilibrium. Indicate by numerical values all the known forces, angles, and dimensions and, by symbols, the unknown quantities.

(3) Construct a set of rectangular axes on the force diagram, placing the body in equilibrium at the coordinate origin.

(4) Apply the first condition of equilibrium, thus obtaining two simultaneous equations.

(5) Solve the equilibrium equations for the unknowns. If a graphical solution is desired it may be obtained by the methods of Chapter 2. When the polygonal method of adding the vector forces is employed, the first condition of equilibrium is imposed by the fact that the forces acting on the body must form a closed polygon.

Example 7.1. A knot is made in a cord forming two sections of unequal lengths. The free ends are attached to an overhanging horizontal rigid support and a body of 100 pounds force hangs from the knot by a vertical cord. The two sections of supporting cord make angles of 60.0° and 25.0° with the horizontal. Find the tensions in each of these cords by analytical means and by graphical construction. The weights of the cords are negligible.

Analytical Solution. In Figure 7.1a is shown a sketch of the hanging weight and supporting cords and in (b) are shown three vector forces acting

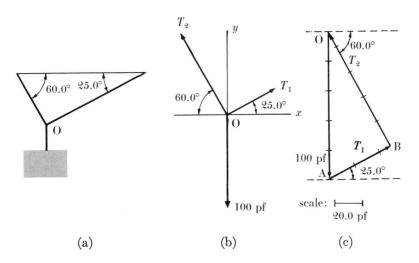

(a)   (b)   (c)

Figure 7.1.

on the knot O as the particle in equilibrium. (Note that other bodies or particles may be chosen as the equilibrium body for purposes of analysis but the choice of the knot at O most directly involves the unknown tensions T_1 and T_2.) Now applying the first condition of equilibrium we have

$$\Sigma F_x = 0; \qquad T_1 \cos 25.0° - T_2 \cos 60.0° = 0$$
$$\Sigma F_y = 0; \qquad T_1 \sin 25.0° - T_2 \sin 60.0° - 100 = 0$$

This yields the two simultaneous equations

$$0.906 T_1 - 0.500 T_2 = 0$$
$$0.423 T_1 + 0.866 T_2 = 100$$

and solving these for T_1 and T_2 we have

$$T_1 = 50.2 \text{ pf}$$
$$T_2 = 91.0 \text{ pf}$$

Observe that here the shorter cord supports the greater amount of weight.

Graphical Solution. The graphical solution is shown in Figure 7.1c. A vertical vector OA is scaled off to represent 100 pounds force. A line drawn from A upward at 25.0° represents the direction along which T_1 acts, and a line drawn from O downward at 60.0° represents the direction along which T_2 acts. The intersection point B represents the terminating point of vector T_1 and the origin of vector T_2. From the measured length values of AB and BO we obtain

$$T_1 = 51 \text{ pf}$$
$$T_2 = 92 \text{ pf}$$

which values agree with the analytically determined values to within about 1.5%, the accuracy of the graphical construction.

It is instructive to point out that any one of the forces in Figure 7.1b is equal and opposite to the resultant of the other two forces. Such a force is known as an *equilibrant*, which is that one force which, when added to an unbalanced system of concurrent forces, will form a force system in translational equilibrium.

Example 7.2. A weight of 50.0 pounds force is supported by a vertical cord whose free end is attached to a ceiling. The cord has a knot a short distance above the weight. A horizontal force F is applied at the knot until the portion of cord from knot to ceiling makes an angle of 30.0° with the vertical. Find the tension in the sloping cord and the magnitude of F. Neglect the weight of the cord.

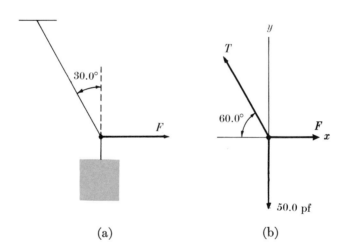

(a)   (b)

Figure 7.2.

Solution. The diagram revealing the features of the problem is shown in Figure 7.2a and the diagram of the forces acting on the knot, considered as the particle in equilibrium, is shown in Figure 7.2b. Applying the first condition of equilibrium yields

$$\Sigma F_x = 0; \quad F - T \cos 60.0° = 0$$
$$\Sigma F_y = 0; \quad T \sin 60.0° - 50.0 = 0$$

Solving this pair of simultaneous equations leads to the solution

$$F = 28.8 \text{ pf}$$
$$T = 57.7 \text{ pf}$$

7.2.   Torque or Moment of a Force.   Let us consider under what conditions the application of a force on a body tends to produce rotation.   In Figure 7.3a is shown a force F applied perpendicular to a rigid bar which is

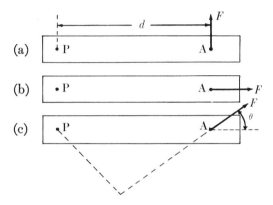

Figure 7.3.   *Illustrating that torque is the product of force and the perpendicular distance from the axis of rotation to the line of action of the force.*

pivoted at the point P.   It is clear that F tends to rotate the body counterclockwise about an axis through P perpendicular to the plane of the figure. *The tendency of a force to produce rotation about an axis is called the torque or the moment of the force.*   If the perpendicular distance d from the axis to the line of action of the force is considered fixed, then the torque increases as F increases, and decreases as F decreases.   On the other hand, if F is held fixed in magnitude and direction but its point of application on the bar is varied, the torque increases as d increases, and decreases as d decreases.   Experiment shows that the torque L is given by the product of F and d:

$$L = Fd \tag{7.3}$$

The distance d is called the *lever arm* or the *moment arm* of the force and, we repeat, is defined as the perpendicular distance from the axis to the line of action of the force.   It is not the distance PA from the axis to the point of application of the force!   For example, in Figure 7.3b the same force as that in (a) is applied so that its line of action passes through P; the distance PA is the same as in (a), but there is no turning tendency and $L = 0$.   This, then, means that the lever arm in (b) is zero. In (c) the force acts at an angle θ with the bar. If we consider the rectangular components of the force, only the vertical component $F \sin \theta$ has a rotating tendency, and the torque is

$$L = (F \sin \theta)\text{PA} = F(\text{PA} \sin \theta)$$

where PA sin θ, the lever arm, as we see from the diagram, is the perpendicular distance from the axis to the line of action of the force. As is evident, the maximum torque results when $\theta = 90°$.

The unit of torque is compounded from the unit of force and the unit of distance. In the cgs absolute system the unit of torque is the centimeter-dyne (cm·dyne), in the mks absolute system the unit of torque is the meter-newton (m·nt), and in the English gravitational system the unit of torque is the pound-force–foot (pf·ft).

Torques are tendencies to rotation either clockwise or counterclockwise, and it is general practice to consider counterclockwise torques as positive and clockwise torques as negative. A torque, then, possesses magnitude and direction and is represented by a vector whose length is proportional to the magnitude and whose direction is along the axis of rotation. It is a convention that the arrowhead of the torque vector is placed so that it points in that direction in which a right-handed screw would advance if rotated in the same sense as the action of the torque; for example, in Figure 7.3a the torque vector points perpendicularly up out of the plane of the figure at P.

7.3. Second Condition of Equilibrium. When several coplanar forces act on a body, each force produces its own turning tendency and the resultant torque is the algebraic sum of the torques due to the individual forces. We shall later show (Chapter 10) that there is a rotational analogue of Newton's second law for translation, in accordance with which a body experiences a rotational acceleration, also called angular acceleration, under the action of a nonzero resultant or unbalanced torque. We shall see that the sum $\sum L$ of the torques about an axis of rotation is directly proportional to the angular acceleration. Since *rotational equilibrium* means the absence of angular acceleration the second condition of equilibrium states that the sum of the torques produced by all the forces acting on a body must be zero, or

$$\sum L = 0 \tag{7.4}$$

It is clear that Equation 7.4 must be valid for *any* chosen axis of rotation. Like translatory equilibrium, an absence of angular acceleration means that the body either is at rest or is rotating with uniform angular velocity.

In applying Equation 7.4 it is advantageous to appraise one's problem with respect to the choice of an axis of rotation and then to choose that axis about which there is the least number of unknown quantities. This procedure is illustrated in the examples following the next section.

7.4.   Total Equilibrium.   We are now in a position to state the conditions that are necessary and sufficient for a rigid body to be in translational and rotational equilibrium.   Total equilibrium is ensured when Equations 7.2 and 7.4 are satisfied simultaneously.   Thus, for total equilibrium

$$\left.\begin{array}{l} \sum F_x = 0 \\ \sum F_y = 0 \\ \sum L \;= 0 \end{array}\right\} \tag{7.5}$$

The words "necessary" and "sufficient" mean the following: given that a body is in total equilibrium, it is necessary that Equations 7.5 be satisfied; given that Equations 7.5 are satisfied, they are sufficient to prove that the body is in total equilibrium.   When the forces are oriented in the x-y plane, $\sum L$ is always calculated about the z axis, which is perpendicular to the plane of the forces.

We shall now illustrate by examples the computations of torque, the application of the second condition of equilibrium, and the application of the conditions of total equilibrium. The outline given in Section 7.1 of a procedure for solving problems applies here.   A clear sketch showing all the forces acting on the body is essential. For total equilibrium, Equations 7.5 are applied.   The axis about which the torque equation is expressed should be clearly indicated on the diagram and correspondingly as a subscript to L, such as $\sum L_A$, which means the sum of the torques about an axis passing through the point A.   These conditions yield three simultaneous equations which may be used to determine three unknown quantities.

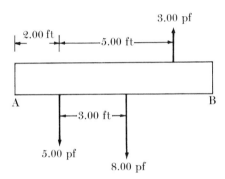

Figure 7.4.   *Resultant torque due to parallel coplanar forces.*

Example 7.3.   (a) Find the sum of the torques about an axis through A acting on the body shown in Figure 7.4.   (b) Where must an upward force of 10.0 pounds force be acting so as to produce rotational equilibrium?   (c) Solve the problem by considering the torques about an axis through B.
Solution.   (a) Using $\sum L_A$ to indicate the sum of the torques about an axis through A we have

$$\sum L_A = -5.00 \times 2.00 - 8.00 \times 5.00 + 3.00 \times 7.00 = -29.0 \text{ pf} \cdot \text{ft}$$

The unbalanced torque is 29.0 pounds-force–foot acting clockwise.
(b) Let x represent the distance to the right of A where the 10.0 pounds force is acting.   Then, for equilibrium,

$$10.0x - 29.0 = 0$$
$$x = 2.90 \text{ ft}$$

(c) Let a be the distance from the 3.00 pounds force to end B, and let z be the distance measured from the 3.00 pounds force to the left where the 10.0 pounds force must act to produce equilibrium. Then,

$$\Sigma L_B = -3.00a + 8.00(2.00 + a) + 5.00(5.00 + a) = 41.0 + 10.0a$$

and

$$41.0 + 10.0a - 10.0(a + z) = 0$$
$$z = 4.10 \text{ ft}$$

which checks with the result obtained in (b).

Example 7.4. A rigid uniform rod 10.0 feet long is supported at a point 4.00 feet from one end on a frictionless knife edge, with a weight of 10.0 pounds suspended from the end nearest the support and another weight w suspended 2.00 feet from the other end. The weight of the rod is 3.00 pounds and acts from its center. Find the reaction of the support on the rod and the weight w.

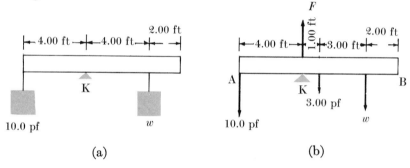

(a)   (b)

Figure 7.5.

Solution. Figure 7.5a shows the rod supported on the knife edge at K and the two weights. In (b) are shown the forces acting on the rigid body, the unknown forces being the reaction F and the weight w. Although the coordinate axes have not been placed on the diagram it is sufficient here to imagine the x axis to be horizontal and the y axis to be vertical.

In applying Equations 7.5 we note that $\Sigma F_x = 0$ yields no information, since there are no horizontal forces present. Applying the second of Equations 7.5 we obtain

$$\Sigma F_y = 0; \qquad F - 10.0 - 3.00 - w = 0$$
$$F - w = 13.0$$

In applying $\Sigma L = 0$ we observe that if we choose an axis through K the torque due to F will be zero and we shall obtain an equation involving the single unknown w. Hence

$$\Sigma L_K = 0; \qquad 10.0 \times 4.00 - 3.00 \times 1.00 - w \times 4.00 = 0$$

from which $w = 9.25$ pounds force and $F = 13.0 + w = 22.2$ pounds force.

To illustrate that any other axis of rotation may have been chosen we shall form the torque equation about an axis through B.   Then

$$\sum L_B = 0; \quad w \times 2.00 + 3.00 \times 5.00 + 10.0 \times 10.0 - F \times 6.00 = 0$$
$$3.00F - w = 57.5$$

and combining this with $F - w = 13.0$ leads to the solution $w = 9.25$ pounds force and $F = 22.2$ pounds force.

Example 7.5.   A cable supports a horizontal beam whose end A is pivoted as shown in Figure 7.6a, and from whose end B a 100-pound weight is suspended.   The weight of the beam, acting from its center, is 30.0 pounds. Find the tension in the cable and the force exerted by the wall on the beam at A.

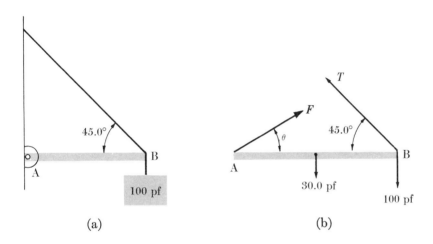

(a)   (b)

Figure 7.6.

Solution.   In Figure 7.6b are shown all the forces acting on the isolated body AB in equilibrium.   At A the force exerted by the wall on the beam has unknown magnitude and direction.   There are thus three unknowns: T, F, and θ.   We apply the conditions of equilibrium and take the x and y directions in the usual manner:

$$\sum F_x = 0; \quad F \cos \theta - T \cos 45.0° = 0$$
$$\sum F_y = 0; \quad F \sin \theta + T \sin 45.0° - 30.0 - 100 = 0$$

The moments about an axis are taken through A as the best choice, since this eliminates both F and θ from the equation:

$$\sum L_A = 0; \quad (T \sin 45.0°)l - 100l - 30.0(l/2) = 0$$

where l is the length of the beam.   Note that l divides out of the equation, yielding the value

$$T = 115\sqrt{2} = 162 \text{ pf}$$

The first two equations now yield

$$F \cos \theta = 115 \qquad \text{and} \qquad F \sin \theta = 15.0$$

which are the horizontal and vertical components of F. By squaring these and adding,

$$F^2 = (115)^2 + (15.0)^2; \qquad F = 116 \text{ pf}$$
and
$$\tan \theta = 15.0/115; \qquad \theta = 7.43°$$

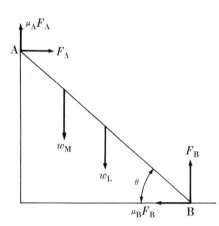

Figure 7.7. *The ladder problem.*

Example 7.6. In this example we shall illustrate the solution of the ladder problem. In Figure 7.7 is shown a uniform ladder AB leaning against a rough wall and rough ground. The weight of the ladder acting from its center is w_L. The ladder is on the point of slipping when a man whose weight is w_M is three fourths of the way up the ladder. Express the conditions of equilibrium as applied to the ladder. The coefficients of static friction are μ_A at the wall and μ_B at the ground.

Solution. Figure 7.7 shows the forces acting on the ladder. The friction forces are expressed as the product of the coefficient of static friction and the normal reactions F_A at A and F_B at B. The conditions of equilibrium give

$$\sum F_x = 0; \quad F_A - \mu_B F_B = 0$$
$$\sum F_y = 0; \quad \mu_A F_A + F_B - w_M - w_L = 0$$
$$\sum L_A = 0; \quad -w_M(l/4) \cos \theta - w_L(l/2) \cos \theta - \mu_B F_B l \sin \theta + F_B l \cos \theta = 0$$

where l is the length of the ladder and need not be known. Four of the seven quantities being given, the other three are readily determined by solving the three simultaneous equations. If one of the surfaces, say the wall, were considered to be smooth (meaning *perfectly smooth*), one would say that it could exert no force tangent to its surface, so that $\mu_A F_A$ is zero in Figure 7.7 and only the normal reaction F_A exists at A.

7.5. Couples. Two equal and oppositely directed noncollinear forces acting on a rigid body, as shown in Figure 7.8, constitute what is known as a *couple*. Although the resultant of the forces is zero so that there is translational equilibrium, the body is not in rotational equilibrium. We can see this by calculating the resultant torque about any axis such as one through O. Thus

$$\sum L_O = Fb - Fa = F(b - a)$$

which shows that the resultant torque is equal to one of the forces multiplied by the perpendicular distance between their lines of action. This product is known as the moment of the couple. Since the value of the torque is inde-

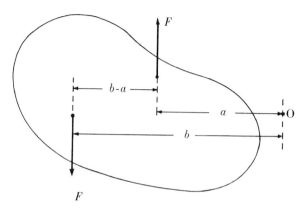

Figure 7.8. *Equal and oppositely directed non-collinear forces form a couple.*

pendent of the position of O through which the axis passes, the moment of a couple is the same about any axis perpendicular to the plane containing the forces F.

Couples have certain other useful and significant characteristics. For example, a single force acting on a rigid body may be replaced by a couple and a force having the same magnitude and direction as the original force but with a displaced line of action. Figure 7.9a shows the original force F (solid arrow). At any point O there are constructed two collinear oppositely directed

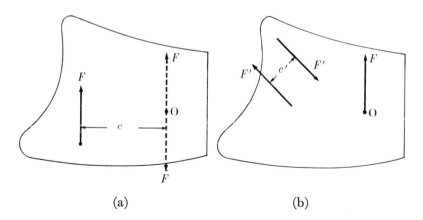

(a)   (b)

Figure 7.9. *Illustrating the resolution of a force into a force and a couple.*

forces (dotted arrows) each equal in magnitude to and, with their common line of action, parallel to, the original force. These added forces cancel and hence do not introduce any change in the system. However, we can now look at the system as composed of a couple of moment Fc and a force F acting upward at O. Since the effect of a couple is the same if its moment is the same we can represent the transformed system as in Figure 7.9b where the force F is applied in the same direction and at the same point O as in (a) and a couple is oriented in any way having a moment $F'c' = Fc$. Thus, a force has been replaced by a force and a couple. Likewise, any couple and a force may be combined into a single force. It follows also that the rotating effect of a couple can never be nullified by a single force; there is needed another couple equal in magnitude but opposite in sense to the given couple to bring about a condition of equilibrium.

7.6. Resultant of a System of Parallel Coplanar Forces Acting on a Rigid Body. In Figure 7.10a is shown a rigid bar AB acted upon

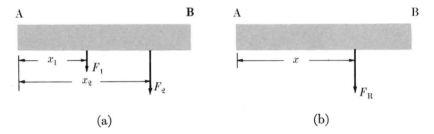

Figure 7.10. *Resultant of parallel coplanar forces.*

by two parallel forces F_1 and F_2 distant x_1 and x_2, respectively, from end A. By definition, the resultant of a system of parallel coplanar forces is a force whose magnitude and point of application are such that when it acts alone it produces the same effect as the system of forces. The forces shown in (a) have both a translational and a rotational effect on the body. The one force having the same effects is shown in (b); its magnitude is F_R and it is distant x from end A. The magnitude of the resultant is

$$F_R = F_1 + F_2$$

The turning tendency of F_R must be the same as the sum of the turning tendencies of F_1 and F_2 about any axis. Taking an axis through A we have, for equality of torques,

$$F_R x = (F_1 + F_2)x = F_1 x_1 + F_2 x_2$$

$$x = \frac{F_1 x_1 + F_2 x_2}{F_1 + F_2} \tag{7.6}$$

which locates the position of the line of action of the resultant. It can easily be shown (see Problem 7.30) that the resultant lies between F_1 and F_2 and divides the distance between the forces into two parts which are inversely proportional to the magnitudes of the forces.

We notice that the location of the resultant is given by a fraction whose numerator is the sum of the torques of the two forces and whose denominator is the sum of the forces. This result can be extended to any number of parallel coplanar forces acting on a rigid body, the magnitude of the resultant and the position of its line of action being given by

$$F_R = \sum_i F_i \qquad i = 1, 2, 3, \ldots \tag{7.7}$$

and

$$x = \sum_i F_i x_i / \sum_i F_i \qquad i = 1, 2, 3, \ldots \tag{7.8}$$

where $\sum_i F_i$ and $\sum_i F_i x_i$ are, respectively, the algebraic sum of the forces and the algebraic sum of the torques or moments.

7.7. Center of Gravity. In Section 4.5 we defined the weight of a body on the earth's surface as the gravitational force exerted on it by the earth. Actually, the expression "gravitational force" means the resultant of all the gravitational forces acting on each element of mass of the body. Each

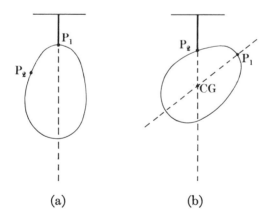

(a)   (b)

Figure 7.11. *Experimental method of locating the center of gravity of a flat object.*

small part of an extended rigid body has acting on it a gravitational force which is directed vertically downward, and the resultant of all of these vertical forces of gravity is called the weight of the body. Being a resultant of parallel forces, the weight of a body acts downward through a definite point called the *center of gravity*.

The center of gravity of a homogeneous body of regular shape is at the geometric center of the body: for a sphere it is at the center, for a uniform rod it is located on its axis midway between its ends, for a cube it is at the intersection point of its interior diagonals, for a circular sheet it is at the center. A body of irregular shape may have its center of gravity determined experimentally by suspending the body successively from two different points near its periphery by a single string. Each time the body is suspended it assumes an equilibrium orientation with its center of gravity directly below its point of suspension. Thus the intersection point of the extended vertical lines of the supporting string marks the center of gravity CG of the body. For a flat plate the location of the center of gravity by this method is easily demonstrated, as shown in Figure 7.11, the two points of suspension being P_1 and P_2. The center of gravity, although fixed relative to a body, does not necessarily lie within the body: the center of gravity of a doughnut-shaped body lies outside the body, at the geometric center of the hole.

The weight of a body may be represented by a single downward force applied at the center of gravity, although actually only the line of action of the weight passes through this point. This is in accord with the principle of the transmissibility of forces, which states that, whenever a force acts on a body, *any* point in the line of action of that force may be considered the point of application.

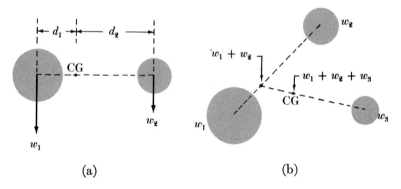

(a)   (b)

Figure 7.12. *Center of gravity of: (a) two bodies and (b) three bodies.*

Center of Gravity of a Group of Bodies. The center of gravity of a group of bodies whose centers of gravity are known is located by successive applications of Equation 7.8. This is illustrated by Figure 7.12. In (a) the center of gravity CG of the two bodies lies on a line joining their centers of gravity. Through the center of gravity passes the line of action of the resultant of the two parallel forces. In accordance with the development in Section 7.6, the combined weight $w_1 + w_2$ acts through the point that divides the distance between the centers of gravity of the two bodies in inverse ratio to the two weights, or $w_1/w_2 = d_2/d_1$. In (b) the center of gravity of three bodies is found by first locating the center of gravity of any two. Then consider that the two bodies are replaced at this center of gravity by a single body having a weight equal to the sum of the weights of the two bodies. This imaginary body is then combined with the third body to give, in like manner, the center of gravity of the three bodies. In Figure 7.12b, where for convenience the weights are considered to act in and perpendicular to the plane of the paper, w_1 and w_2 combine to yield their center of gravity along the line joining their centers. Then the center of gravity of the entire system is located on the line joining w_3 and the center of gravity between the first two bodies. The point CG divides the distance between the point through which $w_1 + w_2$ acts and the point through which w_3 acts in inverse ratio to $(w_1 + w_2)/w_3$.

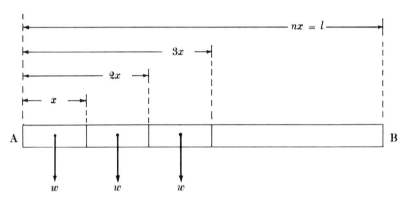

Figure 7.13.   *Center of gravity of a homogeneous uniform rod.*

Center of Gravity of a Straight Rod Containing a Longitudinal Axis of Symmetry. A straight rod possessing a longitudinal axis of symmetry exemplifies a one-dimensional body in so far as calculating the location of its center of gravity is concerned. A uniform rod or a rod in the shape of a flagpole has a longitudinal axis of symmetry along which the center of gravity must lie. It is then only necessary to find the magnitude and the position of the line of action of the resultant of the parallel forces of gravity acting on the body, by the method of Section 7.6. In this case the forces F_i of Equation 7.8 are the weights w_i of the segments into which the rod is considered to be divided, and the center of gravity $\bar{x}$ is given by

$$\bar{x} = \frac{\sum\limits_{i=1}^{n} w_i x_i}{\sum\limits_{i=1}^{n} w_i} \tag{7.9}$$

Here
$$\sum\limits_{i=1}^{n} w_i x_i = w_1 x_1 + w_2 x_2 + \cdots + w_n x_n$$

and
$$\sum\limits_{i=1}^{n} w_i = w_1 + w_2 + \cdots + w_n = W$$

where W is the resultant of the n parallel forces of gravity or the weight of the rod, and the x's and $\bar{x}$ are measured from some fixed origin containing the axis about which the torques are expressed.

As an example we shall compute the position of the center of gravity of a straight uniform homogeneous rod. In what follows, the left column of the divided page contains a noncalculus treatment while in the right column the calculus is employed to obtain the same result.

Let the rod of length l, Figure 7.13, be divided into n sections each of length x and of weight w acting from the geometric center. The resultant weight W acting through the center of gravity produces the same torque about any axis of rotation as the sum of the torques of the weights of the individual sections. Thus, considering an axis of rotation through A and designating $\bar{x}$ the distance of the center of gravity from A, we have

$$W\bar{x} = w\frac{x}{2} + w\frac{3x}{2} + w\frac{5x}{2} + \cdots$$
$$+ w(2n - 1)\frac{x}{2}$$
$$= \frac{wx}{2}(1 + 3 + 5 + \cdots + 2n - 1)$$

Expressing the sum of the n terms of the arithmetic progression and using for W its equal nw leads to

$$nw\bar{x} = \frac{wx}{2}\left[\frac{n}{2}(1 + 2n - 1)\right]$$
$$\bar{x} = \frac{nx}{2} = \frac{l}{2}$$

Let the rod of length l, Figure 7.14, be divided into n segments each of length dx and of weight per unit length w_u. For convenience the origin is chosen at O, and the torque due to the weight $w_u\,dx$ about an axis through O is $w_u x\,dx$. The sum of the torques due to n such segments taken throughout the length of the rod, as n is made to approach infinity, is given by the integral

$$\lim_{n\to\infty} \sum_{i=1}^{n} w_i x_i = \int_0^l w_u x\,dx$$

The resultant weight W acting through the center of gravity distant $\bar{x}$ from O produces the same torque about O as the sum of the torques of the weights of the elemental sections dx. Hence

$$W\bar{x} = \int_0^l w_u x\,dx$$
$$\bar{x} = \frac{\int_0^l w_u x\,dx}{W}$$
$$= \frac{\int_0^l w_u x\,dx}{\int_0^l w_u\,dx}$$

For a homogeneous uniform rod w_u is a constant. Thus

$$\bar{x} = \frac{x^2/2]_0^l}{x]_0^l} = \frac{l^2}{2l}$$
$$\bar{x} = \frac{l}{2}$$

so that the center of gravity lies at the geometric center of the rod.

Center of Gravity of a Two-Dimensional Body. The center of gravity of a two-dimensional body may be obtained by locating the lines of action of the resultant in two different directions through the body in accordance with the experimental method depicted in Figure 7.11. It is convenient to consider the lines of action as being in perpendicular directions. For this purpose we construct a set of x and y axes and denote the position of the center of gravity

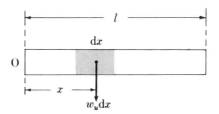

Figure 7.14. *Determining the center of gravity of a homogeneous uniform rod by means of the calculus.*

of each weight-element by its (x, y) coordinates, as in Figure 7.15a. Then we consider that all the forces of gravity act parallel to the y axis, and we apply Equation 7.9. This yields the x coordinate of the center of gravity.

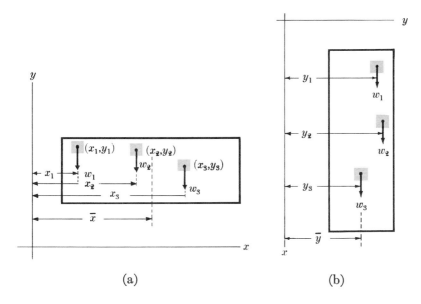

(a)   (b)

Figure 7.15. *Locating analytically the center of gravity of a two-dimensional body.*

Then we imagine that the axes and body are rotated through 90° so that the forces of gravity act parallel to the x axis, as shown in Figure 7.15b. The y coordinate of the center of gravity $\bar{y}$ is thus given by:

$$\bar{y} = \frac{\sum\limits_{i=1}^{n} w_i y_i}{\sum\limits_{i=1}^{n} w_i} \qquad (7.10)$$

This general method of locating the center of gravity is applicable to finding the center of gravity of a group of bodies (Figure 7.12) or to finding the center of gravity of a composite body if the centers of gravity of its component parts (obtained by arbitrary division) are known. These applications are illustrated by the examples that follow.

With a three-dimensional body we must find the three coordinates $(\bar{x}, \bar{y}, \bar{z})$ of the center of gravity where $\bar{z}$ is given by

$$\bar{z} = \frac{\sum\limits_{i=1}^{n} w_i z_i}{\sum\limits_{i=1}^{n} w_i} \qquad (7.11)$$

Example 7.7. Find the location of the center of gravity of a rectangular homogeneous thin plate of length a and width b.

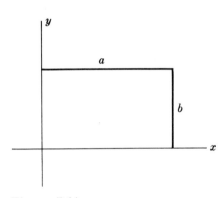

Figure 7.16.

Solution. Figure 7.16 shows the plate with x and y axes. Considering the gravitational forces as acting parallel to the y axis, and applying the method used in locating the line of action of the resultant weight of a thin homogeneous uniform rod, we have

$$\bar{x} = \frac{\sum w_i x_i}{\sum w_i} = \frac{a}{2}$$

Considering the gravitational forces as acting parallel to the x axis gives

$$\bar{y} = \frac{\sum w_i y_i}{\sum w_i} = \frac{b}{2}$$

Hence the center of gravity is at the geometric center of the plate.

Example 7.8. Find the location of the center of gravity of a homogeneous equilateral trapezoid, given that the center of gravity of a triangle is at the point of intersection of its medians or at a distance of one third of the altitude from any base.

Solution. The equilateral trapezoid OBCD in Figure 7.17 is considered a body composed of the equal triangles OBF and CDE of areas A_1 and A_3, respectively, and the rectangle BCEF of area A_2. Let (x_1, y_1), (x_2, y_2), and (x_3, y_3) be the coordinates of the centers of gravity of OBF, BCEF, and CDE, respectively. These are indicated by the dots in Figure 7.17. Then the x coordinate of the center of gravity of the trapezoid is given by:

$$\bar{x} = \frac{\sum\limits_{i=1}^{3} \sigma A_i x_i}{\sum\limits_{i=1}^{3} \sigma A_i} = \frac{A_1 x_1 + A_2 x_2 + A_3 x_3}{A}$$

where σ is the weight per unit area, and $A = A_1 + A_2 + A_3$ is the area of the trapezoid. We now observe that

$$A_1 = A_3 \qquad\qquad x_1 = \frac{2}{3}\left(\frac{a-b}{2}\right)$$

$$= \frac{1}{2}\left(\frac{a-b}{2}\right)h \qquad x_2 = \frac{a}{2}$$

$$A_2 = bh$$

$$A = \left(\frac{a+b}{2}\right)h \qquad x_3 = \frac{2a+b}{3}$$

Substituting, we have

$$\bar{x} = \frac{\dfrac{(a-b)^2 h}{12} + \dfrac{abh}{2} + \dfrac{(a-b)h(2a+b)}{12}}{\dfrac{(a+b)h}{2}}$$

$$= \frac{a}{2}$$

This result is evident from symmetry considerations. The y coordinate of the center of gravity is given by

$$\bar{y} = \frac{\sum\limits_{i=1}^{3} \sigma A_i y_i}{\sum\limits_{i=1}^{3} \sigma A_i} = \frac{A_1 y_1 + A_2 y_2 + A_3 y_3}{A}$$

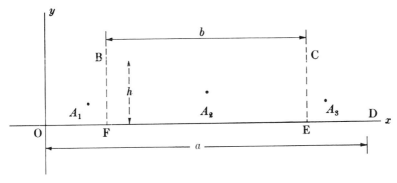

Figure 7.17.

Substituting $y_1 = h/3$, $y_2 = h/2$, $y_3 = h/3$, we have

$$\bar{y} = \dfrac{\dfrac{2(a - b)h^2}{12} + \dfrac{bh^2}{2}}{\dfrac{(a + b)h}{2}}$$

$$= \dfrac{(a + 2b)}{3(a + b)} h$$

7.8.   Center of Mass.   By carrying through the development given in the previous section but using the masses of the elements m_i instead of the weights w_i, we obtain, instead of Equations 7.9, 7.10, and 7.11 for the center of gravity, the following set of equations:

$$\bar{x} = \frac{\sum\limits_{i=1}^{n} m_i x_i}{\sum\limits_{i=1}^{n} m_i} \qquad \bar{y} = \frac{\sum\limits_{i=1}^{n} m_i y_i}{\sum\limits_{i=1}^{n} m_i} \qquad \bar{z} = \frac{\sum\limits_{i=1}^{n} m_i z_i}{\sum\limits_{i=1}^{n} m_i} \qquad (7.12)$$

These equations define the point known as the *center of mass*.   It is the center of mass which possesses this very important property: *As far as translational motion is concerned, the entire mass of a body may be considered as concentrated at the center of mass.*   This means that when a body is under the action of a number of forces, the translational motion of its center of mass is precisely the same as when its entire mass is concentrated at its center of mass and all the forces, maintaining their original magnitude and direction, act at the center of mass.   Thus a springboard diver, twisting and turning, may execute a complicated-looking motion through the air, but his center of mass traces out a parabola.

If $w_i = m_i g$, then Equations 7.12 reduce to the corresponding equations 7.9, 7.10, and 7.11, and the center of gravity becomes identical with the center of mass.   This, however, is true only when g is assumed to be the same for all the mass particles composing the body, an assumption that is valid for bodies that are small enough for g not to vary appreciably over their extents. On the other hand, in the case of very large objects such as mountains or continents, g is not the same for every mass particle and the center of gravity is not coincident with the center of mass.   Most of the bodies with which we shall be dealing are relatively small and we shall consider the center of gravity to be coincident with the center of mass.

7.9.   Stable, Unstable, and Neutral Equilibrium.   Figure 7.18 illustrates the three states of equilibrium under the action of gravity. In (a) is shown a cone resting on its base and the same cone slightly displaced.   This gives rise to an unbalanced torque, produced by the couple due to the weight w and the normal reaction F_N, which restores the body to its original position. When the condition is such that a small displacement gives rise to a restoring torque the equilibrium is *stable*.

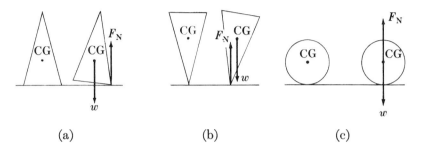

(a)   (b)   (c)

Figure 7.18.   (a) *Stable*, (b) *Unstable*, (c) *Neutral equilibrium.*

In (b) is shown the cone balanced on its apex and the same cone slightly displaced.   Here the unbalanced torque acts to increase the displacement and the cone will fall, getting farther and farther away from its original position. This kind of equilibrium is called *unstable.*

In (c) is shown a sphere (or cylinder) on a level surface and the same body displaced from its original position.   Here there is no torque brought into play either to return the body to its initial position or to increase the displacement.   This type of equilibrium is called *neutral.*

The location of the center of gravity of a body determines the degree of stability that the body possesses.   The lower the center of gravity the greater the stability.   When the line of action of the weight of the body falls inside the base of the body, as in (a), the body is stable; when it falls outside the base, the body is unstable, as would be the case if the cone were placed on a sufficiently elevated inclined plane.   When a wagon, overloaded so that its center of gravity is very high, is driven on an inclined road, the outer wheels may be sufficiently raised above the inner wheels for it to overturn when the line of action of the weight falls outside the wheel base.

7.10.   The Equal-Arm Analytical Balance.   The equal-arm analytical balance, an instrument employed in the laboratory for determining masses, is an excellent example of the principles of equilibrium.   The essential features of the balance are indicated in Figure 7.19.   A rigid beam of length $2l$, pivoted at its midpoint O, supports equal-mass scale pans at its ends A and B.   The student will observe in the laboratory that the pivots at A, O, and B actually are knife edges resting on hard polished plane plates, the system being relatively free of friction.   A vertical pointer P, fastened to the beam at O, plays across a scale as the beam rotates about an axis through

O. When the beam is horizontal and the pointer is at scale zero, its center of gravity is situated a distance a directly below O and remains in nearly the same position after the beam is displaced. Suppose a body of unknown mass m_x is placed in the left pan and a known standard mass m_s, slightly larger

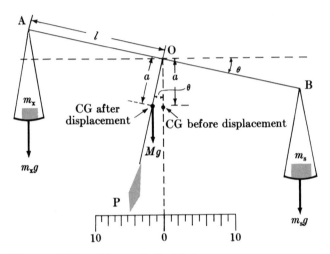

Figure 7.19. *The analytical balance.*

than m_x, is placed in the right pan. The beam of mass M is under the action of three torques due to the action of the parallel downward forces $m_x g$, Mg, and $m_s g$. (The upward reaction force acting at O has no turning tendency about the central pivot point.) The beam assumes an equilibrium position, as shown in the figure, so that in accordance with the second condition of equilibrium we have, computing the torques about an axis through O,

$$m_x g l \cos \theta + Mga \sin \theta - m_s g l \cos \theta = 0$$

or
$$(m_s - m_x)l \cos \theta = Ma \sin \theta \qquad (7.13)$$

in which the left-hand member represents the deflecting torque and the right-hand member denotes the opposing restoring torque. Solving for m_x:

$$m_x = m_s - \frac{Ma}{l} \tan \theta \qquad (7.14)$$

Now the balance comes to rest at the equilibrium angle θ and $\tan \theta$ may be found from the corresponding scale reading (the ratio of the distance along the scale to the perpendicular distance from O to the scale is $\tan \theta$). Hence m_x is determinable if we know the value of Ma/l; the latter may be ascertained by observing $\tan \theta$ for a known mass difference, $m_s - m_x$. On the other hand, the standard mass may be adjusted until $\theta = 0$; then $m_x = m_s$. In actual practice one does not wait for a sensitive balance to come to rest but calculates the rest position of the pointer by observing several successive swings.

A balance is termed sensitive when a small mass difference results in a large deflection.   From Equation 7.13 we see that this is measured by the ratio $\tan \theta / (m_s - m_x)$ which in turn is equal to l/Ma.   Thus:

$$\text{sensitivity} = l/Ma \qquad (7.15)$$

and we see that for great sensitivity the balance arms should be large and yet its mass should be small.   To satisfy these requirements along with that of rigidity, the moving system is usually designed in the form of a truss.   For a given l/M, the sensitivity varies inversely with the distance of the center of gravity below the central point of support.   Some balances are provided with a movable weight on the axis of the pointer, so that it is possible to increase or decrease a and thus provide varying degrees of sensitivity.

For very precise determinations it is advisable to employ the method of *double weighing* which helps to eliminate error due to any inequality existing in the lengths of the balance arms.   First, the unknown mass is placed in one pan, whose suspension point is distant l_1 from the central knife edge, and it is balanced by a standard mass m_1, placed in the other pan, whose suspension point is distant l_2 from the central knife edge.   Then the unknown mass is placed in the other pan and balanced by a standard mass m_2.   We now have

$$m_x g l_1 = m_1 g l_2 \qquad \text{and} \qquad m_2 g l_1 = m_x g l_2$$

Dividing one equation by the other yields $m_x = \sqrt{m_1 m_2}$ so that the true mass is the geometric mean of the standard masses.

7.11.   The Truss.   For another example of the application of the principles of equilibrium we shall consider how the stresses in a truss may be

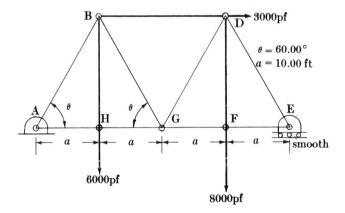

Figure 7.20.   *The bridge truss.*

obtained.   Engineers, practicing structural design, must know the forces acting on all members of a structure subjected to loading conditions before they can decide on the sizes of the various members.

A truss is a mechanical structure composed of a series of triangular frames; the triangular form is employed because a triangle is the structural unit that affords the greatest degree of rigidity. Figure 7.20 shows a symmetrical bridge truss loaded as indicated. To allow for expansion, the support at E is on rollers. The problem is to find the external reactions and the stresses in each of the members.

For purposes of simplicity the engineers obtain a solution to such a problem under the following assumptions:

(1) It is assumed that the truss members are connected at the joints by frictionless pins B, D, E, F, etc. (Figure 7.20). This, of course, is never true and errors incurred in view of such an assumption must eventually be taken into account in the final decision on the sizes of the members.

(2) It is assumed that the loads are applied only on the pin joints, as at H and F. This assumption is substantially valid in actual engineering structures.

(3) It is assumed that the truss members have negligible weight relative to the applied loads. Under this simplifying assumption it follows that all members are subject only to two forces, which are at the extremities of each member and exerted by the joining pin on the member. Furthermore, since each member is a body in equilibrium under the action of two forces, these forces must be equal, opposite, and collinear. Hence the forces act along the members. Such a member is called a *two-force member*. When the forces in a two-force member act toward each other, the member is in compression; when they act away from each other the member is under tension.

One of the methods of analysis of a truss is the *method of sections*, which we shall here illustrate. The first step is to solve for the normal reactions at the points of support A and E, Figure 7.20. For this purpose we construct a free-body diagram of the entire truss as shown in Figure 7.21a, where R_h and R_v are respectively the horizontal and vertical components of the reaction at A, and R_N is the total reaction at E. Applying the conditions $\sum F_x = 0$ and $\sum F_y = 0$,

$$R_h = 3{,}000 \text{ pf} \quad \text{and} \quad R_v + R_N = 14{,}000 \text{ pf}$$

Applying the condition $\sum L_A = 0$, we have

$$-6{,}000(10.00) - 8{,}000(30.00) - 3{,}000(20.00 \times 0.8660) + R_N(40.00) = 0$$

with the result that

$$R_N = 8{,}799 \text{ pf} \quad \text{and} \quad R_v = 5{,}201 \text{ pf}$$

The next step is to make a free-body diagram of a portion of the truss formed by passing a section across truss members. Such sections are illustrated by aa, bb, and cc in Figure 7.21b. Consider the section aa that divides the truss into two parts each of which will be in equilibrium if we apply the external forces F_{AB} along AB, F_{HB} along HB, and F_{HG} along HG, equal to the internal forces that exist respectively in AB, HB, and HG owing to the mutual action of one part of the truss on the other. The free body of the left-hand part of the truss formed by section aa is shown in Figure 7.22a.

The three unknowns F_{AB}, F_{HB}, and F_{HG} may now be determined by applying the first and second conditions of equilibrium. This also brings to light the fact that the section cuts are chosen so as never to involve more than three unknowns. Applying the conditions of equilibrium we have

$$\sum F_x = F_{HG} + F_{AB} \cos 60.00° - 3,000 = 0$$
$$\sum F_y = F_{AB} \sin 60.00° + F_{HB} + 5,201 - 6,000 = 0$$
$$\sum L_A = F_{HB}(10.00) - 6,000(10.00) = 0$$

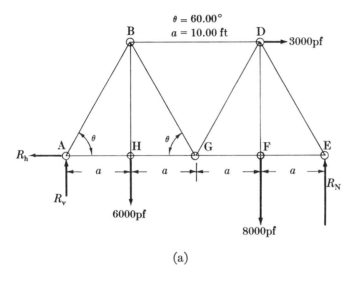

(a)

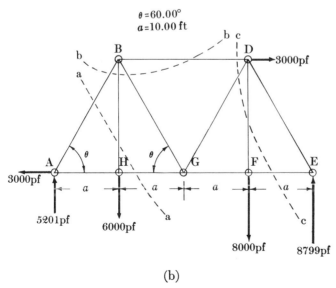

(b)

Figure 7.21. *Solution of the bridge truss by the method of sections.*

Solving these three simultaneous equations yields

$$F_{HB} = 6,000 \text{ pf tension}$$
$$F_{AB} = -6,006 \text{ pf compression}$$
$$F_{HG} = 6,003 \text{ pf tension}$$

The direction of each of these vectors was arbitrarily assumed to act away from the pin joint. Hence, if the value obtained is positive, as in F_{HB} and F_{HG}, the assumed direction was correct and the pin reacts on the member to produce a state of tension. When the value obtained is negative, as in F_{AB}, the force acts toward the pin and the pin reacts to produce a state of compression.

Now consider the section bb and the free body of the lower part of the truss, Figure 7.22b. Here only two of the four members cut by the section

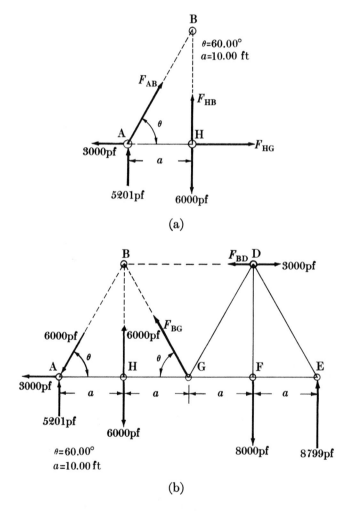

(a)

(b)

Figure 7.22.

are unknown. We need only employ two of the three equilibrium equations to determine F_{BG} and F_{DB}. Thus

$$\sum F_x = -F_{BD} - F_{BG} \cos 60.00° - 6,006 \cos 60.00° = 0$$
$$\sum F_y = F_{BG} \cos 30.00° + 6,000 + 8,799 + 5,201$$
$$- 6,006 \sin 60.00° - 6,000 - 8,000$$
$$= 0$$

from which

$$F_{BG} = -922.0 \text{ pf compression}$$
$$F_{BD} = -2,542 \text{ pf compression}$$

By considering the section cc the student should verify that the stresses in the unknown members are

$$F_{GD} = 924.0 \text{ pf tension}$$
$$F_{FD} = 7,999 \text{ pf tension}$$
$$F_{FE} = 5,080 \text{ pf tension}$$

The stresses in the remaining members of the truss may likewise be determined.

Problems

7.1. A mass of 5.00 kgm is supported by two cords which are 6.00 cm and 8.00 cm long. The cords are fastened to an overhead horizontal beam at points 10.0 cm apart. Find the tension in each cord. Solve analytically and graphically.

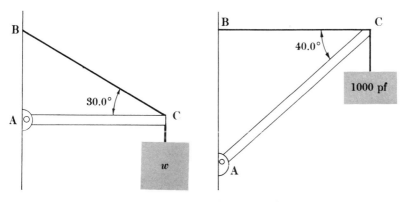

Figure 7.23. *Problem 7.2.*   **Figure 7.24.** *Problem 7.4.*

7.2. A horizontal bar AC (the strut) is attached at A to a vertical wall and supported by a cable BC, the system supporting a weight w as shown in Figure 7.23. Find the tension in the cable and the compression in the strut when $w = 400$ pounds force.   Solve analytically and graphically.   Consider AC weightless.   (*Note:* The force exerted by the wall on a strut considered weightless is along the strut.)

7.3.   If the compressive force in Problem 7.2 is 3,000 pounds force, find the tension in the cable and the weight w.

7.4.   Find the tension in the cable BC and the compressive force in the strut AC shown in Figure 7.24.   Neglect the weight of the strut.   Solve analytically and graphically.   See the note, Problem 7.2.

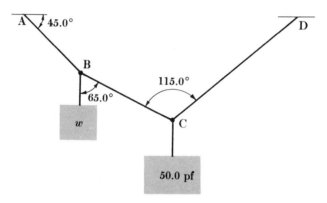

Figure 7.25.   *Problem 7.5.*

7.5.   Figure 7.25 shows two weights suspended from a flexible cable. Find the three tensions in the cable and the weight w.

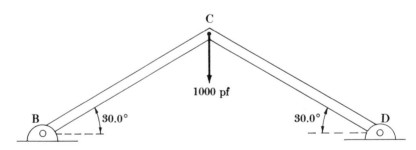

Figure 7.26.   *Problem 7.6.*

7.6.   Figure 7.26 shows a weight of 1.00×10^3 pounds force supported by the pin-jointed A-structure.   Determine the horizontal and vertical components of the compressive force on each member.   (*Hint:* Observe that BC and CD are two-force members.)

7.7.   In Problem 7.6, if the angle at B is 60.0° and that at D is 20.0°, what is the compressive force in each member?   See the hint, Problem 7.6.

7.8. A girl weighing 50.0 pounds force is on a swing weighing 2.00 pounds force which is pulled aside until the supporting chain makes an angle of 30.0° with the vertical. Find the tension in the chain and the horizontal force on the girl and swing.

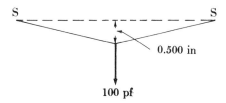

Figure 7.27. *Problem 7.9.*

7.9. Figure 7.27 shows 100 pounds force applied to the midpoint of a chain which has been stretched taut between two fixed supports S, 15.0 feet apart. What force is exerted on the supports?

7.10. A child slides without acceleration down a 15.0-foot slide whose upper end is 5.00 feet above the lower end. What is the coefficient of kinetic friction between child and slide?

7.11. A body whose mass is 2.00 kgm is just supported on a 20.0° inclined plane by two forces passing through its center of gravity, one of 0.980 nt directed upward and parallel to the incline, and the other of 2.94 nt directed upward at an angle of 60.0° with the incline. Find the coefficient of static friction.

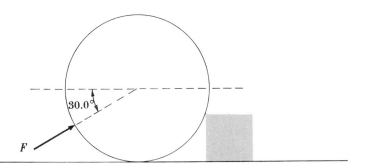

Figure 7.28. *Problem 7.12.*

7.12. Figure 7.28 depicts a wheel of 600 pounds force with a radius of 4.00 feet being pushed over an obstacle, whose height is 2.00 feet, by a force F directed radially at an angle of 30.0° with the horizontal. Without employing the second condition of equilibrium, find F for when the wheel is on the point of moving. Assume that the wheel is in contact with smooth surfaces. (*Hint:* For smooth surfaces the reaction is normal to the common tangent plane. Observe that when the wheel is on the point of moving the reaction of the ground on the wheel is zero.)

7.13. Solve Problem 7.12, using the second condition of equilibrium.

7.14. One end of an 8.00-foot cord is attached to the rim of a ball with a 5.00-foot radius and the other end is attached to a point on a vertical smooth wall. The ball, weighing 900 pounds force, is thus suspended, leaning against the wall. Find the reaction of the wall on the ball and the tension in the cord.

7.15. If the wall in Problem 7.14 is rough and the ball is in equilibrium when the cord makes an angle $\theta = \sin^{-1}(5/8)$ with the vertical, what is the coefficient of static friction? Does the magnitude of the weight of the ball influence the result?

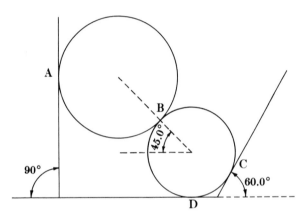

Figure 7.29. *Problem 7.16.*

7.16. Figure 7.29 shows two spheres in equilibrium, all surfaces of contact being smooth. The mass and radius of the large sphere are 1.00×10^3 pounds mass and 3.00 feet and those of the small sphere are 300 pounds mass and 2.00 feet. Find the reactions at A, B, C, and D.

7.17. A rigid horizontal bar has three parallel coplanar vertical forces acting on it; the outer two forces, similarly directed, are each 500 pounds force, and the in-between force, oppositely directed, is 200 pounds force. The distance between adjacent forces is 6.00 inches. Find their resultant (the magnitude, direction, and location of that one force which produces the same effect as the system of forces).

7.18. Find the resultant of the system of parallel coplanar forces shown in Figure 7.30.

7.19. A uniform plank 12.0 feet long and weighing 40.0 pounds force is held horizontally by two supports, one 2.00 feet from the left end and the other 1.00 foot from the right end. When a 200-pound man stands on the plank 2.00 feet to the left of its center, what are the reactions at the supports?

7.20. A tapering pole 15.0 feet long is supported horizontally by two equal upward forces situated 1.50 feet from the heavier end and 3.50 feet from the other end. Find the center of gravity of the pole.

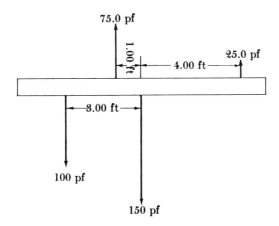

75.0 pf

1.00 ft

25.0 pf

4.00 ft

3.00 ft

100 pf

150 pf

Figure 7.30. *Problem 7.18.*

7.21. A wedge-shaped rod is balanced horizontally when a knife-edged fulcrum is placed between its center of gravity and a downward force applied 5.00 feet from the fulcrum. When the position of the fulcrum is moved 1.00 foot farther away from the center of gravity the applied force must be moved 5.00 feet in the same direction to restore balance. Where is the center of gravity? Neglect friction at the support.

7.22. A uniform beam 6.00 m long has a weight of 50.0 kgf. It is supported horizontally by a man 50.0 cm from one end and a girl 150 cm from the other end. Where should a load of 1.00×10^3 nt be placed so that the man will support four times as much as the girl?

7.23. A uniform plank 20.0 feet long and weighing 50.0 pounds force is supported horizontally by three vertical forces, two equal forces at each end and the third 4.00 feet from one end. Find how great these forces are when a load of 500 pounds force is situated midway between the third support and the center of the plank.

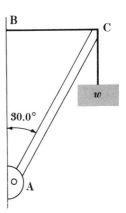

B

C

w

30.0°

A

Figure 7.31. *Problem 7.24.*

7.24. Figure 7.31 shows a crane boom AC, hinged at A and supported by the horizontal cable BC. The length of the boom is 20.0 feet, its weight is 300 pounds force, and its center of gravity is 5.00 feet from A. The weight w is 1.00 ton force. Find (**a**) the tension in the cable and (**b**) the horizontal and vertical components of the reaction at A.

7.25. When the angle shown in Problem 7.24 is 60.0° what effect does this have?

7.26. A uniform door weighs 75.0 pounds force and has a height and width of 8.00 feet and 3.60 feet respectively. It is hinged 1.50 feet from the lower end and 2.00 feet from the upper end. Find the total reaction of each hinge on the door, assuming that the lower hinge supports all the weight of the door.

7.27. A derrick consists of a 25.0-foot uniform boom weighing 500 pounds force, hinged at the lower end of a vertical mast; the outer end of the boom is supported by a cable attached to the upper end of the mast. The boom and cable make angles of 60.0° and 45.0°, respectively, with the mast. A load of 3.00×10^3 pounds force hangs from the outer end of the boom. Find (a) the tension in the cable and (b) the horizontal and vertical forces exerted by the boom on the mast.

7.28. Prove that, when three nonparallel forces acting upon a body produce equilibrium, their lines of action must pass through a common point. (*Hint:* Apply the second condition of equilibrium about an axis passing through the intersection of two of the lines of action.)

7.29. For Figure 7.7 find the equation resulting from $\sum L_B = 0$ and combine this with the expression from $\sum L_A = 0$. Show that this leads to either of the equations obtained from $\sum F_x = 0$ or $\sum F_y = 0$. What do you conclude from this?

7.30. Show that the resultant of F_1 and F_2 in Figure 7.10 lies between F_1 and F_2 and divides the distance between the forces into two parts which are inversely proportional to the magnitudes of the forces. (*Hint:* Find $x - x_1$ and $x_2 - x$, and form their ratio.) For this relationship to hold, what can you say about the two forces?

7.31. A 13.0-foot uniform ladder rests with its upper end against a smooth vertical wall and with its lower end 5.00 feet from the wall. The weight of the ladder is 60.0 pounds force and the weight of a man, standing 10.0 feet up the ladder, is 140 pounds force. Find the reaction of the wall on the ladder and the vertical and horizontal components of force on the foot of the ladder. Solve the problem analytically and graphically. For the graphical solution, observe that the total reactions at the ends of the ladder and the resultant between the weights of the ladder and man form an equilibrium system of three forces which must intersect at one point.

7.32. A 25.0-foot uniform ladder weighing 75.0 pounds force rests with one end against a smooth vertical wall and the other end on rough horizontal ground 7.00 feet from the wall. The ladder supports a painter weighing 125 pounds force who is 20.0 feet up the ladder. A tame bear cub, weighing 50.0 pounds force, climbs the ladder which starts to slip when the cub is 15.0 feet up the ladder. What is the coefficient of static friction?

7.33. A uniform ladder weighing 50.0 pounds force rests against a smooth vertical wall at an angle of 50.0° with the horizontal. A man weighing 150 pounds force stands two thirds of the way up from the foot of the ladder.

What horizontal force must be applied at the base of the ladder in the direction perpendicular to the wall to keep the ladder from slipping?

7.34. A uniform ladder weighing 100 pounds force leans with one end against a smooth vertical wall at an angle of 30.0° with the wall. The other end is on rough horizontal ground. A horizontal force applied to the ladder at a point one quarter of the way up the ladder in the direction perpendicular to the wall causes the ladder to be on the point of slipping upward. If the coefficient of friction is 0.200 what is the magnitude of the applied force and the normal reactions of the wall and the ground?

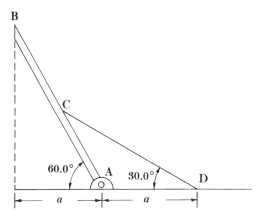

Figure 7.32. *Problem 7.36.*

7.35. A uniform ladder weighing 100 pounds force rests with its upper end against a smooth vertical wall and its lower end on horizontal ground; the coefficient of friction between ground and ladder is 0.0800. The ladder makes an angle of 60.0° with the horizontal and is kept from slipping by a rope extending from the base of the wall to a point one fourth of the way up from the foot of the ladder. Find the tension in the rope and the normal reactions of the wall and the ground.

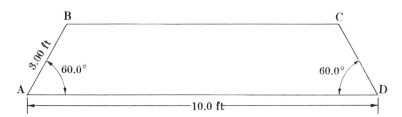

Figure 7.33. *Problem 7.40.*

7.36. Figure 7.32 shows a uniform ladder weighing 50.0 pounds force, hinged on the horizontal platform at A and supported by the cable CD. Find the tension in the cable and the components of the reaction at A when a man weighing 150 pounds force is three quarters of the way up the ladder.

7.37. A wheel 5.00 feet in diameter has a tangential force of 250 pounds force acting on it, tending to produce a clockwise torque. Replace the force on the wheel by a force acting through its center and a couple.

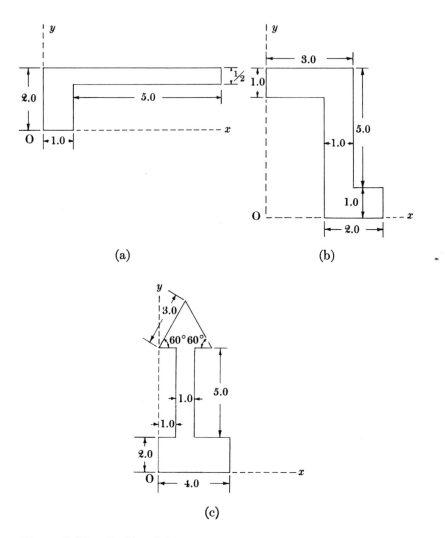

(a)

(b)

(c)

Figure 7.34. *Problem 7.42.*

7.38. A uniform door weighing 50.0 pounds force and of width 3.00 feet has two hinges equally spaced above the horizontal center line. The distance between the hinges is 5.00 feet, and each hinge bears half the load. Find the horizontal and vertical components of force exerted by each hinge, using the theory of couples.

7.39. The base of an isosceles triangle is 18.0 cm and the equal sides are each 41.0 cm. A weight of 10.0 kgf is at each of the corners joining the base line and another of 30.0 kgf is at the apex. Find the position of the center of gravity of the three weights.

7.40. Weights of 3.00, 5.00, 4.00, and 8.00 pounds force are situated respectively at the corners A, B, C, D, of the trapezoid shown in Figure 7.33. Find the position of the center of gravity of the weights.

7.41. When are the center of mass and the center of gravity at the same point?

7.42. Find the centers of gravity, with respect to O as origin, of the three homogeneous laminar objects shown in Figure 7.34. All dimensions are in feet.

7.43. Using the result of Example 7.8, find the location of the center of gravity of an isosceles triangle by **(a)** applying $\bar{x} = \sum w_i x_i / \sum w_i$ and $\bar{y} = \sum w_i x_i / \sum w_i$ and **(b)** the use of the calculus.

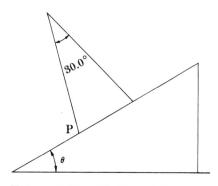

Figure 7.35. *Problem 7.44.*

7.44. A right circular cone with an apex angle of 30.0° rests on an inclined plane as shown in Figure 7.35. For what value of θ is the cone in unstable equilibrium about an axis through P perpendicular to the plane of the figure? Assume that the friction is great enough to prevent sliding.

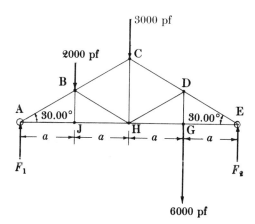

Figure 7.36. *Problem 7.46.*

7.45. In the method of double weighing, show that if the standard masses m_1 and m_2 differ by a very small amount, the true mass is very nearly the arithmetic mean of the standard masses.

7.46. Using the method of sections, find F_1, F_2, and the stresses in all the members of the symmetrical truss loaded as shown in Figure 7.36. The value of a is 10.00 feet. State whether the member is in compression (C) or tension (T).

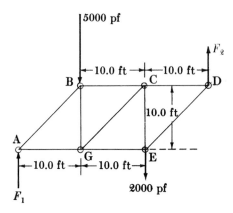

Figure 7.37. *Problem 7.47.*

7.47. The truss in Figure 7.37 is supported and loaded as shown. Find the supporting forces F_1 and F_2, and the stresses in all the members. Employ the method of sections and state whether the member is in compression (C) or tension (T).

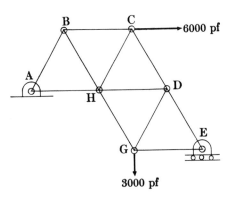

Figure 7.38. *Problem 7.48.*

7.48. Find the reactions at the supports of the loaded truss shown in Figure 7.38 and the stresses in all the members. The equilateral triangles have 10.0-foot sides. Employ the method of sections and state whether the member is in compression (C) or tension (T).

Angular Quantities

*I*N CHAPTERS *3, 4, AND 5* we considered the elements of linear motion and the dynamics of translation. In the following two chapters we shall be concerned with the developments of circular motion and the dynamics of rotation. The most general sort of motion can be resolved into a translational motion and a rotational motion. In pure translational motion all parts of a body have the same velocity or acceleration. In pure rotational motion, such as a flywheel spinning about a fixed axis, each particle of the body, remaining at a fixed distance from the axis of rotation, moves in a circle of a radius equal to the distance of the particle from the axis of rotation. In this chapter we shall discuss and study the quantities employed to describe this *angular motion* and then we shall be in a position to proceed with the mechanics of circular motion and the developments of the dynamics of rotation.

8.1.   The Radian.   The familiar process of dividing a circle into 360 equal sectors provides a means of designating and measuring an angle in degrees. It is particularly useful and convenient to designate angular measure in rotation by the *radian*. We can get at the meaning of this measure by considering the characteristics of the circle. In Figure 8.1 is shown a circular arc of length s formed by two radii r making an angle θ between them. If we keep θ constant and observe the variation in s corresponding to a variation in r we find that $s \propto r$. On the other hand, if r is kept constant and we observe the variation in s corresponding to a variation in θ, we observe that $s \propto \theta$. We can thus state the combined variation as $s = \theta r$ or

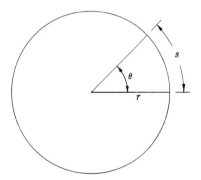

Figure 8.1. *Diagram used to define the radian.*

$$\theta = s/r \qquad (8.1)$$

Equation 8.1 states that an angle may be measured by the ratio of the arc length to its radius. When the lengths s and r are expressed in the same unit the angle is said to be measured in *radians* rather than in degrees. A radian (rad), being a ratio of two lengths which are expressed in the same unit of length, is a pure number, the word 'radian" merely indicating this kind of measure rather than degrees.

From Equation 8.1 we can obtain both the definition of one radian and its degree equivalence. When the angle θ is of such size that it is subtended by an arc s equal in length to its radius r, its magnitude is *one radian*. Now applying Equation 8.1 to an angle of 360° subtended by an arc length equal to a circumference, we have

$$\theta = 2\pi r/r = 2\pi \text{ rad}$$

Hence

$$2\pi \text{ rad} = 360°$$
$$1 \text{ rad} = 360°/2\pi$$
$$\doteq 360°/6.28$$
$$= 57.3° \text{ approximately}$$

8.2. Angular Velocity. Consider a disk of radius r rotating about an axis passing perpendicularly through O, as shown in Figure 8.2. Let the rate of rotation be such that a point on the rim moves from P to P', traversing the arc length s in a time t. The angular displacement of the disk is the

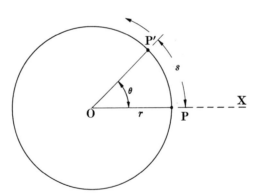

Figure 8.2. *Illustrating angular velocity.*

angle θ that the radius OP' makes with some reference direction OX. As described in connection with linear motion in Section 3.1, we may here have *uniform angular speed or velocity*, *average angular speed or velocity*, and *instantaneous angular speed or velocity*, where in general by *angular speed* we mean *angular displacement in a unit of time*.

In uniform-speed rotation equal angular displacements are swept through in equal time intervals, and the time rate of change of angular displacement is the same for each succeeding unit of time.

For variable-speed rotation, we define the average speed as the ratio of the total angular displacement θ to the corresponding total elapsed time t or

$$\omega_{av} = \theta/t \qquad (8.2)$$

where ω is the symbol used to represent angular speed or angular velocity.

The concept of instantaneous angular speed is derived in a manner analogous to that employed for instantaneous linear speed.   The value of the average angular speed depends on the size of the angular displacement.   One then takes the time interval as progressively shorter and shorter and it is then observed that the ratio of the displacement interval to the time interval approaches a definite limiting value which is the instantaneous angular speed. When the symbol ω is employed we shall mean, unless we indicate otherwise, the instantaneous angular speed or velocity.

The distinction between angular speed and angular velocity is the same as that existing between linear speed and linear velocity.   Angular speed is a scalar quantity, and angular velocity is a vector quantity.

Angular velocity is a directed quantity and its vector representation is illustrated in Figure 8.3.   The arrow representing ω is drawn along the axis of rotation and is of length PQ, proportional to the magnitude of the angular velocity. By convention, the direction of the arrow is the

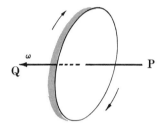

Figure 8.3.   *Vector representation of angular velocity.*

same as the direction in which a right-handed screw would advance if it were rotated in the sense of ω.   Thus, viewed along the direction PQ, the rotation is clockwise.

The unit generally used to express angular speed or angular velocity is the radian per second.   Often the revolution per minute (rev/min) is employed. Since there are 2π radians per revolution we have

$$\omega(\text{rad/sec}) = 2\pi(\text{rad/rev}) \times N(\text{rev/sec}) \qquad (8.3)$$

8.3.   Angular Acceleration.   *Angular acceleration is defined as the time rate of change of angular velocity.*   Again, the pattern for defining uniform, average, and instantaneous angular acceleration follows that laid down for the corresponding linear quantities.   Calling ω_0 the initial angular velocity and ω the angular velocity after a time interval t, the angular acceleration α is given by

$$\alpha = (\omega - \omega_0)/t \qquad (8.4)$$

The angular acceleration given by Equation 8.4 is constant if the angular velocity is changing at a uniform rate.   When the angular velocity does not change by equal amounts in equal time intervals, Equation 8.4 defines the average angular acceleration.   Angular acceleration is a vector and is represented in the same manner as ω in Figure 8.3.

The instantaneous angular acceleration is described in a manner analogous to the way in which the instantaneous linear acceleration was described. The limiting value of the ratio of the change in angular velocity to the change in the time interval as the latter is considered to approach zero is the instantaneous angular acceleration. Unless otherwise specified the symbol α will be employed to indicate the instantaneous angular acceleration.

The unit of angular acceleration, as can be seen from Equation 8.4, is the radian per second, per second (rad/sec^2).

8.4. Relation between Angular and Linear Quantities. When a body is rotating about an axis each point of the body, in describing a circle about the axis, has a linear motion. The relation between the angular displacement θ and the linear displacement s is given by Equation 8.1. Likewise, there exists a similar simple relationship between the angular and linear velocities and between the angular and linear accelerations. These relationships are readily obtained with the aid of Figure 8.4 which shows any point P in a body at a distance r from an axis passing through O. When the body rotates through an angle $\Delta\theta$ in the time Δt, the point P moves to P', traversing an arc distance Δs. In the following development the left column contains the more elementary treatment while the right column employs the calculus.

The average angular velocity is given by

$$\omega_{av} = \Delta\theta/\Delta t$$

and

$$\Delta\theta = \Delta s/r$$

Therefore,

$$\omega_{av} = \frac{\Delta s}{\Delta t} \times \frac{1}{r}$$

Now, permitting Δt to approach zero, then in the limit ω_{av} approaches the instantaneous angular velocity ω and $\Delta s/\Delta t$ approaches the instantaneous velocity v at P and we have

$$\omega = v/r \qquad (8.5)$$

From Figure 8.4,

$$\Delta\theta = \Delta s/r$$

Dividing both sides of the equation by Δt,

$$\frac{\Delta\theta}{\Delta t} = \frac{1}{r} \times \frac{\Delta s}{\Delta t}$$

Taking the limit of both sides as Δt approaches 0,

$$\lim_{\Delta t \to 0} \frac{\Delta\theta}{\Delta t} = \frac{1}{r} \lim_{\Delta t \to 0} \frac{\Delta s}{\Delta t}$$

We now recognize the limit expressions as derivatives so that

$$\frac{d\theta}{dt} = \frac{1}{r} \times \frac{ds}{dt}$$

and since the time rate of change of θ is the instantaneous angular velocity ω and the time rate of change of s is the linear instantaneous tangential velocity v at P, we have

$$\omega = v/r \qquad (8.5)$$

where it is to be observed that the direction of v is perpendicular to the radius.

In the same way the student should prove to himself that the instantaneous angular acceleration is related to the instantaneous linear acceleration by the equation

$$\alpha = a/r \qquad (8.6)$$

Equations 8.1, 8.5, and 8.6 are of extreme importance since they express the relationship between the linear quantities s, v, and a and the corresponding angular quantities θ, ω, and α. It is easy to remember them since each expresses a direct proportion between the linear quantity and the corresponding angular quantity, the radius playing the role of the proportionality constant. We have obtained these relationships in considering rotation about a fixed axis; they are, however, valid in general if the quantities a, α, ω, and r are reckoned with respect to the appropriate instantaneous axis of rotation.

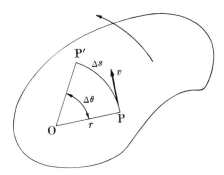

Figure 8.4. *Illustrating the relation between angular and linear quantities.*

An essential fact that must be kept in mind concerning Equations 8.5 and 8.6 is that when a body is rotating about an axis all of its points have the same angular velocity or angular acceleration but any given point has a linear velocity or linear tangential acceleration that is proportional to its distance from the axis of rotation.

8.5. Kinematics of Rotation. We have seen that for constant linear acceleration the kinematic equations of translation are given by Equations 3.7. For constant angular accelerated rotational motion we may derive in a similar manner the kinematic equations of rotation. The first of these, relating ω, ω_0, α, and t, is given by Equation 8.4. The other two may be easily obtained or they may be set down by analogy. We thus have the set of equations

$$\left. \begin{aligned} \omega &= \omega_0 + \alpha t \\ \theta &= \omega_0 t + \tfrac{1}{2}\alpha t^2 \\ \omega^2 &= \omega_0^2 + 2\alpha\theta \end{aligned} \right\} \qquad (8.7)$$

In these equations a consistent set of units that is generally employed is the following: ω is expressed in radians per second, α in radians per second, per second, θ in radians, and t in seconds. Since the student is already familiar with Equations 3.7 it is relatively easy for him to remember and learn to employ Equations 8.7 by fixing in mind the similarity between both sets of equations. For this purpose we give below in tabular form the corresponding kinematic equations for translation and rotation of motion under constant linear and constant angular acceleration.

Table 8.1. *Kinematic equations for translation and rotation.*

Translation (linear acceleration, a = constant)	Rotation (angular acceleration, α = constant)	Relation between linear and angular quantities
$v = v_0 + at$	$\omega = \omega_0 + \alpha t$	$s = \theta r$
$s = v_0 t + \frac{1}{2}at^2$	$\theta = \omega_0 t + \frac{1}{2}\alpha t^2$	$v = \omega r$
$v^2 = v_0^2 + 2as$	$\omega^2 = \omega_0^2 + 2\alpha\theta$	$a = \alpha r$
$v_{av} = (v_0 + v)/2$	$\omega_{av} = (\omega_0 + \omega)/2$	

Example 8.1. How long does it take for a wheel, rotating at a constant angular speed of 100 radians/sec, to make 50.0 revolutions?

Solution. The time is given by

$$t = \theta/\omega$$

$$= \frac{2\pi \dfrac{\text{rad}}{\text{rev}} \times 50.0 \text{ rev}}{100 \dfrac{\text{rad}}{\text{sec}}}$$

$$= \pi \text{ sec}$$
$$= 3.14 \text{ sec}$$

Example 8.2. A motor accelerates uniformly from 300 to 1.50×10^3 revolutions/minute in 5.00 sec. Find (**a**) the angular acceleration, (**b**) the average angular speed, and (**c**) the total angle turned through.

Solution. (**a**) Applying Equation 8.4:

$$\alpha = (\omega - \omega_0)/t$$
$$= \frac{(157 - 31.4) \text{ rad/sec}}{5.00 \text{ sec}}$$
$$= 25.1 \text{ rad/sec}^2$$

$$\omega_0 = \frac{300 \text{ rev}}{\text{min}} \times \frac{2\pi \text{ rad}}{\text{rev}} \times \frac{\text{min}}{60.0 \text{ sec}}$$
$$= 31.4 \text{ rad/sec}$$
$$\omega = 1,500 \text{ rev/min}$$
$$= 157 \text{ rad/sec}$$

(**b**)
$$\omega_{av} = (\omega_0 + \omega)/2$$
$$= (31.4 + 157)/2$$
$$= 94.2 \text{ rad/sec}$$

(**c**)
$$\theta = \omega_{av}t$$
$$= 94.2 \frac{\text{rad}}{\text{sec}} \times 5.00 \text{ sec}$$
$$= 471 \text{ rad}$$

The solution to this part may also be obtained by using the second of Equations 8.7. Thus

$$\theta = \omega_0 t + \tfrac{1}{2}\alpha t^2$$

$$= 31.4 \frac{rad}{sec} \times 5.00\,sec + \frac{1}{2} \times 25.1 \frac{rad}{sec^2} \times 25.0\,sec^2$$

$$= 157\ rad + 313.8\ rad$$
$$= 471\ rad$$

Example 8.3. The propeller of an airplane is rotating at 1.00×10^3 revolutions/minute. If each of the blades is 6.00 feet long what are **(a)** the tangential velocity of the tip of each blade and **(b)** the tangential velocity of a point on the blade distant 2.00 feet from the axis?

Solution. **(a)** Applying Equation 8.5,

$$v = \omega r$$

$$= 1{,}000 \frac{rev}{min} \times 2\pi \frac{rad}{rev} \times \frac{min}{60.0\ sec} \times 6.00\ ft$$

$$= 628\ ft/sec$$

(b)
$$v = \frac{1{,}000 \times 2\pi}{60.0} \times 2.00$$

$$= 209\ ft/sec$$

Example 8.4. A grindstone 2.00 feet in diameter and rotating at 1.50×10^3 revolutions/minute decelerates at a constant rate and comes to rest in 12.0 sec. Find the tangential velocity of a point on its rim 8.00 sec before it comes to rest.

Solution. The deceleration is given by

$$\alpha = (\omega - \omega_0)/t \qquad\qquad \omega = 0$$

$$= \frac{-157\ rad/sec}{12.0\ sec} \qquad \omega_0 = 1{,}500 \frac{rev}{min} \times 2\pi \frac{rad}{rev} \times \frac{min}{60.0\ sec}$$

$$= -13.1\ rad/sec^2 \qquad\quad = 157\ rad/sec$$

and the angular velocity 8.00 sec before ceasing to rotate is given by

$$\omega = \omega_0 + \alpha t$$

$$= 157 \frac{rad}{sec} - 13.1 \frac{rad}{sec^2} \times 4.00\ sec$$

$$= 105\ rad/sec$$

so that the tangential linear velocity is

$$v = \omega r$$

$$= 105 \frac{rad}{sec} \times 1.00\ ft$$

$$= 105\ ft/sec$$

The angular velocity may alternatively be found by determining the total angle turned through in 4.00 sec. Thus:

$$\theta = \omega_0 t + \tfrac{1}{2}\alpha t^2$$

$$= 157\,\frac{\mathrm{rad}}{\mathrm{sec}} \times 4.00\,\mathrm{sec} - \frac{1}{2} \times 13.1\,\frac{\mathrm{rad}}{\mathrm{sec}^2} \times 16.0\,\mathrm{sec}^2$$

$$= 523\ \mathrm{rad}$$

Now apply

$$\omega^2 = \omega_0{}^2 + 2\alpha\theta$$

$$= (157)^2\,\frac{\mathrm{rad}^2}{\mathrm{sec}^2} - 2 \times 13.1\,\frac{\mathrm{rad}}{\mathrm{sec}^2} \times 523\ \mathrm{rad}$$

$$= 10,946\ \mathrm{rad}^2/\mathrm{sec}^2$$

$$\omega = 105\ \mathrm{rad}/\mathrm{sec}$$

and $v = 105$ ft/sec as before.

Problems

8.1. Make the following conversions: 5.00×10^3 radians to degrees; 1.50×10^3 rev/min to rad/sec; 50.0 rad/sec^2 to rev/min^2; 24.0 hr/rev to rad/sec; 365 days/rev to rad/sec.

8.2. A flywheel starting from rest acquires a speed of 250 revolutions/minute in 10.0 sec. Find (**a**) the angular acceleration and (**b**) the total angle turned through.

8.3. In Problem 8.2 find (**a**) the maximum linear speed of a point 0.500 feet from the rotation axis and (**b**) the maximum tangential acceleration of the same point.

8.4. Into Equations 3.7 substitute for s, v, and a their values given respectively by Equations 8.1, 8.5, and 8.6. What are the resulting equations?

8.5. Starting with Equation 8.4 derive Equations 8.5 and 8.6 following the method used to derive the analogous equations for linear motion.

8.6. An automobile engine is making 300 revolutions/minute when it is subjected to a constant angular acceleration of 25.0 radians/sec^2 for 5.00 sec. Find (**a**) the number of revolutions made during the accelerating period and (**b**) the angular velocity at the end of the 5.00 sec.

8.7. The extranuclear electron of a hydrogen atom rotates about the proton as a center with an angular speed of 41.5×10^{15} radians/sec. Find (**a**) the number of revolutions the electron makes in one second and (**b**) the speed of the electron which is considered to be at a constant distance of 0.530×10^{-8} cm from the proton.

8.8. A large gear of effective diameter 12.0 cm engages a smaller gear of effective diameter 5.00 cm. The large gear accelerates from rest to a speed of 60.0 revolutions/minute in 10.0 sec. Find (**a**) the maximum angular velocity of the larger gear, (**b**) the maximum angular velocity of the small gear, and (**c**) the maximum tangential velocity and acceleration of a point on the effective periphery of the small gear.

8.9. A flywheel is making 1.20×10^3 revolutions/minute when a brake is applied. It slows down to 300 revolutions/minute in 8.00 sec. Find (**a**) the angular speed at the end of 6.00 sec, (**b**) the angle turned through after 8.00 sec, and (**c**) how long after the brake is applied the flywheel comes to rest. Assume a constant angular deceleration.

8.10. A pulley 10.0 cm in diameter is connected by a belt to a pulley 18.0 cm in diameter. The 10.0 cm pulley rotates with an angular speed of 120 revolutions/minute. Find (**a**) the linear speed of the belt and (**b**) the angular speed of the larger pulley. Assume no slippage of the belt.

8.11. A wheel rotates through 300 radians in 5.00 sec and at the end of this time its angular velocity is 100 radians/sec. Find (**a**) the angular acceleration and (**b**) the angular velocity at the start of the 5.00 sec interval.

8.12. A flywheel with constant angular acceleration makes 10.0 revolutions in 4.00 sec. The angular velocity at the start of the 4.00 sec interval is 6.00 radians/sec. Find (**a**) the angular acceleration and (**b**) the angular velocity at the end of the 4.00 sec interval.

8.13. At what times between twelve and one o'clock is the angle between the minute hand and the hour hand of a clock equal to $\pi/2$ radians?

8.14. A child, riding a bicycle whose wheels are 20.0 inches in diameter, starts from rest and attains a speed of 6.00 miles/hour in 4.00 sec. The front and rear sprockets contain respectively 25.0 and 5.00 teeth. Find (**a**) the angular acceleration of the wheels and (**b**) the maximum frequency of the vertical rise and fall of the child's knees.

8.15. Two circular wheels A and B are mounted on different motor shafts and placed with their rotation axes horizontal and collinear. Wheels A and B are given clockwise angular velocities of 1.20×10^3 and 900 revolutions/minute, respectively. At the precise instant that a brake is applied simultaneously to each wheel some paint is sprayed on the rim of each wheel in its twelve o'clock position. Wheel A decelerates uniformly at 10.0 radians/sec^2 and wheel B decelerates uniformly at 6.00 radians/sec^2. Find (**a**) when the paint marks will next again coincide and (**b**) the angle from the twelve o'clock position where this coincidence occurs.

Circular Motion

*W*E HAVE SEEN THAT whenever a body is in rotational mo-
tion there is associated with this motion the quantities angular displacement,
angular velocity, and angular acceleration. When the motion is uniform so
that the angular velocity ω is constant, the linear tangential speed of a point
in the body distant r from the rotation axis is ωr, a constant. However, as
we shall see, this uniform circular motion of a point or body is linearly accelerated motion, the acceleration being a result of a change in linear tangential velocity which in turn is due to a constantly changing direction. Analysis
shows that this acceleration is always directed toward the center of rotation,
giving rise to the corresponding unbalanced force known as the *centripetal*
force. We shall see that for all bodies that move along a curve there must
necessarily be present a centripetal force which maintains their curved motion.

Whenever the rotational motion is such that the angular velocity is changing, then, as we have seen, there is present an angular acceleration α, and a
point distant r from the rotation axis has a linear tangential acceleration αr.
In addition, there is present also the linear centripetal acceleration, so that
the point has a linear acceleration which is the resultant between the component radial and tangential accelerations.

In this chapter these motions will be studied in detail. The student
should concentrate as fully as possible, since the principles involved form the
basis of the study of the dynamics of rotation.

9.1. Uniform Circular Motion. Consider a point mass moving with
uniform speed v in a circle of radius r, as shown in Figure 9.1a. Let P_1 and P_2
represent two closely neighboring positions of the point which traverses the
arc distance Δs in the time Δt, the radii from the center O to P_1 and P_2 forming
the small angle $\Delta \theta$. The vector velocity at P_1 is represented by v_1 and at P_2
by v_2. Since the motion is assumed to be uniform the magnitude or length
of v_1 and v_2 is constant and equal to v, but the vectors differ by a change in
direction. Since a vector possesses both magnitude and direction a change
in either or both of these means a change in the vector: the rotating point
mass has a continuously changing vector velocity and thus experiences an
acceleration. We must now determine both the magnitude and direction of
this acceleration.

First consider Figure 9.1b, with the aid of which we can deduce the direction of the acceleration. Let us assume that the acceleration vector acts in any general direction PA. We may then resolve vector PA into two rectangular components: a component acceleration PC acting radially or centrally inward toward O and a component PT acting tangentially. However, since we are dealing with motion in which the magnitude of the velocity does not change there can be no tangential component of acceleration. Hence the acceleration PA must lie along the direction PO, being at every instant perpendicular to the path of motion, directed radially inward toward the center and so producing an effect which results in only a change in direction of the velocity. This acceleration is therefore designated *centripetal* or *center-seeking acceleration* and we shall denote it by the symbol a_c.

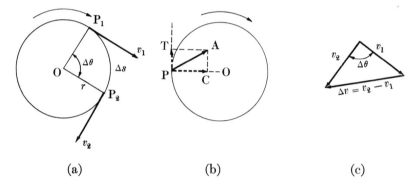

(a)   (b)   (c)

Figure 9.1. *Radial acceleration in uniform circular motion.*

Our next step is to compute the magnitude of the centripetal acceleration. The change in velocity $\Delta v = v_2 - v_1$ is shown by the vector triangle in Figure 9.1c. This vector triangle is similar to the physical triangle OP_1P_2 in (a). Hence the corresponding magnitudes of the sides are proportional, or

$$\frac{|\Delta v|}{|v_1|} = \frac{\overline{P_1P_2}}{r}$$

where $|\Delta v|$ and $|v_1|$ represent the absolute or magnitude values of Δv and v_1 respectively and $\overline{P_1P_2}$ represents the chord connecting P_1 and P_2. We have uniform circular motion so that $|v_1| = |v_2| = v$ and

$$|\Delta v| = \frac{v}{r}\,\overline{P_1P_2}$$

Since we are interested in infinitesimally small changes in evaluating the time rate of change of velocity, $\Delta\theta$ is small and $\overline{P_1P_2}$ may be replaced by the intercepted arc Δs. Hence

$$|\Delta v| = \frac{v}{r}\,\Delta s$$

Now divide both sides of this equation by the time interval Δt:

$$\frac{|\Delta v|}{\Delta t} = \frac{v}{r} \times \frac{\Delta s}{\Delta t}$$

Although this equation is approximate we may now obtain an exact expression by considering that the time interval approaches zero in the limit.   Thus

$$\lim_{\Delta t \to 0} \frac{|\Delta v|}{\Delta t} = \frac{v}{r} \lim_{\Delta t \to 0} \frac{\Delta s}{\Delta t}$$

We now recognize the limiting value of the ratio on the left as the instantaneous acceleration and that on the right as the tangential speed v.   Therefore

$$a_c = v^2/r \tag{9.1}$$

which states that the magnitude of the radial or centripetal acceleration varies directly as the square of the speed of the rotating mass and inversely as the radius of curvature.   Equation 9.1 may be expressed in terms of the angular velocity.   Since $v = \omega r$ we have

$$a_c = \omega^2 r \tag{9.2}$$

That the direction of a_c is perpendicular at all times to the instantaneous direction of v is again evident if we remember that the direction of the acceleration is the same as that of Δv.   As the angle $\Delta \theta$ becomes smaller, v_1 and v_2 approach one another and the direction of Δv becomes more nearly normal to v_1 and v_2.   In the limit when $\Delta \theta$ is zero the vector Δv is exactly normal to the direction of v and the direction of the acceleration is radially inward toward the center of the circular motion.

9.2.   Nonuniform Circular Motion.   The more general case in which a rotating body has an angular acceleration α is illustrated by Figure 9.2.   In Figure 9.2a, P_1, P_2, and the vector v_1 are the same as in Figure 9.1a,

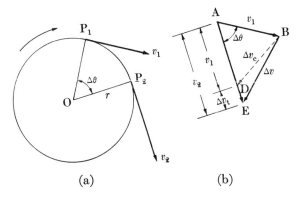

(a)   (b)

Figure 9.2.   *Radial and tangential components of acceleration in nonuniform circular motion.*

but the magnitude of the vector v_2 is greater in Figure 9.2a since we have an increasing angular velocity. In Figure 9.2b is shown the corresponding vector triangle formed by the vector velocity v_1, the vector velocity v_2 (from A to E), and the change in velocity $\Delta v = v_2 - v_1$. The point D on AE defines the vector AD equal to v_1. Then the vector BD is identical with the vector Δv in Figure 9.1c and in the limit when $\Delta\theta \to 0$ is the change in velocity Δv_c, which gives rise to the radial or centripetal acceleration given by Equations 9.1 or 9.2. In the vector triangle BDE, vector BD and vector DE are the two components of vector Δv and in the limit when $\Delta\theta \to 0$, v_1 coincides with v_2, vector BD is perpendicular to either, and vector DE coincides with the direction of either and lies along the tangent at P_2. This means that the total change in velocity Δv distributes as follows: it gives rise to two component changes in velocity, a radial or centripetal component Δv_c, and a tangential component Δv_t. The component Δv_c is the change in velocity due to a change only in direction of motion. The component Δv_t is the change in velocity due to the change in the magnitude of v_1 and v_2. The centripetal component results in the radial or centripetal acceleration a_c given by Equations 9.1 and 9.2. The tangential component gives rise to a tangential acceleration a_t which, obviously, is given by

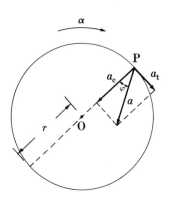

Figure 9.3. *Resultant acceleration in nonuniform circular motion.*

$$a_t = \alpha r \qquad (9.3)$$

The magnitude of the resultant acceleration of a point P whose instantaneous angular velocity is ω is given by the following (see Figure 9.3):

$$a = \sqrt{a_c^2 + a_t^2} = \sqrt{(\omega^2 r)^2 + (\alpha r)^2}$$
$$= r\sqrt{\omega^4 + \alpha^2} \qquad (9.4)$$

and the angle φ that this acceleration vector makes with the radial acceleration direction is given by

$$\tan\varphi = a_t/a_c$$
$$= \alpha/\omega^2 \qquad (9.5)$$

9.3. Centripetal and Centrifugal Forces. We now consider the force that must be present to produce the radial acceleration that a body experiences when it is rotating. In accordance with Newton's second law of motion this force is given by ma_c where m is the mass of the rotating body and a_c is the centripetal acceleration. The direction of the force is the same as that of a_c, being radially inward toward the center of rotation. It is therefore called a *centripetal force* and we shall represent it by the symbol F_{cp}:

$$F_{cp} = mv^2/r$$
$$= m\omega^2 r \qquad (9.6)$$

Several significant facts must be emphasized at this point of the development.

(1) *The magnitude of the centripetal force varies directly as the mass of the body, directly as the square of the tangential speed of the body, and inversely as the radius of curvature.* (This is the more usual statement, instead of the variation in terms of m, ω^2, and r.)

(2) *The direction of the centripetal force is always radially inward toward the center of rotation.*

(3) *The centripetal force always acts on the rotating mass and is responsible for maintaining the body in a curved path.*

The centripetal force is constant if v and r are constant, as with a body which rotates with constant angular velocity in a circle. On the other hand, F_{cp} may vary from point to point, as when a body revolves in a circle with an angular acceleration (see Figure 9.3) or when a body rotates with either uniform or nonuniform elliptic motion. In any case, whenever there is curved motion there is present some physical situation or phenomenon that supplies the centripetal force necessary to maintain this motion, which is characterized by a continuously changing direction. The truth of this statement can again be deduced from Newton's first law of motion. When there is no agent to supply the centripetal force, there is no radial acceleration, hence no unbalanced centripetal force, and the body moves with uniform motion in a straight line.

It will now be recalled that to every action there is an equal and opposite reaction. If the centripetal force is the action, there must be present a reaction force which is exerted upon the agent of the accelerating force. This force, which is the reaction to F_{cp}, is known as the *centrifugal force*, which we shall represent by F_{cf}. Its nature can be stated as follows:

(1) *The magnitude of the centrifugal force is equal to the magnitude of the centripetal force.*

(2) *The direction of the centrifugal force is always opposite to that of the centripetal force, being radially outward away from the center of rotation.*

(3) *The centrifugal force is always exerted by the accelerating body upon the agent which supplies the centripetal force.*

The centripetal and centrifugal forces always form an action-and-reaction pair, but it must be remembered that of these two only the centripetal force acts upon the rotating body; the centrifugal force is exerted by the rotating body. Hence it is well here to caution the reader never to consider the action of centrifugal force as a cause in describing the behavior of the rotating body since the centrifugal force never acts on the body.

9.4.   Examples of Centripetal and Centrifugal Forces. We shall now consider six examples of these forces.

1. Motion in a Horizontal Circle. First we consider a mass m rotating on a perfectly smooth horizontal plane with an angular velocity ω, as shown in Figure 9.4. The cord joining the body to the fixed center of rotation O be-comes taut and keeps the body rotating in a circle. If friction is neglected, there are three forces acting on the body. There is the weight of the body mg acting downward, and the vertical normal reaction of the plane on the body. These forces, which are balanced, are not shown in the diagram. The third force is the centripetal force F_{cp} which is supplied by the tension in the cord and is exerted by the cord on the body at the point of contact. The centrifugal force (not shown) is exerted radially outward by the pull of the body on the cord at the point of con-tact. If the cord breaks, doing away with the centripetal force, the body flies off at a tangent to the curved path, in accordance with Newton's first law of motion.

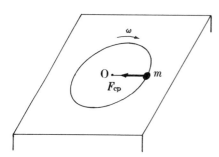

Figure 9.4. *Motion in a horizontal circle.*

As another illustration, we cite the motion of a track trolley rounding a curve on a horizontal plane. The centripetal force here is supplied by the radial push of the outer rail against the flanges of the outer wheels. This maintains the motion in a curved path. The centrifugal force is exerted radially outward by the flanges of the outer wheels of the trolley against the outer railing.

As a familiar illustration, consider the rounding of a curve by an auto-mobile on horizontal ground. In order that the car may accomplish the turn at a given speed without skidding, enough friction between the tires and ground must be present to supply the requisite centripetal force. On wet and icy ground such turns become quite hazardous to execute even at rela-tively low speeds, and the car skids in a direction tangent to the curved path.

2. The Centrifuge. The centrifuge is a device for separating liquids of different densities (i.e., mass per unit volume; see Section 17.1). Centripetal force is the governing phenomenon in its operation. One form of centrifuge is shown in Figure 9.5. It consists of a rotatable frame in a horizontal plane. The frame has attached to it several cylindrical tubes which hang vertically when the frame is at rest and assume a horizontal position when the frame is given a high angular velocity. When a mixture of liquids of different densi-ties is introduced into the tubes and the frame rotates with high angular ve-locity the liquids separate, the denser liquids moving farther from the axis of rotation and the less dense liquids remaining closer. The particles of the denser liquid require a greater centripetal force $m\omega^2 r$ than those of the less dense liquid to keep them in a given circular path.   Therefore, the particles of the denser liquid move outward to positions more remote from the axis of rotation than do the less dense particles.   In a cream separator the milk is denser than the cream so that it accumulates near the outer edge of the centrifuge while the cream remains nearer the axis of the separator.   In the

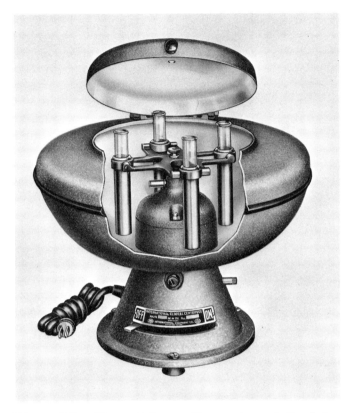

Figure 9.5.   *The centrifuge.   (By courtesy of the International Equipment Company).*

fields of chemistry, medicine, and biology there are put into use high-speed rotors called ultracentrifuges that can be rotated at extremely high speeds, greater than 10^6 revolutions per minute.   With such a machine the process of sedimentation occurs rapidly.

   3. Motion in a Vertical Circle.   Figure 9.6 represents a body of mass m rotating in a vertical circle of radius r.   A cord of negligible mass is attached to the body at one end and to a fixed center O at the other end.   Three positions of the mass are shown: at A the lowest position, at B the topmost position, and at C a general position making an angle θ with the downward vertical. The body is at all times under the action of two forces only. One of these is the tension T in the cord and the other is the weight of the body mg. Considering the more general position of the body and remembering that the centripetal force is the resultant radially inward force acting on the body in circular motion, we have

$$T - mg \cos \theta = mv^2/r \qquad (9.7)$$

where v is the instantaneous speed at C. Physically speaking, motion in a vertical circle is not uniform since the mass speeds up on the way down and slows on the way up owing to the presence of the gravitational field, so that the centripetal force and the tension vary at different points of the circular path.

In particular, the tensions T_1 at A and T_2 at B are given by

$$T_1 = mg + (mv_1^2/r) \qquad (9.8)$$
$$T_2 = (mv_2^2/r) - mg \qquad (9.9)$$

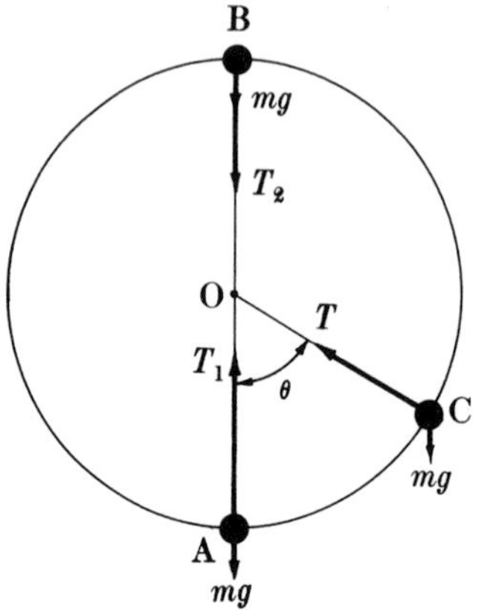

Figure 9.6. *Vertical circular motion.*

where v_1 is the speed at A and v_2 is the speed at B. These equations state that the centripetal force at B is supplied in part by the weight of the body and in part by the tension in the string, and the centripetal force at A is supplied by an amount equal to the difference between the value of the tension there and the weight of the body.

It should be clear that the body must have a speed at A equal to or greater than some minimum value if it is to get over the top at B. Hence there is a corresponding minimum value for the speed at B below which the cord becomes slack there. To find this value of v_2 we set $T_2 = 0$ in Equation 9.9; then:

$$0 = (mv_2^2/r) - mg$$
$$v_2 = \sqrt{gr} \qquad (9.10)$$

With this critical value of v_2 at B, the value necessary for the body to get over the top, we can now find the corresponding minimum speed at A. For this purpose, using the kinematic equations for translation, we need to know the average tangential acceleration. The instantaneous tangential acceleration at C in Figure 9.6 is obtained by applying Newton's second law of motion. The unbalanced tangential force acting on the body at C is $mg \sin \theta$, so that

$$mg \sin \theta = ma_t$$
$$a_t = g \sin \theta \qquad (9.11)$$

which shows that the tangential acceleration varies as the sine of the angle. It can be shown (see Problem 9.16) that the average tangential acceleration over the half-circumference B to A is:

$$(a_t)_{av.} = 2g/\pi$$

so that, applying the kinematic equation relating velocity to distance, we have

$$v_1^2 = v_2^2 + 2(2g/\pi)(\pi r)$$
$$= gr + 4gr$$
$$v_1 = \sqrt{5gr} \tag{9.12}$$

and the body must have at least this speed at A to insure the minimum speed $\sqrt{gr}$ at B needed for the body to get over the top. The student should keep in mind that, since the tangential acceleration is not constant, the average of the tangential acceleration depends on the angular displacement interval.*

The familiar demonstration of swinging a pail of water in a vertical circle without having any of the water fall out is similarly explained by the above analysis.

4. Rotational Motion of the Earth. The earth's own rotation of 2π radians every 24 hours causes a flattening at the poles and a bulging at the equator. Because of this, the earth, instead of being spherical, is an oblate spheroid

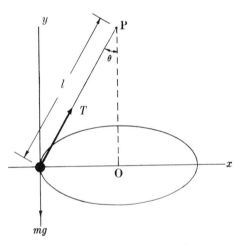

Figure 9.7. *The conical pendulum.*

with the equatorial diameter about 28 miles greater than the polar diameter. A point on the surface of the earth at the equator is farther from the center of the earth than a point at the poles and there is a progressive increase in the gravitational acceleration from the equator to the poles. In addition, at the equator a body is farther from the earth's rotation axis. Consequently, the body at the equator experiences a greater centripetal force which subtracts from the gravitational force to yield an apparent weight smaller than at the

---

* The average of the tangential acceleration for the angular displacement $\theta_2 - \theta_1$ is

$$(a_t)_{av} = \frac{g}{\theta_2 - \theta_1}(\cos\theta_1 - \cos\theta_2).$$

poles. The presence of rotation therefore gives rise additionally to a progressive increase in the weight of a body from the equator to the poles. This change in apparent weight of an object due to the earth's rotation is small, amounting to about 0.34% from the equator to the poles. Hence the amount by which the apparent weight of a body is less than the force of gravitational attraction mg is negligible for most purposes.

5. *The Conical Pendulum.* A conical pendulum is a mass, supported by a light cord, revolving with uniform circular motion in a horizontal plane, as shown in Figure 9.7. The cord of length l, fixed at P directly above the center of the circular path of radius r, generates a cone of semiapex angle θ. We choose rectangular axes through the mass m and observe that there are only two forces acting on m: the tension T and the weight mg. There is no vertical acceleration and an equilibrium condition prevails, and we have

$$\Sigma F_y = T \cos \theta - mg = 0$$

Horizontally in the x direction there is centripetal acceleration; hence

$$\Sigma F_x = T \sin \theta = mv^2/r$$

Eliminating T from these two equations of motion yields

$$\tan \theta = v^2/gr = \omega^2 r/g \tag{9.13}$$

Putting $r = l \sin \theta$, Equation 9.13 becomes

$$\cos \theta = g/\omega^2 l \tag{9.14}$$

Equation 9.14 gives the relationship that must exist between θ, ω, and l. We see that as ω increases, for a pendulum of given length, $\cos \theta$ decreases or θ increases. Hence, as the angular velocity of the mass is increased it rotates in a circle of larger and larger radius.

The conical pendulum affords a convenient means of studying the law of centripetal force. From Equation 9.13,

$$\omega^2 = g/\sqrt{l^2 - r^2} \tag{9.15}$$

For a given pendulum bob and a fixed value of r, the centripetal force $F_{cp} = m\omega^2 r$ is proportional to ω^2. Hence, by keeping r constant a series of determinations of ω corresponding to a series of chosen pendulum lengths l may be made by observing N, the number of revolutions per second, and using $\omega = 2\pi N$. For each value of ω there is a corresponding determined value of the right-hand side of Equation 9.15. A plot of ω^2 versus $1/\sqrt{l^2 - r^2}$ yields a straight line whose slope is the value of the acceleration due to gravity.

6. *Banking of Curves.* We have seen that when a vehicle or trolley makes a turn on level ground or on level rails it must rely upon the presence of friction, and the trolley must depend upon the pressure of the rails against the wheel flanges for the necessary centripetal force. However, it is possible for a car to round a curve at a given speed without relying upon friction or for a train to move in a circle without having the rails press laterally against the wheel flanges. This is accomplished by having curves banked so that the

roadbed, or trolley or train track, slopes upward from the inner to the outer edge. We shall describe how this works, using an automobile for illustration.

Figure 9.8a shows the front view of a car of mass m moving on level ground with speed v and rounding a curve whose center of curvature is a distance r from the center of gravity of the car. Three forces act on the car: the weight mg acting downward, the normal reaction $F_N = mg$ acting upward, and the centripetal force F_{cp} supplied by friction. These forces are shown as acting through the center of gravity, to facilitate the analysis. The resultant reaction of the ground on the car is represented by the dotted arrow F. Thus F and mg, whose resultant is the centripetal force F_{cp}, adjust to keep the car in curvilinear motion, provided there is a sufficient amount of friction present.

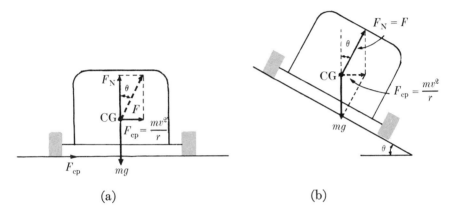

(a)   (b)

Figure 9.8. *Forces on an automobile rounding a curve:* (a) *on level road-bed and* (b) *on a banked roadbed.*

In Figure 9.8b the road is banked so that its surface is perpendicular to the direction of F given in the picture (a). Now the force, whose horizontal component provides the centripetal force and whose vertical component supports the weight of the car, is the normal force F_N exerted by the roadbed on the car. Friction is therefore not required, and the car can move in a circle without skidding. The vectors F and mg are precisely the same in both diagrams and result in the same centripetal force. The angle of banking θ is obtained from the equations

$$F_N \sin \theta = mv^2/r \quad \text{and} \quad F_N \cos \theta = mg$$

which combine to yield

$$\tan \theta = v^2/gr \tag{9.16}$$

Since the angle of banking for a given turn depends on the speed, the banking of highways and railroads are designed for some safe average speed. For an additional analysis of the forces acting on the car see Problem 9.24.

The same considerations apply to other familiar situations. In the case of a plane making a turn, sideslip is prevented by having the angle of banking and the speed so adjusted that the resultant thrust is perpendicular to the wing surfaces, providing a vertical component of lift and a horizontal component that supplies the requisite centripetal force. A person running, riding a bicycle, or skating on level ground, with speed v, leans inward at an angle θ with the vertical, given by Equation 9.16, when rounding a curve of radius r. The adjustment again satisfies the condition that the resultant reaction of the ground (resultant between the friction force and the force of normal reaction) passes through the person's center of gravity and has a vertical component that equalizes the person's weight and a horizontal component that provides the necessary centripetal force. On a racecourse the angle of bank is θ, and the same reaction necessary to supply the same vertical and horizontal components is normal to the track. Friction is then not relied upon and there is no tendency to slipping.

Example 9.1. A horizontal turntable is rotating at 30.0 revolutions/minute. Up to what distance from the rotation axis can a block be placed and not fly off at a tangent? The coefficient of friction between block and turntable is 0.250.

Solution. The limiting distance is given by the fact that the centripetal force at this distance is just equal to the frictional force. Hence

$$m\omega^2 r = \mu_s mg$$

where μ_s is the coefficient of static friction.

$$
\begin{aligned}
r &= \mu_s g/\omega^2 \\
r &= (0.250 \times 980)/(3.14)^2 \\
&= 24.8 \text{ cm}
\end{aligned}
\qquad
\begin{aligned}
\mu_s &= 0.250 \\
g &= 980 \text{ cm/sec}^2 \\
\omega &= (2\pi \times 30.0/60.0) \text{ rad/sec} \\
&= 3.14 \text{ rad/sec}
\end{aligned}
$$

For distances larger than this the friction force is less than the necessary centripetal force.

Example 9.2. A wheel 30.0 cm in diameter is rotating clockwise in a vertical plane at 45.0 revolutions/minute. When a brake is applied the wheel slows to 30.0 revolutions/minute in 15.0 sec. For a point located on the rim directly below the center of rotation at the instant of applying the brake, find (**a**) its position 0.500 sec after the brake is applied and (**b**) its resultant acceleration.

Solution. First find the angular acceleration (see Figure 9.9):

$$
\begin{aligned}
\alpha &= (\omega - \omega_0)/t \\
&= (3.14 - 4.71)/15.0 \\
&= -1.57 \text{ rad/sec}^2
\end{aligned}
\qquad
\begin{aligned}
\omega_0 &= (45.0 \times 2\pi)/60.0 = 4.71 \text{ rad/sec} \\
\omega &= (30.0 \times 2\pi)/60.0 = 3.14 \text{ rad/sec}
\end{aligned}
$$

(**a**) The position is given by

$$
\begin{aligned}
\theta &= \omega_0 t + \tfrac{1}{2}\alpha t^2 \\
&= 4.71 \times 0.500 - \tfrac{1}{2}(1.57)(0.500)^2 \\
&= 2.16 \text{ rad}
\end{aligned}
$$

(b) At this location the angular velocity ω_1 and the radial and tangential components of acceleration are given by

$$\omega_1 = \omega_0 + \alpha t$$
$$= 3.14 - 1.57(0.500)$$
$$= 2.36 \text{ rad/sec}$$
$$a_c = \omega_1{}^2 r$$
$$= (2.36)^2 \times 15.0$$
$$= 83.6 \text{ cm/sec}$$
$$a_t = \alpha r$$
$$= -1.57 \times 15.0$$
$$= -23.6 \text{ cm/sec}^2$$

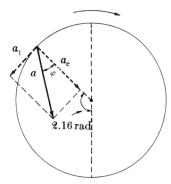

and the resultant acceleration is

$$a = \sqrt{a_c{}^2 + a_t{}^2}$$
$$= \sqrt{(83.6)^2 + (23.6)^2}$$
$$= 86.7 \text{ cm/sec}^2$$

Figure 9.9.

The angle φ that this resultant makes with the radial acceleration direction is

$$\tan \varphi = a_t/a_c$$
$$= 23.6/83.6$$
$$= 0.282$$
$$\varphi = 15.8°$$

Figure 9.9 illustrates the solution.

Example 9.3.   The turn on a highway has a radius of curvature of 125 feet and the angle of banking is 15.0°.   For what speed is it ideally banked?
   Solution.   Applying the equation for the angle of banking,

$$v^2 = gr \tan \theta$$
$$= 32.0 \times 125 \times 0.268$$
$$v = 32.7 \text{ ft/sec}$$
$$= 22.3 \text{ mi/hr}$$

Problems

   Where it is necessary to employ g, use the values 980 cm/sec^2 = 9.80 m/sec^2 = 32.0 feet/sec^2 unless another is specified.

   9.1.   A mass of 2.00 kgm at the end of a wire 2.00 m long is whirled in a circle at 90.0 revolutions/minute.   Find (a) the centripetal force and (b) the angle turned through in 5.00 sec.   Neglect gravity.

   9.2.   A weight of 2.00 pounds force is whirled at the end of a wire 5.00 feet long with a speed of 120 revolutions/minute.   Find (a) the centripetal force and (b) the tangential speed of a small section of wire distant 2.00 feet from the axis of rotation.   Neglect gravity.

9.3. For the electron in Problem 8.7, find (**a**) the centripetal acceleration and (**b**) the centripetal force. The mass of the electron is 9.11×10^{-28} gm.

9.4. The centripetal force acting on a person whose weight is 150 pounds force is 90.0 pounds force when he is standing on a merry-go-round which is rotating at 6.00 revolutions/minute. How far out from the axis of rotation is the person?

9.5. A child sits on the floor of a merry-go-round at a distance of 6.00 m from the axis of rotation. If the coefficient of static friction is 0.500, how many revolutions per minute must the merry-go-round make before the child begins to slide?

9.6. An automobile of 4.00×10^3 pounds mass is rounding a curve of 120 feet in radius at a constant speed of 30.0 miles/hour. Find (**a**) the radial acceleration, (**b**) the centripetal force, and (**c**) the coefficient of friction when the car is on the point of sliding.

9.7. A Ferris wheel 2.50 m in diameter is rotating at 5.00 revolutions/minute. What is the unbalanced force acting on a 25.0 kgm boy riding in one of the cars when it is (**a**) at the top and (**b**) at the bottom?

9.8. A small object whose mass is 150 gm is whirled in a vertical circle at the end of a cord 100 cm in length. Find the tension in the cord when the body is (**a**) at the top, (**b**) at the bottom, and (**c**) at a position 60.0° from the top. The speed of the body when at the top is 500 cm/sec.

9.9. A pail of water is rotating at the end of a cord in a vertical circle 2.00 feet in radius without any liquid's escaping, passing the highest point with twice the critical value of speed. Find (**a**) the minimum speed in its path, (**b**) the maximum speed in its path, and (**c**) the speed when the pail is at a position midway between the top and the bottom.

9.10. In Problem 9.9, find the tension in the cord corresponding to the three positions of the pail of water whose weight is 3.00 pounds force.

9.11. Assume that the earth is a sphere 8.00×10^3 miles in diameter. Find (**a**) the centripetal acceleration at the equator and (**b**) how fast the earth would have to rotate to make the apparent weight of a body at the equator zero. Use $g = 32.2$ feet/sec².

9.12. Find the apparent weight of a 150-pound pilot when he is at the top of a vertical loop 900 feet in radius and is traveling with a speed of 180 miles/hour.

9.13. A wheel 40.0 cm in diameter is rotating at 3.00 revolutions/minute when it is given an acceleration of 0.400 revolution/sec². At 0.500 sec after the acceleration is applied what are (**a**) the angular velocity, (**b**) the tangential velocity of a point on the rim, and (**c**) the magnitude of the resultant acceleration of a point on the rim?

9.14. In each of the following identify the centripetal and centrifugal forces and tell by what and on what each force is exerted: (**a**) a ball whirling at the end of a cord in a horizontal circle, (**b**) a ball whirling at the end of a cord in a vertical circle, (**c**) an electron revolving around a proton, (**d**) a planet revolving around the sun, (e) an airplane making a vertical loop, (f) a train rounding a curve on tracks that are banked.

9.15.   A disk 15.0 cm in radius starts from rest and accelerates uniformly, attaining an angular velocity about a horizontal axis of 3.00 radians/sec clockwise in 0.500 sec.   For a position on the rim situated at the start vertically above the center find (a) its position and (b) the magnitude and direction of its acceleration at the end of 0.800 sec.

9.16.   Show that the average of the tangential acceleration as stated by Equation 9.11 is given by $2g/\pi$ for a half- or quarter-cycle. (*Hint:* Integrate the right-hand member of Equation 9.11 over a half-cycle of a sine curve and divide the result by π.)

9.17.   A car rounds an unbanked curve 110 feet in radius with a speed of 30.0 miles/hour.   The coefficient of friction is 0.500.   (a) Will the car skid? (b) What should the angle of banking be for twice this speed?

9.18.   The breaking strength of a cord is 60.0 pounds force.   A smaller weight, supported by the cord, whose other end is fixed, is pulled aside through a vertical angle φ and then released.   The cord breaks when the weight reaches the bottom of the circular arc.   Find the weight for (a) $\varphi = 90.0°$, (b) $\varphi = 60.0°$.

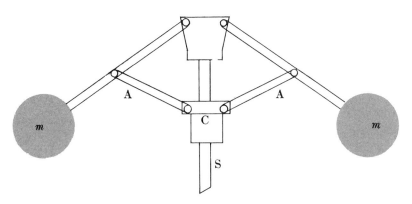

Figure 9.10.   *Problem 9.19.*

9.19.   One form of a centrifugal governor, which is a device for controlling the speed of a steam engine, is shown in Figure 9.10.   It consists of a pair of masses m attached to rigid rods which are hinged on a vertical spindle S. The engine communicates its rotary motion to S and when it is running too fast the masses move farther out from the rotation axis.   This motion, with the aid of arms A, raises the collar C which, by a system of levers not shown, actuates a valve which decreases the supply of steam.   If the rotation is too slow the masses fall and the valve opens to admit more steam.   In this way the engine speed is kept constant within narrow limits.

The rods are 18.0 inches long, the masses are 8.00 pounds mass each and the governor is making 90.0 revolutions/minute.   Find (a) the angle that the rods make with the vertical and (**b**) the tension of the rods. Neglect the weights of the rods and arms.

9.20. A skater rounds a curve 100 feet in radius with an angular speed of 0.250 radians/sec. By how much is his body inclined to the vertical if he is experiencing maximum stability?

9.21. A trolley rounds an unbanked curve 500 m in radius with a speed of 12.0 m/sec. For a 1.00 kgm plumb line hanging in the trolley find (**a**) its inclination to the vertical and (**b**) the tension in the supporting cord.

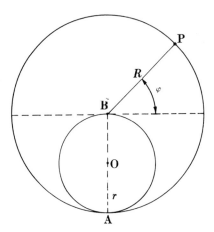

Figure 9.11. *Problem 9.27.*   **Figure 9.12.** *Problem 9.29.*

9.22. A rigid lightweight frame is in the form of an isosceles right triangle whose hypothenuse is 2.00 feet in length. A 4.00-pound weight is attached to the right-angled corner and the frame is rotated at 5.00 radians/sec about the hypotenuse as a vertical axis. Find the stresses in the two slanting members.

9.23. The 50.0 gm bob of a conical pendulum is suspended from a cord 30.0 cm long and swings in a horizontal circle at 90.0 revolutions/minute. Find (**a**) the angle the cord makes with the vertical, (**b**) the tension in the string, and (**c**) the radius of the circle.

9.24. The wheel base of a car that rounds a curve of radius r is b and the height of the center of gravity above the ground is h. Show that the greatest speed at which the car can round the curve without tipping over is given by $v^2 = grb/2h$. (*Hint:* The forces acting on the outer wheel of Figure 9.8a are the upward reaction R_1 and the friction force f_1. The corresponding forces on the inner wheel are R_2 and f_2. These, together with the force mg acting through the center of gravity, are all the forces. Set up the conditions $\sum F_x = mv^2/r$, $\sum F_y = 0$, and $\sum L = 0$ about an axis through the center of gravity. Solve these equations for R_1 and R_2 and obtain the condition for $R_2 = 0$.) Fully interpret all equations.

9.25. A car has a wheel base of 5.00 feet and a center of gravity that is 2.00 feet above the ground. The car rounds a curve at a speed of 60.0

miles/hour.   If the car does not slip, what is the smallest radius of curvature for rounding without tipping?   (*Hint:* Either use the result of Problem 9.24 or use the condition $\sum L = 0$ about an axis through the contact point of the outer wheel at the instant of tipping.)

9.26.   An airplane is looping-the-loop in a circle 500 feet in radius.   At the top of the loop the pilot is just starting to drop from his seat.   What is the speed of the plane?

9.27.   Figure 9.11 shows a loop-the-loop of radius r situated as shown inside a larger track of radius R, where $R = 2r$.   A car starts at P and acquires sufficient speed at A to reach B with the critical speed.   (**a**) What is the value of φ?   (**b**) What is the vertical height of P above B?

9.28.   A pilot weighing 160 pounds force executes a vertical loop of radius 2.00×10^3 feet at 300 miles/hour.   With what force does he press downward on his seat when he is at the bottom of the loop?

9.29.   A small ball originally at the bottom of a hemispherical bowl, radius 20.0 cm, takes up a position P when the bowl rotates about a vertical diametral axis with an angular speed of 10.0 radians/sec as shown in Figure 9.12.   Find the perpendicular distance from P to the rotation axis.

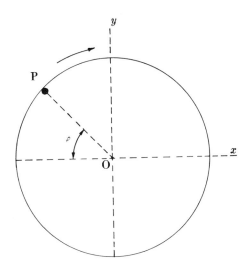

Figure 9.13.   *Problem 9.30.*

9.30.   Figure 9.13 shows a vertical circular inside track of radius r.   A small ball moving with insufficient speed to loop-the-loop leaves the track when it reaches a point P defined by the angle φ indicated.   (**a**) Show that the ball strikes the track at the point given by

$$x = r \, (4 \sin^2 \varphi - 1) \cos \varphi \qquad \text{and} \qquad y = r \, (1 - 4 \cos^2 \varphi) \sin \varphi$$

the coordinate origin being the track center O.   (**b**) For what angle φ, after leaving the track, will the ball strike the lowest point of the track?

Dynamics of Rotation

IN SECTION 7.3 WE INTRODUCED the second condition of equilibrium $\sum L = 0$, which states that the sum of the torques produced by all the forces acting on a body is equal to zero. We indicated that rotational equilibrium demands that there be no angular acceleration and further stated that there is a rotational analogue of Newton's second law for translation. In this chapter we shall derive the equation that defines Newton's second law for rotation, a relationship which states that the resultant torque about an axis of rotation is directly proportional to the resulting angular acceleration. We shall find that the development brings into the picture a new concept, that of *moment of inertia*, which is a significant property possessed by all bodies. In discussing this property we shall see that the value of the moment of inertia depends on the choice of rotation axis about which it is computed or determined.

With these developments at our command it will be possible to deal with the dynamics of a rotating body as completely as we have found it possible to study the dynamics of translation.

10.1. Newton's Second Law: Rotation. Consider a rigid body, Figure 10.1, free to rotate about a fixed axis passing through O perpendicular to the plane of the paper. Now let the body be acted upon by some force F distant r (both not shown) from O. This force F may be resolved into two components, a radial component F_r acting along r and a tangential component F_t acting at right angles to r. Since the radial component produces no turning moment about O, the torque acting on the body is $F_t r$ which gives rise to an angular acceleration α of the body. Now F may be replaced by its vector components F_1, F_2, F_3, etc., that act upon the particles composing the body whose masses are respectively $m_1, m_2, m_3, \ldots$, and whose corresponding distances from O are $r_1, r_2, r_3, \ldots$. Again, only their tangential components $F_{1t}, F_{2t}, F_{3t}, \ldots$, shown in the figure, are effective in producing the torque action. We thus have

$$F_t r = F_{1t} r_1 + F_{2t} r_2 + F_{3t} r_3 + \cdots \tag{10.1}$$

This equation states that the resultant torque L is equal to the sum of the component torques considered to be acting on all the particles of the body. Hence

$$L = F_{1t}r_1 + F_{2t}r_2 + F_{3t}r_3 + \cdots \tag{10.2}$$

Now, by Newton's second law for translation, $F_{1t} = m_1a_{1t}$, $F_{2t} = m_2a_{2t}$, $F_{3t} = m_3a_{3t}, \ldots$, where $a_{1t}, a_{2t}, a_{3t}, \ldots$ are the linear tangential accelerations of the mass particles. Hence,

$$L = m_1r_1a_{1t} + m_2r_2a_{2t} + m_3r_3a_{3t} + \cdots \tag{10.3}$$

From the relationship between linear and angular acceleration we have $a_{1t} = \alpha r_1$, $a_{2t} = \alpha r_2$, $a_{3t} = \alpha r_3, \ldots$, where α is the common angular acceleration of all particles of the body. Therefore

$$L = (m_1r_1^2 + m_2r_2^2 + m_3r_3^2 + \cdots)\alpha \tag{10.4}$$

The quantity in parentheses has fundamental significance in rotation and we designate it by the symbol I:

$$I = m_1r_1^2 + m_2r_2^2 + m_3r_3^2 + \cdots + m_nr_n^2$$

$$= \sum_{i=1}^{n} m_ir_i^2 \tag{10.5}$$

the last expression being the condensed notation for the sum of the products mr^2 over all the particles of the body. This quantity I is called the *moment of inertia* or *rotational inertia* of the body, and we shall soon discuss it more thoroughly. Equation 10.4 now becomes $L = I\alpha$ where, as we have seen, L is the torque due to the external force F. In the more general situation in which a rigid body is under the action of several external torques the left-hand side of Equation 10.4 is the resultant torque represented by $\sum L$. Therefore,

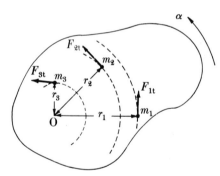

Figure 10.1. *Diagram used to obtain the relation between torque and angular acceleration.*

$$\sum L = I\alpha \tag{10.6}$$

Equation 10.6 is Newton's second law for rotation and expresses the relationship between the resultant external torque acting on a body and the resulting angular acceleration of the body.

10.2.   Discussion of the Laws of Motion for Rotation.   Equation 10.6 is easily recognized as the rotational analogue of Newton's second law for translation, $\sum F = ma$, where the resultant torque, moment of inertia, and angular acceleration in rotation correspond respectively to resultant force, mass, and linear acceleration in translation. The equation states that a resultant torque acting on a rigid body causes an angular acceleration which is directly proportional to, and in the same directional sense as, the resultant torque, and inversely proportional to the moment of inertia about the axis of rotation. Also, when a body possesses an angular acceleration, an unbalanced torque is acting. Furthermore, since rotational equilibrium means that there is no angular acceleration we have the second law of equilibrium $\sum L = 0$ which we have already studied in Section 7.3.

The analogy may be carried through to Newton's first and third laws of translational motion. If $\sum L = 0$, then $\alpha = 0$, and we have Newton's first law for rotation: *A body in rotation continues in rotation with a constant angular velocity about an axis, unless acted upon by an external unbalanced torque.* Finally, there is Newton's third law for rotation which states: *To every torque there is an equal and opposite reactive torque.*

Care should be exercised in the employment of the units in Equation 10.6. When the cgs absolute system is employed, L is given by the centimeter-dyne (cm·dyne), I by the gram-mass–square-centimeter (gm·cm²), and α by the radian per second, per second (rad/sec²). When the mks absolute system is employed, L is given by the meter-newton (m·nt), I by the kilogram-mass–square-meter (kgm·m²), and α by the radian per second, per second (rad/sec²). When the English gravitational system is employed, L is given by the pound-force–foot (pf·ft), I by the slug–square-foot (slug·ft²), and α by the radian per second, per second (rad/sec²). The student is urged at this point to write the units for each of the quantities in Equation 10.6 in each of these systems and observe that both sides of the equation have the same or equivalent units.

10.3. The Moment of Inertia. From Equation 10.6 we see that the moment of inertia of a body is *that property that requires an unbalanced torque to give the body an angular acceleration.* A body with a large moment of inertia sets up a greater resistance to angular acceleration than one with a smaller moment of inertia.

Equation 10.5 shows that the moment of inertia of a body about a specified axis of rotation is given by the sum of the products obtained by multiplying each constituent mass of the body by the square of its distance from the axis of rotation. The moment of inertia, then, depends not only on the mass of the body but—what is particularly significant—on the manner in which this mass is distributed about this axis. Thus the moment of inertia of the parallelopiped shown in Figure 10.2 is smaller about axis AA than about axis BB, for, although the mass involved is the same in both cases, more of it is concentrated at a greater distance, on the average, with respect to axis BB. About another axis the moment of inertia would, in general, have a different value. Hence, although moment of inertia in rotation corresponds to mass in translation, the mass of a body is always the same, while its moment of inertia depends upon the axis of rotation. In dealing with a rotationally accelerated body we must observe the axis about which the body is rotating and then use the appropriate moment of inertia in our analysis. For instance, a flywheel rotates about a fixed axis and the desired moment of inertia is about this axis. On the other hand, the rotation of a cylinder on a plane may be considered a rotation about its center of mass, or a rotation about an instantaneous axis which is tangent to the surface of the cylinder and passes

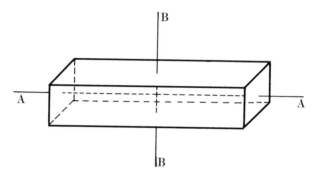

Figure 10.2. *Illustrating the dependence of moment of inertia on the distribution of mass.*

through the points of contact of cylinder and plane. Examples 10.5 and 10.8 at the end of this chapter illustrate the solution of problems in accordance with either of these considerations.

Another characteristic of moment of inertia is that it is a scalar quantity. Hence, for a body that is composed of parts made of different materials and different shapes the entire moment of inertia is obtained by taking the arithmetic sum of the moments of inertia of the different parts with respect to the desired axis of rotation.

10.4.   Calculation of Moment of Inertia.   First consider a system that is composed of discrete point-masses. In Figure 10.3 are shown three mass points m_1, m_2, m_3 situated at the corners of an equilateral triangle of side length b. The moment of inertia of this system about an axis passing normal to the paper through O situated midway between m_2 and m_3 is

$$I = m_1r_1^2 + m_2r_2^2 + m_3r_3^2$$

Here
$$r_1 = b \cos 30° = b\sqrt{3}/2$$
$$r_2 = r_3 = b/2$$
and
$$I = (b^2/4)(3m_1 + m_2 + m_3)$$

Naturally, this simple procedure holds when each mass is concentrated in a mathematical point, a condition which is purely idealistic. However, when the dimensions of the masses are small in relation to their distances from the rotation axis it may be employed to yield a result that, although approximate, is acceptable for practical purposes.   This is again exemplified by considering the moment of inertia of a very thin ring about an axis passing through its center and normal to its plane.   If the thickness of the ring is small compared with its radius r, then the ring may be considered as composed of very

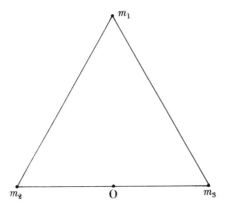

Figure 10.3.   *Moment of inertia of a system composed of discrete mass points.*

small circumferential elements of masses m_1, m_2, m_3, . . . , each considered a mass point distant r from the axis so that the moment of inertia is

$$I = m_1r^2 + m_2r^2 + m_3r^2 + \cdots$$

or $$I = mr^2$$

where m is the total mass of the ring.

Now consider a system whose mass is continuously distributed, such as a sphere, cylinder, or rod.   Again one may divide the body into a finite number of small discrete masses at correspondingly known distances from the rotation axis and use the simple computation.   At best such a procedure would yield a crude approximation to the true value of the moment of inertia.   By choosing elements of decreasing size and thus increasing the number of mass elements the approximation is improved.   The best procedure, of course, is to take elements of infinitesimal size, which in turn entails adding an infinite number of elementary moments of inertia.   Such a mathematical procedure is made possible by the methods of the calculus and leads to the correct evaluation of the moments of inertia of bodies.   The moments of inertia so obtained, for some simple but significant situations, are listed for reference in Table 10.1, where m is the mass of the indicated body.

When the body under consideration is a composite figure made up of two or more basic simple geometric figures, such as those listed in Table 10.1, its moment of inertia is readily computed by taking the sum of the moments of inertia of the parts, the same axis being used for each part. If a body has a void in it, such as a drilled hole, its moment of inertia is equal to the moment

Table 10.1. *Moments of inertia.*

Body	Location of axis	Moment of inertia
Thin rod of length l	Normal to the length at the center	$ml^2/12$
Thin rod of length l	Normal to the length at one end	$ml^2/3$
Thin rectangular sheet of sides a and b	Through the center parallel to b	$ma^2/12$
Thin rectangular sheet of sides a and b	Through the center normal to the sheet	$m(a^2+b^2)/12$
Sphere of radius r	Any diameter	$\frac{2}{5}mr^2$
Spherical shell of inner radius r_1 and outer radius r_2	Any diameter	$\frac{2}{5}m\dfrac{r_2{}^5 - r_1{}^5}{r_2{}^3 - r_1{}^3}$
Right circular cylinder of radius r and any length	Longitudinal axis of symmetry	$mr^2/2$
Right circular cylinder of inner radius r_1 and outer radius r_2	Longitudinal axis of symmetry	$m(r_1{}^2 + r_2{}^2)/2$
Right circular cylinder of radius r and length l	Through the center normal to the longitudinal axis	$\dfrac{m}{4}\left(r^2 + \dfrac{l^2}{3}\right)$
Right cone of base radius r	Longitudinal axis of symmetry	$\dfrac{3mr^2}{10}$

of inertia of the body considered homogeneous throughout, minus the moment of inertia of the removed material, both being about the same axis.

10.5.   Radius of Gyration.   In engineering mechanics there is a useful concept that is employed for the purpose of designating moments of inertia of irregularly shaped parts rotating about a designated axis. One employs a fictitious radius called the *radius of gyration* which is *the distance k from any given axis at which the mass m of the body may be imagined concentrated without altering the moment of inertia of the body about that axis.* Thus, if the mass m of the body is concentrated at this distance k, then its moment of inertia is

$$I = mk^2$$

or
$$k = \sqrt{I/m} \tag{10.7}$$

where I is the actual moment of inertia about the axis.

10.6.   Theorem of Parallel Axes.   Often we know the moment of inertia of a body about a certain axis and we desire to know it about another axis which is parallel to the first axis.   Instead of hunting through tables for the result, which usually cannot be found be-
cause all possible parallel axes are not given, or instead of solving the problem
from basic principles, we can readily com-
pute the value about the desired axis by using the theorem of parallel axes.   We
shall not prove this theorem, although to do so is relatively easy (see Problem 10.10),
but shall state it with the aid of Figure 10.4.   There two axes are shown: one, aa,
passing through the center of mass C of the body and another, bb, parallel to aa
and distant h from it.   The theorem of parallel axes is as follows: *The moment of*

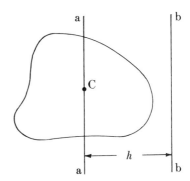

Figure 10.4.   *Illustrating the parallel-axes theorem.*

inertia of a body about any axis is equal to the moment of inertia about a parallel axis passing through the center of mass of the body plus the product of the mass of the body and the square of the perpendicular distance between both axes.   Thus, if I_C is the moment of inertia about aa and I is the desired moment of inertia about bb, then

$$I = I_C + mh^2 \tag{10.8}$$

If one knows the moment of inertia about an axis not passing through the center of mass and desires to know the moment of inertia about a parallel axis not passing through the center of mass, then two applications of Equation 10.8 will yield the result.

10.7.   Rolling Bodies.   A frequently occurring class of problems is that involving wheels, spheres, cylinders, and similar bodies rolling on a plane. This rolling may take place in either of two ways: the body will roll without slipping or it will roll and slip.

First consider a body that rolls without slipping.   In this case there is a simple relation between the angular motion of the body about its center of mass and the linear motion of its center of mass.   This relationship may be obtained by considering a symmetrical body such as a sphere or cylinder rolling without slipping on a horizontal plane.   In the time it takes the body to rotate through an angle θ about an axis through its center, the point of con-
tact of the body with the plane moves a linear distance s, which is given by $s = \theta r$ where r is the radius of the rolling body.   The center of mass, being always directly above the point of contact, also progresses a linear distance $s = r\theta$ parallel to the plane.   Dividing each side of the equation by the time

will lead to $v = \omega r$ and, again applying the time factor, we have $a = \alpha r$; here v and a are respectively the linear velocity and the acceleration of the center of mass and ω and α are respectively the angular velocity and acceleration. The equation $a = \alpha r$ for the acceleration of the mass center must be used with the equations of motion to yield a solution of a given problem. For a body that rolls without slipping the maximum limiting friction, given by the product of the coefficient of friction and the normal reaction force, is ordinarily not developed, and the friction force is an unknown which is determined from the equations of motion. In the case in which slipping impends, friction does have its limiting maximum value.

Now consider that the body both rolls and slips. In this case the friction force has its limiting maximum value and is given by the product of the coefficient of friction and the normal reaction force. Since there is slippage it is no longer true that a is equal to αr.

It is well to point out again that the motion of a rolling body may be analyzed in either of two ways, (1) as a combination of translation of its center of mass plus a rotation about this center or (2) as a pure rotation about the instantaneous rotation axis which passes through the points of contact of rolling body and plane. It can be shown (see Problem 10.22) that the angular velocity and angular acceleration of a rolling body about its instantaneous axis are equal, respectively, to the angular velocity and angular acceleration about an axis through the center of mass of the body.

10.8. Angular Momentum. Analogously to our defining of linear momentum in Section 4.3 we now define *angular momentum* of a rotating body about an axis as the product of the moment of inertia about this axis and the angular velocity, or

$$\text{angular momentum} = I\omega \tag{10.9}$$

Angular momentum is a vector quantity and has the direction of the angular velocity ω as described in Section 8.2. In the metric cgs and mks absolute systems the units of angular momentum are respectively the gram-mass–square-centimeter per second (gm·cm²/sec) and the kilogram-mass–square-meter per second (kgm·m²/sec). In the English gravitational system the unit of angular momentum is the slug–square-foot per second (slug·ft²/sec).

Again, as with Newton's second law for translation, the dynamical law for rotation is more generally stated in terms of angular momentum change. Thus we say that the measurable resultant torque acting on a body is equal to the time rate of change of angular momentum, and for an unchanging value of I this leads to $\sum L = I\alpha$.

One also speaks of the *angular momentum of a single particle*. We can get at the meaning of this by considering one of the masses, say m_1, of the rotating body shown in Figure 10.1. The moment of inertia of m_1 about O is $m_1 r_1^2$ and its instantaneous angular momentum is $m_1 r_1^2 \omega$. We now observe that the product $r_1\omega$ is the tangential speed v_1 of the mass m_1. Hence the instantaneous angular momentum of the particle is $m_1v_1r_1$ or, in general, mvr. In view of the fact that mv is a vector and r is the perpendicular distance from the axis to the line of action of this vector, the definition of the angular momentum of a particle is analogous to that of the moment of a force. In fact, mvr is often called the *moment of momentum*.

The concept of angular momentum is of fundamental significance not only in mechanics but also in the fields of molecular, atomic, and nuclear physics. The earth has an angular momentum due to its orbital motion and an angular momentum due to rotation about its own axis. Likewise, the concept of an electron, moving around the nucleus of an atom in planetary fashion, gives rise to an orbital angular momentum and a spin angular momentum. These motions are subject to laws and principles which we shall consider in subsequent chapters.

Example 10.1. A slim rod 200 cm long has two small 50.0 gm bodies fastened to its ends and a 25.0 gm body fastened at its midpoint, as shown in Figure 10.5. Neglecting the mass of the rod, find the moment of inertia

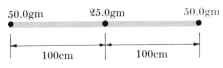

50.0gm   25.0gm   50.0gm

|← 100cm →|← 100cm →|

Figure 10.5.

and the radius of gyration of the system about a transverse axis intersecting the rod and 50.0 cm from one end.

Solution. The moment of inertia about the specified axis is

$$I = \sum_{i=1}^{3} m_i r_i^2$$

$$= 50.0(50.0)^2 + 25.0(50.0)^2 + 50.0(150)^2$$
$$= 1.31 \times 10^6 \text{ gm} \cdot \text{cm}^2$$

The radius of gyration is

$$k = \sqrt{I/m}$$
$$= \sqrt{1.31 \times 10^6/125}$$
$$= 102 \text{ cm}$$

Example 10.2. Derive the formula for the moment of inertia of a thin uniform rod of mass m and length l about an axis normal to the length and passing through one end.

Solution. We shall do this in two ways, first by the approximate method of dividing the mass into a finite number of smaller masses and considering each of these as a point-mass and, second, by employing the method of exact solution by considering an infinite number of infinitesimal masses. In what follows the approximate treatment is given in the left column and the calculus solution in the right.

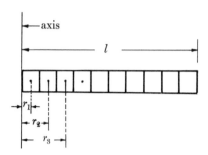

Figure 10.6.

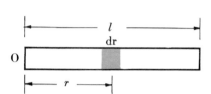

Figure 10.7.

Figure 10.6 shows the rod divided into ten equal masses, the distance of the center of each mass from the rotational axis being as indicated. The moment of inertia is

$$I = \sum_{i=1}^{10} m_i r_i^2$$

$$= \frac{m}{10} \left(r_1^2 + r_2^2 + r_3^2 + \cdots + r_{10}^2 \right)$$

$$= \frac{m}{10} \left[\left(\frac{1}{20} \right)^2 + \left(\frac{3}{20} \right)^2 + \left(\frac{5}{20} \right)^2 \right.$$

$$\left. + \cdots + \left(\frac{19}{20} \right)^2 \right] l^2$$

$$= 0.3325 m l^2$$

The true value, derived in the right-hand column and shown in Table 10.1, is $\frac{1}{3} m l^2 = 0.3333 m l^2$. Hence, dividing the rod into ten equal parts and using this approximate method yields a value which is 0.24% lower than the true value.

Let the rod of length l, Figure 10.7, be divided into n small segments of length dr and mass per unit length m_u. Then the moment of inertia of one of these elements of mass dm distant r from the axis through O is given by $r^2 \, dm$, and the limit of the sum expressed by Equation 10.5 defines t he integral

$$I = \lim_{n \to \infty} \sum_{i=1}^{n} m_i r_i^2 = \int_0^l r^2 \, dm \quad (10.10)$$

Here $dm = m_u \, dr$ and

$$I = m_u \int_0^l r^2 \, dr = m_u l^3 / 3$$

Since $m_u = m/l$ where m is the total mass of the rod,

$$I = m l^2 / 3$$

which is the value given in Table 10.1. The integral in Equation 10.10 with appropriate integration limits may be employed to obtain the moment of inertia of any integrable mass system.

Example 10.3. Find the moment of inertia and radius of gyration of the composite system about the geometric axis shown in Figure 10.8. The middle and two sections are solid cylinders which weigh 480 pounds-force/cubic-foot.

Solution. The total moment of inertia is the sum of the moments of inertia of sections A, B, and C. Each of these has a moment of inertia given by $m r^2 / 2$. Hence

$$I = \tfrac{1}{2} (m_A r_A^2 + m_B r_B^2 + m_C r_C^2)$$

Here $$m_A = m_C = \frac{480 \times \pi(1.50)^2(0.500)}{32.0} = 53.0 \text{ slugs}$$

$$m_B = \frac{480 \times \pi(1.00)^2(3.00)}{32.0} = 141 \text{ slugs}$$

$$I = \tfrac{1}{2}[106(1.50)^2 + 141(1.00)^2]$$
$$= 380 \text{ slug} \cdot \text{ft}^2$$

The radius of gyration is

$$k = \sqrt{I/m} = \sqrt{380/(106 + 141)}$$
$$= 1.24 \text{ ft}$$

Example 10.4. A flywheel, in the form of a uniform metal disk 2.00 feet in radius, has a weight of 640 pounds force. A cord wrapped around its periphery is used to apply an unbalanced torque of 200 pound-force–foot (pf·ft). What is the angular acceleration?

Solution. Applying Equation 10.6,

$$\sum L = I\alpha$$

Here $\sum L = 200$ pound-force–foot. The moment of inertia of a disk is obtained from Table 10.1:

$$I = \tfrac{1}{2}mr^2 = \frac{1}{2} \times \frac{640 \text{ pf}}{32.0 \text{ ft/sec}^2} (2.00)^2 \text{ ft}^2 = 40.0 \text{ slug} \cdot \text{ft}^2$$

Therefore,

$$200 \text{ pf} \cdot \text{ft} = 40.0 \text{ slug} \cdot \text{ft}^2 \; \alpha$$
$$\alpha = 5.00 \text{ rad/sec}^2$$

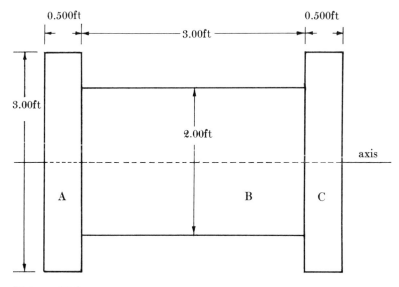

Figure 10.8.

Example 10.5. A solid homogeneous cylinder of mass m and radius r rolls down an inclined plane which makes an angle θ with the horizontal. If the cylinder starts from rest at the top and does not slip, in what time does it traverse the length l of the incline?

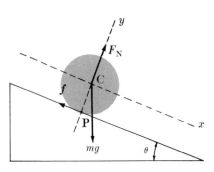

Solution 1. As a first method of solution we shall consider that the cylinder shown in Figure 10.9 is rotating about the instantaneous axis passing perpendicular to the plane of the figure through P. This instantaneous axis moves downward, but it always remains parallel to itself and to the axis through the center of mass C. The forces acting on the cylinder are the weight mg, the normal reaction F_N, and the friction force f which must exist if the body is to roll without slipping. Only the force mg tends to produce rotation about an axis through P and the effective component is $mg \sin \theta$. Hence, using the second law for rotation, we have

Figure 10.9. *A cylinder rolling without slipping down an inclined plane.*

$$(mg \sin \theta)r = I_P \alpha \qquad (10.11)$$

where I_P, the moment of inertia of the cylinder about an axis through P, has, by the parallel-axes theorem, the value

$$I_P = \tfrac{1}{2}mr^2 + mr^2 = \tfrac{3}{2}mr^2$$

Substituting, we have

$$\alpha = \frac{2g \sin \theta}{3r} \qquad (10.12)$$

Now we apply the kinematic equation for rotation:

$$\theta = \omega_0 t + \tfrac{1}{2}\alpha t^2$$

Here $\omega_0 = 0$ and, since a linear distance $2\pi r$ is covered when the cylinder rolls through 2π radians, in a linear distance l we have

$$\theta = 2\pi l/2\pi r = l/r$$

and

$$t^2 = 3l/g \sin \theta \qquad (10.13)$$

Solution 2. In this method we consider the motion as consisting of a rotation of the cylinder about an axis through its center of mass and an additional motion of the cylinder with a linear velocity down the plane. Using the x and y axes indicated in Figure 10.9 we have an equilibrium condition existing in the y direction with $\sum F_y = F_N - mg \cos \theta = 0$. In the x direction we have linearly accelerated motion with acceleration a, so that

$$mg \sin \theta - f = ma$$

Also, the torque causing the cylinder to rotate about an axis through C is fr. Hence,

$$fr = I_C \alpha$$

where I_C, the moment of inertia about an axis through C, is given by

$$I_C = mr^2/2$$

Therefore,

$$fr = (mr^2/2)\alpha$$

Combining this with the equation for linear acceleration and remembering that $a = \alpha r$, we have

$$f = ma/2$$

and

$$\alpha = 2g(\sin\theta)/3r$$

which leads to the same value for t as that obtained in Equation 10.13.

Example 10.6.   Compare the rates of roll down a given incline for uniform cylinders, uniform spheres, and uniform hoops.

Solution.   In the solution of the previous example we see from Equation 10.13 that the time of descent of a solid homogeneous cylinder is independent of both its mass and radius.   In fact, this independence holds whether we consider a hollow cylinder, a hoop, or a sphere, as can be verified by tracing through Equations 10.11 to 10.13.   Hence, regardless of size, all uniform and homogeneous solid cylinders roll down at the same rate, all uniform and homogeneous hoops roll down at the same rate, and all uniform and homogeneous solid spheres roll down at the same rate.   To compare the rates of solid cylinders, hoops, and spheres it is helpful to obtain Equation 10.13 in terms of the radius of gyration of the rolling body about an axis passing through the center of mass.   In place of Equation 10.11 we have

$$(mg\sin\theta)r = (mk^2 + mr^2)\alpha$$

where k is the radius of gyration of the rolling body about an axis passing through its center of mass (longitudinal axis for the cylinder and hoop and diametral axis for the sphere).   This leads to

$$\alpha = (gr\sin\theta)/(k^2 + r^2)$$

and solving for the time of descent we have

$$t^2 = \frac{2l[1 + (k/r)^2]}{g\sin\theta} \tag{10.14}$$

Now, resorting to Table 10.1, we observe that the ratio k^2/r^2 is 0.4 for the solid sphere about a diametral axis, 0.5 for the solid cylinder about a longitudinal axis of symmetry, and 1.00 for the hoop about an axis passing through its center of mass and perpendicular to its plane.   Hence, when a sphere, cylinder, and hoop start simultaneously from rest at the top of the incline, the sphere reaches the bottom of the plane first, the cylinder arrives second, and the hoop arrives last.

Example 10.7.   A flywheel 2.00 feet in radius is mounted so that it is free to rotate about a horizontal axis through its center.   An 8.00-pound mass hangs from a rope which is wound around the rim of the flywheel.   When the system starts from rest, what are the angular acceleration of the wheel, the linear acceleration of the mass, and the tension in the rope?   The moment of inertia of the flywheel about an axis through its center is 3.00 slug–square-foot.

Solution. The system is shown in Figure 10.10a. First isolate the fly-wheel as a free body. The forces acting are shown in (b), where T is the rope tension, w is the weight of the wheel, and F_N is the reaction of the mounting

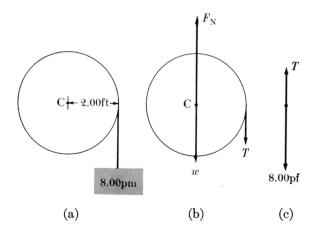

(a)   (b)   (c)

Figure 10.10.

support. We need consider only the torque produced by T and apply Equation 10.6. This yields $2T = 3\alpha$. Now isolate the 8-pound mass as a free body. The forces acting are shown in (c). Applying Newton's second law for translation yields

$$8.00 - T = \frac{8.00}{32.0} a$$

where a, the linear acceleration of the mass, is equal to the tangential acceleration of the rim of the wheel, or

$$a = 2\alpha$$

Solving the above three equations yields the solutions

$$\alpha = 4.00 \text{ rad/sec}^2, \qquad a = 8.00 \text{ ft/sec}^2, \qquad T = 6.00 \text{ pf}$$

Example 10.8. A 3.00-foot cylinder whose weight is 288 pounds force has a cord of negligible weight wrapped around it. The other end of the cord being fixed, the cylinder is released from rest as shown in Figure 10.11. Find the angular acceleration and the tension in the cord.

Solution. The forces acting on the cylinder are its weight and the tension T, as shown in the figure. Consider the cylinder as rotating about an axis through C and normal to the plane of the figure. Applying Equation 10.6 gives

$$1.50T = I_C\alpha = \frac{288}{32.0} \times \frac{(1.50)^2}{2} \alpha$$

$$T = 6.75\alpha$$

Now apply Newton's second law for translation. This yields

$$288 - T = \frac{288}{32.0} a$$

where a, the linear acceleration, is given by

$$a = 1.50\alpha$$

Solving these equations leads to the solutions

$$\alpha = 14.2 \text{ rad/sec}^2 \quad \text{and} \quad T = 96.0 \text{ pf}$$

Alternatively, the cylinder may be considered as rotating about the instantaneous axis through P and normal to the plane of the figure. Application of Equation 10.6 about this axis gives

$$288 \times 1.50 = I_P\alpha$$

where

$$I_P = mr^2/2 + mr^2 = \tfrac{3}{2} mr^2 = \frac{3}{2} \times \frac{288}{32.0} (1.50)^2$$

so that $\alpha = 14.2$ radians/sec^2 as before.

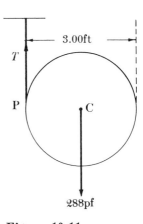

Figure 10.11.

Problems

Unless otherwise specified, use for g where necessary 980 cm/sec^2 = 9.80 m/sec^2 = 32.0 feet/sec^2.

10.1. Three small masses of 20.0, 30.0, and 50.0 gm are situated at the corners of a right triangular framework as shown in Figure 10.12. Neglecting the mass of the framework, find the moment of inertia of the system about an axis through the median point of the triangle and perpendicular to its plane.

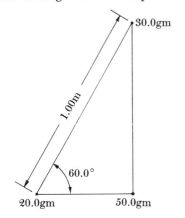

Figure 10.12. *Problem 10.1.*

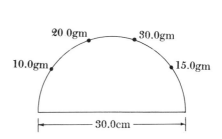

Figure 10.13. *Problem 10.2.*

10.2. A light semicircular frame has four equally spaced small masses attached as shown in Figure 10.13. Find the moment of inertia of the system about the diameter as an axis. Neglect the moment of inertia of the frame.

10.3. Using Table 10.1, find the moment of inertia of a thin rod of length l and mass m about an axis normal to its length and $l/4$ from one end.

10.4. Using Table 10.1, find the moment of inertia of a thin rectangular sheet of sides a and b and mass m about an axis normal to the sheet and passing through a corner.

10.5. Using Table 10.1, find the moment of inertia of a right circular annular cylinder of mass m and inner and outer radii r_1 and r_2, respectively, about a longitudinal axis of symmetry. Do this by the method outlined at the end of Section 10.4.

10.6. Using Table 10.1 find the moment of inertia of a spherical shell of mass m and inner and outer radii r_1 and r_2, respectively, about any diametral axis. Do this by the method outlined at the end of Section 10.4.

10.7. Show that the moment of inertia of a very thin spherical shell of mass m and mean radius r about any diameter is $\frac{2}{3}mr^2$. (*Hint:* Use the result of Problem 10.6 and let $r_1 = r - \epsilon$ and $r_2 = r + \epsilon$, where r_1 and r_2 are respectively the inner and outer radii of the spherical shell and ϵ is a very small quantity whose quadratic and higher power values may be neglected.)

10.8. A dumbbell is made of two spheres, each of 1.00 kgm in mass and 6.00 cm in radius, separated by a cylindrical rod 25.0 cm in length, 4.00 cm in diameter, and 0.500 kgm in mass. Find the moment of inertia of the dumbbell about an axis coincident with the longitudinal axis of the cylinder and passing through the centers of the spheres.

10.9. Find the moment of inertia of the dumbbell in Problem 10.8 about an axis transverse to the cylinder and passing through its center.

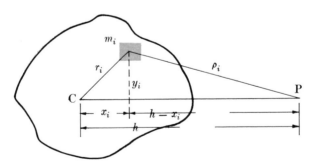

Figure 10.14. *Problem 10.10.*

10.10. Using Figure 10.14, prove the parallel-axes theorem $I_P = I_C + mh^2$. The figure shows a section of a rigid body with any particle of mass m_i distant r_i from an axis through the center of mass C and distant ρ_i from an axis through P. The axes through C and P are perpendicular to the plane of the figure, are parallel, and are separated a distance h. The origin of rectangular coordinates is at C, the x axis passes through P, and the coordinates of m_i are (x_i, y_i). (*Hint:* Observe that $I_C = \sum m_i r_i^2$, $I_P = \sum m_i \rho_i^2$, $\rho_i^2 = h^2 + r_i^2 - 2hx_i$, $\sum m_i x_i = 0$, and $\sum m_i y_i = 0$.)

10.11. A solid cylinder of diameter 6.00 inches has a cylindrical hole of diameter 2.00 inches drilled into it. If the edge of the hole just touches the center of the cylinder, whose mass before drilling was 1.00 pound, what is the moment of inertia of the drilled cylinder about its longitudinal axis of symmetry.

10.12. Find the moment of inertia of the drilled cylinder in Problem 10.11 about a longitudinal axis through the center of the hole.

10.13. Figure 10.15 shows a solid cylinder A of mass m and a right circular cone B of mass $5m$, both of radius r. Find the moment of inertia of the composite body about an axis parallel to the longitudinal axis of symmetry and tangent to the surface of the cylinder.

10.14. What torque is required to accelerate a body with a moment of inertia of 3.00 kgm·m² to a speed of 20.0 revolutions/minute from rest in 10.0 sec?

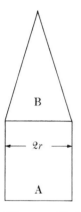

Figure 10.15.
Problem 10.13.

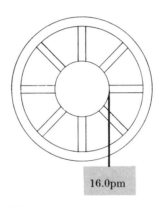

Figure 10.16. *Problem 10.18.*

10.15. A flywheel has a mass of 640 pounds and a radius of gyration of 2.50 feet. What unbalanced torque will speed the wheel from rest to 600 revolutions/minute in 5.00 minutes?

10.16. A flywheel, initially at rest, is acted upon by a constant torque of 200 m·nt and thus gains a speed of 5.00 revolutions/sec in 40.0 sec. Find the radius of gyration of the wheel which has a mass of 300 kgm.

10.17. The rotor of an electric motor, whose moment of inertia is 30.0 slug–square-foot is rotating at 1.80×10^3 revolutions/minute. What constant frictional torque is needed to bring it to rest in 1.50 minutes?

10.18. Figure 10.16 shows a body of 16.0 pounds mass suspended from a cord wrapped around the hub of a flywheel. The rotating system has a mass of 5.00 slugs and a radius of gyration of 1.50 feet, the hub radius being 6.00 inches. When the system is released what are (**a**) the angular acceleration, (**b**) the tension in the cord, and (**c**) the length of unwrapped cord after 3.00 sec? Neglect friction.

10.19. A flywheel of 10.0 kgm and radius of gyration of 1.00 m has a hub of radius 20.0 cm. The wheel is rotating with a speed of 1.20×10^3 revolutions/minute when a brake shoe is applied to the hub, bringing the wheel to rest in 80.0 revolutions. If the coefficient of friction between hub and brake shoe is 0.200, what normal force is exerted by the shoe on the hub?

10.20. Solve the Atwood machine problem, Example 5.10, and obtain an expression for the linear acceleration of the system whose pulley has a mass m. Assume that the cord is perfectly flexible, inextensible, and has negligible weight, and consider that the friction is negligible. Compare the result with that obtained in Example 5.10. (*Hint:* Call the tension on the left side of the pulley T_1 and that on the right T_2; then the pulley is accelerated by the unbalanced torque due to the different tensions.) Use the moment of inertia of a circular cylinder for the pulley.

10.21. An Atwood machine has a pulley with a mass of 400 gm and a radius of 4.00 cm. The masses on opposite sides of the pulley are 800 gm and 1.20×10^3 gm. Assuming no friction, find (**a**) the linear acceleration of the system, (**b**) the cord tension on each side of the pulley, and (**c**) the angular acceleration of the pulley. See Problem 10.20.

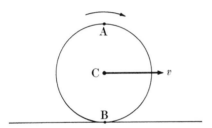

Figure 10.17. *Problem 10.22.*

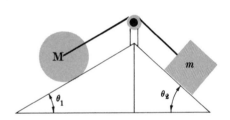

Figure 10.18. *Problem 10.25.*

10.22. Figure 10.17 shows a symmetrical body such as a wheel, cylinder, or sphere of radius r rolling on a horizontal plane with an angular velocity ω about its center C which is moving with a linear velocity v. The rolling may be regarded as a combination of translation and rotation about the central axis through C. Show that the following are true: (**a**) $v = \omega r$, (**b**) $v_A = 2v$ where v_A is the tangential velocity of point A, (**c**) $v_B = v - \omega r = 0$ where v_B, the tangential velocity of the instantaneous axis through B, is zero for rolling without slipping, and (**d**) the angular velocity (and angular acceleration) about the instantaneous axis through B is equal to the angular velocity (and angular acceleration) about the axis through the center C. The significance of the last result is that the combined effects of translation and rotation about C are equivalent to a pure rotation with the same angular velocity about B.

10.23. A Yo-yo whose mass is 10.0 gm is released from rest and descends vertically a distance of 100 cm in 2.00 sec. The thread is initially wrapped around its central axle of radius 2.00 mm. Assuming that the radius of unwinding remains constant, find (**a**) the tension in the thread, (**b**) the moment of inertia of the Yo-yo about its central axis, and (**c**) its angular momentum about the same axis 1.00 sec after it starts to descend.

10.24. A solid cylinder, 4.00 feet in diameter and 900 pounds force in weight, rolls down a 30.0° incline from rest. Find (a) the linear speed of the cylinder after it has rolled 50.0 feet, (b) the friction force, and (c) the angular momentum of the cylinder about its instantaneous axis at the end of 1.00 sec.

10.25. In Figure 10.18 the cylinder of mass M and radius r is connected by a cord, passing over a frictionless pulley of negligible mass, to a block of mass m, the coefficient of friction between block and plane being μ. The cylinder's axle is attached to the cord so as to permit the cylinder to roll without slipping, the cord's line of action passing through the cylinder's center of mass. Prove that the condition for the cylinder to descend is $\mu m \cos \theta_2 < M \sin \theta_1 - m \sin \theta_2$ and the condition for the block to descend is $\mu m \cos \theta_2 < m \sin \theta_2 - M \sin \theta_1$.

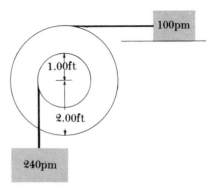

Figure 10.19. *Problem 10.26.*

10.26. The pulley shown in Figure 10.19 has a weight of 40.0 pounds force and a radius of gyration about its central axis of 2.00 feet. The coefficient of friction between block and horizontal surface is 0.200. Neglecting friction in the pulley bearing, find (a) the angular acceleration of the pulley and (b) the tensions in the horizontal and vertical cords.

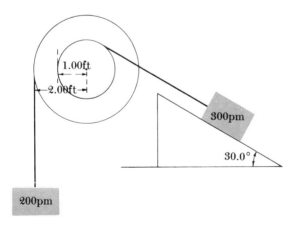

Figure 10.20. *Problem 10.27.*

10.27. The pulley shown in Figure 10.20 has a weight of 100 pounds force and a radius of gyration about its central axis of 1.50 feet. The coefficient of friction between block and plane is 0.200. Neglecting friction in the pulley bearing, find (a) the angular acceleration of the pulley and (b) the tensions in the vertical and slant cords.

10.28. The rolling body in Figure 10.21 has a weight of 200 pounds force and radius of gyration about its central axis of 1.00 feet. Neglecting the friction and mass of the pulley and considering rolling without slipping, find (**a**) the angular acceleration, (**b**) the linear acceleration of both bodies, and (**c**) the tension in the cord.

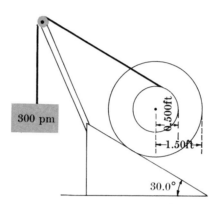

Figure 10.21.   *Problem 10.28.*

10.29. The homogeneous sphere S in Figure 10.22 is free to roll without slipping on the horizontal surface of the cart C. If the cart accelerates in the direction F at 8.00 feet/sec² find the acceleration of the center G of the sphere. (*Hint:* Note that $a_G = a_{GC} + a_C$, where a_G is the vector linear acceleration of G, a_{GC} is the vector linear acceleration of G relative to C, and a_C is the vector linear acceleration of C.)

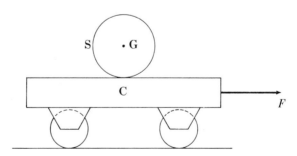

Figure 10.22.   *Problem 10.29.*

10.30. Given also that the mass of the sphere in Problem 10.29 is 96.0 pounds and that of the cart is 160 pounds, find (**a**) the friction force between S and C and (**b**) the force *F*. Neglect the mass of the rollers. See the hint given in Problem 10.29.

10.31. A cylindrical spool, with a mass of 32.0 pounds and with a radius of gyration about its central axis through C of 1.25 feet, is pulled by a cord

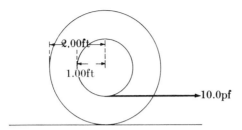

Figure 10.23. *Problem 10.31.*

which exerts a horizontal force of 10.0 pounds force, as shown in Figure 10.23. The cylinder rolls without slipping. Find (a) the linear acceleration of C and (b) the friction force between cylinder and horizontal surface.

Work, Energy, and Power

*T*HE PHYSICIST AND ENGINEER must acquire a thorough understanding of work and energy in order to solve many kinds of problems. Not only do the applications of these concepts lead more directly to solutions, but also in such fields as heat and thermodynamics the concepts of work and energy are basic. So far we have employed Newton's laws of motion relating force, mass, and linear acceleration, or torque, moment of inertia, and angular acceleration, in solving problems of kinetics. The scheme was to equate the unbalanced force acting on a particle or body to the mass times the acceleration for translation, and the application of an analogous equation for rotation. To ascertain a displacement or a velocity change during a given time interval it was necessary to make use of the kinematic principles. We shall now see that such problems frequently may be solved more readily by employing the principle relating work and energy. When the nature of the force involved is such that the force varies as a function of the position of the body the method of work and energy is particularly effective for obtaining a solution.

In this chapter we shall therefore concern ourselves first with the definitions of work and energy. We shall then develop the work-energy principle and the principle of the *conservation of energy*. We shall see that there are two forms of mechanical energy that a body may possess: it may possess *potential energy* owing to its position, or it may possess *kinetic energy* because of its motion. Further, as will become apparent in our discussions, the element of time is not involved in the definition of *work*. However, it is often necessary to consider the time rate at which an agent is performing work as well as to know the total amount of work that is accomplished. For this purpose we shall need to introduce the concept of *power*.

The student is urged to give a great deal of thought and effort to mastering the material dealt with in this chapter, since the methods of work and energy are of prime significance in physics and engineering.

11.1. Work Done in Translation. In popular language the word *work* is used to denote any form of physical or mental effort. In physics and engineering, however, the term *work* is employed in a technical sense only. If physical translational work is to be accomplished, two things are necessary:

a force must act on a body and the body must move in such a way that its displacement has a component parallel to the direction in which the force is acting.   As an example, consider the work done on an object which a person lifts through a vertical height and then carries as he walks horizontally, keeping the object at the same height.   Technically, work is done on the object only during the lifting process when the lifting force, which acts vertically, moves through a vertical distance.   During the walking process, the force necessary to support the object at a given height acts vertically while the displacement, being horizontal, has no vertical component, and no work is accomplished by the force supporting the object.

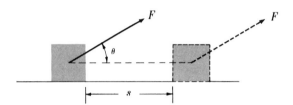

Figure 11.1.   *Work done by the force F in moving the body through a distance s.*

Figure 11.1 represents a body which has moved a horizontal distance s to the right under the action of a constant force F directed at an angle θ with the horizontal.   *The work W done by F is defined as the product of the displacement s and the component of F parallel to the direction of the displacement.*   Thus

$$W = (F \cos \theta)s \qquad\qquad (11.1)$$

Since $(F \cos \theta)s = F(s \cos \theta)$ the work done may alternatively be defined as the product of the force and the component of the displacement in the direction of the force.   We note that when $\theta = 0$ the force and the displacement are in the same direction and the work is given by their product.   When $\theta = 90°$, then $W = 0$ and a force does no work when the displacement of its point of application is normal to the direction along which it acts.   Although work is a product of two vector quantities it is a scalar quantity, there being no sense, or direction, associated with it.   Nevertheless, work does possess an algebraic sign, and a force does positive work when the direction of the displacement and the direction of the force component along the displacement are the same, and it does negative work when these directions are opposite.   This sign convention follows from the definition of work given by Equation 11.1: when θ is less than 90° or is between 270° and 360° the component of force is in the same direction as the displacement and $\cos \theta$ is positive; if θ is greater than 90° and less than 270°, $\cos \theta$ is negative.   For example, in Figure 11.1, if there is present an amount of friction acting to the left when the body is being displaced to the right, the work done on the body by the friction force is considered negative.

The unit of work is compounded from the unit force and the unit of displacement. In the cgs absolute system the unit of work is the dyne-centimeter (dyne·cm), in the mks absolute system the unit of work is the newton-meter (nt·m), and in the English gravitational system the unit of work is the foot–pound-force (ft·pf). [Notice that the dimensions of torque (see Section 7.2) are the same as those of work, but the order of the units forming the compound unit is changed, to distinguish the unit of work from the unit of torque.] We may rigorously define the dyne-centimeter as *the work done by a constant force of one dyne when the body on which the force acts moves through a distance of one centimeter in the same direction as the force.* The student should make similar definitions for the newton-meter and the foot–pound-force. The dyne-centimeter is called an *erg;* the newton-meter is called a *joule* after the British scientist James P. Joule (1818–1889). Since 1 nt is 10^5 dynes, it follows that

$$1 \text{ nt·m} = 10^7 \text{ dyne·cm} = 10^7 \text{ ergs}$$

or $\qquad$ 1 joule $= 10^7$ ergs

and $\qquad$ 1 ft·pf $= 1.356$ joules

If the force varies in either magnitude or direction during a displacement, Equation 11.1 holds only for a very small or infinitesimal change in s, and the total work done during a given displacement is a sum of the individual amounts of work accomplished during each successive infinitesimal displacement. In the special case, in which the force varies in magnitude but its direction coincides with the direction of displacement, the work done may more simply be obtained. We shall illustrate this case by computing the work done in stretching an elastic spring. The force required to stretch a spring increases as the spring is stretched; it follows *Hooke's law*, in accordance with which the force of stretch F is directly proportional to the amount of stretch s. Thus

$$F \propto s \qquad \text{and} \qquad F = Ks \qquad (11.2)$$

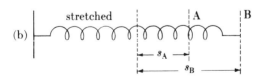

Figure 11.2. *Work done in stretching a spring.*

where K, the constant of proportionality, is called the *force constant*, the *spring constant*, the *stretch modulus*, or the *stiffness coefficient* of the spring. The constant K indicates the force per unit elongation in pounds force per foot, newtons per meter, or dynes per centimeter. Figure 11.2 shows in (a) a spring in an unstretched or normal state and in (b) the same spring in a stretched state under the action of a force (not shown) acting to the right. We wish to calculate the work necessary to stretch the spring from position A distant s_A from the unstretched position O to position B distant s_B from O. In the following, the left-hand column contains the noncalculus treatment and the right-hand column contains the calculus treatment.

Applying Equation 11.1 with $\cos\theta = 1$, we have for the work done

$$W = F_{av}(s_B - s_A)$$

where the average force F_{av} is given by

$$F_{av} = \frac{F_A + F_B}{2}$$

F_A and F_B are the values of the stretching forces at A and B respectively. In view of Equation 11.2, $F_A = Ks_A$ and $F_B = Ks_B$ and

$$W = \frac{K}{2}(s_A + s_B)(s_B - s_A)$$

or

$$W = \frac{K}{2}(s_B{}^2 - s_A{}^2) \qquad (11.3)$$

The work done dW for an infinitesimal displacement ds is given by

$$dW = F\, ds$$

and by integration the total work done in stretching the spring from A to B is

$$W = \int_{s_A}^{s_B} F\, ds$$

Substituting for F the value given by Equation 11.2 we have

$$W = K \int_{s_A}^{s_B} s\, ds$$

$$= \frac{K}{2} s^2 \Big]_{s_A}^{s_B}$$

and this yields

$$W = \frac{K}{2}(s_B{}^2 - s_A{}^2) \qquad (11.3)$$

Equation 11.3 shows that the work done in stretching (or compressing) a spring depends only upon its stiffness coefficient and the initial and final positions of its displacement.

11.2. Work Done in Rotation. In Figure 11.3 is shown a wheel of radius r, which is free to rotate about an axis through O. A cord fastened to its rim is pulled with a constant force F for a distance s along its length, as shown. The work done upon the wheel is $W = Fs$. The constant torque acting is given by $L = Fr$ so that $F = L/r$. Also, during the motion the wheel turns through an angle θ given by $s = \theta r$. Hence, the work expressed in terms of torque and angle is given by

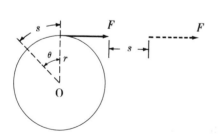

Figure 11.3. *Work done in rotational motion.*

$$W = L\theta \qquad (11.4)$$

This equation, which states that the work is equal to the product of the torque and the angular displacement, is a general expression for the work done upon a rotating body which, under the action of a constant torque L, rotates through an angular displacement of θ radians. When the torque is not constant the work may be found by adding the work accomplished during infinitesimal angular displacements in a manner analogous to that outlined in the previous section for work done in translation.

11.3. Energy. In physics and engineering the term *energy* is used in a strictly technical sense. *Energy is defined as a measure of the capacity or ability to perform work.* Thus, whereas work, involving the motion of a force through a distance, is a measure of accomplishment, energy is a measure of ability. Hence an agent is said to possess energy if it is able to do work. On the other hand, if an agent is not capable of doing work we say it has no energy. For example, a wound watch spring possesses energy because it is able to do work by moving the watch mechanism; steam within the cylinder of a steam engine possesses energy since it can move the piston within the cylinder; a moving bullet, a rotating flywheel, and a moving motorcycle give evidence of their possessing energy by the fact that they all do work during the process of being brought to rest. On the other hand, when the watch spring has run down, or when a car battery has become discharged, the energy they possessed has been expanded and they can no longer do work. However, in all cases in which an agent has done work its energy is reduced by an amount which is precisely equal to the amount of work done. The units in which energy is expressed are the same as those used for work.

The study of physics is principally a study of energy and the student should now realize that the development of the concept of force is essential to a thorough understanding of the concept of energy. Energy exists in various forms: as mechanical energy, a form of which is sound energy; as thermal energy, a form of which is heat energy; as magnetic energy; as electrical energy; as chemical energy; as radiant energy, a type of which is light energy; as atomic and nuclear energy. As examples of these, the wound watch spring, the moving bullet and motorcycle, and the rotating flywheel have mechanical energy, the steam possesses thermal energy, coal has chemical energy, a charged capacitor has electrical energy, a glowing ember has radiant energy, and the nucleus of an atom possesses nuclear energy. A little thought makes us aware of the transformations that occur from one form of energy to another. For instance, a car battery converts chemical energy into electrical energy, part of which goes into mechanical energy, part into heat and light energy, and part into sound energy by means of the radio and horn. A photoelectric cell, present in photographic exposure meters, converts light into electrical energy which, in the presence of the magnetic element of the meter, becomes transformed into mechanical energy necessary to cause a deflection of the meter indicator. In nuclear reactions, mass, a form of energy, disappears, and there becomes available by transformation a tremendous amount of mechanical, heat, and light energy.

The mechanical energy that a body or system of bodies may possess may appear in either or both of two forms, viz., *potential* energy or *kinetic* energy. The potential energy of a body or system of bodies is due to the position or configuration of the body or system of bodies. The kinetic energy of a body or system of bodies is due to the motion of the body or bodies. We shall now discuss these two forms of mechanical energy in greater detail and obtain quantitative expressions for calculating their magnitudes.

11.4. Potential Energy. The potential energy of a body is the capacity of the body to do work as a result of its position or configuration. Two commonly encountered types of mechanical potential energy are *elastic potential energy* and *gravitational potential energy*. In the elastic type a body acquires potential energy whenever work is done against elastic forces, whereas in the gravitational type a body acquires potential energy whenever work is done upon it against the earth's gravitational force of attraction. We shall now elaborate somewhat on each of these types.

The subject of elasticity will be taken up in Chapter 14. For the present it will be sufficient to state that when a solid body is distorted it generally follows the law that the force causing the distortion is directly proportional to the magnitude of the distortion. This will be recognized as Hooke's law which we met in Section 11.1 in connection with the calculation of the work done in stretching or compressing an elastic spring. When a spring is stretched or compressed, internal elastic restoring forces tend to bring the body back to its normal condition or original configuration, and the work that these forces can do is a measure of the elastic potential energy of the body in its distorted state. We saw that the work done in stretching a spring whose force constant is K through a distance s from an unstretched configuration is $\frac{1}{2}Ks^2$ and this, then, is the elastic potential energy we attribute to the spring. Likewise, a clock spring has elastic potential energy imparted to it when it is wound, and can do work in regaining its original configuration.

A body that possesses gravitational potential energy has acquired this energy by virtue of the fact that it has been lifted vertically against the gravitational force of the earth's attraction. Hence it is the kind of potential energy that is a result of the position of the body in the gravitational field of the earth, and the amount of potential energy that the body has is measured by the amount of work the body is capable of doing in returning to its initial position. For example, the water above a dam, because of its position, does work as it passes through the hydraulic turbine, and the hammer of a pile driver, possessing gravitational potential energy in its elevated position, does work when the hammer descends. To generalize, let us now consider a mass m which has been elevated vertically with uniform speed from the horizontal level AB to the horizontal level CD as shown in Figure 11.4. The vertical force necessary to displace the center of gravity of the body a vertical distance h is mg. The work done *on* the body is mgh, assuming that g remains essentially constant over the distance h, and the force mg is capable of doing an amount of work mgh in returning the body to level AB. Hence, at the level CD the gravitational potential energy E_P of the body, relative to the level AB is

$$E_P = mgh \qquad (11.5)$$

which, as we have already observed (Section 11.1), is expressed in terms of the erg, joule, or foot–pound-force in the cgs, mks, and English gravitational systems, respectively. A significant fact is that this potential energy is a relative amount. If the body is now elevated an additional distance h' to

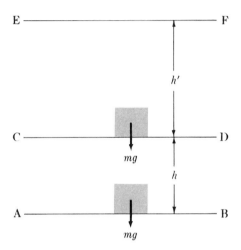

Figure 11.4. *Illustrating gravitational potential energy.*

the level EF the gravitational potential energy is $mg(h + h')$ with respect to level AB but it is mgh' with respect to level CD. That level relative to which the potential energy is computed is designated the base, reference, or zero level of potential energy; very often the earth's surface is considered the zero level of potential energy. From Equation 11.5 we see that the gravitational potential energy is directly proportional to the height above some reference level, the choice of which is purely arbitrary since, physically, we are principally interested only in differences in potential energy corresponding to two different levels. With our body at level EF, the potential energy mgh' with respect to level CD is given by the difference between its potential energy with respect to an arbitrary reference level AB and the potential energy of level CD with respect to the same reference level, or

$$mgh' = mg(h + h') - mgh$$

and this equality is independent of the value of h, that is, on the location of the reference level.

Let us return to the situation in which the body in Figure 11.4 is at the level CD. With respect to level CD as a reference, the gravitational potential energy is zero. With respect to level AB considered as a reference the potential energy is mgh. With respect to level EF taken as a reference the potential energy must then be negative and equal to $-mgh'$. Accordingly, if we compute the potential energy of the body at CD with respect to AB by considering level EF as the reference level we have $-mgh' - [-mg(h + h')]$ which is mgh, as it should be.

It is also desirable and instructive to consider Figure 11.4 from the viewpoint of changes in gravitational potential energy when a body changes its position relative to some reference level. Let us consider that the body falls from level CD to level AB. In its downward motion, the amount of potential energy the body possesses, with reference to level AB, decreases since h decreases. Hence the change in gravitational potential energy is negative. However, the force of gravity, acting downward, does positive work on the body. On the other hand, if we apply an upward force that is just sufficient to lift the body from level AB to level CD, this upward force does positive work against the force of gravity, the force of gravity does negative work, and the change in gravitational potential energy is positive. This is an illustration of the fact that the change in gravitational potential energy is the negative of the work done by the gravitational force. The same relationship is true for the work done by an elastic force.

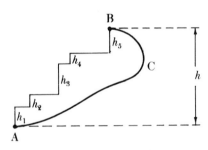

Figure 11.5. *Illustrating that the work done against gravity is independent of the path.*

There is another aspect of gravitational potential energy that is very significant. Suppose, in the absence of friction, a body of mass m is lifted, without acceleration, a vertical height h from a point A to a point B along the zigzag vertical and horizontal path shown in Figure 11.5. The work done against gravity in effecting this transfer is $mg(h_1 + h_2 + h_3 + h_4 + h_5) = mgh$, since no work is done against gravity in the horizontal steps. Hence the result is the same as when the body has been raised vertically a distance h.

Since any curved path is composed of infinitesimal vertical and horizontal steps the same result is obtained if the mass is transported from A to B along a path such as ACB. *The work done against gravity is therefore independent of the path and depends only on the vertical distance between the initial and final points.* Furthermore, if the mass is moved from B to A by either path the work done is $-mgh$. Hence, if the mass is lifted by the zigzag path and returned that way, the total work done is zero; or if we go up along ACB and return along BCA, the total work done is zero; or if we go up along the zigzag path and return along BCA, the total work done is zero. *This illustrates the principle that when a mass is carried completely around a closed path, the total work done against gravity is zero.* It is important to realize that this principle holds only in the absence of friction since otherwise some of the work, done against friction, goes into the form of heat. When the condition is such that the work done in a round trip is zero, we say that the force performing the work is *conservative*. The gravitational force is a conservative force. Friction force, always acting in a direction opposite to that of motion, is not a conservative force and there is no potential energy that can be associated with it. Only when work has been done on a body against a conservative force is the body said to have acquired potential energy.

In our discussion of potential energy we have regarded the potential energy as residing in or being associated with the body. Actually, this is not so, since, when a mass is lifted, the separation between the mass and the earth is increased and work is done against the initial force of attraction that exists between both bodies. Hence the potential energy is to be associated jointly with the system which is composed of the earth and the body. It is true that when a body is lifted the downward displacement of the earth is very much smaller; nevertheless, the potential energy of the system has been increased. The lifted body, however, is that part of the system from which the energy becomes available, and for convenience the potential energy is regarded as being associated with the body. We therefore say that, when a mass is elevated some distance above a reference level, it possesses gravitational potential energy.

Besides mechanical potential energy, in later chapters we shall have occasion to deal with chemical potential energy, electrostatic potential energy, nuclear potential energy, and other types. Whatever the nature of a potential energy, it must be remembered that potential energy always involves forces, i.e., work done by, or work potentially available from, the action of forces.

11.5. Kinetic Energy. When a body is in translational or rotational motion, observation reveals that it can do work in being brought to rest. A body that is moving in a straight line or in a curve possesses energy by virtue

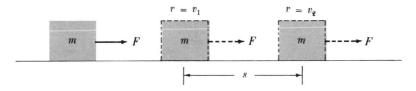

Figure 11.6. *Illustrating kinetic energy.*

of its motion; this energy of motion is called *kinetic energy*. The total motional energy possessed by a body that is simultaneously translating and rotating is a sum of its kinetic energy of translation and its kinetic energy of rotation. We shall now derive the mathematical expressions for kinetic energy, by means of which we can calculate the kinetic energy possessed by a moving body, considering first translation and then rotation.

Consider that a body of mass m, free to move on a horizontal frictionless surface, has a horizontal force F acting on it, as shown in Figure 11.6. In the displacement s shown suppose the body increases its speed from a value v_1 to a value v_2. Since friction is absent and there is no storage of elastic potential energy due to distortion, the work done by the force F goes into producing motion. The weight and normal reaction have been left out of the diagram since they are balanced and do not contribute to the horizontal motion. In what follows, the left-hand column contains the algebraic derivation and the right-hand one sets forth the same development with the calculus.

Taking F in Figure 11.6 as a constant force, the work W done during the displacement s is

$$W = Fs = mas$$

where a is the linear acceleration in the direction of the force. From the kinematic Equation 3.6b we have

$$as = (v_2{}^2 - v_1{}^2)/2$$

Hence

$$W = \tfrac{1}{2}mv_2{}^2 - \tfrac{1}{2}mv_1{}^2 \qquad (11.6)$$

Equation 11.6, although derived for the case in which the acceleration is constant, is true when F is not constant, as is shown by the calculus method in the adjoining column.

The work W done by the force F in an element of displacement ds is

$$W = \int F \, ds$$

and, by Newton's second law for translation, we have

$$W = \int ma \, ds$$

where a, the linear acceleration, is given by the time derivative of the velocity dv/dt. Now

$$\begin{aligned} a &= dv/dt \\ &= (dv/ds)(ds/dt) \\ &= v(dv/ds) \end{aligned}$$

so that $\quad W = m \displaystyle\int_{v_1}^{v_2} v \, dv$

and $\qquad W = \tfrac{1}{2}mv_2{}^2 - \tfrac{1}{2}mv_1{}^2 \qquad (11.6)$

This derivation of Equation 11.6 makes no assumption regarding the nature of F and holds independently of the way in which the body is accelerated.

The work done on the body has gone into motional energy to increase the speed of the body. We thus define the translational *kinetic energy* E_K as *the product of one-half the mass of the body and the square of its speed*, or

$$E_K = \tfrac{1}{2}mv^2 \qquad (11.7)$$

It is significant to point out that Equation 11.7 holds under the condition that the mass m is considered constant. The expression for the kinetic energy when m varies with its speed is given in Section 11.7. If in Equation 11.6 we set $v_1 = 0$, we see that the kinetic energy represents the work done by the force in giving the body a speed v. In general, we have

$$W = E_{K2} - E_{K1} \qquad (11.8)$$

where E_{K1} and E_{K2} are the kinetic energies at the positions where the body in Figure 11.6 has the speeds v_1 and v_2 respectively. Equation 11.8 is a symbolic representation of the *Work-Energy Theorem* which states that *the work done against inertia by a force on a body is equal to the change in kinetic energy of the body resulting from this force.*   The work-energy theorem is powerful in its application to the solution of problems that are most difficult and at times impossible to solve by ordinary methods.   When a body executes a rather complex motion between two instants of time and the speeds of the body at the beginning and end of the time interval are known, the work done against inertia may be easily computed by means of the work-energy theorem, even when nothing is known about the kind of motion performed between the end points.

Kinetic energy is expressed in ergs if m is in grams mass and v is in centimeters per second.   If m is in kilograms mass and v is in meters per second the unit of kinetic energy is the newton-meter (nt·m), the joule.   If m is in slugs and v is in feet per second the unit for kinetic energy is the foot–pound-force (ft·pf).

To find the expression for the kinetic energy of rotation we may proceed in a manner similar to the above.   We suppose that a rigid body is free to turn in a frictionless bearing and an external torque L is applied.   The work done, which goes into rotational energy, is given by Equation 11.4, $W = L\theta$, where θ is the angular displacement in radians.   From Newton's second law for rotation and the kinematic formula for rotation the result follows.   We shall not carry through the details of the derivation, and shall assign this as an exercise in the problems at the end of this chapter.   We here state the results and the student can see the correctness of the form of the equations by remembering that in rotation the quantities m and v appearing in translation are replaced by the moment of inertia I and the angular velocity ω, respectively.   The work-energy theorem for rotation is

$$W = \tfrac{1}{2}I\omega_2^2 - \tfrac{1}{2}I\omega_1^2 \tag{11.9}$$

where ω_1 and ω_2 are the angular speeds at the beginning and end of the displacement interval, respectively.   The rotational kinetic energy is given by

$$E_K = \tfrac{1}{2}I\omega^2 \tag{11.10}$$

In Equation 11.10, ω is in radians per second.   If the unit for I is the gram-mass–square-centimeter (gm·cm²), kinetic energy is given by the dyne-centimeter (dyne·cm), the erg; if it is the kilogram-mass–square-centimeter (kgm·cm²), kinetic energy is given by the newton-meter (nt·m), the joule; and if it is the slug–square-foot (slug·ft²), kinetic energy is given by the foot-pound-force (ft·pf).

A body that is simultaneously translating and rotating has an amount of translational kinetic energy that is given by Equation 11.7 and an amount of rotational kinetic energy given by Equation 11.10.   Therefore its total motional or kinetic energy is

$$W = \tfrac{1}{2}mv^2 + \tfrac{1}{2}I\omega^2 \tag{11.11}$$

The student should realize that it is for convenience that we consider an object at rest in the laboratory as having zero speed and hence no kinetic energy. This merely means that we are considering the earth our frame of reference and, although the body has no kinetic energy relative to the earth, it is revolving about the rotation axis of the earth which in turn has orbital motion around the sun, and these motions are relative to other stellar systems.

11.6. Conservation of Energy. One of the most important principles in the physical sciences is the principle of *conservation of energy*, which can be stated as follows. *Energy can neither be created nor destroyed, although it is subject to change from one form to another.* The most painstaking experiments on detection and measurement of energy indicate that when energy disappears in one form an equal amount appears in another or several other forms. Although there exists no general proof of the principle there is no record of any evidence that it has ever been violated. Accordingly, we are justified in stipulating that the total amount of energy which is confined in an isolated system remains forever constant; i.e., the energy is conserved. An isolated system is one into or out of which there is no passage of energy and, although there may occur energy transformations, the total energy of the system remains constant. When energy is changed from mechanical to electrical form as in an electric generator, from electrical to light form as in a lamp, or from mechanical energy of translation to mechanical energy of rotation as in the reciprocating mechanism of an engine, some of the energy is expended in work against friction. Some of this energy, which we often find most difficult to harness and make available for useful purposes, we say is wasted. However, it is not destroyed because it is converted into heat which, as we shall see, is a form of energy.

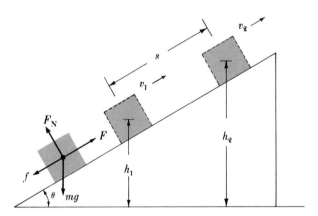

Figure 11.7. *Illustrating conservation of energy.*

As an illustration of the principle of conservation of energy consider a body of mass m being drawn up a rough inclined plane by a constant force F, as shown in Figure 11.7. The resultant force $F - f - mg \sin \theta$, where f is the force of friction, accelerates the body up the plane. At points h_1 and h_2 vertically above the horizontal base line the body has the respective velocities v_1 and v_2 directed up the plane. Expressing Newton's second law for translation along the plane direction we have

$$F - f - mg \sin \theta = ma$$

where a is the linear acceleration up the plane. The acceleration is given by the kinematic equation

$$v_2{}^2 = v_1{}^2 + 2as$$

where s is the displacement of the body between the points where its velocities are v_1 and v_2. Eliminating a between these equations and observing that $s \sin \theta = h_2 - h_1$, we have

$$Fs = \tfrac{1}{2}m(v_2{}^2 - v_1{}^2) + mg(h_2 - h_1) + fs \tag{11.12}$$

In Equation 11.12, Fs is the work done by the agent supplying the force F, $\tfrac{1}{2}m(v_2{}^2 - v_1{}^2)$ is the change in kinetic energy, $mg(h_2 - h_1)$ is the change in the gravitational potential energy, and fs is the work done against friction. The work done against friction represents the amount of energy which is transformed into heat. We here have, in accordance with the principle of conservation of energy, that the mechanical energy Fs, supplied by the lifting agent, has been converted in part into an increase in kinetic energy, in part into an increase in gravitational potential energy, and in part into heat energy.

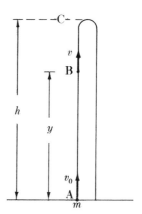

As a further illustration, suppose a mass m, Figure 11.8, is projected vertically upward from position A with a velocity v_0. We have already found, by using the principles of kinematics, that the body in its motion upward passes any intermediate point B at a height y above the starting point with a velocity v which is less than v_0, and attains a maximum height h with a zero velocity. Neglecting air resistance it then returns, passing B with the same speed it had at B on its upward motion, and reaches the starting point A with the initial speed. Taking the origin at the starting point A and considering the upward direction as positive, we have

Figure 11.8. *Conservation of mechanical energy for a ball thrown vertically upward in a frictionless medium. At C the energy is all potential:* $E_P = mgh$, $E_K = 0$. *At B the energy is partly potential and partly kinetic. At A the energy is all kinetic:* $E_K = \tfrac{1}{2}mv_0{}^2$, $E_P = 0$.

$$v^2 = v_0{}^2 - 2gy$$

We now convert this kinematic relationship into an energy equation by multiplying each term by $m/2$. Then

$$\tfrac{1}{2}mv^2 + mgy = \tfrac{1}{2}mv_0{}^2 \tag{11.13}$$

Equation 11.13 states that at all times the total mechanical energy—that is, the sum of the kinetic energy and gravitational potential energy—is equal to the initial kinetic energy which is constant for a given v_0. Hence, the total mechanical energy, which is all kinetic energy initially at $y = 0$, is a constant. As the body rises, the potential energy increases because of the increase in y, and the kinetic energy decreases by just the right amount to preserve the constancy of their sum. At the top C, the total mechanical energy is all gravitational potential energy $mgh = \frac{1}{2}mv_0^2$. At any point between A and C the total mechanical energy is in part kinetic and in part gravitational potential. The constancy of the total mechanical energy, as illustrated by this example of a vertical projectile experiencing no frictional resistance, is an illustration of conservation of mechanical energy. In this example the initial kinetic energy, expended and transformed into potential energy in the upward motion, is recoverable in the downward motion. Hence the net work done in a round trip is zero and, as we have seen, this means that the force operating is conservative. That this is as it should be is clear when we realize that the only force present in this example is the gravitational force which we have already shown is a conservative force. Hence, provided there is no friction present, mechanical energy is conserved.

On the other hand, suppose we consider the effect of the presence of air resistance, Figure 11.8. This gives rise to a friction force which at all instants acts in a direction opposite to that of motion. In the upward motion some of the initial energy $\frac{1}{2}mv_0^2$ is expended in the formation of heat, and the height h' that the body attains is less than h, with the result that mgh' is not equal to $\frac{1}{2}mv_0^2$. On the return trip, friction again is present and the body returns to the starting point with kinetic energy that is less than mgh' and hence smaller than $\frac{1}{2}mv_0^2$. Friction is a nonconservative or dissipative force, giving rise to heat energy which may be converted into mechanical or other useful forms of energy. Whenever friction is present, the sum of the potential energy and kinetic energy is never constant, and the mechanical energy is not conserved. The student should realize, however, that while the mechanical energy is not conserved in a system in which friction is present, the total energy, which includes all forms of energy such as heat, is constant under all conditions.

11.7. Equivalence of Mass and Energy.   In Section 4.2 we stated Einstein's equation

$$m = \frac{m_0}{\sqrt{1 - (v/c)^2}}$$

which shows that the mass m of a particle is not a constant but increases with increasing speed v in such a way that it approaches an infinite value as the speed of the particle approaches the speed of light c. The quantity m_0 is the rest mass of the particle, i.e., the mass of the particle when at rest or, for all practical purposes, when the particle moves with a speed small compared with that of light.   This equation has been directly verified by experiments on high-speed electrons.   By calculating the kinetic energy of a particle as the work necessary to increase the particle s speed from 0 to v and taking into account the variation of mass with speed, it can be shown (see Problem 11.45) that

$$E_K = mc^2 - m_0c^2 = (m - m_0)c^2 \tag{11.14}$$

Equation 11.14 is the famous Einstein relationship between mass and energy and states that the kinetic energy of a body is equal to c^2 times the difference between its motional mass and rest mass.   When v is small compared with c the kinetic energy reduces to the familiar Newtonian form $\frac{1}{2}mv^2$.   This is shown as follows:

$$E_K = \left[\frac{m_0}{\sqrt{1 - (v/c)^2}} - m_0\right]c^2 = m_0c^2\{[1 - (v/c)^2]^{-1/2} - 1\}$$

Now expanding the quantity in square brackets by the binomial theorem we have

$$E_K = m_0c^2\left[1 + \frac{1}{2}\left(\frac{v^2}{c^2}\right) + \frac{3}{8}\left(\frac{v^4}{c^4}\right) + \cdots + \cdots - 1\right]$$

$$= m_0c^2\left[\frac{1}{2}\left(\frac{v^2}{c^2}\right) + \frac{3}{8}\left(\frac{v^4}{c^4}\right) + \cdots\right] = \frac{1}{2}m_0v^2\left[1 + \frac{3}{4}\left(\frac{v^2}{c^2}\right) + \cdots\right]$$

and neglecting the higher-power terms in comparison with unity,

$$E_K = \tfrac{1}{2}m_0v^2$$

For bodies whose speeds are small compared with that of light the change in mass is undetectably small and we ordinarily employ for the kinetic energy the expression $\frac{1}{2}mv^2$.

Equation 11.14 shows that the total energy of a particle

$$mc^2 = m_0c^2 + E_K \tag{11.15}$$

is equal to its rest mass energy plus its kinetic energy.   From this relationship Einstein concluded that mass and energy are two different forms of the same physical quantity and that whenever there is a change in mass there is a corresponding change in energy.   Thus, when there is a change in mass Δm there is a corresponding change in energy ΔW given by

$$\Delta W = c^2 \Delta m \tag{11.16}$$

The equivalence of mass and energy is revealed by the above mass-energy relationships, and the principle of the conservation of energy has thereby been broadened to include mass as a form of energy.

The intrinsic energy of one gram of any material at rest is

$$W = m_0c^2 = 1 \text{ gm } (3 \times 10^{10})^2 \text{ cm}^2/\text{sec}^2$$
$$= 9 \times 10^{20} \text{ ergs} = 9 \times 10^{13} \text{ joules}$$

a truly tremendous amount of energy.   This means that if one gram of material could be made to disappear as mass, there would be generated 9×10^{13} joules of energy.   Direct experimental confirmation of such mass-energy conversions has been accomplished in nuclear reactions which we shall study in Chapter 37. In fact, the sun sends to the earth each day about one hundred tons of its mass in the form of radiant energy and the reality of the atomic bomb, in which there is a conversion of mass into energy, is incontestable evidence of the equivalence of mass and energy.

11.8.   Power.   Very often we are interested not only in the amount of work that an agent can perform but also in the speed with which a given amount of work can be accomplished. The time element did not enter into our discussion of work and energy. However, a powerful agent can do a sizeable amount of work in a relatively short time. The word *power* is employed to represent the time rate of doing work. When a quantity of work W is performed in a time interval t the average power is defined by the relation

$$P_{av} = W/t \qquad (11.17)$$

The power is constant if the work is performed at a uniform rate. However, if the work done varies during succeeding time intervals, the power fluctuates and Equation 11.17 defines the average power.

Instantaneous power is described in a manner analogous to the way in which instantaneous velocity and acceleration were described. If ΔW is the work performed in a short time interval Δt, the instantaneous power P is given by the limiting value of the ratio $\Delta W/\Delta t$ as Δt approaches zero, or

$$P = \lim_{\Delta t \to 0} \Delta W/\Delta t \qquad (11.18)$$

In the special case in which the agent operates in a steady fashion and performs the same amount of work during each succeeding time interval, Equation 11.17 represents the instantaneous power.

Suppose now that a constant force F acts on a body in the direction of the displacement Δs for a time interval Δt. Then

$$\frac{\Delta W}{\Delta t} = F \frac{\Delta s}{\Delta t}$$

and

$$\lim_{\Delta t \to 0} \frac{\Delta W}{\Delta t} = F \lim_{\Delta t \to 0} \frac{\Delta s}{\Delta t}$$

Recognizing that the limiting expression on the right side of the equation is the instantaneous velocity and using Equation 11.18 leads to

$$P = Fv \qquad (11.19)$$

which gives the relationship between the instantaneous power, the force performing the work, and the instantaneous velocity. In Equation 11.19, F and v have the same direction. If F does not have the same direction as v, then only the component of F in the direction of v is effective in the calculation of power. Similarly, the instantaneous power in terms of rotational quantities is

$$P = L\omega \tag{11.20}$$

where L is the torque and ω is the instantaneous angular velocity.

The unit for power is obtained by dividing the work unit by the time unit. In the cgs system the unit of power is the erg per second. In the mks system the unit of power is the joule per second which is called the *watt*. In the English gravitational system the unit of power is the foot–pound-force per second (ft·pf/sec).

In defining a unit the procedure is first to mention the physical quantity the unit represents and then to indicate the defining magnitude of the unit. Thus, a watt is defined as *a unit of power accomplished when an agent performs work at the rate of one joule per second.* The other units may be similarly defined.

The watt is an inconveniently small unit and power is more commonly expressed in kilowatts (kw) or megawatts. The equivalence is as follows: 1 kilowatt = 1,000 watts; 1 megawatt = 1,000,000 watts. Likewise, it is more convenient to use the horsepower (hp) in the English system. Thus 1 horsepower = 550 foot–pound-force/sec = 33,000 foot–pound-force/min. Employing the relations between the newton, pound force, meter, and foot it can be easily verified that 1 horsepower = 746 watts.

From the defining equation for power we see that work is equal to the product of power and time. Hence we may alternatively define a unit of work in terms of a unit of power. The horsepower and the kilowatt are commonly employed to define two large work units, the horsepower-hour (hp·hr) and the kilowatt-hour (kw·hr). Thus *one horsepower-hour is a unit of work accomplished in one hour by an agent working at a constant rate of one horsepower. One kilowatt-hour is a unit of work accomplished in one hour by an agent working at the constant rate of one kilowatt.*

The equivalents in terms of the foot–pound-force and the joule are:

$$1 \text{ hp·hr} = 33,000 \frac{\text{ft·pf}}{\text{min}} \times 1.00 \text{ hr} = 33,000 \frac{\text{ft·pf}}{\cancel{\text{min}}} \times 60.0 \frac{\cancel{\text{min}}}{\cancel{\text{hr}}} \times 1.00 \cancel{\text{hr}}$$

$$= 1.98 \times 10^6 \text{ ft·pf}$$

$$1 \text{ kw·hr} = 1,000 \text{ watts} \times 1.00 \text{ hr} = 1,000 \frac{\text{joules}}{\cancel{\text{sec}}} \times 3600 \frac{\cancel{\text{sec}}}{\cancel{\text{hr}}} \times 1.00 \cancel{\text{hr}}$$

$$= 3.60 \times 10^6 \text{ joules}$$

For convenience an equivalence listing of the commonly employed power and energy units is given in Table 11.1. It is to be carefully noted that horsepower-hour and kilowatt-hour are units of work or energy and not of power. The electric company, in the sale of its product, charges for energy and not power. Users of electricity pay for kilowatt-hours of energy, the unit cost varying from a fractional part of a cent to a few cents per kilowatt-hour, depending upon how much energy is utilized and where it is being delivered.

Table 11.1. *Units of power and energy.*

$1 \text{ watt} = 10^7 \text{ ergs/sec} = 1 \text{ joule/sec}$

$1 \text{ hp} = 550 \text{ ft·pf/sec} = 33{,}000 \text{ ft·pf/min} = 746 \text{ watts}$

$1 \text{ kw} = 1{,}000 \text{ watts} = 1.341 \text{ hp}$

$1 \text{ ft·pf/sec} = 1.356 \text{ watts}$

$1 \text{ hp·hr} = 1.98 \times 10^6 \text{ ft·pf}$

$1 \text{ kw·hr} = 3.60 \times 10^6 \text{ joules}$

Although electrical power and utility rates are invariably expressed respectively in watts or kilowatts and kilowatt-hours, they may also be expressed respectively in horsepower and horsepower-hour. However, common practice in the field of electrical engineering is to employ the metric system. On the other hand, in the field of mechanical engineering in the United States the practice is to use the English system of units and to rate the power of an engine in horsepower although it would not be out of place to stipulate the power in kilowatts.

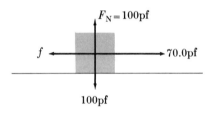

$F_N = 100\text{pf}$

f

70.0pf

100pf

Figure 11.9.

Example 11.1. A constant horizontal force of 70.0 pounds force acts for 5.00 sec on a body of 100 pounds mass which is initially at rest on level ground. The average coefficient of friction is 0.200. Find (**a**) the total work done against friction, (**b**) the kinetic energy attained by the body, and (**c**) the average horsepower expended.

Solution. (**a**) The diagram in Figure 11.9 shows the forces acting on the body. The friction force f is given by

$$f = 0.200 \times 100 = 20.0 \text{ pf}$$

To obtain the displacement s of the body effected in 5.00 sec first apply Newton's second law for translation, which will yield the acceleration a, and then apply the kinematic equation. Thus

$$\Sigma F = ma$$

$$70.0 - 20.0 = \frac{100}{32.0} a$$

and $\qquad a = 16.0 \text{ ft/sec}^2$

$$s = \tfrac{1}{2}at^2 = \tfrac{1}{2} \times 16.0 \times (5.00)^2 = 200 \text{ ft}$$

The work W done against friction is

$$W = fs = 20.0(200) = 4.00 \times 10^3 \text{ ft·pf}$$

(**b**) The speed obtained by the body in 5.00 sec is

$$v = at = 16.0 \times 5.00 = 80.0 \text{ ft/sec}$$

and the kinetic energy is

$$E_K = \frac{1}{2} mv^2 = \frac{1}{2} \times \frac{100}{32.0} \times (80.0)^2 = 10.0 \times 10^3 \text{ ft·pf}$$

This is the same as the work done by the unbalanced force, or $50.0 \times 200 = 10.0 \times 10^3$ foot–pound-force.

(c) The total work done is a sum of the work done against friction and the work necessary to increase the kinetic energy from zero to the value obtained in (b), or 1.40×10^4 foot–pound-force. This is the same as the applied force times the displacement, or $70.0 \times 200 = 1.40 \times 10^4$ foot–pound-force.

$$P = \frac{4.00 \times 10^3 + 10.0 \times 10^3}{5.00} = \frac{3.20 \times 10^3 \text{ ft·pf}}{\text{sec}}$$

$$= 3.20 \times 10^3 \frac{\text{ft·pf}}{\text{sec}} \times \frac{\text{hp}}{550 \frac{\text{ft·pf}}{\text{sec}}} = 5.82 \text{ hp}$$

Example 11.2. If the applied force in Example 11.1 acts upward at 30.0° with the horizontal, what are (a) the work done against friction and (b) the total work done?

Solution. (a) The values of f, a, and s are obtained by using Figure 11.10. From $\sum F_x = ma$ we have

$$70.0 \cos 30.0° - f = \frac{100}{32.0} a$$

From $\sum F_y = 0$ we have

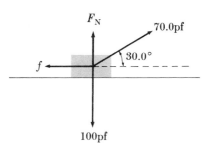

Figure 11.10.

$$F_N + 70.0 \sin 30.0° = 100$$

and using $f = 0.200 F_N$ we obtain

$$f = 13.0 \text{ pf}, \quad a = 15.2 \text{ ft/sec}^2, \quad s = 190 \text{ ft}$$

The work done against friction is

$$W = fs = 13.0 \times 190 = 2.47 \times 10^3 \text{ ft·pf}$$

(b) In using the applied force for this calculation we must employ the component in the direction of motion. Hence

$$\text{total work} = F (\cos \theta) s = 70.0 \times 0.866 \times 190 = 11.5 \times 10^3 \text{ ft·pf}$$

Example 11.3. What force is required to pull a 200 kgm body up a 30.0° inclined plane with uniform speed? The force is directed parallel to the incline and the coefficient of kinetic friction is 0.100.

Solution. Consider that the body of mass m is pulled up a distance l along the incline and is thus elevated a vertical height h, as indicated in

Figure 11.11. The force F does work against the force of friction and against the force of gravity. Hence

$$Fl = fl + mgh$$

But

$$h = l \sin 30.0° \quad \text{and} \quad f = 0.100 F_N = 0.100 \times mg \cos 30.0°$$

$$Fl = 0.100 mgl \cos 30.0° + mgl \sin 30.0°$$

The common factor l divides throughout, and with $m = 200$ kgm and $g = 9.80$ m/sec^2:

$$F = 200 \times 9.80(0.100 \times 0.866 + 0.500) = 1.15 \times 10^3 \text{ nt}$$

The student should check this result by working the problem with the equations for translational equilibrium.

Example 11.4. A body is looping-the-loop in a vertical circle of radius r. The body, passing the bottom of the loop with a speed $v_1 = \sqrt{5gr}$, barely reaches the top of the loop. Find the speed v_2 at the top of the loop, using energy principles.

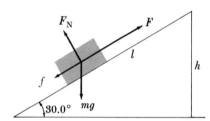

Solution. As the body rises it gains potential energy and loses kinetic energy and, by conservation of energy, the gain in potential energy is equal to the loss in kinetic energy.

Figure 11.11.

At the bottom of the loop the kinetic energy of the body of mass m is $\frac{1}{2}mv_1^2$. At the top of the loop the kinetic energy is $\frac{1}{2}mv_2^2$ and the increase in potential energy is $mg(2r)$. Hence

$$2mgr + \tfrac{1}{2}mv_2^2 = \tfrac{1}{2}mv_1^2$$

But

$$v_1^2 = 5gr$$

so that

$$4gr + v_2^2 = 5gr$$

$$v_2 = \sqrt{gr}$$

which is a result identical with that obtained in Equation 9.10, Section 9.4, by the method of centripetal and centrifugal forces.

Example 11.5. A children's slide is 20.0 feet long and makes an angle of 30.0° with the horizontal. If a child starts from rest at the top, with what speed does he reach the bottom? Take the coefficient of kinetic friction as 0.0500.

Solution. The loss in potential energy of the child is equal to the gain in kinetic energy of the child plus the work done against friction. Hence, if m is the mass of the child, and h is the elevation of the top of the slide, as shown in Figure 11.12, we have

$$mgh = \tfrac{1}{2}mv^2 + 20.0f$$

where v is the speed at the bottom and f is the force of friction. Now,

$$f = 0.0500 F_N = 0.0500 mg \cos 30.0° \quad \text{and} \quad h = 20.0 \sin 30.0°$$

Therefore
$$20.0mg \sin 30.0° = \tfrac{1}{2}mv^2 + 20.0 \times 0.0500mg \cos 30.0°$$

The solution, which is independent of m, is
$$v = 24.2 \text{ ft/sec}$$

Example 11.6. Using energy principles, solve the problem of the solid cylinder rolling down an inclined plane given in Example 10.5 of the previous chapter.

Solution. The potential energy at the top of the incline of height h above the horizontal, as shown in Figure 11.13, is converted into kinetic energy of

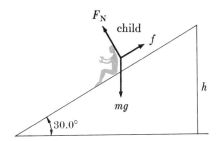

Figure 11.12.   **Figure 11.13.**

translation and kinetic energy of rotation at the bottom of the incline. Hence
$$mgh = \tfrac{1}{2}mv^2 + \tfrac{1}{2}I_C\omega^2$$

where m is the mass of the cylinder, v its linear speed at the bottom of the incline, I_C its moment of inertia about an axis through C, and ω its angular velocity. Here we have
$$h = l \sin \theta, \quad I_C = mr^2/2, \quad \omega = v/r$$
Therefore
$$mgl \sin \theta = \frac{1}{2} mv^2 + \frac{1}{2} \times \frac{mr^2}{2} \times \frac{v^2}{r^2} = \frac{3}{4} mv^2$$

and
$$v^2 = \tfrac{4}{3}gl \sin \theta$$

The linear acceleration along the incline is obtained by employing the kinematic equation involving velocities, acceleration, and displacement:
$$\tfrac{4}{3}gl \sin \theta = 2al$$
or
$$a = \tfrac{2}{3}g \sin \theta$$

The time t it takes to descend is obtained by using the kinematic relationship between the velocities and time, or
$$\sqrt{\tfrac{4}{3}gl \sin \theta} = \tfrac{2}{3}g (\sin \theta)t$$
which yields
$$t^2 = 3l/g \sin \theta$$

This is the result obtained in Example 10.5 by the methods of dynamics.

Example 11.7. When the system shown in Figure 11.14 is released from rest the 112-pound weight descends and the solid cylinder, whose weight is 320 pounds force, rolls without slipping. Using energy principles, find the speeds v_w of the weight and v_c of the cylinder after the weight has descended 5.00 feet. Neglect friction and the mass of the pulley.

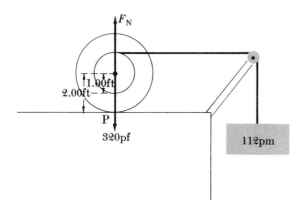

Figure 11.14.

Solution. The friction force acting at P, and necessary for the cylinder to roll without slipping, does no work since it is a static frictional force. In this problem we are neglecting the small amount of rolling friction against which work must be performed. Hence the work done by the falling weight is equal to the increase in the kinetic energies of the weight and the cylinder. The work-energy theorem thus yields the equation

$$112 \times 5.00 = \frac{1}{2} \times \frac{112}{32.0} v_w{}^2 + \frac{1}{2} I_P \omega^2$$

where I_P is the moment of inertia of the cylinder about an axis through P and ω is the angular velocity of the cylinder. Now

$$I_P = \frac{3}{2} \times \frac{320}{32.0} (2.00)^2 \quad \text{and} \quad \omega = \frac{v_w}{3.00}$$

Substituting, we have

$$112 \times 5.00 = \frac{1}{2} \times \frac{112}{32.0} v_w{}^2 + \frac{1}{2} \times \frac{3}{2} \times \frac{320}{32.0} (2.00)^2 \frac{v_w{}^2}{9.00}$$

and solving for the speed of the weight,

$$v_w = 17.3 \text{ ft/sec}$$

The linear speed of the cylinder is

$$v_c = 2_\omega = 2v_w/3.00 = (2 \times 17.3)/3.00$$
$$v_c = 11.5 \text{ ft/sec}$$

Example 11.8. A locomotive starts up a 1.00% grade with a speed of 60.0 miles/hour and exerts a constant drawbar pull of 22.0×10^3 pounds force on a train whose gross weight is 2.00×10^3 tons force (tf). The total train resistance is 20.0 pounds-force/ton-force. The grade is 5.00×10^3 ft. What are (**a**) the speed of the train when it reaches the top, (**b**) the final drawbar horsepower developed, and (**c**) the total work done against the train resistance expressed in horsepower-hours?

Solution. (a) Using the work-energy theorem and observing that the drawbar pull does positive work while the force of gravity and the train resistance each do negative work we have:

work by drawbar pull — work against gravity
— work against resistance = change in kinetic energy

Since a 1.00% grade means a vertical rise of 1.00 foot in a horizontal displacement of 100 feet we have:

$$\text{work done by drawbar pull} = 22.0 \times 10^3 \text{ pf} \times 5.00 \times 10^3 \text{ ft}$$
$$= 110 \times 10^6 \text{ ft} \cdot \text{pf}$$
$$\text{work against gravity} = 2.00 \times 10^3 \text{ tf} \times 2.00 \times 10^3 \frac{\text{pf}}{\text{tf}} \times 50.0 \text{ ft}$$
$$= 100 \times 10^6 \text{ ft} \cdot \text{pf}$$
$$\text{work against resistance} = \frac{20.0 \text{ pf}}{\text{tf}} \times 2.00 \times 10^3 \text{ tf} \times 5.00 \times 10^3 \text{ ft}$$
$$= 200 \times 10^6 \text{ ft} \cdot \text{pf}$$

Therefore

$$(110 - 100 - 200) \times 10^6 = \frac{1}{2} \times \frac{4.00 \times 10^6}{32.0} v^2 - \frac{1}{2} \times \frac{4.00 \times 10^6}{32.0} (88.0)^2$$

where v is the speed of the train at the top of the grade. Solving, we have

$$v = 68.6 \text{ ft/sec} = 46.7 \text{ mi/hr}$$

(**b**) The final drawbar horsepower is given by

$$P = Fv/550$$

where F is the drawbar pull. Hence

$$P = \frac{(22.0 \times 10^3)(68.6)}{550} = 2.74 \text{ hp}$$

(**c**) Work against resistance $= 200 \times 10^6 \text{ ft} \cdot \text{pf} \times \dfrac{\text{hp} \cdot \text{hr}}{1.98 \times 10^6 \text{ ft} \cdot \text{pf}}$
$$= 101 \text{ hp} \cdot \text{hr}$$

Example 11.9. When the system shown in Figure 11.15 is released it accelerates for a distance h after which m_1 comes to rest and m_2 coasts an additional distance d before coming to rest. Neglecting friction and motion of the pulley, find an expression for the coefficient of kinetic friction between m_2 and the table in terms of m_1, m_2, h, and d.

Solution. The potential energy of the falling weight m_1gh goes into work necessary to accelerate m_1 and m_2 equal respectively to m_1ah and m_2ah, and into work against friction equal to $fh = \mu_k m_2gh$ or

$$m_1gh = m_1ah + m_2ah + \mu_k m_2gh$$

where μ_k is the coefficient of kinetic friction. During the time the mass m_2

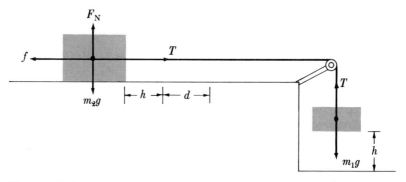

Figure 11.15.

coasts a distance d the unbalanced force acting on it is $\mu_k m_2gd$ and this is equal to m_2ah. Hence the energy equation is

$$m_1gh = m_1ah + \mu_k m_2g(h + d)$$

The acceleration of the system may be obtained by applying Newton's second law to the system. This yields the expression

$$m_1g - \mu_k m_2g = (m_1 + m_2)a$$

and eliminating a between this equation and the energy equation leads to

$$\mu_k = \frac{m_1h}{m_2(h + d) + m_1d}$$

When m_1 and m_2 are made equal, then,

$$\mu_k = h/(h + 2d)$$

which affords a simple and convenient laboratory method of determining the coefficient of kinetic friction between two surfaces. The value of the tension T in the cord is obtained by utilizing the equation $m_1g - T = m_1a$ or $T - \mu_k m_2g = m_2a$, which are the respective equations of motion for the free bodies m_1 and m_2.

Example 11.10. A body of 100 pounds force falls 22.5 inches from rest and strikes the upper end of a vertical spring whose force constant is 25.0 pounds-force per inch. Find **(a)** the maximum compression of the spring in bringing the body to rest and (**b**) the maximum kinetic energy of the body. Neglect the mass of the spring and friction.

Solution. (**a**) Let y_1 be the maximum distance in inches that the spring is compressed downward, measured as positive. Then the weight falls a distance $(y_1 + 22.5)$ inches, the potential energy being converted into kinetic energy, which in turn is expended in the work necessary to compress the spring. Hence

$$(y_1 + 22.5) \times 100 = \frac{K}{2} y_1{}^2 = \frac{25.0}{2} y_1{}^2$$

where y_1 is in inches and the work is expressed by the inch–pound-force (in·pf). This yields the quadratic expression

$$y_1{}^2 - 8.00 y_1 - 180 = 0$$

or

$$(y_1 - 18.0)(y_1 + 10.0) = 0$$

Since only the positive value of y_1 is admissible:

$$y_1 = 18.0 \text{ in}$$

(**b**) The solution to this part of the problem may be obtained from the energy equation

$$E_K = (y + 22.5) \times 100 - \frac{25.0}{2} y^2$$

which expresses the fact that the kinetic energy of the body for any value of y is equal to the potential energy minus the work needed to compress the

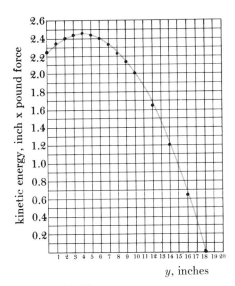

kinetic energy, inch x pound force

y, inches

Figure 11.16.

spring. When $y = 0$, no work has as yet been done on the spring and the kinetic energy is 2,250 inch–pound-force. The first term in the expression, which contributes to the increase in kinetic energy, is linear in y, while the second term, which opposes an increase in kinetic energy, depends on the square of y. Hence, up to a certain critical value $y = y_c$ the kinetic energy increases beyond the value 2,250 inch–pound-force, reaching a maximum value at $y = y_c$, and for values of y greater than y_c the kinetic energy decreases, reaching a value zero when $y = 18.0$ inches and the body comes to rest. This is shown by the graph of E_K versus y in Figure 11.16. From the graph we see that the critical value y_c is in the neighborhood of 4 inches. We shall now find this value mathematically and from it the maximum kinetic energy. In what follows the left-hand column contains an algebraic solution and the right-hand column contains the calculus solution.

The equation for the kinetic energy is

$$E_K = \frac{-25.0}{2}(y^2 - 8.00y - 180)$$

Completing the square inside the parentheses we have

$$E_K = \frac{-25.0}{2}[(y - 4.00)^2 - 196]$$

so that

$$E_K = \frac{-25.0}{2}(y - 4.00)^2 + 2,450$$

Since the term in y is always negative, the maximum value for the kinetic energy results when this term is zero. This yields the critical value

$$y_c = 4.00 \text{ in}$$

with maximum kinetic energy of 2.45×10^3 inch–pound-force.

The derivative of E_K with respect to y is

$$\frac{dE_K}{dy} = 100 - 25.0y$$

and equating this to zero as the condition for an extreme yields

$$100 - 25.0y = 0$$

or $$y = 4.00 \text{ in}$$

That this value of y corresponds to the maximum E_K is revealed by finding the second derivative or

$$\frac{d^2E_K}{dy^2} = -25.0$$

and since this is negative we have a maximum. Hence the critical value is

$$y_c = 4.00 \text{ in}$$

with a maximum kinetic energy of 2.45×10^3 inch–pound-force.

Problems

Unless otherwise specified, use for g the values 980 cm/sec² = 9.80 m/sec² = 32.0 feet/sec².

11.1. Find the work done in lifting (**a**) 200 pm to a height of 30.0 feet, (**b**) 200 gm to a height of 30.0 cm, and (**c**) 200 kgm to a height of 30.0 m.

11.2. A man whose mass is 67.5 kgm climbs a mountain whose elevation is 225 m in 2.50 hours. Find (**a**) the work done, (**b**) the power expended.

11.3. It takes 6.00 sec to accelerate a mass of 120 pounds from rest through a distance of 36.0 feet along a smooth horizontal surface. Find (**a**) the work necessary, (**b**) the average speed, and (**c**) the average power expended.

11.4. A body whose mass is 600 gm is moved with uniform speed along a horizontal surface. If the coefficient of kinetic friction between the body and the surface is 0.250, what is the work required to move the block a distance of 150 cm?

11.5. A sled with occupants, weighing 100 pounds-force, is pulled along level snow by a rope which makes an angle of 20.0° with the horizontal. (a) How much work is done on the sled in moving it through a distance of 50.0 feet? (b) If the sled is moved through this distance in 10.0 sec, what is the horsepower expended?

11.6. A body of 1.00 kgm is on a table top 2.00 m above the floor. (a) How much potential energy with respect to the floor does the mass possess? (b) If the mass falls, with what speed does it strike the floor?

11.7. A catcher receives a pitched ball having 0.250 pounds mass and a speed of 100 feet/sec. If the ball, in coming to rest, moves the catcher's hand through 4.00 inches, how much force is exerted on the catcher?

11.8. It is found that a force of 500 dynes stretches a spring 2.50 cm. Relative to its unstretched configuration, what is the potential energy of the spring when it is stretched 6.00 cm?

11.9. An unstretched spring is 10.0 inches long and its force constant is 6.00 pounds-force/foot. Find the work necessary to increase its total length from 1.00 foot to 1.50 feet.

11.10. A spring has an unstretched length of 6.00 cm and a force constant of 1.00×10^3 dynes/cm. The spring is stretched from a length of 8.00 cm until 4.00×10^3 ergs of work have been expended. Find the final length of the spring.

11.11. A 2.00 gm body is projected vertically downward, from a height of 800 cm above ground level, with a speed of 1.00×10^3 cm/sec. With respect to ground level, find (a) the total energy of the body at the instant of projection, (b) the kinetic energy 0.200 sec after projection, and (c) how far below the starting point the body is 0.200 sec after projection. Use energy principles and check your result with the kinematic equations.

11.12. A uniform telephone pole 50.0 feet long and weighing 1.00 ton is raised from a horizontal to a vertical position on the ground. How much work is done?

11.13. A flywheel has a mass of 320 pounds and a radius of gyration about an axis through its center of 1.50 feet. Find (a) the work required to give the wheel a speed of 90.0 revolutions/minute from rest in 30.0 sec and (b) the average horsepower developed. Neglect friction.

11.14. A constant force of 30.0 nt acts tangent to the rim of a wheel of radius 2.00 feet. Find the work done in turning the wheel through 120.0°.

11.15. A solid sphere of mass 16.0 pounds rolls on a level surface at a constant speed without slipping, covering 30.0 feet in 2.00 sec. Find the motional energy possessed by the sphere. Neglect rolling friction.

11.16.   Derive the work-energy theorem for rotation, Equation 11.9, in a manner similar to that employed for translation in Section 11.5.

11.17.   A flywheel, with a mass of 64.0 pounds and a radius of gyration about an axis through its center of 1.00 foot is put into rotation by a cord wound around its rim.   When 5.00 feet of cord is unwound by a constant pull of 20.0 pounds force, what is the angular speed of the wheel?   Neglect friction.

11.18.   Prove that the total mechanical energy is conserved by showing that the potential energy plus the kinetic energy is a constant for the following, assuming no frictional or other dissipative effects: (**a**) a body projected vertically upward from the earth's surface, (**b**) a projectile fired at an angle with the horizontal, (**c**) a body sliding down a frictionless inclined plane, and (**d**) the system composed of the two bodies in an Atwood machine.

11.19.   The car of a roller coaster, poised for an instant 100 feet above the ground, starts from rest down its curved path.   With what speed does it pass the lowest point 10.0 feet above the ground level?   Neglect friction.

11.20.   A locomotive develops 3.00×10^3 horsepower and draws a train on level track at a speed of 20.0 miles/hour.   Find the drawbar pull exerted by the engine, assuming no resistance.

11.21.   It takes 20.0 horsepower to keep a car moving at a speed of 30.0 miles/hour on level road.   The mass of the car is 3.60×10^3 pounds.   How much horsepower is required to keep the car moving at the same speed if the road slopes upward at an angle of 10.0°?

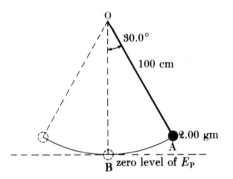

Figure 11.17.   *Problem 11.22.*

11.22.   A simple pendulum is composed of a small 2.00 gm mass attached to a 100 cm light cord whose other end is fixed at O as shown in Figure 11.17. The bob is pulled aside so that the string makes an angle of 30.0°, and is then released.   Taking the horizontal level through the lowest point B of the swing as the reference level of potential energy find (**a**) the potential energy of the bob when at A, (**b**) the speed with which the bob passes through point B, (**c**) the potential energy of the bob when it is midway along the arc between A and B, and (**d**) the kinetic energy of the bob when it is midway along the arc between A and B.

11.23. The hammer of a pile driver has a weight of 1.50 tons force. After falling 20.0 feet it strikes a pile which is driven 6.00 inches into the ground. What is the average force acting on the pile?

11.24. The amount of power put out by an engine or motor is usually measured by means of a Prony or other kind of friction brake, one form of which is shown in Figure 11.18. The band passing around the rotating pulley of the machine is attached to spring balances. Rotating of the pulley of radius r drags the band around by friction and the effective force of friction is given by the difference in the spring balance readings, $T_1 - T_2$. If the machine has a speed of n revolutions/minute, then the horsepower output is $P = Fv = 2\pi rn(T_1 - T_2)/33,000$, which is known as the *brake horsepower*. Find the power output of a motor if $r = 6.00$ inches, $T_1 = 50.0$ pounds force, $T_2 = 20.0$ pounds force, and $n = 2.00 \times 10^3$ revolutions/minute.

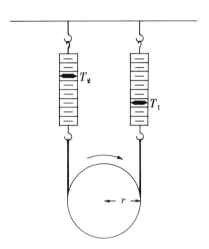

Figure 11.18. *Problem 11.24.*

11.25. A bullet with a mass of 20.0 gm and a speed of 350 m/sec is stopped in a distance of 5.00 cm. Find the average stopping force.

11.26. A 3/4-horsepower electric motor operates continuously at rated load. (**a**) Find the work done in 24.0 hours and express the result in horse-power-hours and kilowatt-hours. (**b**) If the charge for electric energy is 6.00 cents per kilowatt-hour, what is the cost per day to operate this motor?

11.27. Using the first two terms of the relativity expression for kinetic energy, $E_K = \frac{1}{2}m_0v^2[1 + \frac{3}{4}(v/c)^2]$, find for each of the following bodies (*1*) the kinetic energy, neglecting relativity correction, (*2*) the kinetic energy including the relativity correction $\frac{3}{4}(v/c)^2$, and (*3*) the percentage error incurred when the relativity correction is neglected: (**a**) an electron whose rest mass is 9.11×10^{-28} gm and whose speed is 2.70×10^{10} cm/sec, and (**b**) a bullet whose rest mass is 5.00 gm and whose speed is 5.00×10^4 cm/sec. Take the speed of light as 3.00×10^{10} cm/sec.

11.28. If it were possible to annihilate completely one pound mass of matter, how many kilowatt-hours of energy would be produced?

11.29. A 10.0 kgm block resting on a horizontal surface is pulled by a constant horizontal force of 50.0 nt for 5.00 sec. The average coefficient of friction is 0.200. Find (**a**) the total work done, (**b**) the work done against friction, (**c**) the speed of the body at the end of 5 sec, and (**d**) the average power expended.

11.30. Solve Problem 11.29 under the condition that the applied force of 50.0 nt acts upward at 25.0° with the horizontal.

11.31. A sled and occupants weighing 100 pounds force is accelerated on a horizontal snow surface under the action of a horizontal constant force of 30.0 pounds force. After the sled has moved 20.0 feet from rest the force is removed and the sled continues for another 10.0 feet before coming to rest. What is the coefficient of kinetic friction between snow and sled?

11.32. A 100 kgm body is resting at the bottom of a 10.0 m plane inclined at an angle of 30.0° with the horizontal. A constant force applied parallel to the plane causes the body to reach the top with a speed of 5,00 m/sec. The coefficient of friction between body and plane is 0.300. Find (**a**) the total energy acquired by the body when at the top of the incline, (**b**) the work done against friction, (**c**) the work done against gravity, and (**d**) the magnitude of the applied force.

11.33. A body with a mass of 16.0 pounds is projected up a 20.0° inclined plane with a speed of 10.0 feet/sec. The coefficient of friction is 0.100. Find (**a**) how far up the plane the body momentarily comes to rest, (**b**) the work done against friction in rising, and (**c**) the speed with which the body returns to its starting point. Is mechanical energy conserved? Explain your answer.

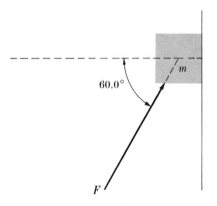

Figure 11.19. *Problem 11.34.*

11.34. A body is pushed up against a vertical wall by a force F making an angle of 60.0° with the wall, as shown in Figure 11.19. The body starts from rest at ground level and in 4.00 sec attains a speed of 6.00 feet/sec. The mass m equals 20.0 pounds and the coefficient of friction is 0.200. Find the following during the 4.00 sec interval: (**a**) the force F, (**b**) the work done against friction, (**c**) the potential energy acquired by the body at the end of the time interval, and (**d**) the average power expended over this time interval.

11.35. A train of 25 cars, each of which has a weight of 20.0 tons force, is pulled up a 1.00% grade at a constant speed of 3.00 miles/hour. If the train resistance is 5.00 pounds force per ton weight, what is the horsepower developed by the locomotive?

11.36. A locomotive, starting from rest, pulls a train weighing 3.00×10^3 tons force down a 2.00% grade. The constant drawbar pull is 1.00×10^4 pounds force. The train resistance is 6.00 pounds force per ton weight. Find (**a**) the kinetic energy of the train after it has moved 1.00 mile and (**b**) the final horsepower developed by the engine.

11.37. A body weighing 50.0 pounds force is dropped from a height of 1.00 foot onto a vertical spring whose force constant is 8.00 pounds-force/inch. (**a**) Find the maximum compression of the spring in bringing the body to rest. (**b**) Find the maximum velocity of the falling body. (**c**) Plot the velocity of the body as a function of the spring displacement from the instant the body comes in contact with the spring until it is brought to rest. Neglect friction and the mass of the spring.

11.38. Figure 11.20 shows a compressed spring with one end fixed and the other end in contact with a 100-pound block. The spring has a force constant equal to 25.0 pounds-force/inch and its initial compression is 1.00 foot. When the system is released the body moves up the plane and loses contact with the spring at the instant it has re-gained its unstretched length. If the coefficient of friction between block and plane is 0.100 what are (**a**) the speed of the body at the instant it loses contact with the spring and (**b**) the total distance the body moves up the incline? Neglect other dissipative effects.

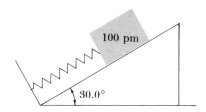

Figure 11.20. *Problem 11.38.*

11.39. Solve Problem 9.27 using the principles of energy.

11.40. Solve Problem 10.19 using the principles of energy.

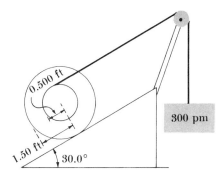

Figure 11.21. *Problem 11.41.*

11.41. When the system shown in Figure 11.21 is released from rest the 300-pound mass descends and the cylinder, of weight 200 pounds force and radius of gyration of 1.00 foot about an axis through its center, rolls without slipping. Using energy principles find (**a**) the speed of the falling weight and (**b**) the linear speed of the cylinder after the weight has descended 5.00 feet. Neglect friction and the mass of the pulley. Check your answers by using the kinematic equations and the results for the linear accelerations obtained in Problem 10.28.

11.42. The pulley shown in Figure 11.22 has a weight of 100 pounds force and a radius of gyration of 1.50 feet about an axis through its center, and is free to rotate about this same axis. The coefficient of friction between block and plane is 0.200. When the system is released from rest find, using energy principles, (**a**) the speed of the 200-pound weight, (**b**) the speed of the 300-

pound weight, and (c) the angular acceleration of the pulley after the weight
has descended 5.00 feet.   Neglect friction in the pulley bearing.   Check your
answers with the results obtained by dynamical methods in Problem 10.27.

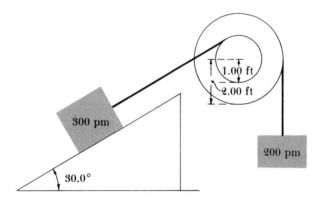

Figure 11.22.   *Problem 11.42.*

11.43.   Figure 11.23 shows a solid sphere of radius r released from rest
at a height h above the lowest point of a loop-the-loop of radius R.   For
what value of h will the sphere barely complete the loop without leaving the
track?   Neglect the effect of friction.   Take $R = 6.00$ feet and $r = 1.00$ foot.

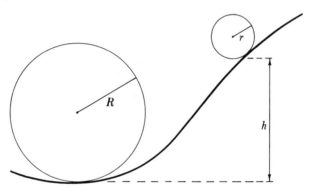

Figure 11.23.   *Problem 11.43.*

11.44.   An automobile traveling on horizontal ground enters at the bottom of a vertical loop-the-loop of 40.0-foot radius.   The car, whose center
of gravity is 1.60 feet above the ground, just goes around the loop without
falling.   Neglecting friction, find the speed with which the car enters the
loop-the-loop.

11.45.   Show that Equation 11.14 is true.   (*Hint:*

$$E_K = \int F\, ds = \int \frac{d(mv)}{dt}\, ds = \int v\left(m\frac{dv}{dt} + v\frac{dm}{dt}\right) dt$$

Now substitute $m = m_0/\sqrt{1 - (v/c)^2}$ and integrate.)

Simple Machines

*T*HERE ARE TWO GENERAL types of machine. One type is the devices that transform energy of one kind into energy of another. For instance, the household iron transforms electric energy into heat energy, the electric motor transforms electric energy into mechanical energy, the electric light bulb transforms electric energy into light energy, the photoelectric cell transforms light energy into electric energy, and the loud-speaker transforms electric energy into sound energy. The second type is the devices that yield on the output the same kind of energy as is fed in at the input, the machine being employed because of convenience or because of an advantage. Among these are the electric transformer, the electron tube and modern transistor, the hydraulic press, the crowbar, the automobile jack, the nutcracker.

In this chapter we shall study the mechanical devices that belong to the second type of machine. Any mechanical machine, of the most complex kind, is a combination of a few simple ones, known as simple machines. The devices generally considered simple machines are the lever, the wheel and axle, the pulley, the inclined plane, the wedge, and the screw. We shall study each of these individually, although the wheel and axle and the pulley are basically modified levers, and the wedge and screw essentially inclined planes.

Since work is given by force times distance, a simple machine may deliver a given amount of work by exerting a large force through a small displacement or by exerting a small force through a large displacement. Hence we shall see that a simple machine may be employed to increase the magnitude of a force, to decrease the magnitude of a force, or to change the direction of a force.

We shall first introduce and discuss two quantities, *mechanical advantage* and *efficiency*, which are significant in describing the operation of a machine, and we shall see that the mechanical advantage is a quantity describing the force-multiplication property of a machine while the efficiency is a quantity measuring the amount of energy loss due to friction.

12.1. Mechanical Advantage. Any machine has what may be termed an input end and an output section. In using a mechanical machine the operator applies a force to the input section, and the machine exerts a force at the output section. Usually the output force is greater than the input force. However, as we shall see, the output force may be equal to, and even less than, the input force.

Let us consider in Figure 12.1 the general case of a mechanical machine to whose input end there is applied an input force F_i through a distance s_i and

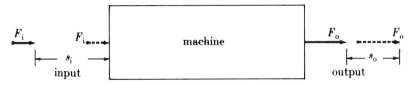

Figure 12.1. *Diagram used to define mechanical advantage and efficiency of a machine.*

at whose output end there is exerted an output force F_o through a distance s_o. There is, then, an amount of work W_i put into the machine which puts out or delivers an amount of work W_o and these, in accordance with the principle of conservation of energy, are related by the equation

$$W_i = W_o + W_f + W_m \tag{12.1}$$

where W_f is the work done against friction in the machine and W_m is the work required to give translatory and rotary motion to the parts of the machine. Because of friction and the finite mass of the moving machine parts, the work output is always less than the work input.

A measure of the ability of the machine to transform an input force F_i into an output force F_o is the ratio F_o/F_i which is called the *actual mechanical advantage* M_a. Thus

$$M_a = F_o/F_i \tag{12.2}$$

This ratio of the force exerted by the machine on a load to the force applied to the machine is never exactly calculable since the calculation always involves friction and its attendant heat loss. One obtains M_a by actual test, finding the experimental values of F_i and F_o and forming their ratio. The quantity M_a may be greater than, or equal to, or less than 1. The presence of friction and the moving machine parts always effectively decreases the output force, so that the actual mechanical advantage is always less than it would be if there were no friction or moving parts present. Hence it is customary to define another quantity that is useful in describing the overall performance of a machine. This quantity is called the *ideal or theoretical mechanical advantage* M_t which is the mechanical advantage that the machine would have if friction were absent and the moving parts of the machine were weightless. In this case, setting $W_f = W_m = 0$ in Equation 12.1 we have

$$W_i = W_o$$
$$F_i s_i = F_o s_o$$

and
$$M_t = F_o/F_i = s_i/s_o \tag{12.3}$$

in which F_o is the output force the machine would exert under ideal conditions.

Thus M_t is the ratio of the distance through which the applied force acts to the distance through which the output force acts, and this ratio can usually be calculated from the geometry of the device.

12.2. Efficiency. Referring to Equation 12.1 we see that even when a machine is exceptionally well designed, such that W_m is negligibly small, the energy delivered by the machine is less than that supplied to it, because of the presence of friction which causes the production of some wasteful energy. For a given machine we may therefore indicate the output work as the input work times a fraction less than 1. This fraction represents the machine's efficiency, which is defined as the ratio of the output work or energy to the input work or energy. Since Equation 12.1 is converted into a power equation by dividing each term by the same interval of time the efficiency may alternatively be represented by the ratio of output power to input power. Thus, if ε is the symbolic representation of the efficiency of a machine we have

$$\varepsilon = \text{output work (or energy) / input work (or energy)}$$
$$= \text{output power / input power} \tag{12.4}$$

Substituting $F_o s_o$ for output work and $F_i s_i$ for input work we have

$$\varepsilon = F_o s_o / F_i s_i$$

and with the use of Equations 12.2 and 12.3 there follows

$$\varepsilon = M_a / M_t \tag{12.5}$$

so that the efficiency may also be calculated by dividing the actual mechanical advantage by the ideal or theoretical mechanical advantage. The ratio represented by ε is usually multiplied by 100, to convert it into *per cent efficiency.*

The efficiency of a machine may be almost 100% or it may be just a few per cent. Steam engines have efficiencies as low as 10 or 20% while some electrical machines operate at efficiencies between 95 and 100%. It is generally desirable that the efficiency of a machine be as high as is possible, and modern research is constantly aiming at increase in efficiency. The objection to having a low-efficiency machine when a reasonably large output is needed is that this requires an unusually large amount of energy input that is expensive. Also, the large energy loss due to friction results in a heat problem, causing damage to the machine, that may be very costly to control. In some cases, such as the jackscrew described in Section 12.8, a low efficiency is desirable and a great amount of friction is needed for the successful operation of the machine.

In the sections that follow we shall consider that we have the ideal condition of 100% efficiency and calculate the theoretical mechanical advantages of the simple machines enumerated in the introductory portion of this chapter.

12.3.   The Lever.   In its simplest form, a lever is a rigid bar which is free to rotate about a fixed axis.   The well-known three classes of the lever are shown in Figure 12.2.   In each of the classes the bar rests on the fulcrum

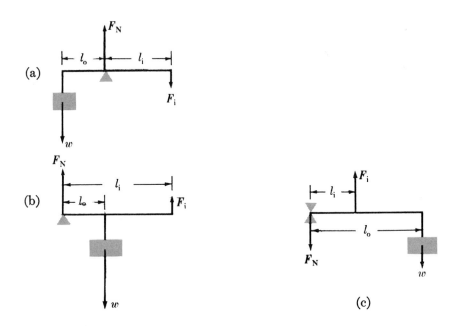

(a)

(b)

(c)

Figure 12.2.   *The lever: (a) first class, (b) second class, (c) third class.*

(shaded triangle) and is free to rotate about an axis passing through the contact point of bar and fulcrum.   The input force is represented by F_i and the output force F_o, exerted upward by the bar on the weight w, is equal in magnitude to w, so that $F_o = w$.   The normal reaction of the fulcrum on the bar is F_N.   When the fulcrum is between the load w and F_i as in (a), we have a lever of the first class; when the load w is between the fulcrum and F_i we have a lever of the second class; and when F_i is between the fulcrum and the load w we have a lever of the third class.   In the three cases shown let l_i be the lever arm from the fulcrum to the line of action of F_i and l_o be the lever arm from the fulcrum to the line of action of w.   At the instant that the weight is on the point of being raised the system is in equilibrium.   Applying the second law of equilibrium about an axis of rotation through the fulcrum, and neglecting friction and the weight of the bar, we have

$$wl_o = F_i l_i$$

and, since $F_o = w$,

$$F_o l_o = F_i l_i$$

which holds for the three classes shown in Figure 12.2.   This equation may also be derived by considering that F_i moves downward through a small displacement s_i and that F_o moves upward through a corresponding displacement s_o. Equating the output and input work and observing that $l_i/l_o = s_i/s_o$ leads to the lever equation. The theoretical mechanical advantage of the lever is

$$M_t = F_o/F_i = l_i/l_o \qquad (12.6)$$

From Equation 12.6 we see that M_t is greater than, less than, or equal to 1, according as l_i is greater than, less than, or equal to l_o respectively.

A lever of the first class usually has its fulcrum situated such that l_i is greater than l_o. When the fulcrum is placed very close to the load the ratio l_i/l_o can be made effectively very large, the magnitude of the mechanical advantage being limited by how closely the fulcrum may be placed to the load consistent with the breaking strength of the lever end. This class of lever is exemplified by the crowbar, the scissors, and a screwdriver when it is used to pry up the lid of a paint can.

In the case of a lever of the second class (see Figure 12.2b) l_i is always greater than l_o and M_t is always greater than 1. (When $l_o = l_i$, we have the condition of lifting a load vertically without the use of a lever.) By utilizing this lever so that w is close to the fulcrum, a high mechanical advantage may be achieved. The wheelbarrow, and the claw hammer when used for pulling nails, belong to this class.

In the case of a lever of the third class (see Figure 12.2c) l_o is always greater than l_i and M_t is less than 1 except, again, in the trivial case that $l_o = l_i$ and no lever principle is employed. Here the force output is less than the force input and the lever is ordinarily employed for convenience. To this class belong such devices as a pair of fire tongs or tweezers. Also, the flexion of the forearm in lifting a weight held in the hand operates as a lever of the third class: the elbow joint is the pivot point, the load is in the palm of the hand, and the input force is supplied by the tension of the biceps applied at a point between weight and elbow and close to the latter.

12.4. The Wheel and Axle. The wheel and axle is a simple machine which consists of a wheel of radius R and a smaller wheel (the axle) of radius r fastened together and free to rotate about the common central axis; see Figure 12.3. The ropes around wheel and axle are wound in opposite directions so that an input force F_i raises a weight w. This machine is actually a lever of the first class. Let F_i be displaced downward through a distance s_i; then w and, hence, F_o move upward through a distance s_o. Neglecting friction and the weights of wheel, axle, and ropes we have:

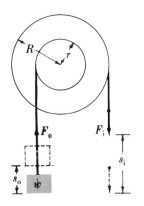

Figure 12.3. *The wheel and axle.*

$$F_o s_o = F_i s_i$$

When the wheel rotates through an angle θ, then $s_i = \theta R$ and $s_o = \theta r$. Therefore:

$$M_t = R/r \tag{12.7}$$

and the theoretical mechanical advantage is equal to the wheel radius divided by the smaller axle radius, so that $M_t > 1$.

12.5.   Pulleys.   A pulley consists of a wheel whose rim is grooved, and this sheave, as it is called, is mounted in a frame called a block so that it can rotate about an axle that passes through it and is attached to the block, as shown in Figure 12.4a.   One end of a cord or rope which passes over the

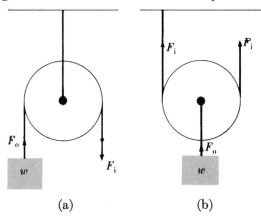

(a)   (b)

Figure 12.4. *Single pulleys: (a) fixed, (b) movable.*

groove is attached to a weight which may be raised by applying a force to the other end.   Hence this pulley is in reality an equal-arm lever of the first class.   A single pulley may be a *fixed pulley*, as in (a), or a *movable pulley*, as in (b).

For the case of a single fixed pulley, if F_i moves down a distance s_i, the weight and F_o move up a distance $s_o = s_i$.   Hence $F_o = F_i$ and $M_t = 1$. Although there is no multiplication in force it is more convenient to lift a weight by applying an equal force in a downward rather than an upward direction.

For the case of a single movable pulley, if F_i is displaced upward through a distance s_i both of the supporting cords are displaced upward by an amount $s_i/2$.   The weight w and F_o are displaced upward by an amount $s_o = s_i/2$. Hence $F_o s_i/2 = F_i s_i$ and $M_t = 2$.   Another way of obtaining the value of the ideal mechanical advantage is to observe that when the weight is on the point of moving upward it is in equilibrium.   Hence, applying $\sum F_y = 0$ to w,

Figure 12.4b, leads to $F_i + F_i = w = F_o$ or $2F_i = F_o$ and $M_t = 2$. To retain this mechanical advantage and have the convenience of exerting the input force downward, the free end of the movable pulley is passed over a fixed pulley, which simply changes the direction of F_i.

Fixed and movable pulleys are usually combined to form a system that has a high mechanical advantage. Such an arrangement is shown in Figure 12.5 which illustrates the use of a fixed and a movable block, each of

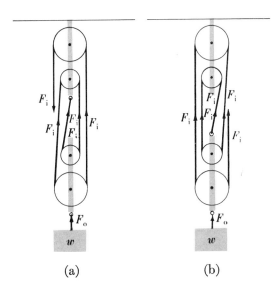

(a)   (b)

Figure 12.5.   *The block and tackle:* (a) M_t
$= 4$, (b) $M_t = 5$.

which contains two sheaves. In (a) the fixed end of the rope is attached to the fixed block while in (b) it is attached to the movable block. Such arrangements are called blocks and tackle and there may be two or more sheaves in each block. Some blocks contain equally sized pulleys mounted side by side, while others contain differently sized pulleys mounted one above the other as is shown in Figure 12.5. Assuming that friction is absent, that the weights of the components are negligible, and that all the ropes are vertical, the theoretical mechanical advantage is obtained by applying $\sum F_y = 0$. This yields, for (a), $4F_i = F_o$ or $M_t = 4$ and, for (b), $5F_i = F_o$ or $M_t = 5$. The same result is derivable from energy considerations, and the student should be certain that he can obtain the result also in this way. Notice that the mechanical advantage is increased by 1 when the fixed end of the rope is attached to the movable rather than the fixed block. When no assumption is made regarding the parallelism of the ropes a more exact value for M_t may be obtained by dealing with the vertical components of each tension force. It is useful to observe that in Figure 12.4a, where one rope supports the load, $M_t = 1$; in Figure 12.4b, where two parallel ropes support w, $M_t = 2$; in a block and tackle in which the fixed block contains two sheaves, the movable block contains a single sheave, and the fixed end of the rope is attached to the movable block, the number of parallel ropes supporting w is 3 and $M_t = 3$; in a block and tackle in which the fixed block contains a single sheave, the movable block contains two sheaves, and the fixed end of the rope is attached to the fixed block, the number of parallel ropes supporting w is 4 and $M_t = 4$; in Figure 12.5a the number of parallel ropes is 4 and $M_t = 4$; in Figure 12.5b the number of parallel ropes supporting w is 5 and $M_t = 5$. In other words, the theoretical mechanical advantage of any block and tackle is given by the number of parallel ropes supporting the load. Such a rule cannot, however, be extended to a system such as that shown in Figure 12.6a, which, the student should verify, has an ideal mechanical advantage of 8.

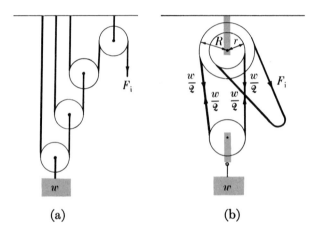

(a)   (b)

Figure 12.6. (a) *Fixed and movable pulley system with $M_t = 8$.* (b) *The differential pulley.*

A machine that is suitable for lifting very heavy weights is the differential pulley, which utilizes the principle of the wheel and axle and a movable pulley; it is shown in Figure 12.6b. The fixed block contains two rigidly attached sheaves of slightly different diameters and free to turn about an axis through their common center. A continuous chain passes over the pulleys. When an input force F_i is applied as indicated by the arrow, the weight w may be raised, the two chains supporting it each having a tension $w/2$. To obtain the expression for the ideal mechanical advantage, we again assume that friction is absent and the weights of all moving parts are negligible, and apply the second law of equilibrium for the upper pulleys, the smaller having a radius r and the larger a radius R. Expressing the torques about an axis through their common center we have

$$F_i R + \frac{wr}{2} = \frac{wR}{2}$$

Since $F_o = w$, this leads to

$$M_t = 2R/(R - r) \tag{12.8}$$

Since the difference $R - r$ usually is rather small, the mechanical advantage is large. To prevent slipping when heavy loads are raised the grooves of the sheaves are provided with toothlike projections over which the chain links fit.

12.6. The Inclined Plane. An inclined plane is used to lift a heavy load w vertically a distance h by applying a smaller input force F_i through a distance l along the incline, as shown in Figure 12.7. Neglecting friction, the

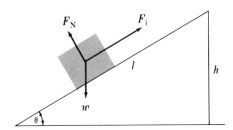

Figure 12.7. *The inclined plane.*

theoretical mechanical advantage is obtained by observing that the input work is $F_i l$ and the output work is $wh = F_o h$. The normal reaction F_N does no work since there is no displacement in the direction F_N. Hence

$$F_o h = F_i l$$

and
$$M_t = l/h = 1/\sin \theta \tag{12.9}$$

Equation 12.9 shows that the smaller the angle θ the greater the mechanical advantage, which is always greater than 1 since l is always greater than h. Notice again that the smaller force F_i acting through the larger distance l overcomes the larger force $F_o = w$ acting through the smaller distance h.

12.7. The Wedge. A wedge is an inclined plane which raises a heavy load w by driving it under the load with an input force F_i as shown in Figure 12.8. Thus, instead of pulling the load up an incline, as in Figure 12.7,

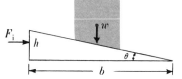

Figure 12.8. *The wedge.*

the inclined plane is pushed under the load. When the wedge has been forced in a distance b, the input work, neglecting friction, is $F_i b$ and w has been raised a height h, with a consequent output work $wh = F_o h$. Hence

$$F_o h = F_i b$$
and
$$M_t = b/h = 1/\tan \theta \qquad (12.10)$$

As with the inclined plane, the smaller the angle θ the larger the mechanical advantage. Wedges may be single or double inclined planes and are exemplified by such devices as the ax, the razor, the knife, the chisel, and the wood plane.

12.8. The Screw. A screw is a cylindrical rod around which there is a spiral groove or thread. The thread fits snugly into a hollow cylindrical block which is similarly threaded and into which the screw turns. The helical thread of the screw is in effect an inclined plane wrapped around a cylinder, the hypotenuse forming the spiral thread. The screw operates on the principle that its axial displacement is proportional to the angular twist. Hence, when the screw is turned through one revolution it advances axially by a fixed amount called the *pitch*, p, of the screw. The pitch of a screw is the distance between successive threads. See Figure 12.9.

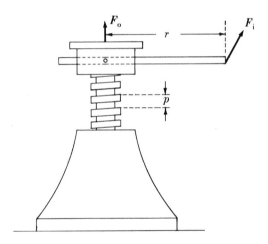

Figure 12.9. *The jackscrew.*

When very heavy bodies such as automobiles are to be raised, a type of screw known as the *jackscrew* is often used. As shown in Figure 12.9, the jackscrew is turned by exerting an input force F_i applied normal to the length of an adjustable rod which slides into the output end or cap of the jackscrew. The output force F_o is thus available for exertion against a load. Neglecting friction, the ideal mechanical advantage is obtained by considering one revolution of the lever arm of radius r. The input work is $F_i \times 2\pi r$ and the output work performed against a load equal to F_o is $F_o p$ where p is the screw pitch. Therefore:

$$2\pi r F_i = F_o p$$

and
$$M_t = 2\pi r/p \qquad (12.11)$$

A high mechanical advantage is achieved when the ratio r/p is large. The actual mechanical advantage of a jackscrew is much smaller than that indicated by Equation 12.11 since a large amount of friction is needed for the screw to be "self-locking" and not to slip or unwind when the applied force is removed. Self-locking jackscrews are usually equipped with square screw threads and their efficiency is less than 50%.

Problems

12.1. A machine lifts without acceleration a weight of 2.25 tons force a vertical distance of 3.00 feet when the applied force of 120 pounds force acts through a distance of 105 feet. Find (**a**) the output work, (**b**) the input work, (**c**) the theoretical mechanical advantage, (**d**) the actual mechanical advantage, and (**e**) the efficiency.

12.2. A man employs a machine to lift a load of 400 kgf through a vertical distance of 3.00 m. He applies a force of 225 nt through a distance of 80.0 m. Find (**a**) the output work, (**b**) the input work, (**c**) the theoretical mechanical advantage, (**d**) the actual mechanical advantage, and (**e**) the efficiency.

12.3. A screwdriver is used as a first-class lever to pry up the lid of a can. The end of the lever is inserted under the lip of the lid 0.500 cm, which marks the location of the fulcrum. The lid opens when a force of 10.0 pounds force is applied 20.0 cm from the inserted end. If the efficiency is 80.0%, what force was applied to the lid?

12.4. A wheelbarrow with contents weighs 250 pounds force. The perpendicular distances from the wheel axle to the lines of action of the load and the input force applied at the handles are respectively 9.00 inches and 45.0 inches. What force applied at the handles will lift the load?

12.5. A 10.0-foot pole is used as a second-class lever, the load being placed 2.00 feet from the fulcrum. If the pole is to be used as a first-class lever, how far must the fulcrum be placed from the load to give an ideal mechanical advantage that is three times that of the second-class lever?

12.6. A nutcracker is 5.00 inches long and a nut, requiring a force of 20.0 pounds force to be cracked, is inserted so that its center is 0.750 inches from the hinged ends. What force applied at the unhinged ends will crack the nut?

12.7. Derive the expression for the theoretical mechanical advantage of the wheel and axle by the principle of torques.

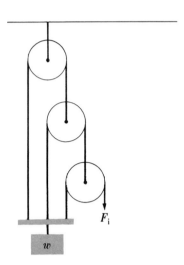

Figure 12.10.   *Problem 12.11.*

12.8.   The diameters of a wheel and axle are 45.0 cm and 5.00 cm respectively. When a force of 200 nt is applied by a rope wound around the rim of the wheel a load of 130 kgf is raised. Find (**a**) the theoretical mechanical advantage, (**b**) the actual mechanical advantage, and (**c**) the efficiency.

12.9.   Using energy principles, obtain the values for the theoretical mechanical advantages given in Figure 12.5.

12.10.   A workman raises himself on a platform attached to the movable block of a block and tackle. The upper block contains three sheaves and the lower block contains two sheaves. If the man and his equipment weigh 300 pounds force, what is the force he exerts? Consider ideal conditions and parallel ropes.

12.11.   (**a**) Find the theoretical mechanical advantage of the system shown in Figure 12.10.   (**b**) What would be the theoretical mechanical advantage of such a system if it contained n pulleys?

12.12.   Find the mechanical advantages of the systems shown in Figure 12.11.

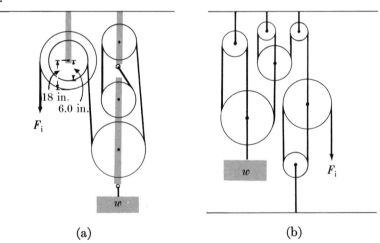

(a)   (b)

Figure 12.11.   *Problem 12.12.*

12.13.   What is the theoretical mechanical advantage of a block and tackle in which (**a**) the fixed block contains two sheaves and the movable block contains one sheave, (**b**) the fixed block contains one sheave and the movable block contains two sheaves?

12.14. A force of 1.00×10^3 pounds force is needed to pull a truck out of a ditch. You have available a pull of 275 pounds force and a block and tackle that contains two sheaves per block and has an efficiency of 75.0%. Show how you would attach the block and tackle between a nearby tree and the truck which can thus be extricated. How much force is exerted on the truck?

12.15. Derive the expression for the theoretical mechanical advantage of the differential pulley, using energy principles.

12.16. In a differential chain hoist the outer and inner pulleys have effective radii of 8.00 inches and 7.50 inches respectively. An applied force of 50.0 pounds force raises a load of 800 pounds force. Find (**a**) the theoretical mechanical advantage, (**b**) the actual mechanical advantage, and (**c**) the efficiency.

12.17. Using Figure 12.7 but including a force of friction, show that for the inclined plane the actual mechanical advantage is $1/(\mu \cos \theta + \sin \theta)$ and the efficiency is $1/(\mu \cot \theta + 1)$ where μ is the coefficient of friction.

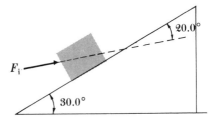

12.18. A body is pushed up a 30.0° inclined plane by the application of a horizontal force. What is the theoretical mechanical advantage?

12.19. If the coefficient of friction between body and plane in Problem 12.18 is 0.200, what are (**a**) the actual mechanical advantage and (**b**) the efficiency?

Figure 12.12. *Problem 12.20.*

12.20. Figure 12.12 shows a body being pushed up a 30.0° inclined plane by a force F_i making an angle of 20.0° with the plane. Taking the coefficient of friction as 0.100, find (**a**) the actual mechanical advantage and (**b**) the efficiency.

12.21. A 3.00×10^3 kgm cable car is pulled 1.00 km up a 20.0° incline in 20.0 minutes. The efficiency is 60.0%. Find (**a**) the theoretical mechanical advantage, (**b**) the actual mechanical advantage, and (**c**) the horsepower expended.

12.22. A wedge like that shown in Figure 12.8 has a 10.0° angle and is employed to lift a weight of 500 pounds force. If the overall efficiency is 40.0% how much driving force must be exerted?

12.23. A jackscrew, with a pitch of 0.250 inch, is turned by a force of 100 pounds force applied at right angles to a lever 1.50 feet long. The efficiency is 40.0%. Find (**a**) the theoretical mechanical advantage, (**b**) the actual mechanical advantage, and (**c**) the weight the jackscrew is capable of lifting.

12.24. A jackscrew is to be used for lifting a weight of 2.00 tons. It has a pitch of 0.200 inch, a 3.00-foot lever, and an efficiency of 35.0%. What minimum force must be applied perpendicular to the lever?

12.25. A screw jack with a pitch of 5.50 mm is used to lift a load of 600 nt. The length of the lever is 50.0 cm and the force applied normal to the lever is 5.00 nt. Find the efficiency of the device.

12.26. If the screw and lever in Problem 12.25 weigh 25.0 nt and the load is raised 0.400 m, what are (**a**) the work done against friction in raising the load, (**b**) the useful output work, and (**c**) the work done in raising the screw and lever?

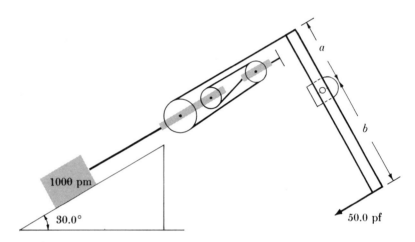

Figure 12.13.   *Problem 12.27.*

12.27. In Figure 12.13 the coefficient of friction between plane and block is 0.250. What must be the ratio b/a if a 50.0-pound force applied at the end of, and normal to, the lever will cause the block to be in impending motion upward? The overall efficiency of the pulley and lever systems is 60.0%. Consider the pulley ropes parallel.

Impulse and Momentum

L ET US FOR A MOMENT REVIEW the methods we have developed and employed thus far in our study of dynamics. First, we used the force-inertia method in which we applied Newton's second law of motion directly in the form $\sum F = ma$ for translation and $\sum L = I\alpha$ for rotation. In this method the analysis of a problem is made by dealing directly with the forces or torques acting on a body and relating their actions to the resulting linear or angular accelerations. We then derived from Newton's second law the work-energy theorem or principle and showed how the principle of conservation of energy may be employed in solving problems often in a simpler, more direct, and more basic fashion. In the method of energy we deal with the work done by the applied forces and relate this to the displacement and velocity of a body. In this chapter we shall see that there is still a third way in which Newton's second law may be expressed, a way which is different in form and leads to two new and useful concepts, viz., *impulse* and *momentum*, These afford the impulse-momentum method for the solution of problems. In the method the forces acting on a body are related to the velocity and time. Although some problems may be solved just as readily with any one of the three methods, the student is by now aware of the fact that there are certain problems that are best handled by applying Newton's second law directly and others by applying the work-energy method, and now in this chapter we shall learn another class of problems that are most easily solved by applying the impulse-momentum principle. We shall see that in problems of impact and collision, where there is an applied force that acts for a very short time interval, it is essential to employ the concepts of impulse and momentum to obtain a solution. The principles of impulse and momentum are also very effective for problems that deal with fluids.

In Sections 4.3 and 10.8 we briefly introduced the meanings of linear momentum and angular momentum respectively. We shall now see how the concept of momentum is related to the concept of impulse and how, as a consequence of the laws of mechanics, there operates, along with the principle of conservation of energy, an equally significant principle known as the *principle of conservation of momentum*. These two principles, conservation of energy and conservation of momentum, are the most significant principles in physics and engineering, and are basic to a thorough understanding of dynamical systems.

13.1.   Linear Impulse and Linear Momentum.   Let us consider the nature or character of the force that exists when a bat strikes a baseball, when a golf ball is struck by a golf club, when a football is kicked, or when a rifle is fired.   That the force which gives rise to subsequent motion is very large is evident from the magnitudes of the accelerations imparted to each of the projectiles.   This force, present during the time of contact of bat (golf club or foot) and ball, during the time the gas, formed by the ignited rifle powder, expands, is not constant but varies in a rather complicated way.   In general, however, the force may be characterized as follows: (*1*) it starts with a zero value, rises rapidly to a large maximum value, and dies away swiftly to zero, and (*2*) it acts for only a very short time interval.   These characteristics are represented in a general fashion by the graph shown in Figure 13.1. A force that has this kind of variation with time is called an *impulsive force*. At the initial instant t_1 the force F commences, rising to a maximum value, and then decreases to zero at a later time t_2.   The time interval $\Delta t = t_2 - t_1$ is so short that the detailed variation of the force is in general undeterminable. With the aid of high-speed photographs it is revealed that the bodies in impact are distorted while in contact.   Although it is practically impossible to determine the magnitude of the impulsive force F or the time interval Δt, the product $F_{av}\Delta t$ may be readily evaluated, F_{av} being the average value of the impulsive force during the time interval.   This is accomplished by employing the concept of momentum and using Newton's second law.   We show this again in the parallel noncalculus and calculus fashion.

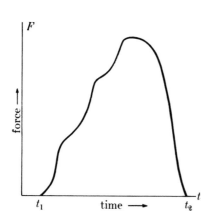

Figure 13.1. *The impulsive force.*

From Newton's second law:

$$F_{av} = ma_{av} = m\,\Delta v/\Delta t \quad (13.1a)$$

where the average acceleration a_{av} is given by the change in velocity $\Delta v = v_2 - v_1$ per time interval Δt.   Therefore

$$F_{av}\,\Delta t = mv_2 - mv_1 \quad (13.1b)$$

where v_1 and v_2 are the velocities of the mass at the instants t_1 and t_2 respectively. The left-hand side of Equation 13.1b, $F_{av}\Delta t$, is called the *linear impulse* which invariably implies a very short time interval.   The quantities mv_1 and mv_2 are the linear momenta corresponding

From Newton's second law:

$$F = m\,dv/dt \quad \text{or} \quad F\,dt = m\,dv$$

and integrating between the time limits t_1 and t_2 at which the corresponding velocities of the mass are v_1 and v_2 we have

$$\int_{t_1}^{t_2} F\,dt = mv_2 - mv_1 \quad (13.1A)$$

The integral in Equation 13.1A is called the *linear impulse*, with which there is usually associated a short time interval, as in a collision.   The quantities mv_1 and mv_2 are the linear momenta to the times t_1 and t_2 respectively. Equation 13.1b expresses the *linear impulse-momentum theorem* which states that the *linear impulse of a force in a given direction is equal to the change of linear momentum, in the same direction, of the body acted on by the force.* Since the average value of the force is given by the area under the curve shown in Figure 13.1, divided by the base line Δt, we have

$$F_{av} \, \Delta t = \frac{\text{area under } F\text{-}t \text{ curve}}{\Delta t} \, \Delta t$$

and we see that the linear impulse is given by the area under the F-t curve. In the special case in which the force entering into the expression for impulse is a constant, the linear impulse is given by this constant force times the time interval. In collision and impact processes the observed data yield information on change in momentum and so determine the impulse. From this, F_{av} may be obtained if the value of Δt is known.

at the corresponding times t_1 and t_2. Expression 13.1A is an expression of the *linear impulse-momentum theorem* which states that the *resultant linear impulse of a force in a given direction is equal to the change of linear momentum, in the same direction, of the body on which this force acts.* Notice that the impulse is the area under the force-time curve of Figure 13.1. Furthermore, since the area under the curve divided by the base line $\Delta t = t_2 - t_1$ gives the average ordinate or, in this case, the average force, we have

$$\frac{\int_{t_1}^{t_2} F \, dt}{\Delta t} \, \Delta t = mv_2 - mv_1$$

or $\qquad F_{av} \, \Delta t = mv_2 - mv_1 \qquad (13.1B)$

Equation 13.1B shows that the linear impulse, expressed as the average force times the time interval, is equal to the change in linear momentum. If the force function shown in Figure 13.1 is known, the integration represented by $\int F \, dt$ may be performed. However, F as a function of t ordinarily is not known, and only the average value of the force as given by Equation 13.1B may be found. In the special case in which F is constant the area or impulse is $F \, \Delta t$.

Both linear momentum and linear impulse are vectors, the momentum vector having the direction of the velocity vector and the impulse vector having the direction of the vector force. The units of linear momentum were given in Section 4.3. The units of linear impulse are the dyne-second (dyne·sec) in the cgs system, the newton-second (nt·sec) in the mks system, and the pound-force–second (pf·sec) in the English gravitational system. The student should see that these are equivalent respectively to the gram-mass–centimeter per second, the kilogram-mass–meter per second, and the slug-foot per second (gm·cm/sec, kgm·m/sec, slug·ft/sec) used for linear momentum.

In the development above we considered that only the magnitude of the impulsive force was varying, as shown by Figure 13.1. In general, the direction of the impulsive force may also vary and when it does F_{av}, which enters into the definition of linear impulse, is obtained by finding the time average of the three components of the impulsive force.

13.2. Principle of Conservation of Linear Momentum. There are three fundamental physical laws which hold for a dynamical system.

One of these we have already met, the principle of conservation of energy. The other two are concerned with momentum, viz., the principle of conservation of linear momentum and the principle of conservation of angular momentum. We shall here take up the first, and the second will be taken up in Section 13.6.

Although the principle of conservation of linear momentum is perfectly general and holds for a system containing any number of particles, we shall derive the principle by considering a system composed of two particles that collide and are thus in contact for a period of time Δt. Let the two particles of masses m_1 and m_2 and respective velocities u_1 and u_2 collide, as shown in Figure 13.2. Consider that the particles experience a *direct central impact*,

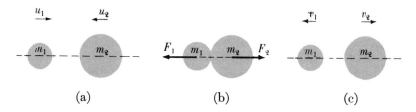

(a)   (b)   (c)

Figure 13.2. *Conservation of linear momentum:* (a) *before impact,* (b) *during impact,* (c) *after impact.*

i.e., that the centers of mass of the particles approach one another along their common line of motion and the force of impact is along the line that joins the centers of mass. We shall assume that no outside force acts on either of the particles so that the only forces that act on the two-body system are those which either body exerts on the other during impact. Figure 13.2a shows the system just before impact; (b) shows the system in the process of interaction during impact, where F_1 is the impulsive force exerted by m_2 on m_1 and F_2 is the impulsive force exerted by m_1 on m_2. Since F_1 and F_2 constitute an action-reaction pair, they are at every instant equal in magnitude and oppositely directed. Hence the variations of both F_1 and F_2 are like those depicted in Figure 13.1. Figure 13.2c shows the system at the instant after impact, the particles m_1 and m_2 receding with the respective velocities v_1 and v_2.

By Newton's third law, at each instant we have

$$F_1 = -F_2$$

Therefore, the time average of F_1 is the negative of the time average of F_2. Hence

$$\text{impulse of } F_1 = -\text{impulse of } F_2$$

or

$$m_1v_1 - m_1u_1 = -(m_2v_2 - m_2u_2)$$

Rearranging the terms we obtain

$$m_1u_1 + m_2u_2 = m_1v_1 + m_2v_2 \tag{13.2}$$

The left side of Equation 13.2 is the total linear momentum of the system before collision and the right side is the total linear momentum of the system after collision. We have therefore arrived at the very significant result, known as the *principle of conservation of linear momentum*, that the *total linear momentum of the system remains unchanged*. Notice that the principle is true only when there is no net external force acting on the system and the only forces operating are the two *internal* impulsive forces which, being equal and opposite at every instant, give rise to equal and opposite changes in linear momentum. If one particle gains an amount of linear momentum because of interaction, the other particle loses the same amount of linear momentum, and the total linear momentum remains unaltered. The only way in which the total linear momentum of a system can change is to have it acted upon by an unbalanced external force. When the system is completely isolated its total linear momentum remains constant.

In applying Equation 13.2 to problems several things should be realized and kept in mind:

(*1*) Momentum is a vector, so that each momentum value that enters into Equation 13.2 carries along with it a sign consistent with the convention of positive and negative directions. For instance, the signs of the momenta in Figure 13.2 would be plus for m_1u_1, minus for m_2u_2, minus for m_1v_1, and plus for m_2v_2. If a velocity is unknown, the corresponding momentum may be assumed to be in an arbitrary direction. If the solution for this velocity is positive, the assumed direction is correct, but if negative the indication is that the corresponding momentum vector is in a direction opposite to that arbitrarily assumed. The magnitude of the velocity will in each case come out to the correct value.

(*2*) The conservation of linear momentum, as exemplified by Equation 13.2, holds true no matter what the direction. Therefore, if the momentum vectors are not all parallel, the x components, the y components, and the z components of momenta are separately conserved.

(*3*) Although we considered two bodies in actual contact they may interact without being in actual physical contact. The impulsive forces may be transmitted through some medium such as a spring acting between the bodies, or the force may be electric or magnetic in nature.

(*4*) Often, when two bodies collide and are in contact for a very short time, it may be assumed that certain external forces present have a negligible effect on the momenta of the interacting bodies during the impact period. For example, when a block resting on rough ground is struck by a rapidly moving projectile such as a bullet it may be true that the impulse of the friction between block and ground during the time of impact is small in comparison with the large linear momenta of block and bullet. Where it is admissible to assume that the forces of interaction are much greater than the external forces, the principle of conservation of momentum may be applied to obtain a useful approximate solution.

(*5*) Any combination of mass and velocity units may be employed in the equation expressing conservation of linear momentum, provided the same combination of units is used for each momentum vector.

The worked examples at the end of this chapter illustrate the significant facts covered in the above items.

13.3. Elastic and Inelastic Collisions.   Two bodies may collide and give rise to an impulsive force in several ways.   When the centers of mass of the bodies approach each other along their common line of motion we have what is called *direct impact*. When the colliding bodies do not move on the common line of motion the situation is termed *oblique impact*.   When the force of impact is along the line that joins the centers of mass of the bodies the impact is called *central;* when this is not the case the impact is termed *eccentric*.   Our discussions will be confined to *direct central impact*, as illustrated by Figure 13.2.   The method employed in the solution of a problem involving oblique impact is illustrated by the worked Example 13.7.

The time of impact is divided into two intervals corresponding to the two mechanical processes that are present.   First, there is the short period of time known as the *period of deformation*.   This period commences at the instant the bodies come in contact, when they begin to compress or deform one another at the surfaces of contact.   During this compression period the force between the surfaces increases and reaches its largest value at the instant the deformation ceases, at which instant the centers of mass of the bodies are moving with the same speed.   The second succeeding time interval is known as the *period of restitution*, which is present for bodies that are partially or entirely elastic.   During this period the mass centers begin separating and the force between the surfaces decreases, reaching a value zero at the instant of separation, when the deformed surfaces have returned to their initial form.

In general, when two or more bodies collide, linear momentum is always conserved; however, the total kinetic energy before impact may or may not be equal to the total kinetic energy after impact, depending on the kind of collision.   If the collision is such that kinetic energy is conserved, the collision is called *perfectly elastic*.   Here the bodies separate after impact with velocities such that the kinetic energy remains constant.   If the collision is of the type in which the bodies do not separate after impact but cling together, the collision is termed *perfectly inelastic*.   If the collision is such that the bodies separate after collision but the kinetic energy is not conserved because some of the initial kinetic energy goes into the dissipative forms of heat, sound, and permanent displacement of surface layers, the collision is termed *inelastic*. We shall now illustrate in greater detail each of these three kinds of collision between two bodies experiencing direct central impact.

Perfectly Elastic Collision.   Although a perfectly elastic collision is an idealized interaction never exactly realized between ordinary laboratory bodies, it is known to occur between submicroscopic particles such as electrons, atoms, and molecules.   If we consider that the impact shown in Figure 13.2

is perfectly elastic, then we have, by the principle of conservation of energy,

$$\tfrac{1}{2}m_1u_1^2 + \tfrac{1}{2}m_2u_2^2 = \tfrac{1}{2}m_1v_1^2 + \tfrac{1}{2}m_2v_2^2 \tag{13.3}$$

or

$$m_1(u_1 - v_1)(u_1 + v_1) = m_2(v_2 - u_2)(v_2 + u_2)$$

Dividing this equation by Equation 13.2, which may be put in the form $m_1(u_1 - v_1) = m_2(v_2 - u_2)$, we have

$$u_1 + v_1 = u_2 + v_2$$

or

$$u_1 - u_2 = -(v_1 - v_2) \tag{13.4}$$

which shows that in a perfectly elastic collision the relative velocity before impact, $u_1 - u_2$, and the relative velocity after impact, $v_1 - v_2$, are equal in magnitude but reversed in direction. Eliminating v_2 between Equations 13.4 and 13.2 leads to

$$v_1 = \frac{(m_1 - m_2)u_1 + 2m_2u_2}{m_1 + m_2} \tag{13.5}$$

and eliminating v_1 between Equations 13.4 and 13.2 yields

$$v_2 = \frac{(m_2 - m_1)u_2 + 2m_1u_1}{m_1 + m_2} \tag{13.6}$$

Equations 13.5 and 13.6 give the velocities of the bodies after impact in terms of the velocities of the bodies before impact and their masses. It is of interest now to examine these two equations for some special and significant cases.

When $m_1 = m_2$ we have $v_1 = u_2$ and $v_2 = u_1$, so that in direct central impact between two bodies of equal mass the bodies interchange velocities after impact. In particular, if one of the bodies is originally at rest, say $u_2 = 0$, then after impact $v_1 = 0$ and $v_2 = u_1$.

As another example, suppose $m_1 \neq m_2$ and $u_2 = 0$; then Equations 13.5 and 13.6 yield the values

$$v_1 = \frac{m_1 - m_2}{m_1 + m_2}u_1 \quad \text{and} \quad v_2 = \frac{2m_1}{m_1 + m_2}u_1$$

In particular, when m_2 is very large compared with m_1, so that m_1/m_2 is vanishingly small, $v_1 = -u_1$ and $v_2 \doteq 0$. Hence, the moving body rebounds with the same speed with which it strikes the stationary body and its momentum is reversed.

Collisions between ivory billiard balls and bronze spheres, although not perfectly elastic, are very nearly so.

Perfectly Inelastic Collision. In collisions of this kind at least one of the colliding bodies suffers a deformation. Collisions between bodies of wet clay or putty, sticking together after impact, fall in this class. If the two bodies in Figure 13.2 do not separate after impact but, instead, move as a unit with the common velocity v, then the conservation of momentum, Equation 13.2, becomes $m_1u_1 + m_2u_2 = (m_1 + m_2)v$. The collision between a bullet and a block of wood in which the bullet becomes embedded is an example of perfectly inelastic impact. Let us examine this example in some detail.

Figure 13.3 shows a heavy block of wood of mass M, initially at rest, in position to receive a rifle bullet having a mass m and a velocity u. The block of wood is supported by four cords (only the front two are shown) so that it can swing in a vertical plane without rotating. Such an arrangement is called a *ballistic pendulum*, which is employed to measure the velocity of the

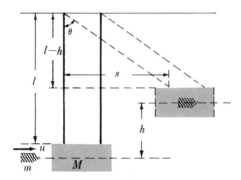

Figure 13.3. *The ballistic pendulum.*

bullet. The bullet is fired horizontally and becomes embedded in the block of wood. After the bullet is brought to rest inside the block, both block and bullet move after impact with the common velocity v. It is assumed that the bullet is brought to rest so quickly that the block M does not move very much during this time and thus acquires its velocity v before having moved any significant distance from its rest position. The conservation of linear momentum applied to bullet and block gives the equation

$$mu = (m + M)v \qquad (13.7)$$

The block and bullet, starting out with a velocity v at the lowest position, swing until the center of gravity of the system has been raised vertically a distance h, as shown. By the conservation of energy the kinetic energy at the bottom is equal to the potential energy at the top of the swing, and we have

$$\tfrac{1}{2}(m + M)v^2 = (m + M)gh$$

or

$$v^2 = 2gh \qquad (13.8)$$

Eliminating v between Equations 13.7 and 13.8 leads to

$$u = \frac{M + m}{m}\sqrt{2gh} \qquad (13.9)$$

Since m, M, and h are measurable, u becomes determinable. Usually h is small, and greater accuracy is afforded if either the angle θ or the horizontal displacement s (Figure 13.3) is measured and h is expressed in terms of either of these quantities. It can easily be shown (see Problem 13.25) that u is given by:

$$u = \frac{2(M + m)}{m} \sqrt{gl} \sin \frac{\theta}{2} \qquad (13.10)$$

where l is the length of cord and, if h is small compared with s, then

$$u = \frac{(M + m)s}{m} \sqrt{g/l} \qquad (13.11)$$

Ordinarily m is small compared with M; then m appearing in the numerator of Equations 13.9, 13.10, and 13.11 may be neglected.

Inelastic Collision: Coefficient of Restitution. Outside the realm of perfectly elastic collisions between certain ultramicroscopic particles, all other collisions in which the bodies separate after impact are called inelastic. For these Newton observed that the relative velocity after impact is proportional to the relative velocity before impact. The constant of proportionality is called the *coefficient of restitution, e,* which is defined* by the expression

$$e = -(v_1 - v_2)/(u_1 - u_2) \qquad (13.12)$$

where u_1 and u_2 are the velocities of the two bodies before impact and v_1 and v_2 are the velocities after impact, as shown in Figure 13.2. The negative sign has the same significance as in Equation 13.4, for perfect elasticity. Since $v_1 - v_2$ is opposite in direction to $u_1 - u_2$, e is a positive number. The coefficient of restitution indicates the degree to which two bodies in impact approach perfect elasticity or perfect inelasticity, and it may have any value between 0 and 1.† When $e = 1$, Equation 13.12 becomes Equation 13.4 and we have a perfectly elastic collision, the kinetic energy being conserved. When $e = 0$, $v_1 = -v_2$ and we have the case of a perfectly inelastic collision in which there is no conservation of kinetic energy, such as the ballistic pendulum and the bullet stopped inside the wood block. For all other values of e the combination of Equation 13.12 and Equation 13.2 is sufficient to determine v_1 and v_2 if u_1 and u_2 are known. The coefficient of restitution is high for such materials as glass and steel, while it is low for lead and other less elastic materials. Experiment shows that e depends not only on the elastic properties of the colliding bodies but also on their relative velocity of approach, on their shapes, and their sizes, on their masses, and on the density of the medium in which the collision takes place. For instance, when the approach velocity of the colliding bodies is high enough to produce permanent deformation, e is small, but when the approach velocity is low and there

---

* For oblique impact, the velocities in Equation 13.12 are *normal* velocities, i.e., the components of the velocities along the normal common to the surfaces at the point of contact.

† The range of e may be considered as extended to infinity (∞) if inelastic collisions of the second kind are included (see the comprehensive treatment by R. H. Bacon, *American Journal of Physics,* 8, 154, 1940). In the inelastic collisions of the first kind, discussed above, the translational kinetic energy is greater before than after impact. In collisions of the second kind, the translational kinetic energy is greater after than before impact, some other form of energy being transformed into translational kinetic energy. In inelastic collisions of the second kind, $e > 1$; examples are the firing of a gun, radioactive disintegration, and nuclear conversion of mass to kinetic energy. Although these are not collisions in the ordinary sense they may be considered as limiting cases of collisions.

is a rapid return to the configuration of the bodies before impact e approaches unity.

13.4.   Jet and Rocket Propulsion.   When a rifle is held against the shoulder and a bullet is fired the bullet is given a large forward linear momentum and the rifle recoils against the shoulder with an equal and opposite momentum in accordance with the conservation of linear momentum.   In the same way the principle of impulse and momentum is employed in the operation of a self-propelled projectile such as the jet or rocket.

In jet propulsion, air is admitted in the forward part of the plane or projectile.   It is then compressed by a compressor, mixed with fuel, and ignited. The products of combustion, at high temperature and pressure, are then discharged at a very high velocity through some kind of jet nozzle at the rear. In keeping with the principle of the conservation of linear momentum, the fast-moving gas continuously ejected from the jet produces a forward thrust on the projectile.   The V-1 buzz bombs used by the Germans in World War II and the jet aircraft illustrate the application of the jet principle.

While a jet-propelled missile requires the intake of large quantities of air for its successful operation, the rocket carries its own oxygen supply to support combustion.   The principle of propulsion, however, is the same, in that the gases in the hot combustion chamber, in issuing from the rear of the missile, cause a forward reaction thrust on the rocket.   The rocket therefore does not need the atmosphere for propulsion and, in fact, performs better in the absence of an atmosphere because there is no air friction.   Rockets are therefore most suitable for stratosphere flight and interplanetary travel. Powerful present-day rockets are able to boost massive earth-orbiting satellites, lunar spacecraft, and interplanetary probes (see Section 16.7).

13.5.   Angular Impulse and Angular Momentum.   In Section 10.8 we introduced the quantity angular momentum.   For a rigid body the angular momentum is given by $I\omega$ where I is the moment of inertia and ω the angular velocity, both about some specified axis.   This is a vector quantity whose direction coincides with the direction of the vector ω, as described in Section 8.2.   We have previously pointed out the analogy between linear and angular quantities and it is again of value to call to mind that when the mass and linear velocity in linear momentum are replaced respectively by the moment of inertia and angular velocity one obtains the analogous quantity angular momentum.

Using angular quantities we can now parallel our detailed development given in Section 13.1 for linear impulse and linear momentum and arrive at the relationship for the analogous angular quantities, angular impulse and angular momentum.   We shall not go through this derivation but shall merely state the analogous result with the hope that the interested student will think through the individual steps given in Section 13.1 as applied to the corresponding angular quantities. It should then become clear, from Newton's second law for rotation, that for a rigid body

$$L_{av} \Delta t = I\omega_2 - I\omega_1 \qquad (13.13)$$

where L_{av} is the average value of the impulsive torque acting during the time interval Δt, I is the moment of inertia of the body, and ω_1 and ω_2 are the angular velocities at two corresponding instants of time t_1 and t_2 such that $t_2 - t_1 = \Delta t$, all considered with respect to some axis of rotation. An *impulsive torque* has a zero-maximum-zero variation with time similar to that shown in Figure 13.1 for the impulsive force. The left-hand side of Equation 13.13, $L_{av} \Delta t$, is called the *angular impulse;* it has the geometric significance of being equal to the area under the impulsive torque-time curve, and the right-hand side represents the change in angular momentum. Equation 13.13 expresses the *angular impulse-momentum theorem* which states that *the angular impulse of a torque, acting upon a body about a given axis, is equal to the change of angular momentum about the same axis.*

The units of angular impulse are the centimeter-dyne-second (cm·dyne·sec) in the cgs system, the meter-newton-second (m·nt·sec) in the mks system, and the pound-force–foot–second (pf·ft·sec) in the English gravitational system. The respectively equivalent units used to express the angular momentum are the gram-mass–square-centimeter per second (gm·cm²/sec), the kilogram-mass–square-meter per second (kgm·m²/sec), and the slug–square-foot per second (slug·ft²/sec).

13.6. Principle of Conservation of Angular Momentum. From Equation 13.13 we see that when $L_{av} \Delta t = 0$ or when there is no unbalanced angular impulse there is no change in the angular momentum: $I\omega_2 = I\omega_1$ or, in general,

$$I\omega = \text{constant} \qquad (13.14)$$

Equation 13.14 expresses the *principle of conservation of angular momentum* which states that *if there is no external unbalanced torque acting, the angular momentum of a body which is rotating about a fixed axis is constant.* In order to preserve the constant relationship expressed by Equation 13.14 we see that if, while a body is rotating, the distribution of mass about the axis of rotation changes so that I changes, then ω must change in inverse proportion. This is strikingly demonstrated by a person's standing at the center of a relatively frictionless turntable. When the person is given an angular velocity about a vertical axis he can, to a certain extent, control his speed of rotation. When he extends his arms outward the moment of inertia I of the rotating system is thus increased and the angular velocity decreases by just an amount that will keep $I\omega$ constant. On the other hand, if the person pulls his arms in, close to his body, I decreases and ω increases.

Pirouetting toe dancers, divers, skaters, and acrobats utilize this means of changing their angular velocities of rotation. The principle of conservation of angular momentum also governs the action of a flywheel in maintaining a constant speed of rotation in a motor. Because of the large moment of inertia of a flywheel its change in angular momentum is small when the motor speed changes. Hence when the motor slows an amount, the flywheel's resistance to change in angular momentum has the effect of supplying a torque that tends to maintain the speed.

Like the principle of conservation of linear momentum, the total angular momentum of an isolated system remains constant. If a system composed of two bodies has initially zero angular momentum and one of the bodies is given an angular momentum by the action of the other body, the latter must acquire an equal and opposite angular momentum.

As we have already stated—and we again emphasize—the principles of conservation of energy, conservation of linear momentum, and conservation of angular momentum are most fundamental to the study of dynamics. The principle of conservation of angular momentum has a significant application in gyroscopic motion, which we treat in Sections 13.8 and 13.9.

13.7. Center of Percussion. The student is perhaps familiar with the fact that when a baseball bat strikes a ball the hands holding the bat will

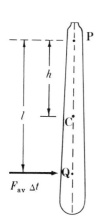

experience a "sting" except when the bat is struck at one specific point. This point is called the *center of percussion* and its position on the bat relative to the location of the hands may be determined by applying the concepts of impulse and momentum. In Figure 13.4 the point P, distant h above the center of mass, C, represents the position of the hand. The linear impulse $F_{av} \Delta t$, due to the impact of ball and bat, occurs at Q a distance l below P. If no sting is to be felt at P, no momentum must be transferred to that point and the bat will rotate about P as a pivot. Hence, by the linear impulse-momentum theorem

$$F_{av} \Delta t = mv = mh\omega$$

Figure 13.4.
Center of percussion.

where m is the mass of the bat, v is the velocity of the center of mass of the bat, and ω is the angular velocity about an axis through P. The angular impulse is $F_{av} l \Delta t$ and the angular impulse-momentum theorem yields

$$F_{av} l \Delta t = I\omega$$

where I is the moment of inertia of the bat about an axis through P. Combining the two equations leads to the result

$$l = I/mh = k^2/h \qquad (13.15)$$

where k is the radius of gyration about an axis through the pivot point.

Equation 13.15 locates the position of the center of percussion, Q, below the axis of rotation, P, which is momentarily at rest and is also known as the *center of oscillation*. If the ball strikes above or below Q, then P receives a horizontal translational motion which is felt as a sting.

13.8. Gyroscopes and Gyroscopic Principles. Every rotating or spinning body is in effect a *gyroscope*, but in more descriptive terms a gyroscope may be defined as a rotating body which is mounted in such a way as to be free to rotate about any one of three orthogonal axes. To understand and fully appreciate gyroscopic motion we must first recall, and keep in mind, the scheme for vectorially representing angular quantities such as angular velocity, angular momentum, angular impulse, and torque. The vector representing each of these quantities is drawn in the manner indicated in Figure 8.3. For instance, the angular momentum is represented by an arrow which is drawn along the axis of rotation. The length of the arrow is scaled to represent the magnitude of the angular momentum and the direction of the arrow is that in which the rotation would advance a right-handed screw. The same convention applies to torque: the vector arrow is drawn along the axis about which the torque tends to produce rotation.

First consider Figure 13.5, which shows a heavy wheel that is mounted with bearings on a stationary shaft AB and is rotating with an angular velocity ω. The wheel has an angular momentum $I\omega$ represented by the indicated arrow. If a force-couple is now applied to the wheel so as merely to increase or decrease the angular velocity, only the magnitude of the angular momentum changes, its direc-

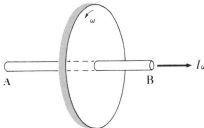

Figure 13.5.

tion remaining along the spin axis AB. On the other hand, suppose the couple is applied to the shaft AB so that it tends to change the direction of the rotation axis. The wheel then exhibits *angular inertia* which is a property of the rotating wheel that resists any tendency to change the direction of its axis of rotation. The system then performs a resultant gyroscopic motion, the nature of which we shall now describe.

Consider the simple gyroscope shown in Figure 13.6a. It is composed of a massive wheel, bearing-mounted in a rigid frame C, so that it can be given a high angular velocity ω about the axis AB. Let the gyroscope be placed at the tip A of the vertical support S with the end B temporarily supported so that the axis AB is horizontal. At the instant that the support at B is removed the gyroscope is free to turn about three mutually perpendicular axes: the wheel may turn about the horizontal axis AB, the wheel and frame may turn about the vertical axis SA of the support S, and the wheel and frame may turn about an axis AD perpendicular to these two. If the wheel is not turning and end B is free, the only forces acting on the gyroscope are its weight mg and the reaction of the support acting upward at A (not shown). The gravitational torque mgl about the axis AD is unbalanced and the gyroscope falls off the support. Now let us consider what happens when the wheel is given a large angular velocity ω about the axis AB. With the end B free we now have two simultaneous effects acting on the gyroscope: owing to the rotation of the wheel the system possesses an angular momentum $I\omega$ where I is the moment of inertia of the wheel about the axis AB, and owing to the action of the constant gravitational torque $L = mgl$ there is superimposed an angular momentum about the axis AD. We can obtain the resultant effect by considering the action of spin and external torque in a short time interval Δt and by depicting the corresponding vectors in the horizontal plane shown in Figure 13.6b in which the letters S, A, D, and B correspond

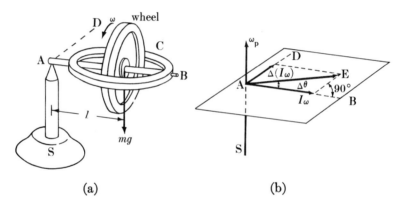

(a)   (b)

Figure 13.6. *Gyroscopic precession.*

exactly to those in Figure 13.6a. Starting at the instant represented by Figure 13.6a, the angular momentum due to the spinning wheel is represented in Figure 13.6b by the vector $I\omega$ pointing to the right along the axle direction AB. In the short time interval Δt the action of the gravitational torque produces an angular impulse $L\,\Delta t$ and, by the angular impulse-momentum theorem, this causes a change in angular momentum, $\Delta(I\omega)$. The vector representing this change in angular momentum is shown in Figure 13.6b as acting in the direction AD. Both $I\omega$ and $\Delta(I\omega)$ act in the same horizontal plane and their resultant angular momentum is the vector AE making a small angle $\Delta\theta$ with the direction that AB had at the beginning of the time interval Δt. Therefore, the gyroscope, instead of falling, has rotated in a horizontal plane about the vertical axis SA. We see that, since the gravitational torque acts continuously, the gyroscope will continuously rotate in a horizontal plane. This kind of motion illustrates the general principle of gyroscopic motion which is stated as follows: *When a body is rotating about an axis* (AB in Figure 13.6) *and an external unbalanced torque simultaneously tends to rotate the spinning body about an axis* (axis AD) *perpendicular to the spinning axis, the resultant motion of the body is a rotation about an axis* (axis SA) *which is perpendicular to the other two axes.* This resultant rotation, which shifts the axis of spin of the rotating body, is called *precession*, and the vertical axis about which the precession takes place is called the *axis of precession*.

Let us now see what quantitative relationships are obtainable for precessional motion. From the vector diagram in Figure 13.6b we have

$$\tan (\Delta\theta) = \Delta(I\omega)/I\omega = L \,\Delta t/I\omega$$

and, since successive positions of the resultant angular momentum vector AE are to be considered for infinitesimally small angles $\Delta\theta$, we may replace $\tan (\Delta\theta)$ by $\Delta\theta$ and obtain

$$\Delta\theta/\Delta t = L/I\omega$$

As it naturally occurs, precession proceeds smoothly and continuously rather than in discrete steps so that we must consider the left-hand member of the last expression as being the ratio of $\Delta\theta$ to Δt when Δt approaches zero. Hence, since $\lim_{\Delta t \to 0} \Delta\theta/\Delta t = \omega_p$ where ω_p is the angular velocity of precession, we have:

$$\omega_p = L/I\omega = mgl/I\omega \qquad (13.16)$$

or

$$L = I\omega\omega_p \qquad (13.17)$$

The vector ω_p is shown in Figure 13.6b as pointing up along the axis SA, and we see from Equation 13.16 that when the torque L is constant the angular velocity of precession is uniform. The equation also shows that ω_p varies directly as the torque and inversely with the angular momentum of the spinning body. When the angular velocity of spin is large the angular velocity of precession is small. Equation 13.17 makes it possible to calculate the torque needed to maintain a precessional velocity ω_p for a given angular spin momentum $I\omega$.

Since no external torques act about the axis of spin AB in Figure 13.6 it is clear that the magnitude of the resultant angular momentum AE must remain constant and the external torque has the effect of changing only the direction of the spin angular momentum $I\omega$. Hence the vector diagram of Figure 13.6b must be interpreted with caution, since the diagram is only an approximate static representation of a dynamic situation. The torque vector $\Delta(I\omega)$ at every instant is perpendicular to the spin angular momentum vector $I\omega$. As soon as the vector $I\omega$ precesses through an infinitesimal angle, the torque vector is again perpendicular to it and the terminating point of the spin angular momentum vector describes a horizontal circle of radius equal to the magnitude $I\omega$. We have met the analogous effect produced by the action of centripetal force on a body moving in a circular path. Recall that centripetal force continuously changes only the direction but not the magnitude of the tangential velocity.

We have already indicated that the axis about which the angular momentum rotates is known as the *precession axis*. The other two axes are descriptively known as the *spin axis* (axis AB) and the *torque axis* (axis AD). Notice that the direction of precession is always toward the positive direction of the torque vector.

If an attempt is made to change the rate of precession by applying to the gyroscope axle a force in the horizontal plane, the center of gravity of the gyroscope either rises above or falls below the horizontal plane. An applied force tending to hurry the rate of precession causes the resultant angular momentum vector to point upward above the horizontal plane while, if the applied force tends to slow down the rate of precession, the resultant angular momentum points downward from the horizontal plane. This behavior again illustrates the two principal characteristics of gyroscope motion, viz., angular inertia and precession.

When a gyroscope is performing only a steady motion of precession in a horizontal plane the motion is dynamically stable. However, when a gyroscope like that shown in Figure 13.6 is started by supporting the free end B, precession will commence, but superimposed on this motion is an unstable up-and-down motion, or oscillation, about the axis AD. This up-and-down oscillation, which also occurs when a gyroscope, performing only a steady precession, is disturbed, is called *nutation*. Nutation can readily be seen in the gyroscopic motion of the spinning top shown in Figure 13.7. The top

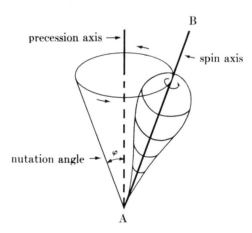

Figure 13.7. *The spinning top.*

rotates about its spin axis AB which itself moves so as to generate an inverted cone of half apex angle φ. The top therefore precesses about the vertical axis of the cone. Usually this motion is accompanied by the periodic oscillation of the spin axis toward and away from the precession axis so that φ alternately decreases and increases and the top is undergoing nutation. This angle φ is called the *nutation angle*. We shall not give a detailed study of the phenomenon of nutation since it is relatively involved and beyond the scope of this text.

Figure 13.8 shows a demonstration gyroscope which is mounted in gimbal rings. As can be seen, this permits the gyroscope wheel to spin about its axis and also have freedom of rotation about the other two mutually perpendicular axes. With the mounting such that very little friction is present at the pivots, the base of the gyroscope can be lifted and turned in any direction without transmitting any appreciable torque to the spinning wheel. The spinning gyroscope then has the property of *stability of the spin axis* and maintains the direction of its spin axis when its position is changed. For example, when such a gyroscope is kept rotating at high speed with its spin axis directed horizontally east and west, then, after the earth has turned through 90°, the spin axis will be vertical. The two properties, stability of the spin axis and precession, are employed in the many

Figure 13.8. *Gyroscope mounted in gimbal rings.*

useful applications of gyroscopes. Some of these applications, as well as examples of some gyroscopic effects, are taken up in the next section.

13.9. Gyroscopic Applications and Gyroscopic Effects. *The Bicycle.* Anyone who rides a bicycle knows what to do to keep from falling when he starts to tip to either side. He brings into play a precessional effect which restores his balance. To see how the principles of gyroscopic motion afford an explanation, consider a bicyclist riding upright in the forward direction. The spin axis of the front wheel coincides with the front wheel axle and the spin angular momentum vector points horizontally to the left. Now suppose the rider rapidly turns the front wheel to the left by applying to the handlebars a torque counterclockwise as seen by the rider. This superimposes on the rotating system an angular momentum vector that points vertically upward. The resultant angular momentum vector now points upward and to the left, the wheel axle slopes downward to the right, and the rider tips to the right. Hence, if a rider starts to tip to either side he restores balance by turning the handlebars in the direction in which he is tipping.

The Automobile. The flywheel of an automobile acts as a gyroscope and when the car turns a curve the axis of the flywheel precesses. As seen by the driver the flywheel spins counterclockwise, so that the spin angular momentum points opposite the direction of motion. When the car makes a right turn the added angular momentum points vertically downward, with the result that the front of the car tends to rise. A left turn causes the rear of the car to rise. If a driver in an emergency must make a rapid turn at high speed and there is a choice in direction, it becomes a matter of whether he can best get along without much steering ability or without much traction.

Airplane Propellers and Ships' Turbines. The propeller of an airplane and the rotating wheel of a ship's turbine rotate at very high speed and possess large moments of inertia. When the airplane or ship turns, the direction of the spinning axis of the propeller or turbine changes, with the result that a gyroscopic torque appears, similar to the turning automobile. When the airplane is put into a turn, the precession causes it to climb or dive, depending upon the sense of the turn. When a ship rolls the bearing force due to the gyroscopic torque may be fifteen or twenty times that existing in the absence of roll. To counteract the ship's roll an antiroll device such as a *gyrostabilizer* may be employed. This consists of one or more very large gyroscopes mounted in the ship, and rotated by a motor at high speed in a horizontal plane about a vertical axis. The vertical axis of the gyroscope can be precessed slowly fore and aft but not athwart ship by a precession motor. This causes a gyroscopic reaction torque on the ship against the direction of the rolling motion. For example, with the spin of the gyroscope counterclockwise as viewed from above, if the boat rolls, say to the left, then the axis of the gyroscope is tilted aft and thus supplies a reaction torque which opposes the roll.

The Earth-Precession of the Equinoxes. Although the earth is nearly spherical it is actually an oblate spheroid, which is a surface generated by revolving an ellipse about its minor, or short, axis. Because the earth is thus short at its poles and bulging at the equator it is acted upon by torques exerted by the gravitational attraction forces of the moon and sun. This results in a torque exerted about an axis which is perpendicular to the axis of spin of the earth. Consequently, the spin angular momentum of the earth precesses about a fixed direction in space. Since the spin angular momentum of the earth is large and the external torque is small, the angular velocity of precession is small, as may be seen from Equation 13.16. This gyroscopic precession causes the axis of spin to describe a cone whose apex opening is 46°54', one complete precession period being 25,800 years. Therefore the pole of the earth points successively to different parts of the heavens and results in the astronomic phenomenon known as the precession of the equinoxes.

Miscellaneous Gyroscopic Devices. The principles of gyroscopic motion are employed also in such instruments and devices as the *gyrocompass* which always indicates the true geographic north-south direction, the *artificial horizon* which indicates to an aircraft operator the horizon when it is visible, the airplane *turn-indicator* which indicates to the pilot his direction and rate of turn, and the *automatic pilot* which combines the principles of the artificial horizon and the directional gyroscope. One of the earliest man-made devices employing the principles of the gyroscope is the boomerang. These are but a few of the many significant and ingenious applications of gyroscopic principles.

Example 13.1. A golf ball weighing 2.00 ounces starts out from rest with a speed of 192 feet/sec after having been struck by a golf club. Find (a) the impulse and (b) the average force, assuming that the duration of impact is 6.00×10^{-4} sec.

Solution. (a) Applying the impulse-momentum theorem we have

$$F_{av} \Delta t = mv_2 - mv_1$$

$$\text{impulse} = F_{av} \Delta t = \frac{2.00}{16.0 \times 32.0} \times 192 - 0 = 0.750 \text{ pf} \cdot \text{sec}$$

(b) $F_{av} = 0.750/(6.00 \times 10^{-4}) = 1.25 \times 10^3 \text{ pf}$

Example 13.2. An automobile with a mass of 4.00×10^3 pounds strikes a concrete wall with a speed of 60.0 miles/hour and is thus brought to rest in 0.200 sec. Find the average force during collision.

Solution. From Equation 13.1b:

$$F_{av} = \frac{mv_2 - mv_1}{\Delta t}$$

$$F_{av} = \frac{0 - \dfrac{4.00 \times 10^3 \times 88.0}{32.0}}{0.200} = -5.50 \times 10^4 \text{ pf}$$

The minus sign indicates that the force acts opposite the direction of motion taken as positive.

Example 13.3. A gun weighing 800 pf fires a 6.00-ounce shell with a muzzle velocity of 600 m/sec. The gun is mounted such that it is free to move. Find its recoil velocity.

Solution. Linear momentum is conserved; hence, the gun recoils with a momentum that is equal and opposite to that of the shell. Therefore:

$$m_{gun} v_{gun} = m_{shell} v_{shell}$$

$$800 \cancel{\text{ pf }} v_{gun} = \frac{6.00}{16.0} \cancel{\text{ pf }} \times 600 \text{ m/sec}$$

$$v_{gun} = 27.5 \text{ cm/sec}$$

Notice that it is permissible to mix English and metric units because the same conversion constants appear as factors on each side of the equation.

Example 13.4. An elastic ball of 5.00 gm is moving with a velocity of 8.00 cm/sec in the positive x direction and collides with a ball of 2.00 gm moving with a velocity of 10.0 cm/sec in the negative x direction. Find the velocities of the bodies after impact, assuming direct, central, and perfectly elastic impact.

Solution. We first make a diagram depicting the bodies before and after impact. In Figure 13.9, both u_1 and u_2 are known in magnitude and direction. However, the directions of v_1 and v_2 are unknown. They may be as assumed, in which case the solution will yield positive values for both. On the other hand, a negative sign in the solution for a velocity indicates that the correct direction is not as assumed but is reversed.

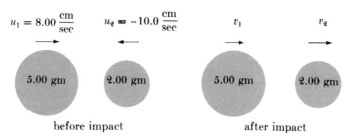

$u_1 = 8.00 \dfrac{\text{cm}}{\text{sec}}$ $u_2 = -10.0 \dfrac{\text{cm}}{\text{sec}}$ v_1 v_2

5.00 gm   2.00 gm   5.00 gm   2.00 gm

before impact   after impact

Figure 13.9.

Applying the principle of conservation of linear momentum,

$$5.00 \times 8.00 - 2.00 \times 10.0 = 5.00v_1 + 2.00v_2$$

or $$5.00(8.00 - v_1) = 2.00(10.0 + v_2) \qquad (13.18)$$

Assuming perfect elasticity, the principle of conservation of energy yields

$$\tfrac{1}{2} \times 5.00(8.00)^2 + \tfrac{1}{2} \times 2.00(10.0)^2 = \tfrac{1}{2} \times 5.00v_1^2 + \tfrac{1}{2} \times 2.00v_2^2$$

or $$5.00(8.00 - v_1)(8.00 + v_1) = 2.00(v_2 - 10.0)(v_2 + 10.0) \quad (13.19)$$

From Equations 13.18 and 13.19 we have

$$v_2 - v_1 = 18.0$$

which may be directly obtained by using Equation 13.4.

Combining this with Equation 13.18 yields the solution

$$v_1 = -16/7 = -2.28 \text{ cm/sec}$$
$$v_2 = 110/7 = 15.7 \text{ cm/sec}$$

which shows that after impact the 2.00 gm ball moves to the right with a speed of 15.7 cm/sec and the 5.00 gm ball moves to the left with a speed of 2.28 cm/sec. The same solutions are readily obtained by applying Equations 13.5 and 13.6.

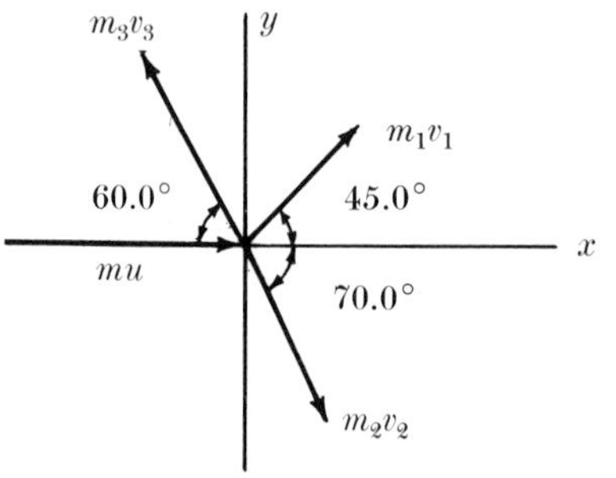

m_3v_3 y

m_1v_1

$60.0°$ $45.0°$

mu x

$70.0°$

m_2v_2

Figure 13.10.

Example 13.5. A bomb whose mass is 2.00 pounds is moving in the positive x direction with a velocity of 50.0 feet/sec when it explodes into three fragments traveling in the same vertical plane. One fragment, of mass 0.750 pound, flies off at an angle of 45.0°; another fragment, of mass 0.250 pound, flies off at an angle of 290.0°; the third fragment, of mass 1.00 pound, flies off at an angle of 120.0° with a velocity of 10.0 feet/sec. The indicated angles are given with respect to the positive extension of the x axis. Find the magnitudes of the velocities of the three-quarter-pound and quarter-pound fragments.

Solution. Figure 13.10 shows the vector diagram of linear momenta. The momentum before impact is represented by mu where m is the mass of the bomb and u is its velocity before explosion. After explosion the momenta of the fragments are indicated by m_1v_1, m_2v_2, and m_3v_3, the masses being m_1, m_2, and m_3 and the corresponding velocities being v_1, v_2, and v_3. Both the x components of momenta and the y components of momenta are conserved. Hence,

$$mu = m_1v_1 \cos 45.0° + m_2v_2 \cos 70.0° - m_3v_3 \cos 60.0°$$
and
$$0 = m_1v_1 \sin 45.0° + m_3v_3 \sin 60.0° - m_2v_2 \sin 70.0°$$

Substituting the given values for m, m_1, m_2, m_3, u, and v_3 we have

$$2.12v_1 + 0.342v_2 = 420$$
and
$$2.12v_1 - 0.940v_2 = -34.6$$

from which are obtained the solutions

$$v_1 = 141 \text{ ft/sec}$$
$$v_2 = 355 \text{ ft/sec}$$

Example 13.6. An inelastic impact occurs between a 10.0 pm body moving in the positive x direction with a velocity of 30.0 feet/sec and a 20.0 pm body moving in the negative x direction with a velocity of 20.0 feet/sec. If the coefficient of restitution is 0.800 what are (**a**) the velocities of each body after impact and (**b**) the fractional loss of kinetic energy?

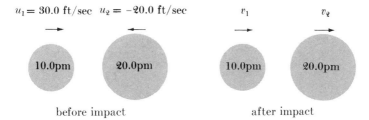

$$u_1 = 30.0 \text{ ft/sec} \quad u_2 = -20.0 \text{ ft/sec} \qquad v_1 \qquad v_2$$

| 10.0pm | 20.0pm | 10.0pm | 20.0pm |

before impact   after impact

Figure 13.11.

Solution. Figure 13.11 shows the condition before impact and the assumed condition after impact; in the latter the unknown velocities are assumed to be in the positive x direction. The sign of the result will indicate whether or not these should be reversed.

(**a**) Applying the principle of the conservation of linear momentum, we have

$$10.0(30.0) - 20.0(20.0) = 10.0v_1 + 20.0v_2$$
or
$$v_1 + 2.00v_2 = -10.0$$

Also, from Equation 13.12 an independent equation between v_1 and v_2 is found:

$$0.800 = -\frac{v_1 - v_2}{30.0 + 20.0}$$

or $$v_1 - v_2 = -40.0$$

Solving the two independent relationships for v_1 and v_2 yields

$$v_1 = -30.0 \text{ ft/sec in the negative } x \text{ direction}$$
$$v_2 = 10.0 \text{ ft/sec in the positive } x \text{ direction}$$

(b) Kinetic energy before impact:

$$= \left(\frac{1}{2} \times \frac{10.0}{32.0}\right)(30.0)^2 + \left(\frac{1}{2} \times \frac{20.0}{32.0}\right)(-20.0)^2 = \frac{17.0 \times 10^3}{64.0} \text{ ft·pf}$$

Kinetic energy after impact:

$$= \left(\frac{1}{2} \times \frac{10.0}{32.0}\right)(-30.0)^2 + \left(\frac{1}{2} \times \frac{20.0}{32.0}\right)(10.0)^2 = \frac{11.0 \times 10^3}{64.0} \text{ ft·pf}$$

Loss in kinetic energy:

$$= 6.00 \times 10^3/64.0 \text{ ft·pf}$$

Fractional loss in kinetic energy:

$$= 6/17$$

Example 13.7.   A smooth ball A of 40.0 gm is rolling in the positive x direction with a velocity of 100 cm/sec when it collides with a second smooth ball B of 20.0 gm moving with a velocity of 200 cm/sec upward at an angle of 30.0° with the horizontal, as shown in Figure 13.12. Assuming perfectly elastic impact, find the velocities of the balls after impact.

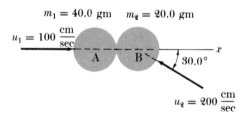

Figure 13.12.

Solution.   The centers of the two bodies are not moving in the same line before impact, so that we have a case of oblique impact. Here we consider that the velocities u_1 and u_2 before impact are resolved into two components, one along the x axis that passes through the centers of A and B at the instant of collision and the other in the perpendicular y direction. Since the spheres are perfectly smooth, only the components of the velocities of the points of contact normal to the surfaces of contact are affected by the impact, the components in the tangential direction remaining unaltered. If the oblique impact were inelastic, the equation defining the coefficient of restitution (Equation 13.12) would be in terms of the components of the velocities in the direction normal to the surfaces of contact. Here, of course, $e = 1$. If the spheres were not smooth, a tangential action between the spheres would take place, resulting in a motion of rotation, which is assumed not to be present here.

Let the x and y components of the velocities before impact be $(u_1)_x$, $(u_2)_x$, and $(u_1)_y$, $(u_2)_y$, respectively. Also, let the x components of the velocities v_1 for A and v_2 for B be respectively $(v_1)_x$ and $(v_2)_x$. Applying the principle of the conservation of linear momentum to the x components we have

$$m_1(u_1)_x + m_2(u_2)_x = m_1(v_1)_x + m_2(v_2)_x$$

and, substituting the given values,

$$40.0 \times 100 - 20.0 \times 200 \cos 30.0° = 40.0(v_1)_x + 20.0(v_2)_x$$

or
$$26.8 = 2.00(v_1)_x + (v_2)_x \qquad (13.20)$$

Also, applying Equation 13.4 to the x components we have

$$100 + 200 \cos 30.0° = -[(v_1)_x - (v_2)_x]$$

or
$$-273 = (v_1)_x - (v_2)_x \qquad (13.21)$$

Solving Equations 13.20 and 13.21 for the x components of velocities after impact yields

$$(v_1)_x = -82.1 \text{ cm/sec} \qquad \text{and} \qquad (v_2)_x = 191 \text{ cm/sec}$$

Therefore, since $(u_1)_y = 0$ the velocity of A after impact is 82.1 cm/sec in the negative x direction and the velocity of B after impact is given in magnitude by $\sqrt{(v_2)_x^2 + (u_2)_y^2} = \sqrt{(191)^2 + (200 \sin 30.0°)^2} = 215$ cm/sec, and in direction by $\tan^{-1}(100/191) = 27.6°$ north of east.

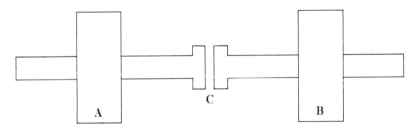

Figure 13.13.

Example 13.8. Figure 13.13 shows two wheels A and B. Viewing the figure from left to right, wheel A rotates clockwise at 3.00 radians/sec and wheel B rotates counterclockwise at 5.00 radians/sec. The moment of inertia of the left unit about the axis of rotation is 8.00 slug–square-foot (slug·ft²) and that of the right unit is 6.00 slug–square-foot (slug·ft²). When the clutch

C suddenly engages both shafts, what is the common angular velocity immediately after the shafts join?

   Solution. During the short time interval that the changes in angular
velocity take place, unit A exerts a torque on unit B, and unit B exerts on
unit A at all times an equal and opposite torque.   The conservation of angular
momentum holds.   Hence,

$$I_A \omega_A + I_B \omega_B = (I_A + I_B)\omega$$

where I_A and I_B are the moments of inertia of A and B respectively, ω_A and ω_B
are the corresponding angular velocities, and ω is the resultant angular velocity.   Substituting the given values

$$8.00 \times 3.00 + 6.00(-5.00) = (8.00 + 6.00)\omega$$

and $\omega = -0.429$ rad/sec counterclockwise.

   Example 13.9.   The rotating wheel of a ship's turbine has a moment of
inertia of 400 slug–square-foot about its axis of rotation and a spin of 1.80×10^3 revolutions/minute about a horizontal axis.   The ship is moving at 30.0
feet/sec and turns around a 600-foot radius.   Find the magnitude of the
gyroscopic torque.
   Solution.   The angular speed of the turbine's wheel is

$$\omega = \frac{2\pi}{60.0}(1800) = 188 \text{ rad/sec}$$

and the precessional angular speed is

$$\omega_p = 30.0/600 = 0.0500 \text{ rad/sec}$$

Applying Equation 13.17, the gyroscopic torque is

$$L = I\omega\omega_p = 400 \times 188 \times 0.0500$$
$$= 3.76 \times 10^3 \text{ pf} \cdot \text{ft}$$

Problems

   Where necessary, use for g the values 980 cm/sec² = 9.80 m/sec² = 32.0
ft/sec².

   13.1.   Find the magnitude of the linear momentum of the following:
(a) an automobile of 4.00×10^3 pounds mass moving with a speed of 60.0
miles/hour, (b) a 2.00-ounce bullet traveling with a speed of 2.00×10^3
feet/sec, and (c) an electron of rest mass 9.11×10^{-23} gm moving with a speed
of 1.50×10^{10} cm/sec (use the relativistic mass).

   13.2.   Find the magnitude of the angular momentum of the following:
(a) a 500-pound-mass flywheel which has a radius of gyration of 2.00 feet and
is rotating at 1.80×10^3 revolutions/minute, (b) the earth about its axis of

spin, taking the mass of the earth as 5.98×10^{24} kgm and its radius as 6.37×10^6 m, and (**c**) an electron of mass 9.11×10^{-23} gm, revolving about a proton nucleus at 6.62×10^{15} revolutions/sec, the radius of revolution being 0.530×10^{-8} cm.

13.3. What is the speed of recoil of a gun weighing 10.0 pounds force when it discharges a half-ounce bullet with a speed of 2.40×10^3 feet/sec?

13.4. A body whose mass is 10.0 kgm is under the action of an impelling force of 75.0 nt directed eastward and a retarding force of 15.0 nt directed westward. Find, considering that the body starts from rest, (**a**) the time rate of change of the momentum of the body, (**b**) the change in momentum after the forces have acted for 5.00 sec, and (**c**) the velocity of the body at the end of 5.00 sec.

13.5. A baseball, weighing 5.00 ounces and initially at rest, is struck with a bat. The impact is of a 0.200 sec duration, after which time the ball separates with a speed of 300 feet/sec. Find (**a**) the impulse and (**b**) the magnitude of the average force exerted.

13.6. A baseball of 100 gm strikes a bat with a speed of 4.50 m/sec and separates in the opposite direction with a speed of 12.0 m/sec. Assuming that the bat and ball make contact for 0.005 sec, find (**a**) the impulse and (**b**) the magnitude of the average force exerted.

13.7. Find the average force that it is necessary to exert over a time interval of 0.002 sec in order to change the velocity of a 4.00-ounce baseball from 80.0 feet/sec to -80.0 feet/sec.

13.8. A hammer whose weight is 6.00 pounds force is used to drive a nail into a hardwood board. If the hammer strikes the nail with a downward velocity of 24.0 feet/sec and comes to rest in 0.002 sec, what are (**a**) the impulse and (**b**) the average force exerted?

13.9. A small steel sphere weighing 20.0 gf is dropped into a vat of tar from a height of 19.6 m. If the ball comes to rest in 0.400 sec, what is the average force exerted in bringing it to rest?

13.10. An experimental rocket of mass 1.50 pounds suddenly ejects from a rear nozzle 0.250 pound mass of gas with a speed of 20.0 feet/sec. Find the speed of the rocket.

13.11. A bullet whose mass is 10.0 gm is moving with a speed of 600 m/sec and passes through a 500 gm wooden block which is initially at rest, emerging with a speed of 400 m/sec. Assuming no retarding forces on the block, find (**a**) its speed immediately after impact and (**b**) the loss in kinetic energy during the process of penetration.

13.12. If the thickness of the block penetrated by the bullet in Problem 13.11 is 2.00 cm, what is the average force exerted by the bullet on the block? Assume the deceleration of the bullet is uniform.

13.13. A sphere A, moving eastward with a velocity of 15.0 feet/sec, collides with a sphere B which is initially at rest. A and B have masses of 10.0 and 5.00 pounds respectively. Assuming direct, central, perfectly elastic impact, find (**a**) the velocity of each body after impact, (**b**) the total momentum, and (**c**) the total kinetic energy.

13.14.   Solve Problem 13.13 where A and B each have a mass of 10.0 pounds.

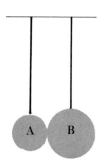

Figure   13.14.
*Problems   13.18,
13.19, and 13.20.*

13.15.   A ball A, whose mass is m_1 and velocity u_1, strikes a stationary ball B whose mass is m_2. For a case of direct, central, perfectly elastic impact, show that, after impact, B has acquired the fraction $4r/(r+1)^2$ of the original energy and A has remained with the fraction $(r-1)^2/(r+1)^2$ of its energy, where r is the ratio of the masses.

13.16.   A 500 gm ball A, moving in the positive x direction with a velocity of 600 cm/sec, overtakes and collides with a 1.00×10^3 gm ball B moving in the same direction with a velocity of 100 cm/sec. For direct, central, perfectly elastic impact, find the velocity of each body after impact.

13.17.   A sphere A moving in the positive x direction with a velocity of 50.0 m/sec collides with a sphere B moving in the negative x direction with a velocity of 75.0 m/sec. The masses of A and B are 2.00 and 3.00 kgm, respectively. Assuming direct, central, perfectly elastic impact, find the velocity of each sphere after impact.

13.18.   Two perfectly elastic spheres are suspended by cords as shown in Figure 13.14. When one or both spheres are pulled aside and released they experience direct, central impact. Mass A is 50.0 gm and mass B is 100 gm. Let A be pulled aside, until its center of gravity has been raised 10.0 cm, and then be released. Find the velocity of each sphere after collision.

13.19.   In Figure 13.14 let A have a mass m and B have a mass $3m$. Now consider that A is pulled aside and released, striking B with a velocity u directed to the right. There then follows a series of impacts, the character of the motion during two successive impacts being a repeating pattern. Show that this pattern has the following character: after the first impact A

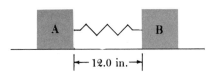

Figure   13.15.   *Problems   13.21 and 13.22.*

and B separate with equal speeds $u/2$ and after the second impact the velocity of B is zero and the velocity of A is $-u$ directed toward the left. Assume perfectly elastic impacts.

13.20.   Solve Problem 13.19 for the case in which B is pulled aside and released, striking A with a velocity $-u$ directed toward the left. Show that the repeating pattern now is as follows: after the first impact A has a velocity

$-3u/2$ and B has a velocity $-u/2$, both directed to the left, and after the second impact the velocity of A is zero and the velocity of B is u directed toward the right. Assume perfectly elastic impacts.

13.21. The 40.0-pound-mass body A and the 25.0-pound-mass body B shown in Figure 13.15 are connected by a spring whose modulus is 50.0 pounds-force/inch. The spring has a normal length of 12.0 inches. The bodies are pushed together until the distance between them is 4.00 inches and then are suddenly released from rest. Find the velocities of A and B when the distance between them is again 12.0 inches. The plane is smooth and the spring has negligible weight.

13.22. In Problem 13.21, let the bodies be pulled apart until the distance between them is 20.0 inches and then be released from rest. Find the velocities of A and B when the distance between them has decreased to 14.0 inches.

13.23. A smooth ball A, moving northward with a velocity of 8.00 m/sec, collides with another smooth ball B moving in a direction 20.0° south of west with a velocity of 12.0 m/sec, as shown in Figure 13.16. The masses of A and B are 0.500 kgm and 0.200 kgm respectively. Assuming perfectly elastic central impact, find the velocities of A and B after impact.

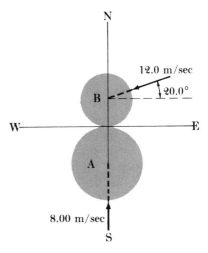

Figure 13.16. *Problem 13.23.*

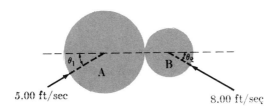

Figure 13.17. *Problem 13.24.*

13.24. Two smooth balls A and B are moving as shown in Figure 13.17, when they collide, with oblique central impact. The masses of A and B are 6.40 and 4.80 pounds respectively, their velocities are 5.00 and 8.00 feet/sec respectively, and the angles shown are given by $\theta_1 = \tan^{-1} (3/4)$ and $\theta_2 = \tan^{-1} (5/12)$. Assuming perfectly elastic impact find the velocities of A and B after impact.

13.25. Using Figure 13.3 for the ballistic pendulum, show that Equation 13.9 may be put in the form

$$u = \frac{2(M + m)\sqrt{gl}}{m} \sin (\theta/2)$$

Now show that if $h \ll s$ then

$$u = \frac{(M + m)s}{m} \sqrt{g/l}$$

13.26. Show that when the bullet embeds itself in the block of the ballistic pendulum, kinetic energy is not conserved and the use of the relation $\frac{1}{2}mv^2 = \frac{1}{2}(m + M)V^2$ leads to an impossible result.

13.27. The block of a ballistic pendulum has a weight of 500 gf and its center of gravity rises 10.0 cm when it is struck by a bullet of 25.0 gm and becomes embedded in the block. Find (**a**) the speed with which the bullet strikes the block and (**b**) the loss in kinetic energy, also expressing this as a percentage of the initial energy.

13.28. A projectile with a mass of 1.00 pound is moving horizontally with a speed of 600 miles/hour. It strikes and becomes embedded in a 500-pound target which hangs at rest from a rope whose length is 10.0 feet. Neglecting the mass of the rope, find (**a**) the speed of the target after impact, (**b**) the loss of kinetic energy, (**c**) the height to which the target is raised, and (**d**) the tension in the rope immediately after impact.

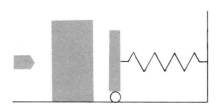

Figure 13.18. *Problem 13.29.*

13.29. The bullet shown in Figure 13.18 has a mass of 10.0 gm and is moving to the right with a velocity of 600 m/sec. It strikes and becomes embedded in a 4.50 kgm block resting on a smooth horizontal surface. Find the amount by which the spring, whose modulus is 500 nt/m, is compressed. Neglect friction and the mass of the spring, and assume that all the kinetic energy after impact is available when the spring is compressed.

13.30. A bullet with a mass of 0.240 ounce is projected horizontally into a 2.00-pound-mass block that is initially at rest on a horizontal surface. The bullet embeds itself in the block which moves a distance of 8.00 feet after impact. If the coefficient of friction between block and surface is 0.200, what is the speed with which the bullet strikes the block?

13.31. A wooden block weighing 10.0 pounds force is moving on a horizontal plane with a velocity of 4.00 feet/sec in the negative x direction when it is struck by a bullet weighing 0.100 pound force which is moving with a velocity of 900 feet/sec in the positive x direction. The bullet becomes embedded in the block. (**a**) Find the resulting velocity of the block after impact. (**b**) If the coefficient of friction between block and plane is 0.100, how far does the block move after impact?

13.32. Consider that the two bodies shown in Figure 13.2 experience an inelastic, direct, central impact. Show that the velocities after impact are given by

$$v_1 = \frac{(m_1 - em_2)u_1 + m_2(e + 1)u_2}{m_1 + m_2}$$

$$v_2 = \frac{(m_2 - em_1)u_2 + m_1(e + 1)u_1}{m_1 + m_2}$$

and observe that these reduce to Equations 13.5 and 13.6 for $e = 1$. Also show that the loss in kinetic energy is given by

$$\frac{1}{2} \times \frac{m_1 m_2}{m_1 + m_2} (1 - e^2)(u_1 - u_2)^2$$

13.33. Using the result of Problem 13.32 show that the fractional loss in kinetic energy for $u_2 = 0$ is independent of the speed of m_1 and is given by $m_2(1 - e^2)/(m_1 + m_2)$.

13.34. A golf ball is dropped from a height of 10.0 feet upon a hard surface. The coefficient of restitution is 0.800. Find **(a)** the height to which the ball rebounds and **(b)** the fractional loss in kinetic energy.

13.35. A smooth spherical ball strikes a smooth immovable vertical wall with a velocity u directed at an angle θ with the wall's normal. The ball rebounds at an angle φ with the wall's normal. Show that the coefficient of restitution is given by $e = \tan \varphi / \tan \theta$. (*Hint:* Combine Equation 13.12, using velocity components normal to the wall, with the equation which expresses the fact that the component of momentum parallel to the wall remains constant.) Explain why an incorrect result is obtained by applying Equation 13.2 using velocity components normal to the wall. Note that, for perfectly elastic impact, $\theta = \varphi$, and we have the angle of incidence equal to the angle of reflection so familiar in optical reflection. On the other hand, for perfectly inelastic impact, $e = 0$ and $\varphi = 90°$; i.e., the ball after impact moves along the wall surface. For example a stream of water striking a fixed flat plate spreads out and the water flows along the surface of the plate, following the result of perfectly inelastic impact.

13.36. A billiard ball strikes and rebounds from the table railing respectively at 30.0° and 31.5° with the railing's normal. Assuming a smooth, perfectly rigid railing and neglecting friction, find **(a)** the coefficient of restitution and **(b)** the ratio of the speed before impact to that after impact (see Problem 13.35).

13.37. A smooth ball is thrown against a smooth vertical wall with a velocity of 50.0 feet/sec in a direction which makes an angle of 70.0° with the wall. Find **(a)** the speed of the ball after impact and **(b)** the angle of rebound. The coefficient of restitution is 0.500.

13.38. A puck A, sliding on smooth ice in the positive x direction, makes a direct central collision with a similar puck B traveling in the negative x direction. The speeds of A and B before impact are 600 cm/sec and 900 cm/sec respectively. Find **(a)** the velocities of A and B after impact and **(b)**

the loss in kinetic energy if the coefficient of restitution is 0.600 and each puck has a mass of 30.0 gm.   (Check your results by the equations given in Problem 13.32.)

13.39.   Solve Problem 13.16, the coefficient of restitution being 0.800, and also find the loss in kinetic energy.

13.40.   Solve Problem 13.24 where the coefficient of restitution is 0.500. (*Hint:* Apply Equations 13.2 and 13.12, using the components of velocities and momenta along the line joining the mass centers.   The components perpendicular to this line remain unchanged for smooth bodies.

13.41.   A machine gun fires 300 bullets per minute, each bullet having a mass of 1.00 ounce.   If the muzzle speed of the bullet is 2.40×10^3 feet/sec, what is the magnitude of the average force needed to hold the gun in place? Neglect the effect of the expanding gas.

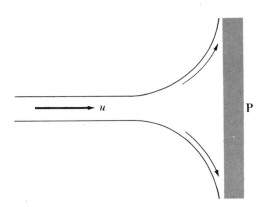

Figure 13.19.   *Problem 13.42.*

13.42.   A cylindrical jet of water, 4.00 inches in diameter and moving horizontally with a velocity $u = 50.0$ feet/sec, strikes a fixed vertical plate P as shown in Figure 13.19.   Find the force required to hold the plate.   The weight of water per cubic foot is 62.4 pounds force.   (*Hint:* The stream of water falling on P is a case of perfectly inelastic collision.   As shown in the figure, during impact the liquid spreads out and flows along the plate surface; see comment in Problem 13.35.   Before collision the water has a linear momentum in the horizontal direction and after collision this momentum is zero. Therefore, the force exerted by the stream on the plate, and hence the equal and opposite force exerted by the plate on the stream, is given by the time rate of change of linear momentum or by the product of the mass of water striking the plate per unit time and the velocity of the jet.)

13.43.   Find the force exerted on the plate in Problem 13.42 when (**a**) P moves horizontally to the right at 10.0 feet/sec and (**b**) P moves horizontally to the left at 10.0 feet/sec.

13.44. A rocket burns fuel at the constant rate of 400 kgm/sec and ejects it in gaseous form with a speed of 2.00×10^3 m/sec with respect to the rocket. (a) Find the magnitude of the reaction force or thrust that accelerates the rocket. (b) If the rocket has an initial mass of 3.00×10^4 kgm what is its upward acceleration 30.0 sec after it starts upward from rest? (*Hint:* The thrust is given by the mass of gas discharged per second, times the velocity of discharge.)

13.45. Figure 13.20 shows a solid cylinder of radius 2.00 feet and mass 320 gm, free to rotate in frictionless bearings. The mass $m = 64.0$ pounds mass is attached to a rope which is wrapped around the cylinder. Employ the impulse-momentum theorems to find (a) the angular speed of the cylinder, (b) the linear speed of m, and (c) the tension in the rope 5.00 sec after the system is released from rest.

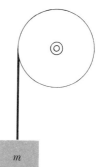

Figure 13.20.
Problem 13.45.

13.46. Two cylinders A and B, respectively 40.0 kgm and 60.0 kgm, are rotating clockwise on the same frictionless shaft. Cylinder A, of radius 20.0 cm, is rotating at 240 revolutions/minute and cylinder B, of radius 30.0 cm, is rotating at 360 revolutions/minute. When a clutch brings the cylinders into contact, what are (a) the common rotational speed and (b) the loss in kinetic energy? Use for the moment of inertia of the rotating bodies the expression for a solid cylinder.

13.47. Solve Problem 13.46 with cylinder A rotating clockwise and cylinder B rotating counterclockwise before the clutch brings them into contact.

13.48. A man is standing at the center of a frictionless turntable and holds a weight of 8.00 pounds force in each hand. With his arms extended horizontally and the weights thus distant 2.50 feet from the rotation axis, he is given a rotational speed of 2.00 revolutions/minute. (a) What is his speed of rotation when he pulls his hands close to his body so that the weights are distant 4.00 inches from the rotation axis? (b) Compare the kinetic energy of the system before the weights are pulled in with that after, and account for the difference. Assume that the moment of inertia of the system without weights is constant and equal to 5.00 slug–square-foot.

13.49. A slender uniform rod, whose radius of gyration about a transverse axis through its center is $10\sqrt{3}$ cm, hangs vertically from a pivot point through its end. What distance below the pivot point must it be struck so that no momentum is transferred to the pivot?

13.50. A slender rod hangs in a vertical position from a smooth pivot O as shown in Figure 13.21. The rod is 90.0 cm long and it has a mass of 18.0 kgm. It is struck a horizontal blow at B by a small object having a mass of 500 gm and a horizontal speed of 7.50 m/sec. Taking the coefficient of restitution as 0.800, find the maximum vertical rise h of the center of mass C as shown.

13.51. The wheel of a gyroscope, with a radius of gyration of 10.0 cm about its axis of spin, spins about a horizontal axis at 2.40×10^3 revolutions/minute clockwise as viewed from its free end. The pivot end of the gyroscope is distant 15.0 cm from the center of gravity of the rotating system. Find the angular velocity of precession as viewed from above. (See Figure 13.6.)

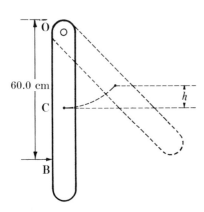

13.52. A top has a radius of gyration about its axis of symmetry of 1.00 inch. When it spins at 1.80×10^3 revolutions/minute with its axis inclined at 30.0° with the vertical it precesses with an angular speed of 0.400 radian/sec. How far up from the pivot point along its axis is the center of gravity located?

Figure 13.21. *Problem 13.50.*

13.53. Each wheel of a car weighs 64.0 pounds force, has a diameter of 32.0 inches, and has a radius of gyration of 12.0 inches. The tread (i.e., the distance separating a pair of wheels on an axle) is 5.00 feet. If the car rounds a horizontal curve of 200-foot radius at 30.0 miles/hour, what is the change of load on each pair of wheels, caused by gyroscopic action? (*Hint:* The gyroscopic couple acting on a pair of car wheels is given by Equation 13.17.)

13.54. Present in tabular form all the translational and corresponding or analogous rotational quantities, equations, laws, and principles that you have thus far studied. Do this as follows: in one column write the name of the quantity, law, or principle; in a second column state the translational symbol, expression, equation; divide a third column into three subcolumns and give the cgs absolute, mks absolute, and English gravitational units for each of the translational listings; in a fourth column state the analogous rotational symbol, expression, or equation; divide a fifth column into three subcolumns and give the cgs absolute, mks absolute, and English gravitational units for each of the rotational listings.

Elasticity and Strength
of Materials

T*HUS FAR IN OUR TREATMENT* of mechanics it has been assumed that bodies were rigid solids which, under the action of impressed forces, experienced as a whole a state of rest, a state of translational motion, a state of rotational motion, or a combination of the last two. We assumed that the distances between the atomic and molecular constituents of a body were fixed and not subject to change under the application of a force. Actually, however, all bodies are more or less deformable and we are justified in ignoring the effects of deformation only when they are negligible in relation to the problem at hand. Members of a structure may be subject to stretching, bending, twisting, and equilateral compression, and the engineer, knowing how to ascertain the extent to which each member distorts, applies his knowledge of the strength of materials to arrive at a correct choice of size and kind of material for structural members.

In this chapter we shall consider the manner in which bodies may change their sizes or shapes under the action of applied forces. Such a study comes under the general subject of *elasticity* and we shall see that the elastic properties of materials find their description in a basic law which was discovered by Robert Hooke (1635–1703). We shall be concerned with the definitions of *stress*, *strain*, and *modulus of elasticity*, concepts which are fundamental to the study of elasticity and strength of materials.

14.1.   Elasticity.   *Elasticity* may be defined as that property of a body by virtue of which it tends to return to its original size or shape when the forces which caused the deformation are removed. A body is said to be *perfectly elastic* when, after removal of the impressed distorting force, the body springs back completely to its original configuration. Although no object is known to possess perfect elasticity there are many substances that are almost perfectly elastic up to an amount of distortion known as the *elastic limit*. If a body is distorted beyond its elastic limit and the forces of distortion are removed, the body acquires a form that is very far removed from its original configuration and, in fact, it is then in a permanently deformed state.   Some substances, such as putty, are almost *perfectly inelastic* and show practically no tendency to return to their original size or shape after the forces of deformation are removed.

To understand what happens internally when an elastic body is subjected to forces tending to cause distortion, consider Figure 14.1 which shows a bar

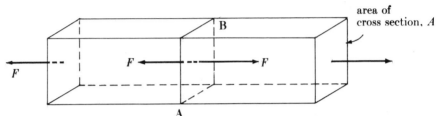

Figure 14.1.   *Internal stress.*

that is under the action of a stretching force *F* applied to its ends.   Since the bar is elastic it will experience an elongation.   There thus occurs a change in the relative positions of the constituent parts of the bar and we say that the body has undergone a *strain* which in this example is of the longitudinal type. This strain is accompanied by *internal forces* which arise between the contiguous parts of the bar because of its elastic properties.   These internal forces react against the applied forces and tend to restore the bar to its initial configuration.   When such internal restoring forces arise in a body, the body is said to be under *stress*.   When the applied forces of deformation increase, the distortion increases and the internal restoring forces increase, but at every instant the internal forces are equal and opposite to the applied forces.   For example, consider a dividing plane AB, Figure 14.1; it is in static equilibrium, the portion of the bar to the left of AB exerting on the portion of the bar to the right of AB a force *F* directed to the left, and the portion of the bar to the right of AB exerting on the portion of the bar to the left of AB a force *F* directed to the right.   When the applied forces are removed the action of the internal forces causes the elastic bar to spring back to its initial configuration. Since the internal force is always equal in magnitude to the applied force we invariably employ the applied force in defining physically and mathematically the three different kinds of stress which will now be illustrated.

One kind of stress is defined with the aid of Figure 14.1.   Here the applied force *F* acts normal to the cross-sectional area *A* and the stress, termed *longitudinal stress*, is the ratio of the force *F* to the area *A*, or *F/A*.   This kind of stress is in the nature of a tension or compression, and the associated distortion is essentially a change in length of the body.

Another kind of stress is illustrated by Figure 14.2a.   Here the area over which the applied force is distributed is parallel to the direction of the force. As indicated, the upper layer of the body is pulled to the right and the lower layer is pulled to the left.   Consequently, each layer of material moves to the right relative to the adjacent layer below it and we have a deformation which is characterized by a change in shape but not in volume. The stress called forth in this kind of deformation is called a *shearing stress* or, simply, a *shear*, which is defined as the ratio of the tangential force F to the area A, or F/A. When the distorting forces are removed and the body returns to its original shape the material is said to possess *shear elasticity* or *rigidity*.

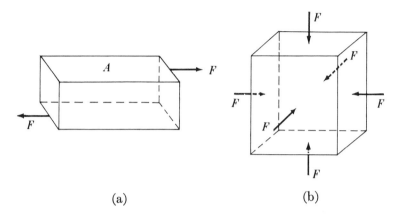

(a)   (b)

Figure 14.2.   (a) *Shearing stress.*   (b) *Volume stress.*

A third type of stress is exemplified by Figure 14.2b which shows a cube of material subjected to one force F acting normal to its faces, each of area A. The cube is thus subjected to a uniform normal force per unit area on all its faces and if the elastic body is *isotropic*—that is, exhibits physical properties that are the same in all directions—it will undergo a change in volume but not in shape. The change in size of the cube gives rise to a stress which is called a *volume stress* and is defined as the ratio of the normal force F to the area A, or F/A. Such a constant force per unit area in all directions may be obtained, as is shown in Chapter 17, by immersing the cube in a liquid, so that it is subjected to an equal increase in pressure in all directions. In fact, the normal force per unit area here has the correct physical significance of a *pressure*. When the external pressures are removed and the body returns to its original volume, the body is said to possess *volume elasticity*. All states of matter possess elasticity of volume, the degree of elasticity being, in general, large for gases, very small for liquids, and practically zero for solids. On the other hand, liquids and gases cannot support shearing stresses.

It is to be noted that the longitudinal stress, the shearing stress, and the volume stress or pressure are given by force per unit area, so that the unit of stress is the dyne per square centimeter (dyne/cm^2) in the cgs system, the newton per square meter (nt/m^2) in the mks system, and the pound force per square foot (pf/ft^2) or pound force per square inch (pf/in^2) in the English gravitational system.

As mentioned above, the three strains associated with the longitudinal stress, the shearing stress, and the volume stress are, respectively, in the nature of a change in length, a change in shape but not volume, and a change in volume but not shape. The manner in which these strains are designated or defined is taken up in the following section where it is shown that the ratio of the stress to the strain is a constant characteristic of an elastic material.

14.2. Hooke's Law. In 1676 Robert Hooke published a statement of the law which bears his name and expresses the relationship existing between the force of deformation and the distortion experienced by an elastic body. Hooke's law states that *the stress called forth in an elastic body that is subjected to an applied force is proportional to the strain experienced by the body, provided the elastic limit is not exceeded,* or:

$$\text{stress/strain} = \text{constant} \qquad (14.1)$$

The constant of proportionality in Equation 14.1 is a characteristic of elastic material and was first assigned physical meaning by Thomas Young who designated it the *modulus*, or measure, of elasticity. The behavior of elastic materials that obey Hooke's law is illustrated in Figure 14.3 which shows a

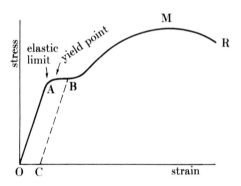

Figure 14.3. *Typical stress-strain diagram.*

typical stress–strain curve for a specimen of steel that is subjected to increasing tensile stress. The variation is linear from O to some point in the vicinity of A which is called the *proportional limit*. In this region the material follows Hooke's law. A point which also is in the vicinity of A and quite close to the proportional limit is the *elastic limit*, which is that stress beyond which the material fails to return to its original state upon removal of the forces of deformation. Although there is this distinction, the proportional limit and the elastic limit are usually considered as coincident since they are generally indistinguishable. Beyond the elastic limit there occurs the *yield point*, which is the stress at which there is a large increase in strain with little or no change in stress and the material takes on a "flow" characteristic very much like a viscous liquid. With further increase in strain the curve exhibits a maximum at M which represents the *maximum* or *ultimate strength* of the material, and soon after that rupture occurs at R. Within the proportional region an elastic material returns to its original configuration after the applied forces are removed, while at some point such as B, beyond the elastic limit, the material returns along the dotted line if the stress is removed and a *permanent set*, OC, results. For medium steel under simple tension the elastic limit is around 3.5×10^4 pounds-force/square-inch and the maximum stress is 7.0×10^4 pounds-force/square-inch.

Corresponding to the three kinds of strain and associated stresses discussed in the preceding section the constant in Equation 14.1 is called by the following names: the *stretch* or *compression* modulus, or *Young's modulus;* the *shear* or *rigidity* modulus; the *volume* or *bulk* modulus. We shall now apply Hooke's law to obtain expressions for each of these elastic moduli.

14.3. Young's Modulus: Elasticity of Stretch or Compression.

Consider the rod of wire in Figure 14.4, of length l and cross-sectional area A, under the action of a stretching force F applied normal to its face. Representing the longitudinal stress by σ we have

$$\sigma = \text{longitudinal stress} = F/A \qquad (14.2)$$

The distortion is principally a change in length, Δl, and since every element of the specimen stretches by the same fractional amount as the entire specimen we define the longitudinal strain as the fractional change in length, $\Delta l/l$. When defined in this manner, the magnitude of the strain is independent of the original length of the specimen, as it should be. Hence

$$\text{longitudinal strain} = \Delta l/l \qquad (14.3)$$

Now applying Equation 14.1 for the region in which Hooke's law holds, we have

$$E = \frac{\sigma}{\Delta l/l} = \frac{F/A}{\Delta l/l} \qquad (14.4)$$

where the symbol E is used to represent Young's modulus. Equation 14.4 applies to a specimen subjected to longitudinal compression as well as to longitudinal tension. Notice that the strain, defined as in Equation 14.3,

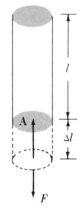

Figure 14.4.
Elasticity of length.

is a pure numeric, so that it has no units and the unit for E is the same as that for the stress. Although for any specimen that experiences an elongation or a contraction there is a simultaneous corresponding change in the transverse dimensions, only the change in the longitudinal dimension as given by Equation 14.4 is employed in calculating Young's modulus. Typical values of Young's modulus for some common materials are given in Table 14.1.

Table 14.1. *Representative elastic constants.*

| Material | Young's modulus E | | Shear modulus G | | Bulk modulus B | |
	pf/in²	nt/m²	pf/in²	nt/m²	pf/in²	nt/m²
Aluminum	10×10^6	69×10^9	3.9×10^6	26×10^9	8×10^6	55×10^9
Brass	13×10^6	90×10^9	5.1×10^6	35×10^9	16×10^6	110×10^9
Copper	16×10^6	110×10^9	6.0×10^6	41×10^9	18×10^6	124×10^9
Glass	9×10^6	62×10^9	3.6×10^6	25×10^9	5×10^6	34×10^9
Steel	29×10^6	200×10^9	11.6×10^6	80×10^9	24×10^6	165×10^9
Alcohol (ethyl)					16×10^4	110×10^7
Ether (ethyl)					9×10^4	60×10^7
Mercury					400×10^4	2800×10^7
Water					31×10^4	210×10^7

14.4.   Shear, or Rigidity, Modulus: Elasticity of Shape.   In Figure 14.2a was shown a rectangular block subjected to a shearing stress, the force F being applied parallel to the area A.   Representing the shearing stress by τ we have

$$\tau = \text{shearing stress} = F/A \qquad (14.5)$$

In this type of deformation the shape of the body changes but its volume remains the same.   Figure 14.5 shows a cross-sectional view of the undis-

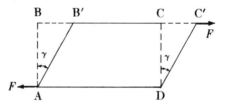

Figure 14.5. *Elasticity of shape.*

torted block ABCD and the distorted body AB'C'D under the action of a shearing stress.   Clearly, a representation of the amount of shearing strain is the ratio BB'/AB which is the tangent of the angle γ shown.   Hence

$$\text{shearing strain} = \tan \gamma \qquad (14.6)$$

Applying Equation 14.1 to this kind of deformation we have

$$G = \tau/\tan \gamma = \frac{F/A}{\tan \gamma} \qquad (14.7)$$

where the symbol G is employed to represent the *shear modulus* or *rigidity modulus*.   Again we note that the shear modulus has the unit of a force divided by an area. For most practical situations γ is small so that γ in radians may be employed in Equation 14.7 in place of $\tan \gamma$.

Only solids can exhibit a permanent shearing strain. Although a fluid can offer resistance to a shearing stress it exhibits no elasticity to one. Typical values of the shear modulus for some common materials are given in Table 14.1.

14.5. Bulk Modulus: Elasticity of Volume. Referring to Figure 14.2b, which shows a body of initial volume V subjected to the same normal force per unit area or the same increase in pressure Δp in all directions, we have

$$\text{volume stress} = \Delta p \tag{14.8}$$

For an isotropic body this increase in pressure is accompanied by a decrease in volume, $-\Delta V$, and the volume strain is defined as the fractional decrease in volume, or

$$\text{volume strain} = -\Delta V/V$$

Therefore, applying Equation 14.1 to this type of deformation, which results in a change in volume but not in shape, we have

$$B = -\frac{\Delta p}{\Delta V/V} \tag{14.9}$$

where the symbol B is used to represent the *bulk modulus*. Since $\Delta V/V$ is a pure numeric, the change in volume and the original volume being expressed in the same cubic units, B has the units of Δp or a force unit divided by an area unit. Since an increase in pressure is accompanied by a decrease in volume, ΔV is negative when Δp is positive and vice versa, so that B is always a positive quantity.

All states of matter possess volume elasticity, the bulk modulus of gases being very low and that of liquids and solids very high. Liquids and solids have bulk moduli that are of the same order of magnitude so that liquids are generally classed as relatively incompressible. It is convenient to utilize the *compressibility*, which is defined as the reciprocal of the bulk modulus. Representing the compressibility by the symbol κ we have

$$\kappa = \text{compressibility} = 1/B = -\Delta V/V\Delta p \tag{14.10}$$

the units for which are the square centimeter per dyne (cm²/dyne) in the cgs system, the square meter per newton (m²/nt) in the mks system, and the square foot per pound force (ft²/pf) or square inch per pound force (in²/pf) in the English gravitational system. However, compressibilities are ordinarily tabulated "per atmosphere" (atm⁻¹) where 1 atmosphere is equal to 1.0132×10^6 dynes/cm², 1.0132×10^5 nt/m², or 14.7 pf/in².

Typical values of the bulk modulus for some common materials or substances are given in Table 14.1.

14.6.   The Helical Spring.   The familiar and significant example that illustrates the truth of Hooke's law for rather large ranges of stress is the spiral or helical spring.   With such a spring it can easily be demonstrated that the applied stretching (or compressing) force F is directly proportional to the spring extension (or compression) displacement s, and Hooke's law for the spring is

$$F = Ks \tag{14.11}$$

where K, as we have previously indicated (see Section 11.1) is called the *force constant* or *stiffness coefficient* of the spring and is accurately constant over wide limits.   Equation 14.11, which is the same as Equation 11.2, may be inferred from Equation 14.4 which states that the applied force is proportional to the longitudinal displacement.   However, when a coiled spring is stretched the deformation of the wire out of which the spring is made is in the form of a twisting strain.   Nevertheless, within the limits of elasticity, the linear displacement of the spring is directly proportional to the applied force, as given by Equation 14.11.   It can be shown that the force constant K depends upon Young's modulus, the rigidity modulus, the spring wire radius, the length of the wire forming the coiled spring, and the radius of the coil.

At this point the student should again read the material having to do with the spring in Sections 11.1 and 11.4.   There it was shown that the elastic potential energy of the spring when elongated or compressed through a distance s from its unstretched configuration is

$$E_{\mathrm{P}} = \tfrac{1}{2}Ks^2 \tag{14.12}$$

This is the work that can be done by the internal elastic force when the applied force is removed and the body returns to its initial configuration, to which is assigned the state of zero potential energy.   The internal elastic restoring force is at all times equal and opposite to the external applied force and when F in Equation 14.11 is thought of as the internal elastic force, then F and s are opposite in direction and a minus sign must be inserted in the right-hand side of the equation.   Then the elastic potential energy as given by Equation 14.12 is the negative of the work done by the internal elastic force when the spring returns from a distorted state to its undeformed state.

14.7.   Torsion of Cylindrical Shells and Rods.   When a thin-walled hollow cylinder, or a solid cylindrical rod, is twisted about its longitudinal axis by keeping one end fixed and applying a torque to the other end, the resulting deformation is one of pure shear.   In each case Hooke's law for rotation is obeyed and the applied torque is directly proportional to the angular twist.

First consider the hollow cylinder of mean radius r, length l, and wall thickness Δr shown in Figure 14.6.   The lower end is assumed to be clamped while the upper end, under the action of a torque indicated by the arrows, is shown twisted through an angle θ.   Any circular section is twisted through an angle which is proportional to its vertical distance above the fixed end. The shearing strain is tan γ and, since γ is small in the elastic range, we have

$$\text{shearing strain} = \gamma = r\theta/l \qquad (14.13)$$

The tangential force, creating the torque across any circular section, is distributed over the area $2\pi r\,\Delta r$ so that the torque L is given by

$$L = (2\pi r\,\Delta r)(\tau r) \qquad (14.14)$$

where τ is the shearing stress defined by Equation 14.5. From Equation 14.7 $\tau = \gamma G$, and using Equation 14.13 we have

$$L = 2\pi G\theta r^3\,\Delta r/l \qquad (14.15)$$

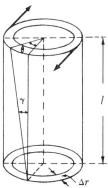

where G is the shear modulus as defined by Equation 14.7. Equation 14.15 gives the relationship between the applied torque and the angular twist and shows that L is directly proportional to θ, the proportionality constant (called the torsion constant of the cylindrical shell) being given by $2\pi Gr^3\,\Delta r/l$. Hence, if experimentally determined values of L and θ are plotted for a cylindrical shell clamped at one end, the slope of the resulting straight line yields the value of the shear modulus since r, l, and Δr for the hollow cylindrical sample are known. The propor-

Figure 14.6. *Torsion of a thin-walled cylindrical shell.*

tionality constant is measured in torque units per radian: the centimeter-dyne per radian (cm·dyne/rad), the meter-newton per radian (m·nt/rad), or the pound-force–foot per radian (pf·ft/rad).

The above development can now readily be extended to the case of a solid cylindrical rod or a wire. The left column of the divided page gives an algebraic treatment while in the right column the same result is achieved by the use of calculus.

Consider that the solid cylinder is composed of a large number n of concentric cylindrical shells like that in Figure 14.6, of mean radii $r_1, r_2, r_3, \ldots, r_n$ and corresponding wall thicknesses Δr_1, Δr_2, Δr_3, $\ldots$, Δr_n. Equation 14.15 gives the torque necessary to twist any hollow cylinder, and the total torque, being a sum of the individual torques, is given by

$$L = (2\pi G\theta/l) \lim_{n\to\infty} (r_1{}^3\Delta r_1 + r_2{}^3\Delta r_2$$

$$+ r_3{}^3\Delta r_3 + \cdots + r_n{}^3\Delta r_n)$$

where the sum in parentheses is to be evaluated in the limit as n approaches

Consider that the solid cylinder or rod is divided into cylindrical shells like that in Figure 14.6, each of mean radius ρ and wall thickness $d\rho$. Then the elementary torque necessary to twist such a cylindrical shell through an angle θ is given by Equation 14.15 where L is replaced by dL, r is replaced by ρ, and Δr is replaced by $d\rho$. Then:

$$dL = \frac{2\pi G\theta\rho^3\,d\rho}{l}$$

The total torque is obtained by integrating the element of torque from a value $\rho = 0$ to the value $\rho = r$ where r is the radius of the solid cylinder.

infinity. In evaluating this sum we shall for simplicity take the wall thicknesses all equal, so that $\Delta r_1 = \Delta r_2 = \Delta r_3 = \ldots = \Delta r_n = \Delta r$. Also, when n approaches in the limit an infinitely large number we have $r_1 = \Delta r, r_2 = 2\Delta r, r_3 = 3\Delta r, \ldots, r_n = n\Delta r$. Then

$$L = (2\pi G\theta/l) \lim_{n\to\infty} (\Delta r)^4 (1^3 + 2^3 + 3^3 + \cdots + n^3)$$

It can be shown by algebra that the sum of the series $1^3 + 2^3 + 3^3 + \ldots + n^3$ is represented by $(n^2/4)(n+1)^2$. Also, $\Delta r = r/n$ where r is the radius of the cylinder. Therefore

$$L = (2\pi G\theta/l) \lim_{n\to\infty} (r^4/n^4)(n^2/4)(n+1)^2$$

$$= (\pi G\theta r^4/2l) \lim_{n\to\infty} (1 + 1/n)^2$$

and this leads to

$$L = \pi Gr^4\theta/2l \qquad (14.16)$$

Therefore:

$$L = \frac{2\pi G\theta}{l} \int_0^r \rho^3 \, d\rho$$

Integrating leads to the equation:

$$L = \pi Gr^4\theta/2l \qquad (14.16)$$

For a given cylindrical rod or wire of radius r, length l, and shear modulus G, the applied torque is directly proportional to the angle of twist, or

$$L = C\theta \qquad (14.17)$$

where the constant of proportionality $C = \pi Gr^4/2l$ is called the *torsion constant* of the rod or wire. By plotting experimentally applied values of L against the corresponding observed values of θ a straight line may be obtained within the limit of elasticity, showing that Hooke's law for rotation is obeyed. A measure of the slope of the line yields the torsion constant C, which in turn leads to the determination of the shear modulus G. Notice that C is a constant for a given specimen whereas G is a constant that is independent of the dimensions of the specimen. We shall make use of Equation 14.16 in our study of periodic rotary motion in the next chapter.

By arguments similar to those employed for the spring in Sections 11.1 and 11.4 it can be shown—and this is left as an exercise in Problem 14.25— that the elastic potential energy stored in a cylindrical rod or wire which has been twisted through an angle θ is given by

$$E_P = \tfrac{1}{2}C\theta^2 \qquad (14.18)$$

This represents the work that could be done by the internal elastic torque when the applied torque is removed and the rod or wire returns to its initial untwisted configuration.

14.8. Poisson's Ratio. Let us here return to a more exact consideration of what happens when a body is subjected to a longitudinal tension or compression. We have indicated that the longitudinal strain is represented by the fractional change in length, $\Delta l/l$, whose magnitude is controlled by Young's modulus. Actually, however, when a body is subjected to tension or compression there is a change in length and a simultaneous change in the lateral or transverse dimension. This is illustrated in Figure 14.7 which shows a wire of original dimensions l and d subjected to a stretching force F. In addition to the longitudinal increase in length Δl there is a transverse contraction Δd resulting in two components of strain, a longitudinal component $\Delta l/l$ and a transverse component $\Delta d/d$. Experiment shows that the ratio of the transverse component to the longitudinal component of strain is practically a constant; it is called Poisson's ratio. Denoting this ratio by ϵ we have

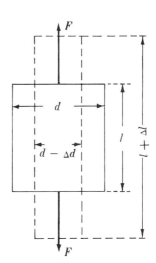

$$\epsilon = \frac{\Delta d/d}{\Delta l/l} \qquad (14.19)$$

Figure 14.7. *Poisson's ratio.*

The Poisson ratio ϵ, named in honor of S. D. Poisson (1781–1840) who introduced it, is a dimensionless quantity whose value lies between $1/4$ and $1/2$ for almost all bodies. Analysis shows (see Problem 14.28) that a body under tension always experiences an increase in volume, and under compression it experiences a decrease in volume; in each case, $\epsilon < 1/2$. When $\epsilon = 1/2$, there is no change in volume.

14.9. Remarks Concerning Elastic Moduli. Elastic moduli are used by engineers in the design and construction of all kinds of structures, and the elastic coefficient the most frequently employed is Young's modulus. There are also many situations which demand the application of the shear modulus, such as in the construction of a torsion balance or in the determination of the greatest amount of power that can be transmitted along an automobile drive shaft. In all applications it must be kept in mind that the elastic moduli are functions of the temperature and the design of a member must take into account any attendant variations in temperature.

Of the three basic elastic moduli which we defined for an isotropic medium only two are independent. For instance, we have seen that the stretching of a wire, governed by the Poisson ratio, actually involves a change in shape and a change in volume; this illustrates the fact that various elastic changes are expressible in terms of the shear and bulk changes. As an example, it can be shown that, for an isotropic solid, Young's modulus E is expressible in terms of the shear modulus G and the bulk modulus B as

$$E = 9BG/(3B + G) \qquad (14.20)$$

The relationship contained in Equation 14.20 is most useful in calculating B since, although E and G are relatively easy to determine experimentally, it is very difficult to determine B directly. Another relationship that is useful is

$$\epsilon = \frac{E}{2G} - 1 \qquad (14.21)$$

which expresses the Poisson ratio in terms of Young's modulus and the shear modulus.

Solid metals are isotropic with respect to their elastic properties, and the above considerations and relationships apply. However, for materials that are elastically anisotropic—that is, those that possess different elastic properties in different directions—more than two basic independent moduli are needed for a description of their elastic behavior. For the most general type of anisotropic body no less than twenty-one elastic constants are required to describe completely its elastic behavior.

Example 14.1. A steel wire 50.0 inches in length and 0.200 inch in diameter is subjected to a tensile force of 1.00×10^3 pounds. Find (**a**) the stress, (**b**) the strain, and (**c**) the length of the wire under load.

Solution. (**a**) Using Equation 14.2:

$$\sigma = F/A = 1000\ \text{pf}/\pi(0.100)^2\ \text{in}^2 = 31.8 \times 10^3\ \text{pf/in}^2$$

(**b**) From Table 14.1, $E = 29 \times 10^6$ pf/in². Now, applying Hooke's law,

$$\text{longitudinal strain} = \sigma/E = \frac{31.8 \times 10^3\ \text{pf/in}^2}{29 \times 10^6\ \text{pf/in}^2}$$

$$= 1.1 \times 10^{-3}$$

(**c**) From Equation 14.3:

$$\Delta l = 1.1 \times 10^{-3} \times 50.0\ \text{in} = 0.055\ \text{in}$$

and the final length is 50.1 inches.

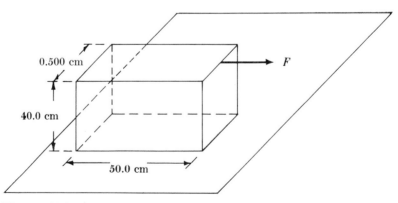

Figure 14.8.

Example 14.2. An aluminum plate of dimensions shown in Figure 14.8 protrudes above a foundation to which it is securely fastened. Find the force F necessary to shear the top of the plate a distance of 0.0200 cm.

Solution. From Equation 14.7 the force is given by $F = GA \tan \gamma$. Here

$$G = 26 \times 10^9 \text{ nt/m}^2 = 26 \times 10^{10} \text{ dynes/cm}^2$$
$$A = 50 \times 0.50 = 25 \text{ cm}^2$$
$$\tan \gamma = 0.020/40 = 5.0 \times 10^{-4}$$

Therefore $F = (26 \times 10^{10})(25)(5.0 \times 10^{-4}) = 3.4 \times 10^9$ dynes.

Example 14.3. One end of a long brass cylindrical rod is clamped tightly and a torque of 10.0 m·nt is applied to the other end which thus rotates through 4.00 degrees. Find (**a**) the torsion constant, (**b**) the radius of the rod if its length is 1.00 m, and (**c**) the potential energy of the twisted rod.

Solution. (**a**) Using Equation 14.17:

$$C = L/\theta = \frac{10.0 \text{ m·nt}}{4.00 \text{ deg} \times \dfrac{\pi}{180} \times \dfrac{\text{rad}}{\text{deg}}} = 143 \text{ m·nt/rad}$$

(**b**) Applying Equation 14.16:

$$r^4 = \frac{2lC}{\pi G} = \frac{2 \times 1.00 \text{ m} \times 143 \text{ m·nt/rad}}{\pi \times 35 \times 10^9 \text{ nt/m}^2}$$
$$r = 9.5 \times 10^{-3} \text{ m} = 9.5 \text{ mm}$$

(**c**) The elastic potential energy is obtained from Equation 14.18:

$$E_p = \tfrac{1}{2}C\theta^2 = (143 \text{ m·nt/rad})(4\pi/180 \text{ rad})^2 = 0.696 \text{ joule}$$

Example 14.4. Find the increase in pressure required to decrease the volume of 1.0000 cm³ of water to 0.9999 cm³.

Solution. Applying Equation 14.9, the increase in pressure is

$$\Delta p = -B \frac{\Delta V}{V}$$

Here $B = 210 \times 10^7$ nt/m² and $\Delta V = -(1.0000 - 0.9999) = -0.0001$ cm³. Therefore:

$$\Delta p = 210 \times 10^7 \frac{\text{nt}}{\text{m}^2} \times \frac{0.0001 \text{ cm}^3}{1 \text{ cm}^3} = 2 \times 10^5 \text{ nt/m}^2$$

Problems

Where necessary employ the values of elastic moduli given in Table 14.1.

14.1. A copper wire 10.0 m in length and 1.60 mm in diameter supports a mass of 5.00 kgm. Find (**a**) the stress, (**b**) the strain, and (**c**) the elongation.

14.2. A steel bar 25.0 feet long, 4.00 inches wide, and 1/4 inch thick, stretches 0.150 inch when subjected to a tensile force. Find (**a**) the strain, (**b**) the stress, and (**c**) the tensile force.

14.3. An aluminum rod whose diameter is 0.200 inch supports a 400-pound mass suspended from its end. (**a**) The elastic limit is 19×10^3 pounds-force/square-inch. Will the rod return to its initial length when the load is removed? (**b**) What per cent change in length occurs when the load is present?

14.4. A vertical steel cylindrical pier is needed to support a load of 50.0 tons force. The pier is to be 20.0 feet high and the allowable stress 2.00×10^4 pounds-force/square-inch. Find (**a**) the radius of the pier and (**b**) the length of the pier when supporting the load.

14.5. Wire A has a length of 100 cm and a diameter of 2.00 mm. Wire B has a length of 150 cm and a diameter of 1.00 mm. The same tensile force produces an elongation of 0.100 mm in wire A and 0.0750 mm in wire B. Find the ratio of the Young's moduli of the wires.

14.6. A brass wire of length 30.0 cm is joined end to end, to a steel wire of length 50.0 cm. When a tensile force is applied the combined wire stretches to a length of 80.0400 cm. If the diameter of the brass wire is 1.60 mm and that of the steel wire is 0.800 mm, what is the stretch experienced by each wire?

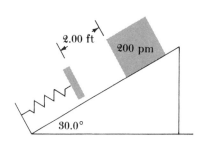

Figure 14.9. *Problem 14.7.*

14.7. The block shown in Figure 14.9 starts from rest in the position shown and is brought to rest by the spring which has a force constant of 50.0 pounds-force/inch. Find (**a**) the maximum compression of the spring in bringing the block to rest and (**b**) the maximum velocity of the block. The coefficient of friction between block and plane is 0.200. Neglect the mass of the spring. (*Hint:* See Example 11.10 and Problem 11.37.)

14.8. An elevator whose mass is 2.50 tons is moving down with a velocity of 8.00 feet/sec when the cable drum is suddenly stopped. Consider that the supporting cable behaves as if it were equivalent to an elastic spring with a force constant of 0.750 tons-force/inch, and find the maximum tensile force experienced by the cable. (*Hint:* Apply the work-energy theorem.)

14.9. A mass m hangs in equilibrium from a vertical spring whose force constant is K. The mass is pulled down a distance s and then released from rest. Show that the speed with which the mass passes upward through the equilibrium position is given by $s\sqrt{K/m}$.

14.10. A truck weighing 3.20×10^3 pounds force and moving at 10.0 feet/sec to the right, as indicated by the arrow in Figure 14.10, is brought to rest by the bumber shields A and B. After striking A, how far has the truck moved before being brought to rest? The force constants of each of the springs attached to A is 500 pounds-force/inch and that attached to B is 5.00×10^3 pounds-force/inch.

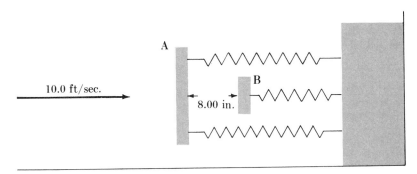

Figure 14.10. *Problem 14.10.*

14.11. A parallelopiped of jelly is 8.00 inches high, 6.00 inches wide, and 4.00 inches thick. A sheairng force of 0.500 ounce, applied by means of a layer of waxed paper adhering to the top surface of the jelly, displaces the top 0.800 inch. Find (**a**) the stress, (**b**) the strain, and (**c**) the shear modulus of the jelly.

14.12. A solid aluminum cube, 27.0 cm³ in volume, is subjected to forces of 8.10×10^3 nt applied parallel to two of its opposite faces. Find (**a**) the stress and (**b**) the angle of shear.

14.13. If the force in Problem 14.12 is applied normal to each of the faces of the cube, what is the percentage decrease in the length of a cube edge?

14.14. Using Equation 14.20 calculate E, employing the values of B and G for the solids listed in Table 14.1. Can you explain why some of the calculated values vary somewhat from those listed in the table?

14.15. Find the increase in pressure necessary to decrease the volume of one cubic centimeter of water by one part in one million.

14.16. For each of the liquids listed in Table 14.1 find the compressibility in reciprocal atmospheres (atm⁻¹). One atmosphere is 14.7 pounds-force/square-inch.

14.17. A certain oil used in a hydraulic machine has a volume of 6.00 cubic feet. When subjected to an increase in pressure of 1.50×10^3 pounds-force/square-inch the oil decreases in volume by 30.0 cubic inches. Find the compressibility of the oil.

14.18. Find the ratio of the density of water at a point in the interior of a lake to the density of the water at the surface. The pressure at the interior point due to the water above it is 5.000×10^4 pounds-force/square-foot. (*Hint:* Density is defined as mass per unit volume.)

14.19. A solid cylindrical rod 1.00 m long and 2.00 mm in radius is securely clamped at one end and a torque of 1.50 m·nt is applied at the free end. If the free end twists through an angle of 30.0° what is the shear modulus of the rod?

14.20. Find the angle through which the free end of a solid cylindrical copper rod will twist when a torque of 100 pounds-force–inch is applied to it. The length of the rod is 50.0 inches and its diameter is 0.250 inch.

14.21. A solid cylindrical rod A has a radius of 4.00 mm, and a hollow cylindrical rod B of the same material has the same length, the same mean radius, and a wall thickness of 1.00 mm. Find the ratio of the torques required to produce equal twists in the rods.

14.22. A solid steel torque rod of length 4.00 feet and radius 0.500 inch is delivering 10.0 horsepower at a speed of 25.0 revolutions/sec. Find the amount by which the rod is twisted.

14.23. A glass tube 50.0 cm in length, 1.50 cm in mean radius, and 3.00 mm in wall thickness is securely fastened at one end; a torque is applied at the other end which twists through 0.0100 radian. Find (**a**) the torsion constant and (**b**) the applied torque.

14.24. Find the radius of a solid cylindrical steel shaft that will transmit 10.0 kilowatts of power at a speed of 30.0 revolutions/sec. The shaft has a length of 200 cm and can have a maximum twist of 5.00°.

14.25. Show that the elastic potential energy stored in a cylindrical wire which has been twisted through an angle θ is $C\theta^2/2$ where C is the torsion constant. Employ methods similar to those used in Section 11.1.

Figure 14.11.
Problem 14.26.

14.26. Figure 14.11 shows a disk suspended by a vertical copper wire which obeys Hooke's law for torsional displacements. When a torque of 2.00 pound-force–foot is applied to the disk it turns through an angle $\theta = 28.0°$. Find (**a**) the elastic potential energy stored in the wire when its lower end is twisted through this angle and (**b**) the length of the wire if its radius is 1/16 inch.

14.27. Combine Equations 14.20 and 14.21 and obtain the relationships

$$\epsilon = \frac{3B - 2G}{2(3B + 2G)} \quad \text{and} \quad \epsilon = \frac{3B - E}{6B}$$

14.28. Show that when a cylindrical rod is under tension it always experiences an increase in volume, while when it is under compression it always experiences a decrease in volume, and that in each case the Poisson ratio ϵ is less than 1/2. Show also that when $\epsilon = 1/2$ there is no change in volume. (*Hint:* The fractional change in length and the fractional change in radius are each small in comparison to 1.)

14.29. A wire, whose length and radius are 6.00 feet and 0.100 inch, respectively, supports a weight of 100 pounds force suspended from its end. Young's modulus for the wire is 15.0×10^6 pounds-force/square-inch and its shear modulus is 5.50×10^6 pounds-force/square-inch. Find (**a**) the increase in length and (**b**) the decrease in radius.

Simple Harmonic Motion

*L*ET US HERE RECAPITULATE the kinds of motion we have thus far treated. We studied motion with constant velocity, which results in a state of equilibrium; this, for translation, means that there is no unbalanced force, that there is motion with zero linear acceleration, and for rotation it means that there is no unbalanced torque, that there is motion with zero angular acceleration. We also studied motion with constant acceleration; this invariably involves either a constant unbalanced force for translation or a constant unbalanced torque for rotation. In each of the developments it was one of our principal aims to arrive at expressions for the energy of the body or bodies of a system, and this involved obtaining expressions for the position and velocity of the body as a function of the time.

The next step in mechanics is to study the motion of a body when the resultant force or torque acting is not constant but takes on different values as the body moves. Such a variable force (magnitude, direction, or both), causing a variable acceleration, can occur in a variety of ways, some of which introduce such complications as to make the motion extremely difficult, if not impossible, to analyze in detail. Fortunately, however, it turns out that it is not very useful to obtain a general solution corresponding to any type of force variation. It is more practical in physics and engineering to consider the different kinds of variable-force motions that commonly occur in nature and treat these individually. One such kind of motion that is particularly important and has wide application in physics and engineering is the kind that brings into play the elastic restoring force or torque which we met in the previous chapter. When an elastic body is distorted by an applied force and then released it vibrates or oscillates about the equilibrium position. It is precisely motion of this kind with which we will be concerned in this chapter, and we shall see that the most significant kind of variation is the one in which the restoring force or torque is proportional and opposite in direction to the corresponding linear or angular displacement. Such motion is *periodic*, the pattern of motion repeating over and over again after equal intervals of time, and is termed *simple harmonic motion* (SHM) because of the particular law of force variation.

Common examples of this kind of motion, whose characteristics we shall soon develop, are the vibratory up-and-down motion experienced by a body at the end of a vertical spring which has been stretched and then released, the vibrations of strings and air columns of musical instruments, the torsional vibrations of the balance wheel of a watch, and the vibrations of bridges and other structures. From a practical engineering point of view may be mentioned the fact that often there are present undesirable vibrations in machines. These are periodic motions that are in general very complicated but, as we shall see, they can quite effectively be analyzed as combinations of the simple harmonic vibrations. It is fortunate that such a procedure yields a practical solution, for it then becomes possible to make a study of, and avoid, excessive stresses, uneven wear, and unwanted noise, all of which may result from improper balance of a rotating machine.

The subject of mechanical vibrations and oscillations is extremely significant in all phases of physics and engineering, and the student is urged to master the developments in this chapter and thus acquire a background that is basic and of extreme practical importance.

15.1.   Linear Simple Harmonic Motion.   Consider Figure 15.1, which shows a particle P oscillating along the x axis through a central position O and between equally spaced positions Q and Q'. The position of P at any time is represented by its displacement x from the point O. It is clear that P could have a great variety of motions, depending upon the nature of the force to which it is subject. However, there is one kind of motion that is of great practical significance, and the corresponding nature of the force is such that it causes the particle to exhibit the following periodic behavior. The speed of P varies from a value zero at the end points Q and Q', where the particle reverses in direction, to a maximum value at the midpoint O. In between

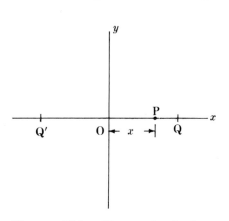

Figure 15.1. *Linear simple harmonic motion.*

Q or Q' and O the square of the speed is a linear function of the square of the displacement x. An equivalent way of describing this behavior is to state that the magnitude of the acceleration of P is a maximum at the end points Q or Q' and is zero at O. For P to pass point O with maximum speed and zero acceleration, and reach points Q and Q' with zero speed and maximum acceleration, the acceleration must always be directed toward the point O and hence in a direction opposite to that of the displacement. In order that P of mass m may have this kind of periodic behavior its variable acceleration a must have the form

$$a = -\omega^2 x \tag{15.1}$$

where ω is a proportionality constant whose physical significance will be brought out later. The corresponding force F acting on P must be

$$F = ma = -m\omega^2 x$$

or $\qquad\qquad F = -Kx \qquad\qquad\qquad\qquad (15.2)$

with $\qquad\qquad K = m\omega^2 \qquad\qquad\qquad\qquad (15.3)$

where K is a constant for any given vibratory mass. Equation 15.1 or 15.2 defines the important type of motion known as *linear simple harmonic motion*. It says that the acceleration is proportional, and opposite in direction, to the displacement, and Equation 15.2 says that the force acting on the oscillating mass is proportional, and opposite in direction, to the displacement. We therefore define linear SHM as follows: *Linear SHM is straight-line to-and-fro motion in which the acceleration (and hence the force) is directly proportional to the displacement of the vibrating mass from a fixed point on that line and always directed toward the fixed point.*

Equation 15.1 or 15.2 completely and uniquely defines linear SHM; conversely, when a vibrating or oscillating mass has an acceleration or a force that is given by Equation 15.1 or 15.2 respectively, the mass must be executing linear SHM. The sign of a and F is at all instants opposite to that of x, thus always yielding a positive value for ω^2 and K. When P in Figure 15.1 is to the right of O, x is positive and both a and F are negative, while when P is to the left of O, x is negative and both a and F are positive. Since P always experiences an acceleration and force which are directed to the origin, the force in Equation 15.2 is called a *restoring force*, and the origin, being the position where this restoring force has a zero value, is called the *equilibrium position*.

When a body vibrates with linear SHM it periodically makes equal excursions on both sides of the equilibrium position, and the displacement OQ or OQ′ in Figure 15.1, when the body is instantaneously at one of its extreme positions, is called the *amplitude*. The motion is periodic: it repeats itself in equal intervals of time. The time for a complete vibration or oscillation is known as the *period*, T, which is represented, for example, by the time it takes P in Figure 15.1 to oscillate over the path OQOQ′O. One completed oscillation or vibration is also referred to as a *cycle*, so the units used to designate the period are vibrations per second or cycles per second. The reciprocal of the period has the units seconds per cycle or seconds per vibration and represents the *frequency*, f, of the periodic motion. It is obvious that

$$T = 1/f \qquad \text{or} \qquad f = 1/T \qquad\qquad (15.4)$$

Although the character of some periodic oscillations is such that there is present only one single frequency or period, there are other vibratory motions, such as sound vibrations, in which there are present simultaneously many different periods. As we shall show later in this chapter, when the instantaneous displacement of a vibratory motion is plotted against the time, there result the mathematical sine or cosine curves which are called *harmonic curves*, and the term *harmonic motion* stems from the early application of harmonic curves to the analysis of sound vibrations. It is for a vibratory motion in which there is present only one period that we reserve the descriptive phrase "simple harmonic motion" which is uniquely defined by Equation 15.1 or 15.2. More complicated, multiple, periodic vibrations are describa'ıle in terms of individual-component simple harmonic vibrations in accordance with the mathematically established work of Fourier (1768–1830) who showed that any complex periodic vibration may be built up or represented by the superposition of a number of suitably chosen simple harmonic vibrations. Therefore, we concentrate on learning the aspects of simple harmonic motion and then apply the *Fourier theorem* to the analysis of complex periodic harmonic motions.

15.2.   The Circle of Reference and Period of SHM.   In pursuing further the study of SHM it turns out that it is very useful to find an ideally dynamic situation that theoretically gives rise to a to-and-fro motion that is perfect simple harmonic motion, i.e., one that obeys Equation 15.1 or 15.2. The solution reveals several significant facts: first, we emerge with the result that there is a close relationship between uniform circular motion and simple harmonic motion; second, this relationship makes it possible to assign physical significance to the constant ω in Equation 15.1; third, we arrive at a generalized means of evaluating the period and frequency of the simple harmonic motion. Let us now see how all this comes about.

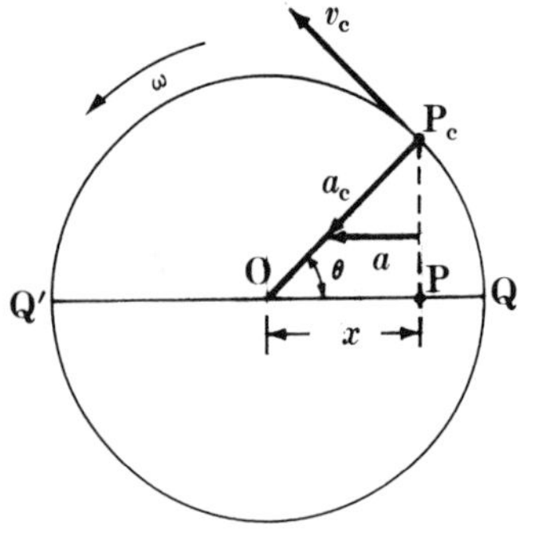

Figure 15.2.   *The circle of reference in simple harmonic motion.*

Figure 15.2 shows a particle P_c rotating in a circle of radius r with uniform speed v_c and angular speed ω. We have already investigated the characteristics of this kind of motion and have found in Section 9.1 that P_c experiences a constant linear acceleration a_c which is always centrally directed toward O and has a magnitude $a_c = v^2/r = \omega^2 r$, as stated by Equations 9.1 and 9.2. We recall also that the angular speed ω in radians per second is given by $\omega = 2\pi f$ where f is the frequency in revolutions per second or cycles per second.

Now consider the type of motion that a particle would execute if it were situated at P, which is the projection of P_c on the horizontal diameter Q′Q. As P_c rotates counterclockwise from Q to Q′, P moves along a straight line from Q to Q′, and when P_c rotates from Q′ to Q, P retraces its linear path by going from Q′ to Q. Hence, when P_c completes one cycle of motion, P executes one to-and-fro vibratory cycle and the period of vibration coincides with the period of rotation $2\pi/\omega$. The acceleration a of the projection particle P is given by the horizontal component of the acceleration of P_c or, taking the positive direction along OQ,

$$a = -a_c \cos \theta \qquad (15.5)$$

The negative sign is necessary because the acceleration of P is to the left, in the negative direction.   Substituting x/r for $\cos \theta$ and v_c^2/r for a_c we have

$$a = -\frac{v_c^2}{r^2} x$$

or

$$a = -\omega^2 x \qquad (15.6)$$

We thus emerge with the result that the to-and-fro vibratory motion of P is of such a character that its acceleration is directly proportional to its displacement from the point O and opposite in direction to this displacement. At the instant shown in Figure 15.2 and for θ between $+90°$ and $-90°$, a is negative and x is positive.   For angles θ which are greater than $90°$ and less than $270°$, a is positive and x is negative.   We thus see (compare Equations 15.6 and 15.1) that the projection particle P executes a to-and-fro motion which is simple harmonic motion.   In fact, we may now alternatively define linear SHM as *the motion of the projection on a straight line of a point which rotates with uniform circular motion, the straight line being in the plane of the circle.*

The point P_c is called the *reference point* and the circle in which it rotates is called the *reference circle*.   Since Equation 15.6 is identical with Equation 15.1, which was introduced to define SHM, and since ω in Equation 15.6 has the physical significance of being the angular speed of the reference point, we see that the period is the same for the particle executing SHM as for the particle moving with uniform circular motion.   This period T, from Equation 15.6, is related to a and x:

$$a = \frac{-4\pi^2}{T^2} x$$

or

$$T = 2\pi \sqrt{-x/a} \qquad (15.7)$$

in which x and a have opposite signs so that T is always positive.   In terms of the vibratory mass, the period, from Equation 15.3, is

$$T = 2\pi \sqrt{m/K} \qquad (15.8)$$

where K is the negative of the force per unit displacement as given by Equation 15.2.

Whenever a mass oscillates with linear SHM and with a given amplitude we set up or imagine the presence of a reference point and circle of reference of radius equal to the amplitude of the vibratory motion.   We may then apply Equations 15.6, 15.7, and 15.8 to the vibratory motion.   Notice that the period depends only upon the vibratory mass and the constant K and is independent of r, the amplitude of vibration.   It is clear that T is in seconds per cycle, whether m is in grams mass and K is in dynes per centimeter, or m

is in kilograms mass and K is in newtons per meter, or m is in slugs and K is in pounds force per foot.

15.3. Velocity in Linear SHM. Equation 15.1 makes it possible to calculate for all values of displacement the acceleration of a body executing SHM. It is also convenient to have an expression that enables us to calculate the velocity of the body for all values of displacement. This is readily obtained from Figure 15.2. There we observe that the velocity v of the projection point P is the horizontal component of the velocity v_c of the reference particle. Hence

$$v = -v_c \sin \theta \qquad (15.9)$$

Substituting for $\sin \theta$ its equivalent $\sqrt{r^2 - x^2}/r$ we have

$$v = \frac{v_c}{r} \sqrt{r^2 - x^2}$$

or

$$v = \omega\sqrt{r^2 - x^2} = 2\pi f\sqrt{r^2 - x^2} \qquad (15.10)$$

the square root yielding a plus value when the oscillating body is moving to the right and a minus value when it is moving to the left. Equation 15.10 states that $v^2 = \omega^2 r^2 - \omega^2 x^2$ which shows that the square of the speed in SHM is a linear function of the square of the displacement. The equation yields the value of v for any value of x, and again we see that when $x = 0$ the body is at the equilibrium position and its speed is a maximum, while when x is equal to the maximum displacement $+r$ or $-r$ the body is at the end points of its motion and its speed is zero.

15.4. Representation of Displacement, Velocity, and Acceleration as Functions of Time in SHM. The time dependence of displacement, velocity, and acceleration may readily be stated with the aid of Figure 15.2. The left column below gives this presentation in elementary form while the right column presents the calculus treatment.

We have seen from Figure 15.2 that the displacement x, the velocity v, and the acceleration a in linear SHM are given by

$$x = r \cos \theta$$
$$v = -v_c \sin \theta = -\omega r \sin \theta$$
$$a = -a_c \cos \theta = -\omega^2 r \cos \theta$$

where θ is known as the *phase angle* or simply the *phase* of the motion. The angle θ varies uniformly with the time

Expressing the acceleration as the time derivative of the velocity, Equation 15.1 defining linear SHM may be written

$$dv/dt = -\omega^2 x$$

To integrate this equation multiply both members by $2v$. Then, since $v\,dt = dx$,

$$2v\,dv = -2\omega^2 xv\,dt = -2\omega^2 x\,dx$$

Integrating yields

$$v^2 = -\omega^2 x^2 + c_1$$

t, and if at $t = 0$ the reference point P_c in Figure 15.2 is located such that the radius from O to P_c makes an angle θ_0 with the horizontal, then θ is, in general, given by

$$\theta = \omega t + \theta_0$$

where θ_0 is known as the *phase constant*. However, if we reckon time from the instant that P_c is at Q, then, when $t = 0$, $\theta = 0$ so that $\theta_0 = 0$. Hence $\theta = \omega t$ and the expressions for displacement, velocity, and acceleration as functions of time are

$$x = r \cos \omega t \qquad (15.11a)$$
$$v = -\omega r \sin \omega t$$
$$= \frac{-2\pi r}{T} \sin \omega t \qquad (15.11b)$$
$$a = -\omega^2 r \cos \omega t$$
$$= \frac{-4\pi^2 r}{T^2} \cos \omega t \qquad (15.11c)$$

where T, as before, stands for the period of the motion.

To evaluate the constant of integration c_1 we take, as the initial condition, that when $x = r$ in Figure 15.2 then $v = 0$. Then $c_1 = \omega^2 r^2$ and we now have

$$v = \omega \sqrt{r^2 - x^2}$$

which we recognize as Equation 15.10. Now substituting dx/dt for v and rearranging we have

$$dx/\sqrt{r^2 - x^2} = \omega \, dt$$

Integration yields

$$-\cos^{-1}(x/r) = \omega t + \theta_0$$
and $\qquad x = r \cos(\omega t + \theta_0)$

where the constant of integration θ_0 is known as the *phase constant*. To evaluate it, we consider that when $t = 0$, P is at Q so that $x = r$. Then $\theta_0 = 0$ and

$$x = r \cos \omega t \qquad (15.11a)$$

which expresses the displacement as a function of the time. The dependence of velocity on time is obtained by differentiating Equation 15.11a with respect to time, yielding

$$v = -\omega r \sin \omega t$$
$$= \frac{-2\pi r}{T} \sin \omega t \qquad (15.11b)$$

and differentiating v with respect to time gives the acceleration:

$$a = -\omega^2 r \cos \omega t$$
$$= \frac{-4\pi^2 r}{T^2} \cos \omega t \qquad (15.11c)$$

where T is the period of the motion.

It is helpful to keep in mind the graphs of Equations 15.11a, 15.11b, and 15.11c. These are shown in Figure 15.3 which depicts displacement, velocity, and acceleration as functions of time. The time scale is in fractions of a period T. The graphs clearly reveal that when the displacement is zero the velocity is a maximum and the acceleration is zero, while when the displacement is a maximum and equal to the amplitude the velocity is zero and the acceleration is a maximum. The fact that the acceleration is opposite in direction to the displacement is seen by comparing graph (a) with graph (c).

15.5. Energy Relations in Linear SHM. Let us now analyze the motion of the particle P in Figure 15.2 from the viewpoint of energy and see what energy relationships are involved in simple harmonic motion. We recall that when P is moving to the right of O there is a restoring force $F = -Kx$ acting on it to the left and when P is moving to the left of O this restoring force acts to the right. Hence, to give the oscillating particle a displacement outward from O, work must be done against this force F and the particle ac-

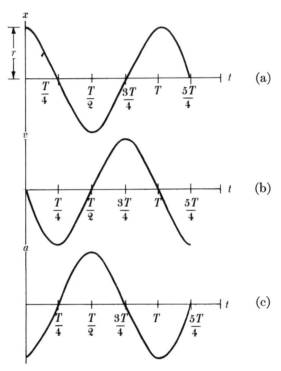

Figure 15.3. *Graphs of:* (a) *displacement,* (b) *velocity, and* (c) *acceleration, as functions of time.*

quires potential energy with respect to O. As P moves outward from O its potential energy increases and its kinetic energy decreases. At the end points Q and Q′ the velocity of the particle is zero, its kinetic energy is zero, and it possesses the maximum potential energy. When the particle moves from Q or Q′ to O its potential energy is continuously converted into kinetic energy and when P is at O the potential energy is zero and all of the energy is in kinetic form. In between O and Q the particle possesses in part kinetic and in part potential energy. In the absence of frictional effects mechanical energy is conserved and the potential plus kinetic energy is at all times constant.

To obtain an expression for the total energy we consider that the particle is passing a point distant x from O with a velocity v. Since the restoring force is proportional to the displacement, the average force needed to overcome the restoring force is $Kx/2$ and the work done by this average force is $(Kx/2)x$, or the potential energy is

$$E_\mathrm{P} = \tfrac{1}{2}Kx^2 \qquad (15.12)$$

which is precisely the expression we obtained for the potential energy stored in a spring due to stretch or compression; this is as it should be, since a spring, following Hooke's law, obeys Equation 15.2. The kinetic energy of the particle is given, with the use of Equations 15.10 and 15.3, by:

$$E_\mathrm{K} = \frac{1}{2}\,mv^2 = \frac{\omega^2 m}{2}\,(r^2 - x^2) = \frac{K}{2}\,(r^2 - x^2) \qquad (15.13)$$

Hence the total energy W is

$$W = \frac{Kx^2}{2} + \frac{K}{2}\,(r^2 - x^2)$$

or

$$W = Kr^2/2 \qquad (15.14)$$

and we see that the *total energy in linear SHM is directly proportional to the square of the linear amplitude r of the motion.*

15.6. Examples of Linear SHM. There are some vibrating systems, such as the prongs of a vibrating tuning fork, which oscillate with almost perfect simple harmonic motion, and there are many illustrations of oscillatory motions which are approximately simple harmonic, such as the bob of an oscillating simple pendulum or the to-and-fro motion of the piston of an engine with a long connecting rod. We shall here discuss in some detail the application of the equations of linear SHM to two significant oscillating systems, the elastic helical spring and the simple pendulum.

The Elastic Helical Spring. We have seen in the previous chapter that an elastic deformation following Hooke's law is characterized by the presence of an elastic restoring force which is proportional, and opposite in direction, to the deformation. Since these are precisely the conditions that define SHM, the vibrations of a mass attached to one end of a helical spring obeying Hooke's law are simple harmonic. Figure 15.4 shows a mass m suspended from a spring and at rest at O where it is in equilibrium under the action of two forces, a downward force equal to the weight of the mass and an equal upward force supplied by the spring tension. Now consider that the mass is pulled down to the position Q', a distance $-A$ below the equilibrium position O, and is held there. There direction above Q being taken as positive and below O as

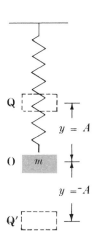

Figure 15.4.
The oscillations of a mass supported by an elastic spring are simple harmonic.

negative, an additional downward force $-KA$ is acting to keep the body in equilibrium at Q′ and the upward spring tension has been increased by the amount KA, where K is the force constant of the spring. If we now release the body, it is no longer in equilibrium, and an upward instantaneous unbalanced force KA acts on the body. The mass moves upward under the action of a resultant force which varies in accordance with Hooke's law:

$$F = -Ky \qquad (15.15)$$

where y is continuously changing from its greatest value $-A$ at Q′ to the value zero at O. At O the resultant force is zero but, because of the velocity which the body has acquired as a consequence of the conversion of potential energy into kinetic energy, it tends to move in the same upward direction with the same speed unless acted upon by an unbalanced force. The mass therefore continues to move upward and as soon as it has passed above the equilibrium position the restoring force given by Equation 15.15 comes into play again, y now varying from zero at O to $+A$ at Q. When the mass is above O the restoring force F acts in the downward negative direction and the tension in the spring is reduced by the amount Ky from its value when m is at the equilibrium position O. The positions Q, O, and Q′ have identical significances in Figure 15.4 to those shown in Figure 15.2, and the mass m oscillates vertically with simple harmonic motion, attaining, in the absence of frictional effects, equal positive and negative amplitude displacements A. Therefore the SHM equations apply, the angular speed of the associated uniform circular motion is ω, and the equations for displacement, velocity, acceleration, period, and energy are those obtained in the preceding sections, the symbols y and A taking the place of x and r respectively. With gravity acting on the vertically oscillating mass the total energy is computed as a sum of the kinetic energy, the elastic potential energy, and the gravitational potential energy (see (**f**) of Example 15.1).

The above development assumes that the mass of the spring is negligible. When this is not the case the mass appearing in Equation 15.8 must be augmented by one third of the mass of the spring (see Problem 15.8).

The Simple Pendulum. As indicated in Figure 15.5, a *simple pendulum* consists of a small concentrated mass m, called the *pendulum bob*, supported by a light inextensible string, the upper end of which is attached to a fixed support at O. The string is assumed to be of negligible weight and m is considered as being a point-mass (see Section 10.4). At the outset we can state that, although the swing of the bob is periodic, oscillating between the extreme

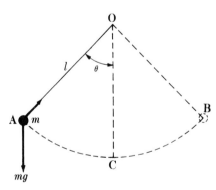

Figure 15.5. *The simple pendulum.*

points A and B about an equilibrium position C, the motion is certainly not simple harmonic in view of the fact that the bob moves in a circular path and does not execute a to-and-fro motion along a straight line. Nevertheless, analysis shows that if the angular displacement θ is limited to relatively small values, then the motion of the bob approximates very closely linear simple harmonic motion, which, as we recall, means that the motion is to-and-fro along a straight line and the restoring force is proportional and opposite in direction to the linear displacement from the equilibrium position. We shall now proceed with this analysis.

There are two forces acting on the bob in Figure 15.5, the weight of the bob mg and the tension in the string (represented by the upward arrow). This is precisely the motion we encountered in our study of motion in a vertical circle, Section 9.4. There it was indicated that the radial component of mg perpendicular to the path of the bob combines with the tension in the string to supply the centripetal force, and the tangential component $mg \sin \theta$ produces a tangential acceleration a_t which acts along the path of the bob and is given by Equation 9.11:

$$a_t = -g \sin \theta$$

Here we have inserted the minus sign because the direction of the acceleration, being toward the equilibrium point C, is opposite to the direction of the angular displacement θ. Now let us impose the condition that the angle θ be restricted to a relatively small value so as to permit the substitution of θ in radians for $\sin \theta$. Then the acceleration of the bob along its path is

$$a_t = -g\theta \tag{15.16}$$

Calling x the displacement from C along the arc CA or CB, and l the length of the pendulum, Equation 15.16 becomes

$$a_t = \frac{-g}{l} x \tag{15.17}$$

which, for given values of g and l, shows that the acceleration of the bob along its path is directly proportional, and opposite in direction, to its displacement from the equilibrium position C. We note also that, when the amplitude of swing is small, the to-and-fro motion takes place approximately along a straight line and the motion is approximately simple harmonic. Therefore, from a comparison of Equation 15.17 with Equation 15.6 or 15.7 the period of the motion is seen to be

$$T = 2\pi \sqrt{l/g} \tag{15.18}$$

which shows that the period of a simple pendulum is independent of the mass of the bob and independent of the amplitude of swing.

It must be kept in mind that the degree to which Equation 15.18 approximates the true period of a simple pendulum is entirely dependent on the magnitude of θ. This is brought to light when we compare Equation 15.18 with the exact equation obtained under a more rigorous derivation involving no assumption regarding the magnitude of θ. The exact equation proves to be:

$$T = 2\pi \sqrt{\frac{l}{g}} \left(1 + \frac{1}{4} \sin^2 \frac{\theta}{2} + \frac{9}{64} \sin^4 \frac{\theta}{2} + \cdots \right) \qquad (15.19)$$

the infinite series in parentheses permitting a calculation to any desired degree of precision. For instance, when $\theta = 15°$, the true period differs from that given by Equation 15.18 by less than 0.5% and when $\theta = 10°$ the difference is less than 0.2%.

The simple pendulum may be employed to determine the acceleration of gravity g at any locality by observing for a series of different pendulum lengths the corresponding periods. A plot of T as a function of $\sqrt{l}$ will yield a straight line whose slope is $2\pi/\sqrt{g}$, from which g is readily obtained. However, a simple pendulum does not provide a method of determining g with a high degree of precision since there are always present sizeable errors, such as those due to neglecting the weight of the cord or the uncertainty concerning the true length of the supporting cord which slackens as the bob approaches its maximum displacement positions. For more precise determinations of g one employs a *physical*, or *compound*, *pendulum* (discussed in Section 15.8 where it is shown that the simple pendulum is really a special case of the physical pendulum).

15.7. Angular Simple Harmonic Motion. There is a rotational analogue of linear SHM so that for a body which rotates periodically clockwise and counterclockwise about an axis, rotational simple harmonic motion may be defined in an analogous manner and described by analogous mathematical equations. In defining angular SHM, linear quantities such as displacement, velocity, and acceleration are replaced by the corresponding angular quantities, mass m is replaced by moment of inertia I, and force F is replaced by torque L. Thus:

Angular simple harmonic motion is periodic rotational motion in which the torque (and hence the angular acceleration) is directly proportional to the angular displacement of the oscillating mass from an equilibrium position and oppositely directed to the sense of this displacement.

Mathematically, this definition yields the equation

$$L = -C\varphi \qquad (15.20)$$

where L is the torque, φ is the angular displacement, and C is the proportionality constant. We recall (see Equation 14.17) that this equation expresses Hooke's law for rotation and the presence here of the minus sign indicates that L is the restoring torque, opposite in sense to the applied torque and producing an angular acceleration α given by

$$\alpha = \frac{L}{I} = -\frac{C}{I}\varphi \qquad (15.21)$$

Comparing Equation 15.21 with the analogous Equation 15.1 we see that the period of the rotational SHM is given by:

$$(2\pi/T)^2 = C/I = -\alpha/\varphi$$

or

$$T = 2\pi\sqrt{-\varphi/\alpha} \tag{15.22}$$

which is analogous to Equation 15.7, and

$$T = 2\pi\sqrt{I/C} \tag{15.23}$$

which is analogous to Equation 15.8. In Equation 15.23 it can readily be verified that T will be in cycles per second if I is given by the gram–square-centimeter (gm·cm²) and C the centimeter-dyne per radian (cm·dyne/rad), or I by the kilogram-mass–square-meter (kgm·m²) and C the meter-newton per radian (m·nt/rad), or I by the slug–square-foot (slug·ft²) and C the pound-force–foot per radian (pf·ft/rad).

The equations for the angular displacement, velocity, and acceleration as functions of time, corresponding to the analogous linear SHM equations 15.11, are, considering that the body is initially displaced through an angle φ_0 and then released,

$$\varphi = \varphi_0 \cos\frac{2\pi}{T} t \tag{15.24}$$

$$\Omega = -\frac{2\pi}{T} \varphi_0 \sin\frac{2\pi}{T} t \tag{15.25}$$

$$\alpha = -\frac{4\pi^2\varphi_0}{T^2} \cos\frac{2\pi}{T} t \tag{15.26}$$

where Ω, the time rate of change of the angular displacement, is the angular velocity of the oscillating mass and is given, as a function of angular displacement, by

$$\Omega = 2\pi f\sqrt{\varphi_0{}^2 - \varphi^2} = \sqrt{C/I}\sqrt{\varphi_0{}^2 - \varphi^2} \tag{15.27}$$

which is analogous to Equation 15.10. Equations 15.24 to 15.27 may be rigorously derived by methods similar to those employed in deriving the corresponding equations for linear SHM. The graphical representations of the time-dependence equations for φ, Ω, and α are those of Figure 15.3 except that the linear quantities there shown are replaced by the corresponding appropriate angular quantities.

The energy relationships may also readily be written down for a body which is executing angular SHM. The potential energy of a body which has been angularly displaced through a value φ is (see Equation 14.18) $\frac{1}{2}C\varphi^2$ and the rotational kinetic energy is $\frac{1}{2}I\Omega^2$ so that the total energy W is

$$W = \tfrac{1}{2}C\varphi^2 + \tfrac{1}{2}I\Omega^2 \tag{15.28}$$

and substituting the value of Ω from Equation 15.27 there results

$$W = \tfrac{1}{2}C\varphi_0{}^2 \tag{15.29}$$

and we again have the result, analogous to Equation 15.14, that the *total energy in angular SHM is directly proportional to the square of the angular amplitude.*

15.8.   Examples of Angular SHM.   We shall here illustrate the application of angular SHM with two examples, the torsion pendulum and the physical pendulum.   The student will have occasion to deal with other systems executing SHM in his further studies of physics and engineering and these two significant illustrations will serve to show the application of the principles of angular SHM to physical systems.

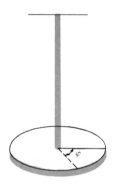

The Torsion Pendulum.   A torsion pendulum consists of a mass, represented by the disk shown in Figure 15.6, supported at its center by a wire whose upper end is clamped.   When the disk is twisted through an angle about the vertical wire as an axis and then released it executes angular vibrations.   Since the wire obeys Hooke's law for rotation it sets up a restoring torque proportional, and opposite in direction, to the angular displacement, and the resulting vibrations are angular simple harmonic.   Hence Equations 15.20 to 15.29 apply.

Figure   15.6.
The torsion pendulum.

Equation 15.23, for the period of the torsion pendulum, may be employed to determine the moment of inertia of a body.   The body is supported as a torsion pendulum from a wire whose torsion constant C is known.   If C is unknown it may first be determined by observing the angle of twist, φ, produced by a known applied torque L, and calculating C from $L = C\varphi$.   Then the period of oscillation is determined experimentally, and I about the wire axis is calculated from Equation 15.23.

Another method that determines both the torsion constant and the moment of inertia of the body from the measurement of oscillation periods alone is as follows.   First, the period T_1 of the body suspended as a torsion pendulum is observed.   Hence

$$T_1 = 2\pi\sqrt{I_1/C} \tag{15.30}$$

where I_1 is the required moment of inertia of the body about the wire axis. Then a mass of known moment of inertia I_2 is placed upon the body at a known distance from the wire axis, and the period T_2 for the oscillation of the combined system is observed.   Therefore

$$T_2 = 2\pi\sqrt{(I_1 + I_2)/C} \tag{15.31}$$

Combining these two equations leads to the expressions

$$I_1 = \frac{T_1{}^2}{T_2{}^2 - T_1{}^2} I_2 \quad \text{and} \quad C = \frac{4\pi^2 I_2}{T_2{}^2 - T_1{}^2} \tag{15.32}$$

which yield the moment of inertia I_1 about the wire axis and the torsion constant C of the wire.

The Physical Pendulum.   Any rigid body, like that shown in Figure 15.7, which is mounted such that it can swing freely under its own weight about a horizontal axis passing through the point of suspension P, is called a *physical*, or *compound, pendulum.* In the figure, m represents the mass of the pendulum and h is the distance from P to the center of mass C. When the pendulum is pulled aside through an angle φ as shown and then released it will oscillate with rotational motion about an axis which passes through P and is perpendicular to the plane of the paper. To find out whether this angular rotation is simple harmonic we shall find an expression for the torque acting on the body and see whether it follows the law given by Equation 15.20.

Assuming that there is no friction at P the body is at all times under the action of two forces: a force mg equal to the weight of the body acting downward through C and an equal upward force (not shown) at P exerted by the support. This couple produces a torque whose magnitude is $mgh \sin \varphi$. When the body's displacement is in a counterclockwise sense the torque acts in a clockwise sense, and vice versa. Hence

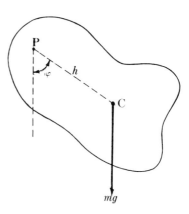

Figure 15.7. *The physical pendulum.*

$$L = -mgh \sin \varphi \qquad (15.33)$$

Since this equation states that L is proportional to $\sin \varphi$ and not to φ the rotational motion of a physical pendulum strictly is not simple harmonic. However, if we restrict the swings to small angular displacements of the order of $\varphi = 10°$ or less, then we may replace $\sin \varphi$ by φ in radians, so that

$$L = -mgh\varphi \qquad (15.34)$$

and we have approximately angular SHM. Comparing this with Equation 15.20 and then employing Equation 15.23 we find, for the period of a physical pendulum, that

$$T = 2\pi \sqrt{I/mgh} \qquad (15.35)$$

where I is the moment of inertia of the swinging body about the suspension axis. Note that the period of oscillation is independent of the amplitude and independent of the mass of the body. (Why?)

Equation 15.35 also reveals that a simple pendulum may be regarded as a special case of a physical pendulum since, when we consider that all of the mass is concentrated at a point and suspended by an inextensible weightless string, this point must be located at C in Figure 15.7. Then the moment of inertia is given by $I = mh^2$ and Equation 15.35 reduces to $T = 2\pi \sqrt{h/g}$ which, h taking the place of l, is the expression for the simple pendulum, Equation 15.18.

A significant concept is that of expressing, as a function of the constants of a given physical pendulum, the length of an *equivalent* simple pendulum whose period is equal to that of the physical pendulum. Calling the length of the equivalent simple pendulum l_e and equating Equation 15.35 to Equation 15.18 yields

$$l_e = I/mh \qquad (15.36)$$

Now l_e is greater than h (why?) and the point Q in Figure 15.8 indicates the position at which the entire mass of the physical pendulum of Figure 15.7 would have to be concentrated to form an equivalent simple pendulum. If we consider that the physical pendulum is pivoted about an axis through Q the period of oscillation is

$$T = 2\pi\sqrt{I_Q/mg(l_e - h)}$$

where I_Q is the moment of inertia about the axis through Q. Using the parallel-axes theorem (Section 10.6):

$$I_Q = I + m(l_e - h)^2 - mh^2 = I + ml_e(l_e - 2h)$$
$$= I(l_e - h)/h$$

so that

$$T = 2\pi\sqrt{I/mgh}$$

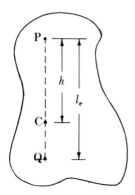

Figure 15.8. *Illustrating the equivalent length of a simple pendulum and the center of oscillation Q.*

which is the period as given by Equation 15.35. In other words, the point P and the point Q have the property that if the pendulum is pivoted about either, the period of oscillation is the same. The point Q is called the *center of oscillation*; we have already met it in Section 13.7, in our discussion of impulse, momentum, and the center of percussion. When the physical pendulum is pivoted about an axis through Q its period is the same as when it is pivoted about an axis through P, and P becomes the new center of oscillation. This property of a physical pendulum is the basis of Kater's reversible pendulum (see Problem 15.39) which is employed for making very precise determinations of g.

15.9. Summary of SHM Equations. It is convenient to summarize the significant equations of linear and angular simple harmonic motion which have been developed in this chapter. Such a summary is given in Table 15.1.

Example 15.1. A vertical helical spring elongates 5.00 cm when a mass of 15.0 gm is suspended from it. From this equilibrium configuration the mass is pulled down 4.00 cm and then released. Find (**a**) the period of the motion, (**b**) the maximum acceleration of the mass, (**c**) the acceleration of the mass when it is 3.00 cm above its equilibrium position, (**d**) the speed of the mass when it is 2.00 cm from its equilibrium position, (**e**) the tension in the spring when the mass is 2.00 cm below its equilibrium position, and (**f**) the total energy of the vibrating mass, showing also that the sum of the

Table 15.1. *Summary of linear and angular SHM equations.*

	Linear SHM		Angular SHM	
Acceleration	$a = -\omega^2 x$	$\omega = 2\pi f$ $= 2\pi/T$	$\alpha = -\dfrac{C}{I}\varphi$	$\sqrt{C/I} = 2\pi f$ $= 2\pi/T$
Force or torque	$F = -Kx$	$K = m\omega^2$	$L = -C\varphi$	$C = I(2\pi f)$ $= I(2\pi/T)$
Period	$T = 2\pi\sqrt{-x/a}$ $= 2\pi\sqrt{m/K}$		$T = 2\pi\sqrt{-\varphi/\alpha}$ $= 2\pi\sqrt{I/C}$	
Velocity as a function of displacement	$v = \omega\sqrt{r^2 - x^2}$	r = amplitude = maximum linear displacement	$\Omega = \sqrt{\dfrac{C}{I}}\ \sqrt{\varphi_0{}^2 - \varphi^2}$	φ_0 = amplitude = maximum angular displacement
Displacement as a function of time	$x = r\cos\omega t$		$\varphi = \varphi_0 \cos\dfrac{2\pi}{T}t$	
Velocity as a function of time	$v = -\omega r \sin\omega t$		$\Omega = -\dfrac{2\pi}{T}\varphi_0 \sin\dfrac{2\pi}{T}t$	
Acceleration as a function of time	$a = -\omega^2 r \cos\omega t$		$\alpha = -\left(\dfrac{2\pi}{T}\right)^2 \varphi_0 \cos\dfrac{2\pi}{T}t$	
Potential energy	$E_P = Kx^2/2$		$E_P = C\varphi^2/2$	
Kinetic energy	$E_K = \dfrac{K}{2}(r^2 - x^2)$		$E_K = \dfrac{C}{2}(\varphi_0{}^2 - \varphi^2)$	
Total energy	$W = Kr^2/2$		$W = C\varphi_0{}^2/2$	

kinetic energy, the elastic potential energy and the gravitational potential energy is a constant. Neglect the mass of the spring.

Solution. We shall represent vertical displacements by y, in place of x, and consider a displacement above an equilibrium position as positive. First determine the elastic constant of the spring:

$$K = -F/y = -15.0 \text{ gf } / -5.00 \text{ cm} = 3.00 \text{ gf/cm} = 2.94 \times 10^3 \text{ dynes/cm}$$

(a) The period of the motion is

$$T = 2\pi\sqrt{m/K} = 2 \times 3.14 \sqrt{\frac{15.0 \text{ gm}}{2.94 \times 10^3 \text{ dynes/cm}}} = 0.448 \text{ sec/cycle}$$

(b) The maximum acceleration when the mass has a displacement equal to its amplitude is

$$a = -\omega^2 r = -\frac{4\pi^2}{T^2}r$$

$$= -\frac{4(3.14)^2(-4.00 \text{ cm})}{(0.448)^2 \text{ sec}^2} = 786 \text{ cm/sec}^2 \text{ upward}$$

(c) $a = -\omega^2 y = -\dfrac{4(3.14)^2(3.00 \text{ cm})}{(0.448)^2 \text{ sec}^2} = -589 \text{ cm/sec}^2$ downward

(d) $v = \omega\sqrt{r^2 - y^2} = \dfrac{2(3.14)}{0.448}\sqrt{(4.00)^2 - (2.00)^2} = 48.5 \text{ cm/sec}$

(e) The spring has a tension equal to the tension at the equilibrium position or the weight of the body, plus the unbalanced force giving rise to the acceleration. Hence

$$\text{tension} = mg + F = mg - Ky$$

$$= (15.0 \times 980) - (2.94 \times 10^3)(-2.00) = 2.06 \times 10^4 \text{ dynes}$$

(f) We shall first obtain an expression for the total energy computed as a sum of the kinetic energy, the elastic potential energy and the gravitational potential energy. Referring to Figure 15.4, consider that the mass m has stretched the spring a distance d from its unstretched configuration. Then $K = mg/d$. Now consider that the oscillating mass is at the position distant y above the equilibrium position O. The kinetic energy of the mass is $\frac{1}{2}mv^2$, its elastic potential energy is $\dfrac{K}{2}(d - y)^2$, and its gravitational potential energy, considered zero at the equilibrium position O, is mgy. Then the total energy W is

$$W = \frac{1}{2}mv^2 + \frac{K}{2}(d - y)^2 + mgy$$

Using $v^2 = \omega^2(A^2 - y^2)$, $K = m\omega^2$, and $mg = Kd$, leads to

$$W = \tfrac{1}{2}KA^2 + \tfrac{1}{2}Kd^2$$

which is a constant, the first term being the energy due to harmonic oscillation and the second being the elastic potential energy associated with stretching the spring to the equilibrium position.

In the problem under consideration, $A = 4.00$ cm, and $d = 5.00$ cm so that

$$W = \frac{1}{2} \times 2.94 \times 10^3 \frac{\text{dynes}}{\text{cm}} \left[(4.00)^2 + (5.00)^2\right] \text{cm}^2$$

$$= 6.03 \times 10^4 \text{ ergs}$$

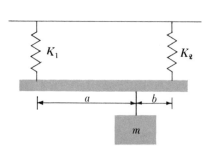

Figure 15.9. *Springs in parallel.*

Example 15.2. The mass $m = 10.0$ pounds mass in Figure 15.9 is suspended by two springs whose force constants are $K_1 = 5.00$ pounds-force/foot and $K_2 = 20.0$ pounds-force/foot. With the ratio $a/b = 4$ find the period of vibration of the suspended mass when it is displaced vertically from its equilibrium position. Neglect the weights of the springs and connecting bar, which remains horizontal during the motion.

Solution. Since the displacement of the mass through a vertical distance y stretches each spring through this same vertical distance it is clear that the equivalent restoring force F is given by

$$F = -(K_1 y + K_2 y) = -(K_1 + K_2)y$$

and the mass vibrates with linear SHM, the system possessing an equivalent spring constant K which is given by

$$K = K_1 + K_2 = 5.00 + 20.0 = 25.0 \text{ pf/ft}$$

These springs are in parallel and, in general, the equivalent force constant of any number of springs in parallel, arranged so that unit displacement in one spring is accompanied by unit displacement in all other springs, is equal to the sum of the individual force constants. Hence

$$T = 2\pi \sqrt{m/K} = 2\pi \sqrt{\frac{10.0}{32\ 0} \text{ slug} / 25.0 \frac{\text{pf}}{\text{ft}}}$$

$$= 0.702 \text{ sec/cycle}$$

Example 15.3. The mass and springs shown in Figure 15.9 are arranged in series as shown in Figure 15.10. Find the period of vibration.

Solution. When the springs are in series a force F applied at m is transmitted through both springs and the total displacement y is a sum of the individual displacements of each spring. Hence

$$y = y_1 + y_2$$

and, since each spring sets up the same restoring force F,

$$F/K = F/K_1 + F/K_2$$

and

$$1/K = 1/K_1 + 1/K_2$$

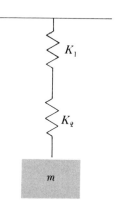

Figure 15.10.
Springs in series.

In general, when the springs are arranged in series the reciprocal of the equivalent force constant is equal to the sum of the reciprocals of the individual force constants; therefore,

$$K = \frac{K_1 K_2}{K_1 + K_2} = \frac{5.00 \times 20.0}{5.00 + 20.0} = 4.00 \text{ pf/ft}$$

and

$$T = 2\pi \sqrt{m/K} = 2\pi \sqrt{\frac{10.0}{32.0} \text{ slug} / 4.00 \frac{\text{pf}}{\text{ft}}} = 1.75 \text{ sec/cycle}$$

Example 15.4. The vibrating system shown in Figure 15.11 consists of a rigid rod of length b fastened at one end to a frictionless hinge, carrying a mass at the other end, and supported by a spring whose force constant is K. When m is displaced vertically from its equilibrium position as indicated, prove that for small amplitude the period of vibration is given by $T = (2\pi b/a)\sqrt{m/K}$, where a is as shown in the figure.

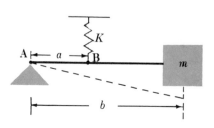

Figure 15.11.

Solution. For small displacements, m and point B move in vertical paths with linear SHM. Let:

F_B = restoring force acting on point B
F_m = restoring force acting on mass m
y_B = vertical displacement of B
y_m = vertical displacement of m

Then $F_B = -Ky_B$.

Now, taking moments about an axis through A yields $F_B = (b/a)F_m$ and, from similar triangles, $y_B = (a/b)y_m$ so that:

$$(b/a)F_m = -K(a/b)y_m$$

or

$$F_m = -K(a/b)^2 y_m$$

and the period of vibration is $T = (2\pi b/a)\sqrt{m/K}$.

Example 15.5. A solid circular disk whose mass is 13.5 kgm and whose radius is 0.500 m oscillates as a torsion pendulum, as in Figure 15.6. The wire, 1.00 m in length and 1.50 mm in radius, has a shear modulus of elasticity of 7.60×10^{10} nt/m². Find the period of vibration.

Solution. From Equations 14.16 and 14.17 the torsion constant C is related to the shear modulus G of the wire of radius r. Therefore

$$C = \frac{\pi G r^4}{2l} = \frac{3.14 \times (7.60 \times 10^{10} \text{ nt/m}^2) \times (1.50 \times 10^{-3})^4 \text{ m}^4}{2 \times 1.00 \text{ m}}$$

$$C = 0.604 \text{ m} \cdot \text{nt/rad}$$

The moment of inertia of the disk of radius R with respect to the wire axis is

$$I = \frac{mR^2}{2} = \frac{13.5 \text{ kgm} \times (0.500)^2 \text{ m}^2}{2} = 1.69 \text{ kgm} \cdot \text{m}^2$$

Now applying Equation 15.23,

$$T = 2\pi\sqrt{I/C} = 6.28\sqrt{\frac{1.69 \text{ kgm} \cdot \text{m}^2}{0.604 \text{ m} \cdot \text{nt/rad}}}$$

$$= 10.5 \text{ sec/cycle}$$

Example 15.6. The balance wheel of a watch executes angular SHM with an amplitude of 15.0°. It takes an applied torque of 14.0×10^3 cm·dyne to rotate the wheel through an angle of 10.0°, and the wheel has a moment of inertia of 81.4 gm·cm² about its oscillating axis. Find (**a**) the period of oscillation, (**b**) the maximum acceleration, (**c**) the angular speed when the angular displacement is 5.00°, and (d) the energy stored in the hairspring when the wheel has its maximum displacement.

Solution. The torsion constant of the hairspring is

$$C = -\frac{L}{\varphi} = -\frac{14.0 \times 10^3 \text{ cm} \cdot \text{dyne}}{-10.0 \times (\pi/180) \text{ rad}} = 80.3 \times 10^3 \text{ cm} \cdot \text{dyne/rad}$$

(a) The period is

$$T = 2\pi \sqrt{\frac{I}{C}} = 6.28 \sqrt{\frac{81.4 \text{ gm} \cdot \text{cm}^2}{80.3 \times 10^3 \text{ cm} \cdot \text{dyne/rad}}} = 0.200 \text{ sec/cycle}$$

(b) The maximum acceleration is given by

$$\alpha = -\frac{C}{I}\varphi_0 = \frac{80.3 \times 10^3 \text{ cm} \cdot \text{dyne} \times 15.0 \times (\pi/180) \text{ rad}}{81.4 \text{ gm} \cdot \text{cm}^2} = 258 \text{ rad/sec}^2$$

(c) The angular speed is

$$\Omega = \sqrt{\frac{C}{I}(\varphi_0{}^2 - \varphi^2)} = \sqrt{\frac{80.3 \times 10^3 \text{ cm} \cdot \text{dyne}}{81.4 \text{ gm} \cdot \text{cm}^2}[(15.0)^2 - (5.00)^2]\left(\frac{\pi}{180}\right)^2 \text{ rad}^2}$$

$$= 7.75 \text{ rad/sec}$$

(d) The maximum energy stored in the hairspring is

$$W = \frac{C\varphi_0{}^2}{2} = \frac{80.3 \times 10^3 \text{ cm} \cdot \text{dyne} \times (15.0)^2(\pi/180)^2 \text{ rad}^2}{2}$$

$$= 2.75 \times 10^3 \text{ ergs}$$

Example 15.7. A uniform thin rod of length 120 cm swings as a pendulum about an axis passing through a point which is $l/6$ from one end. Find (a) the frequency of the motion and (b) the length of the equivalent simple pendulum.

Solution. From Table 10.1 the moment of inertia of the thin rod about an axis through its center and normal to its length is $ml^2/12$ and its moment of inertia about an axis through its pivot point is

$$I = \frac{ml^2}{12} + m\left(\frac{l}{2} - \frac{l}{6}\right)^2 = \frac{7}{36}ml^2 = \frac{7}{36}m(120)^2 = 2800m$$

(a) The frequency is given by the reciprocal of Equation 15.35 with $h = 40.0$ cm. Therefore

$$f = \frac{1}{2\pi}\sqrt{40.0mg/2800m} = \frac{1}{6.28}\sqrt{980/70.0} = 0.596 \text{ cycles/sec}$$

(b) The length of the equivalent simple pendulum is given by Equation 15.36 or

$$2800m/40.0m = 70.0 \text{ cm}$$

Example 15.8. A thin annular cylindrical ring of inner radius 3.00 feet and outer radius 4.00 feet is supported from a knife edge as shown in Fig. 15.12. Find its period of oscillation for small angular displacements.

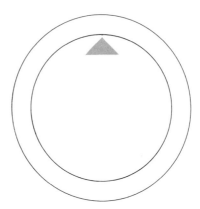

Figure 15.12.

Solution. From Table 10.1 the moment of inertia of the cylindrical ring of inner radius r_1 and outer radius r_2 about its longitudinal axis of symmetry is $m(r_1^2 + r_2^2)/2$. Hence, the moment of inertia about an axis through its point of support is

$$I = \frac{m(r_1^2 + r_2^2)}{2} + mr_1^2 = \frac{m}{2}(3r_1^2 + r_2^2) = \frac{m}{2}(27.0 + 16.0) = \frac{43.0m}{2}$$

The period is

$$T = 2\pi \sqrt{\frac{43.0m}{2m \times 32.0 \times 3.00}} = 2.97 \text{ sec/cycle}$$

Problems

Unless otherwise specified consider the masses of springs as negligible and the amplitudes of oscillation of simple and compound pendula as small.

15.1. When a mass of 5.25 pounds, suspended from a spring, is pulled down 1.55 inches and then released it vibrates with a frequency of 3.00 vibrations/sec. Find (**a**) the force constant of the spring, (**b**) the acceleration when the body is at its extreme upward position, and (**c**) the velocity of the body when it is 0.500 inch from its equilibrium position.

15.2. A spring elongates 4.90 cm when a weight of 24.5 gf is suspended from it. When the spring supports 57.5 gm and the mass is set vibrating with an amplitude of 9.50 cm what are (**a**) the force constant, (**b**) the period, and (**c**) the maximum kinetic energy of the body?

15.3. A spring with a force constant of 50.0 nt/cm supports a mass of 20.0 kgm. The mass is pulled down 5.00 cm and then released. Find (**a**) the period, (**b**) the maximum speed of the body, and (**c**) the tension in the spring when the body has its maximum downward displacement.

15.4. A body suspended from a spring oscillates with a period of 0.485 sec/cycle through a total distance of 5.56 inches. Its maximum kinetic energy is 20.0 foot–pound-force. Find (**a**) the force constant of the spring, (**b**) the mass of the body, and (**c**) the tension in the spring when the mass is 1.50 inches above its equilibrium position.

15.5. A body executes linear SHM with a period of 3.14 sec/cycle and an amplitude of 15.8 cm. Find the speed and acceleration when the body is (**a**) one sixth of a period from the equilibrium position and (**b**) one eighteenth of a period from its maximum displacement position.

15.6. A body, executing linear SHM with an amplitude of 10.0 cm, passes a point displaced 4.00 cm from its equilibrium position with a speed of 60.0 cm/sec. Find (**a**) the angular speed of the reference particle and (**b**) the magnitude of the unbalanced force acting on the body if its mass is 100 gm and it is at its maximum displacement.

15.7. Plot a graph of Equation 15.10, using v as ordinate and x as abscissa and considering ω and f constant, and interpret the result.

15.8. A vertical spring has a force constant of 1.22×10^3 dynes/cm and a mass of 2.00 gm. For a 25.0 gm body suspended from the spring and set vibrating find the error incurred in calculating the period when the mass of the spring is neglected.

15.9. The piston in the cylinder head of a locomotive has a stroke of 2.50 feet. If the drive wheels make 180 revolutions/minute, what is the speed of the piston relative to the cylinder head when the piston passes the center of its stroke? Assume the piston moves with linear SHM.

15.10. Write the equations for displacement, velocity, and acceleration as functions of time in seconds for the mass of Problem 15.1. Let the equations apply to the mass when it is above its equilibrium position and consider upward as positive.

15.11. A spring, which stretches 4.00 cm when loaded with a mass of 37.4 gm, supports two masses, A = 50.0 gm and B = 187 gm. Mass B is suddenly removed and mass A vibrates with linear SHM. Find (**a**) the amplitude of the motion, (**b**) the period, (**c**) the speed of A as it passes its equilibrium position, (**d**) the speed of A when it is 5.00 cm from its equilibrium position, (**e**) the acceleration of A when it is 10.0 cm from its equilibrium position, (**f**) the elastic potential energy of A when it is 15.0 cm below its equilibrium position, (**g**) the tension in the spring when A is at its maximum downward displacement, (**h**) the state (magnitude also) of the spring when A is at its maximum upward displacement, and (**i**) the total energy of A, considering the equilibrium position the zero of gravitational potential energy.

15.12. The period of vibration of mass A suspended from a spring is T_1 and that of a mass A + B suspended from the spring is T_2. If the ratio T_2/T_1 is 3/2 what is the ratio of the masses m_B/m_A?

15.13. When a mass of 0.585 pound is vibrating at the end of a spring the period is observed to be 0.475 sec/cycle. When an unknown mass is added to the system the period is 1.56 sec/cycle. Find (**a**) the unknown mass and (**b**) the spring constant.

15.14. Find the period of a simple pendulum whose length is 120 cm at a place where the gravitational acceleration is 980 cm/sec².

15.15. Find the frequency of a simple pendulum whose length is 5.65 feet at a place where the gravitational acceleration is 32.2 feet/sec².

15.16. A so-called seconds pendulum beats seconds so that its period is 2.000 sec/cycle. What is the length of a seconds pendulum at a place where the gravitational acceleration is 980.0 cm/sec²?

15.17. The bob of a simple pendulum whose length is 1.50 m has a mass of 5.00 gm. The pendulum is given an angular displacement of 10.0° and then released. Find (**a**) the period, (**b**) the speed of the bob as it passes its lowest point, (**c**) the maximum acceleration, and (**d**) what fraction of the total energy is kinetic and what fraction is potential when the bob swings through the 5.00° position. Take $g = 980$ cm/sec².

15.18. Find the per cent error incurred in using the approximate Equation 15.18 rather than the true Equation 15.19 for the period of a simple pendulum having an angular amplitude of 5.00°. Retain only the first two terms in Equation 15.19 for the calculation.

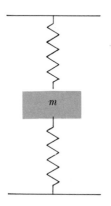

Figure 15.13.
Problem 15.23.

15.19. If the seconds pendulum in Problem 15.16 keeps accurate time where g is 980.0 cm/sec² but loses 1.550 minutes in 24.00 hours at a different location, find g at this location.

15.20. A simple pendulum of length 4.00 feet hangs from the ceiling of an elevator. Find the period of the pendulum when the elevator is (**a**) accelerating upward at 7.00 feet/sec², (**b**) accelerating downward at 7.00 feet/sec², and (**c**) falling freely. The gravitational acceleration is 32.0 feet/sec².

15.21. For the system shown in Figure 15.9 take $K_1 = 225$ nt/m, $K_2 = 900$ nt/m, and $m = 5.00$ kgm. Find (**a**) the period of vibration and (**b**) the work done in displacing the system from its unstretched configuration to its equilibrium position with the mass suspended.

15.22. The frequency of vibration of the system shown in Figure 15.10, with $K_1 = 600$ pounds-force/inch and $m = 688$ pounds mass, is 2.15 cycles/sec. Find the value of K_2.

15.23. In Figure 15.13 the upper and lower springs have force constants of 25.0 and 35.0 pounds-force/inch respectively. If $m = 96.0$ pounds mass what is the period of vibration when m is displaced vertically from the equilibrium position shown?

15.24. Figure 15.14 shows a mass $m = 75.0$ gm resting upon a frictionless horizontal surface between two springs whose force constants are $K_1 = 22.5$ gf/cm and $K_2 = 45.5$ gf/cm. The mass is displaced 1.85 cm from its equilibrium position and released. Find (a) the period of vibration, (b) the

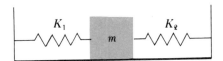

Figure 15.14. *Problem 15.24.*

maximum speed of the body, and (c) the kinetic energy of the body as it passes a point removed 1.55 cm from its position of maximum displacement.

15.25. Find the period of vibration of the system shown in Figure 15.15 where $a = 1.50$ feet, $b = 4.50$ feet, $K_1 = 30.0$ pounds-force/inch, $K_2 = 50.0$ pounds-force/inch, and $m = 2.00 \times 10^3$ pounds mass. Neglect the weight of the rigid supporting rod.

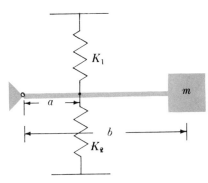

Figure 15.15. *Problem 15.25.*

15.26. Prove that for the system shown in Figure 15.16 the frequency of vibration is given by $f = (b/2\pi a)\sqrt{K/m}$ where K is the force constant of the spring. Neglect the weight of the supporting rod.

15.27. Neglecting the weight of the rigid bar AB in Figure 15.17, show that the period of vibration of the system is given by

$$T = \pi\sqrt{m(4K_1K_2 + K_2K_3 + K_1K_3)/K_1K_2K_3}$$

where K_1, K_2, and K_3 are the force constants of the springs. Note here that the bar AB does not remain horizontal.

15.28. Derive from elementary considerations Equations 15.24, 15.25, and 15.26.

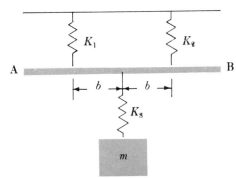

Figure 15.17. *Problem 15.27.*

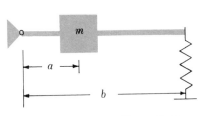

Figure 15.16. *Problem 15.26.*

15.29. A solid circular disk, with a mass of 2.50 slugs and a diameter of 1.50 feet, is mounted as in Figure 15.6. The disk turns through an angle $\varphi = 22.5°$ under the application of an external torque of 25.0 pound-force–foot. Find (a) the torsion constant of the wire, (b) the elastic potential energy stored in the wire, (c) the period of oscillation when the torque is removed, and (d) the angular speed of the disk as it passes a position displaced 10.0° from its equilibrium configuration.

15.30. The oscillating body of a torsion pendulum has a frequency of 2.55 cycles/sec. The suspension wire has a radius of 2.00 mm, a length of 125 cm, and a shear modulus of 40.0×10^{10} dynes/cm². The mass of the body is 5.75 kgm. Find its radius of gyration about the wire axis.

15.31. The period of the disk in Figure 15.6 is 0.575 sec/cycle. When two identical bodies are placed on the disk at equal distances from its center and along a straight line passing through the disk's center the period of vibration is increased to the value 2.56 sec/cycle. What is the torsion constant of the wire and the moment of inertia of each body about the wire axis if the moment of inertia of the disk about the wire axis is 0.285 kgm·m²?

15.32. The balance wheel of a watch, oscillating as a torsion pendulum, has a period of 1.00 sec. The torsion constant of the hairspring is 8.56×10^{-7} m·nt/radian. Find (a) the radius of gyration of the balance wheel about the axis of oscillation if its mass is 1.58 gm and (b) the energy stored in the hairspring when the angular displacement is 7.50°.

15.33. The disk of Figure 15.6 has a mass of 10.5 pounds and a radius of gyration of 0.545 feet about the wire axis. The disk twists under the application of a 9.50-pound-force–foot torque and is then released. The torsion constant of the wire is 4.75 pound-force–foot/radian. Find (a) the period

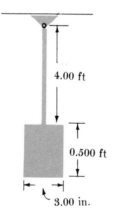

of oscillation and (b) the angular speed of the disk at the instant it passes its half-maximum angular displacement.

15.34. Show that the period of oscillation of a physical pendulum is given by $T = 2\pi\sqrt{(k^2 + h^2)/gh}$ where k is the radius of gyration of the pendulum about an axis, through its center of mass and parallel to the pivotal axis, and h has the significance shown in Figure 15.7.

15.35. A uniform meter stick oscillates as a physical pendulum about a horizontal axis passing through its 10.0 cm mark. Find (a) the period of oscillation and (b) the position of the center of oscillation.

4.00 ft

0.500 ft

3.00 in.

Figure 15.18.
Problem 15.37.

15.36. A homogeneous cylinder 8.00 cm in diameter and 6.00 cm long oscillates as a pendulum about a diametral axis at one end. Find (a) the frequency of vibration and (b) the location of the center of percussion.

15.37. The pendulum shown in Figure 15.18 consists of a solid cylindrical brass bob attached to a brass rod of diameter 0.250 inch. (a) Find the period. (b) What is the period if the rod is replaced by an inextensible cord of negligible weight and the system is considered a simple pendulum? Each cubic foot of brass has a mass of 543 pounds.

15.38. A thin uniform ring of radius r vibrates as a physical pendulum on a knife edge. Show that the period is the same as that of a simple pendulum of length $2r$.

15.39. The properties of Kater's reversible physical pendulum may be obtained by plotting the equation $T = 2\pi\sqrt{(k^2 + h^2)/gh}$ obtained in Problem 15.34. Taking k as a constant, plot T as ordinate and h as abscissa. Do this by plotting T in units of A, and h in units of k where $A = 2\pi\sqrt{k/g} = $ constant, $h = ck$, and $T = A\sqrt{(1 + c^2)/c}$ where c takes on arbitrarily assigned positive values such as 0, 0.2, 0.4, 0.6, . . . , 3.0. Since h is the distance from the center of mass to the axis of suspension, plot the value of T for a given value of h to both the right and the left of the ordinate corresponding to the two possible positions of the axis of suspension on either side of the center of mass. From the plot observe the following:

(1) The graph is symmetrical about a line through the center of mass.

(2) The pendulum has a minimum period of vibration corresponding to $h = k$.

(3) For a given center of suspension, except that for which the period is a minimum, there are three other parallel axes of suspension about which the period is the same.

(4) With respect to the center of mass there are two pairs of symmetrical points (equidistant from the center of mass) and two pairs of unsymmetrical points. One point of an unsymmetrical pair represents the center of suspension and the other point the center of oscillation.

(5) If h_1 is the distance from the center of mass to either of the two axes forming one symmetric pair, and h_2 that to either of the two axes forming the other symmetric pair, show that the corresponding period is $T = 2\pi\sqrt{(h_1 + h_2)/g}$ and interpret the result.

Gravitation

*W*E HAVE SEEN HOW NEWTON'S three laws of motion are fundamental in the study of mechanics. There is another law which Newton formulated, the *law of universal gravitation*, that is not only of great significance in mechanics but, together with the three laws of motion, is basic to the field of astronomy. We have employed the concept of the weight of a body as the gravitational force with which the earth attracts the body on its surface. It is this phenomenon of gravitational attraction with which we shall be concerned in this chapter and we shall see that Newton's gravitation law, which states in precise mathematical fashion the quantities upon which the force of attraction between two bodies depends, is a universal law holding for any two bodies in the universe.

Newton derived his law of universal gravitation from experimental data that had been previously accumulated by astronomers on the motion of the planets around the sun. The Danish astronomer Tycho Brahe (1546–1601) had recorded accurate measurements of the motions of the planets and the sun. Later Johannes Kepler (1571–1630), a student of Brahe's, in studying, analyzing, and interpreting these astronomical observations, deduced three laws which accurately describe the motion of a planet around the sun. Newton (1642–1727) then used these three experimental laws of Kepler to develop his law of universal gravitation.

16.1. Kepler's Laws of Planetary Motion. After years of painstaking study and analysis of astronomical observations accumulated by Tycho Brahe and others, Kepler arrived at the three laws which accurately describe the motion of any planet around the sun. These three laws are as follows:

(1) *The orbit of each planet is an ellipse with the sun at one focus.*

(2) *The radius vector drawn from the sun to a planet sweeps out equal areas in equal time intervals.*

(3) *The square of the period of revolution of a planet is proportional to the cube of the semimajor axis of the elliptical orbit.*

The meanings of the laws may be clarified with the aid of Figure 16.1 which shows the elliptic path of a planet, the sun S as focus, the center O of the ellipse, and the semimajor axis a. The shaded regions show the areas A_1 and A_2 swept out by the radius vector for two equal time intervals corresponding to the planet's motion from P_1 to P_2 and from P_3 to P_4. The second law states that $A_1 = A_2$. The third law states that

$$T^2 = Ka^3 \tag{16.1}$$

where T is the period of rotation, a is the semimajor axis, also known as the *mean distance* of the planet from the sun (i.e., one-half the sum of the maxi-

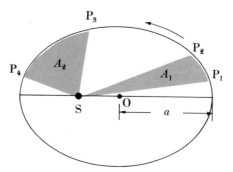

Figure 16.1. *Planetary motion.*

mum and minimum values of the radius vector), and K is a constant of proportionality. The first law simply describes the shape of the orbit. The second law indicates that the planet moves with a speed that varies in such a way as to make the area swept out per unit time a constant. The third law gives the relation between the size of the orbit and the time of revolution.

Although Kepler's empirical laws describe the motion of a planet they do not indicate the nature of the force acting between the sun and a planet. The next section indicates how Newton's law of universal gravitation follows from Kepler's laws of planetary motion.

16.2. Law of Universal Gravitation. The empirical laws of Kepler provided Newton with the experimental results from which he derived his law of gravitation, a law establishing a physical explanation of the cause of all planetary motion. In performing the steps of a derivation we shall treat the planetary orbits as circular since they are actually very nearly circles. By using circular orbits the derivation is very much simplified and the result obtained is valid for elliptical orbits (we shall not, however, prove that here).

For a circular orbit, the sun, which we shall consider stationary,* is at the center of curvature, and the radius vector is constant in magnitude and equal to the semimajor axis of the ellipse. In an interval of time Δt the radius

---

* Actually both the sun and the planet revolve about their common center of mass, and the corresponding, more rigorous treatment leads to the same result for the law of universal gravitation. The sun, being more massive, is relatively undisturbed by the gravitational attraction of the planet.

sweeps through a central angle $\Delta\theta$ which subtends an arc length $r\,\Delta\theta$ where r is the radius of the circle. The area ΔA swept out is the area of the circular sector, or

$$\Delta A = \tfrac{1}{2}r^2\,\Delta\theta \tag{16.2}$$

and dividing both sides of the equation by Δt gives

$$\frac{\Delta A}{\Delta t} = \frac{1}{2}\,r^2\,\frac{\Delta\theta}{\Delta t} \tag{16.3}$$

Considering the limiting values of the ratios on both sides of Equation 16.3 we have

$$\lim_{\Delta t\to 0}\frac{\Delta A}{\Delta t} = \frac{r^2}{2}\lim_{\Delta t\to 0}\frac{\Delta\theta}{\Delta t}$$

It will be recalled that as Δt approaches zero the limiting value of $\Delta\theta/\Delta t$ is the instantaneous angular velocity ω and that of $\Delta A/\Delta t$ is the rate at which the radius vector sweeps out an area which by Kepler's second law is a constant. Therefore

$$\tfrac{1}{2}r^2\omega = \text{constant} \tag{16.4}$$

so that the angular velocity is a constant. This in turn means the tangential speed is constant and there is no tangential acceleration. Hence the entire acceleration of the planet is directed radially inward toward the sun and the value of the centripetal gravitational force is

$$F = m_P\omega^2 r = m_P\frac{4\pi^2}{T^2}r \tag{16.5}$$

where m_P is the mass of the planet and T is its period of revolution. From Equation 16.1 the third law states that $T^2 = Kr^3$, so that

$$F = 4\pi^2 m_P/Kr^2 \tag{16.6}$$

Since K is the same constant for all planets the force of attraction exerted by the sun on a planet is directly proportional to the mass of the planet and inversely proportional to the square of the distance between the planet and sun. Since the sun pulls on a planet with a force given by Equation 16.6, the planet, by Newton's third law of motion, pulls on the sun with an equal and opposite force. Under such considerations and the assumption that the phenomenon of gravitational attraction is a universal property of mass, Newton was led to place the constant in Equation 16.6 proportional to the mass of the sun m_S or

$$4\pi^2/K = Gm_S \tag{16.7}$$

where G is the constant of proportionality. The gravitational law of force between the sun and planets is thus seen to be given by

$$F = G\frac{m_P m_S}{r^2} \tag{16.8}$$

Although we used the approximation of circular orbits in our derivation the same result may be proved exactly by employing elliptical orbits. Newton was able to generalize the result and formulate the law of universal gravitation as valid for all mass points in the universe. This law, stated in a general way, is as follows: *Any particle in the universe attracts any other particle with a force that acts along the line joining the particles and has a magnitude that is directly proportional to the product of the masses and inversely proportional to the square of the distance between them.* Calling the masses of the particles m_1 and m_2 and the distance between them r, the law of universal gravitation is

$$F = G \frac{m_1 m_2}{r^2} \tag{16.9}$$

where G is the *universal gravitation constant.* This law, which has had extensive confirmation by detailed astronomical observations, provides the concept of the force which is responsible for the regularities of all planetary motions. Its formulation, based on astronomically observed relationships, represents one of Newton's greatest contributions. The constant G which, as described in the following section, is experimentally determinable in the laboratory, is a *universal* constant because its value depends only upon the units employed in its measurement and not on any other quantities such as location, time, nature of the masses employed, or other properties of matter.

16.3.   The Cavendish Experiment.   The numerical value of G in Equation 16.9 can be found experimentally by measuring the force of gravitational attraction between two bodies whose separation and masses are known. Such a determination was first made by Henry Cavendish in 1798 by means

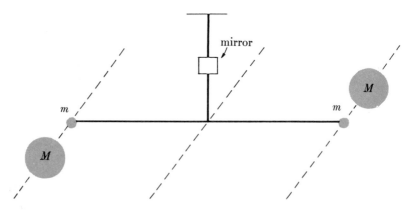

Figure 16.2.   *The torsion balance employed by Cavendish for determination of the gravitation constant G.*

of an apparatus involving a torsion balance. Figure 16.2 shows the essential features of the apparatus. Two small lead spheres of known equal mass m are at the ends of a light rigid rod which is supported from its midpoint by a long vertical fiber whose torsion constant is known. When two massive fixed spheres of known equal mass M (supports not indicated) are brought into position as shown, with the centers of the four spheres in a horizontal plane, the gravitational force of attraction between the large and small spheres produces a torque on the suspended system. This causes the fiber to twist through a small angle which is accurately measured by observing the deflection of a beam of light reflected from a mirror fastened to the fiber. The product of the angle of twist and the torsion constant of the fiber yields the torque. Dividing the torque by the distance between the small spheres gives F in Equation 16.9. With the twisted system at rest under the condition that the attractive forces are balanced by the elastic force of the fiber, the distance r between the centers of the large and small spheres is measurable and the application of Equation 16.9 readily leads to the value of G. In actual practice the torsion balance is enclosed in a glass case to avoid air currents and other disturbing factors. There also is provision for shifting the large spheres to positions 180° from those shown and observing the angle through which the fiber twists when the large spheres are shifted from one position to the other. Also, the apparatus is of sufficient size as to make negligible the gravitational effect of a large sphere on the more remote small sphere.

The value of G has been determined by Cavendish, Boys, and others; the most reliable value, determined by P. R. Heyl and P. Chizanowski at the U.S. Bureau of Standards, is

$$G = 6.67 \times 10^{-8} \text{ dyne} \cdot \text{cm}^2/\text{gm}^2$$

$$= 6.67 \times 10^{-11} \text{ nt} \cdot \text{m}^2/\text{kgm}^2$$

As G is so very small, gravitational forces between bodies ordinarily dealt with in the laboratory may be neglected.

The mass appearing in Newton's law of universal gravitation represents that property of a body by virtue of which it exerts an attractive force on other bodies and is referred to as the *gravitational mass*. The laboratory beam balance affords a method of comparing such masses. On the other hand, in Section 4.2 we introduced the term "mass" as a measure of the property of a body that requires a force to produce a linear acceleration and this is designated the *inertial mass*. These masses are the same. By the principle of equivalence, which Einstein (1879–1955) introduced in his General Theory of Relativity and which has been supported by experiment, the gravitational mass and the inertial mass are equal.

16.4. Gravitational Effect of a Spherical Shell. A significant fact is that the law of universal gravitation as given by Equation 16.9 expresses the force action between point-masses, i.e., mass particles of infinitesimal dimensions. To find the gravitational force action between masses of finite size we consider that Equation 16.9 applies between the elementary particles composing the bodies and we sum or, as we say in calculus, integrate, over the interaction between all the particles.   To say that Equation 16.9 expresses the gravitational force between two irregularly shaped masses m_1 and m_2 whose centers of mass are separated by an amount r is incorrect.   Yet the student may question the direct applicability of Equation 16.9 to the extended objects in the Cavendish experiment, where r is taken as the separation of the centers of mass of the attracting bodies.   The justification lies in the fact that for the special case of a uniform spherical body the gravitational effect is the same as if all the mass were concentrated at the center.   Such a result follows from the consideration of the gravitational effect of a uniform thin spherical shell.

In Figure 16.3 is shown a thin uniform spherical shell of mass M and center O attracting a point-mass m situated at P distant r from O.   It is not difficult to show (by use of the calculus) that the gravitational force of attraction between shell and m is GMm/r^2.   This shows that a uniform spherical shell attracts an external point-mass as if all of its mass were concentrated at its center O.   Since a solid sphere may be considered as made up of a large number of concentric spherical shells, it acts gravitationally on objects external

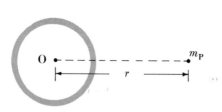

Figure 16.3. *Gravitational effect of a spherical shell.*

to it, as if all of its mass were concentrated at its center, that is, as if it were a mass point.   This is true of any homogeneous sphere.   Bodies such as the sun, the earth, the moon, and other planets are sufficiently spherical to be treated as mass points to a very close approximation.

When the mass m in Figure 16.3 is situated inside the spherical shell, analysis shows that the shell exerts no gravitational force on m.   Therefore, the gravitational force of a solid sphere on a particle in its interior decreases as the particle gets closer to the center, since the gravitational matter more remote from the center than the particle has no effect on the particle interior to it.   In fact, the gravitational attraction of a solid homogeneous sphere on a point-mass in its interior is directly proportional to the distance of the mass from the center of the sphere (see Problem 16.9).

16.5.   Gravitational Field Strength.   The region of space that surrounds a body, when considered with reference to the action of gravitational forces, is called a *gravitational field*.   In regarding the phenomenon of gravitational attraction between two masses it is convenient to consider that each of the masses is in the gravitational field of the other mass.   In accordance with this view any mass sets up a gravitational force field and work must be done against the field when a body is moved farther from the center of the

earth, or work is done by the field when the body and earth come closer together.   A property of the gravitational field is that whenever a given mass
is placed at any point in the field it is acted
upon by a force whose magnitude depends on
the strength of the field at that point.   It is
therefore useful to preassign to every point
of the field a vector which represents in magnitude and direction how strong the field is.
This is accomplished by defining the *intensity
of the gravitational field* or the *gravitational
field strength at a point* as the *gravitational
force per unit mass acting on a mass placed
at the point.*   In Figure 16.4 is shown a small
particle of mass m situated at point P distant
r from the mass point M.   Denoting by I
the gravitational field strength of M we have

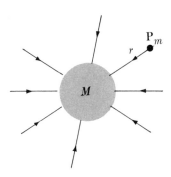

Figure 16.4.   *Gravitational
field of a mass point M.*

$$I = F/m = GMm/mr^2$$

or

$$I = GM/r^2 \tag{16.10}$$

Equation 16.10 shows that the gravitational field strength at any point
P varies inversely as the square of the distance from the mass point M and
has a direction which is inward along a line that connects M and P.   The
force field is then radially inward, as shown by the vectors in Figure 16.4.

Let us, as an example, apply Equation 16.10 to the earth which behaves
like a mass point if we consider it to be spherical.   In this case the force of
gravitational attraction F acting on a mass at its surface is what has been
called the weight w of the body, so the gravitational field strength of the earth
at its surface is w/m and this, as we have seen, is simply the acceleration due
to gravity g.   Hence:

$$g = GM_e/r^2 \tag{16.11}$$

where M_e is the mass of the earth and r its radius.   With $r = 6.38 \times 10^6$ m
and $g = 9.80$ m/sec^2 the mass of the earth is readily computed as

$$M_e = \frac{gr^2}{G} = \frac{(9.80 \text{ m/sec}^2)(6.38 \times 10^6 \text{ m})^2}{6.67 \times 10^{-11} \text{ nt} \cdot \text{m}^2/\text{kgm}^2}$$

$$= 5.98 \times 10^{24} \text{ kgm} = 6.59 \times 10^{21} \text{ tons mass}$$

The concept of field strength, introduced here in connection with gravitation, is significant throughout the various branches of physics.   It is usually
possible to represent a field graphically in such a way that both the magnitude
and direction of the field intensity are revealed.   Figure 16.4 shows a plot
of the gravitational field of a mass point.   It is composed of radial lines that
converge on the field-producing mass M, and the direction of the field is
radially inward along these *lines of force.*   The magnitude of the field strength
at any point of the field is obtained by constructing at the point a surface
of unit area which is at every region normal to the lines of force; the magnitude

of the field strength is then proportional to the number of lines of force that pass perpendicularly through this unit area. A radial field as exemplified by Figure 16.4 varies in both magnitude and direction and we say the field is nonuniform. For the special case of a uniform field, the lines of force are straight, parallel, and uniformly spaced. At the surface of the earth, the gravitational lines of force, directed approximately toward the center of the earth from which the surface is so far distant, are approximately parallel and uniformly spaced over a region that is not too extensive and we have approximately a uniform gravitational field. Actually, at sea level the intensity of the earth's gravitational field g changes over the surface of the earth. We have already indicated (see Sections 3.5 and 9.4) that there are several reasons for this variation. First, the earth is not a sphere but an oblate spheroid with the equatorial diameter greater than the polar diameter. Second, the earth spins about its axis and for points on the surface farther away from the spin axis the value of g is less. Third, the distribution of mass throughout the earth is not uniform so that there are local variations in gravity. Of course, g at any latitude decreases with altitude in accordance with Equation 16.11.

16.6. Gravitational Potential. Since a gravitational field exhibits the vector property of force, work must be done by or against the gravitational force to move a particle in the field. Hence, a gravitational field also exhibits the scalar property of energy. We have seen in Section 11.4 that whenever work is done upon a body against the earth's gravitational force of attraction the body acquires potential energy and that the change in gravitational potential energy is equal to the negative of the work done by the gravitational force. It was there also illustrated that when a body is elevated from one horizontal level to another in the earth's gravitational field the work done against gravity is independent of the path followed in the elevating of the body and that the work depends only upon the initial and final points. We saw that the gravitational force is therefore a conservative force, so that a body acquires potential energy when work is done on it against this force. These concepts were developed for the case of a body elevated above the surface of the earth, in which we neglected the change in weight of the body with elevation and obtained the simple expression mgh for the change in potential energy when the body was elevated through a vertical distance h.

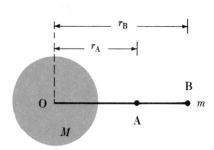

Figure 16.5. *Diagram used for calculating the wrok done by the gravitational force of attraction in moving a mass m from B to A.*

We shall now compute the exact expression for the change in gravitational potential energy and show that the concepts above are true in general in a gravitational field. This development will enable us to introduce the very useful and significant concepts of *difference in gravitational potential* and *gravitational potential at a point*.

In Figure 16.5 is shown a small mass m in the gravitational field of a mass point M located at the origin O. Let us find the work done by the gravitational force exerted by M on m in moving the latter from position B to position A. For simplicity we assume that the motion takes place radially along BO and later justify the fact that the result obtained holds for any path and so is independent of the path followed. We observe that the force is not constant from A to B but varies continuously from the magnitude GMm/r_A^2 at A to GMm/r_B^2 at B. The calculation of the work done by such a variable force will be made in two ways: in the left column below we obtain the result without the use of the calculus and the right column shows the parallel development with the use of the calculus.

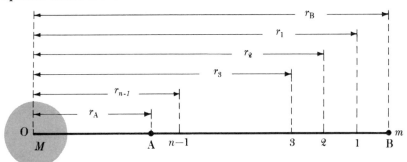

Figure 16.6.

Consider that the path BA is subdivided into a large number n of very small displacements indicated in Figure 16.6 by the points $1, 2, 3, \ldots, (n-1)$, the distances from the center of M represented by $r_1, r_2, r_3, \ldots, r_{n-1}$, respectively.

Let W_1 be the work done when m is displaced from B to 1. The magnitude of the force at B is GMm/r_B^2 and that at 1 is GMm/r_1^2. The representative average force in the range $r_B - r_1$ is the geometric mean, or $GMm/r_1 r_B$. Hence, since the force and displacement are directed in the negative direction toward O we have

$$W_1 = -\frac{GMm}{r_1 r_B}[-(r_B - r_1)]$$

$$= GMm[(1/r_1) - (1/r_B)]$$

Taking an infinitesimal displacement dr, shown in Figure 16.7 as an element

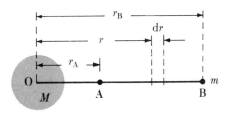

Figure 16.7.

of integration, we have for the work done in displacing m from B to A:

$$W = \int_B^A F\, dr$$

In the same way, representing the work done in the displacement from 1 to 2 by W_2, that in the displacement from 2 to 3 by W_3, etc., there results

$$W_2 = GMm \left(\frac{1}{r_2} - \frac{1}{r_1} \right)$$

$$W_3 = GMm \left(\frac{1}{r_3} - \frac{1}{r_2} \right)$$

.
.
.

$$W_n = GMm \left(\frac{1}{r_A} - \frac{1}{r_{n-1}} \right)$$

The total work W in displacing m from B to A is the sum of $W_1, W_2, W_3, \ldots, W_n$. In this sum we see that $1/r_1, 1/r_2, 1/r_3$, $\ldots, 1/r_{n-1}$ cancel, leaving the result

$$W = GMm[(1/r_A) - (1/r_B)] \quad (16.12)$$

where F, the force acting toward O in the infinitesimal displacement dr, is $-GMm/r^2$. Therefore

$$W = -GMm \int_B^A \frac{1}{r^2} \, dr$$

Integrating this definite integral leads to the result

$$W = GMm[(1/r_A) - (1/r_B)] \quad (16.12)$$

Although Equation 16.12 was obtained for the simplified case of a linear path from B to A it is true for the most general case of any path whatsoever between B and A. We can see why this is so from the following consideration. Any arbitrarily assumed path along which m may be considered to move from B to A may be divided into small segments each of which may be represented by two component displacements, one directed radially toward O and one perpendicular to this radial direction. Since no work is accomplished along the perpendicular displacements, the total work accomplished is the sum of the work done along all the radial paths and again leads to Equation 16.12. The significant fact in the result is that the work done by the gravitational field is independent of the path and depends only upon the end positions B and A and, in fact, this result proves to be true for any central field of force. Hence, the gravitational force as given by Newton's law is a conservative force and the gravitational field is conservative.

If we now consider moving the mass m from position A to position B by applying a force equal to the gravitational force but directed radially outward, we shall be doing an amount of work given by Equation 16.12 against the gravitational field and we shall be increasing the potential energy of the system. Since the change in the gravitational potential energy is equal to the negative of the work done by the gravitational force we have,

$$\Delta(E_P) = -W = -GMm \left(\frac{1}{r_A} - \frac{1}{r_B} \right) \quad (16.13)$$

where ΔE_P represents the change in potential energy. It is now very useful to introduce the concept of *difference in gravitational potential as the negative of the work done by the gravitational force per unit mass m or the change in the gravitational potential energy per unit mass*. Hence:

$$\Delta V = -GM \left(\frac{1}{r_A} - \frac{1}{r_B} \right) \tag{16.14}$$

where $\Delta V = \Delta E_P/m = -W/m$ is the difference in gravitational potential between points A and B. This difference in gravitational potential represents the work necessary to move a unit mass against the gravitational force from point A to point B. Again we see that ΔV depends only upon the distances r_A and r_B, of the initial and final points A and B, respectively, from the field-producing mass M. Equation 16.14 may be written

$$\Delta V = (-GM/r_A) - (-GM/r_B)$$

with the attendant observation that $\Delta V = V_A - V_B$, where $V_A = -GM/r_A$ and $V_B = -GM/r_B$ may be designated respectively the gravitational potential at A and the gravitational potential at B. From this we see that the gravitational potential at A is the difference in gravitational potential between a point A distant r_A from M and a point B at infinity where $V_B = -GM/\infty = 0$. We thus arrive at the result that the gravitational potential at a point distant r from a mass M producing a gravitational field is

$$V = -GM/r \tag{16.15}$$

which means that it takes an amount of work GM/r to move a unit mass against the gravitational field from this point to infinity along any path, or that the gravitational field does an amount of work GM/r in moving the unit mass along any path from infinity to the point distant r from M. The presence of the negative sign in Equation 16.15 is due to the choice of the zero potential. As with potential energy, we are interested in measuring only differences in gravitational potential and it is quite arbitrary to what point, level, or region is assigned the value of zero potential. In expressing the potential energy of a stretched or compressed spring, Hooke's law indicates that the convenient choice for the position of zero potential energy is the force-free unstretched position. When we considered the change in potential energy of a body which is elevated above the surface of the earth, under the assumption that the gravitational force of attraction was approximately constant, we considered the zero level of potential energy as the earth's surface. Under these conditions the gravitational potential is gh where h is the distance above the earth's surface considered as a reference potential. In our present development, where we are taking into account the variation in gravitational force with distance, we could still take the surface of field-producing mass as our position of zero gravitational potential, although it is more convenient and customary to choose as the zero of potential energy the energy of a body infinitely far from the attracting center. This is precisely what was done in deriving Equation 16.15. With such a choice there is the mathematical convenience that the gravitational potential at infinity is zero while its value at any other finite distance from the field-producing mass is negative. As r in Equation 16.15 increases, the potential gets less negative: in other words, the potential increases.

The concept of potential difference and potential, here introduced in the

study of gravitation, is an extremely important one and we shall later see
how it may also be significantly employed in the study of electricity. Potential is a scalar quantity and the gravitational potential is expressed in ergs
per gram mass in the cgs absolute system, in joules per kilogram mass in the
mks absolute system, and in foot–pound-force per slug in the English gravitational system.

16.7.   Earth Satellites.   As a part of the International Geophysical
Year (1957–1958) successful space launchings were accomplished. On October 4, 1957, the first earth satellite, designated 1957α_2 (Sputnik I), and on
November 3, 1957, the second earth satellite, designated 1957β (Sputnik II),
were successfully placed in orbits around the earth by the Russian scientists.
On January 31, 1958, the third earth satellite, designated 1958α (Explorer I),
and on March 17, 1958, the fourth earth satellite, designated 1958β_2 (Vanguard I), were placed in orbit by the United States scientists. The first earth
satellite, of weight about 184 pounds force, remained in orbit until January 4,
1958, and the second earth satellite, of weight about 1120 pounds force, remained in orbit until April 14, 1958, both plunging into the earth's atmosphere and burning to extinction in their rapid descent to the earth. At
the time of this writing, 1958α and 1958β_2 are orbiting the earth, 1958α having
a weight of about 31 pounds force and 1958β_2 a weight of 3.25 pounds force.
In each of these launchings, a multistage rocket was employed to lift the
assembly vertically against the earth's gravitational field and atmospheric
resistance, and gradually, with the attainment of altitude, the assembly was
permitted to curve away from the vertical. When the satellite was at the
proper altitude and traveling in a direction parallel to the surface of the earth
the last-stage rocket produced the final thrust which projected the satellite
with the necessary velocity into its orbit. If this velocity is correct, the force
of the earth's gravitational attraction on the satellite supplies, and is exactly
equal to, the necessary centripetal force, and the satellite follows an orbital
path. The orbiting satellite at all times has an acceleration toward the
earth's center and this centripetal acceleration is at every point equal to the
gravitational acceleration. The orbits, like the planets, are almost always
elliptical, with the center of the earth at one of the foci but with such small
eccentricities as to make them practically circular. It should be clear that
an orbiting satellite is under the action of an unbalanced centripetal force due
to gravitation, and that the satellite is continuously prevented from moving
off in a straight line by the presence of the gravitational force.

In accordance with Kepler's laws, a satellite goes through a point called
perigee, the point in its orbit closest to the earth's center, and through a point
that is farthest from the earth, called *apogee* (see Figure 16.8). At perigee
the satellite has its greatest instantaneous linear speed, at apogee it possesses
its least instantaneous speed, and for points in between it has variable speeds
between these limits. When the satellite is in the region of perigee the den-

sity of the atmosphere is greater than when it is at apogee and, if perigee is of the order of 200 miles, then the density of the atmosphere is of such magnitude as to slow the satellite down somewhat with each revolution and produce a corresponding decrease in the value of apogee. How long a satellite stays aloft depends on its initial values of perigee and apogee. In the case of Sputnik I, initially perigee and apogee were respectively about 143 miles and 583 miles above the earth's surface, the satellite having remained in orbit 92 days. Sputnik II, with about the same initial value of perigee and a larger initial value of apogee (1020 miles), stayed aloft for a longer period, 162 days. Explorer I with significantly larger values of perigee and apogee is expected to remain in orbit about eight years while Vanguard I with still larger initial values of perigee and apogee will probably remain in orbit for 200 years or more. A diagram of the orbits of these first four earth satellites is shown in Figure 16.8. Although the orbits have been drawn in the same plane for

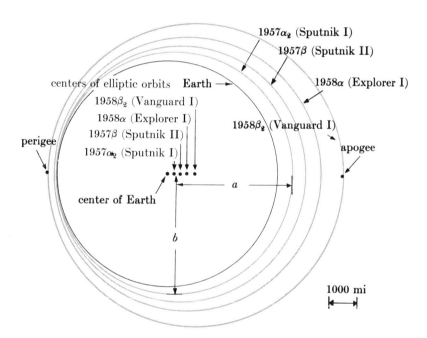

Figure 16.8. *The orbits of the earth satellites 1957α₂, 1957β, 1958α, and 1958β₂.*

comparison, the plane of each orbit is actually inclined at a different angle with the earth's equatorial plane. Table 16.1 lists for each elliptic orbit the period T, the semimajor axis a and the semiminor axis b, the values of perigee and apogee above the surface of the earth, the speed of the satellite at perigee and apogee, and the eccentricity e which indicates the degree of departure from a circular orbit for which $e = 0$. These values correspond to the conditions existing early in the history of each satellite and are for an assumed spherical earth with an average radius of 3,960 miles. The computed values are based on press announcements of the values of the period, perigee, and apogee appearing in October 1957 for Sputnik I and in March 1958 for the other three satellites. Only for the orbit of satellite 1957α_2 are a and b indicated in Figure 16.8; for the other satellites they have been omitted for simplicity and are drawn only approximately with respect to their elliptic centers. For the relationships between the various quantities see Problems 16.24 and 16.25.

Table 16.1. *Orbital characteristics of some earth satellites.*

	U.S.S.R. Sputnik I 1957α_2	U.S.S.R. Sputnik II 1957β	U.S. Explorer I 1958α	U.S. Vanguard I 1958β_2
T, min/rev	96.2	103	115	134
a, mi	4,323	4,540	4,863	5,395
b, mi	4,317	4,519	4,814	5,295
Perigee, mi	143	140	219	404
Apogee, mi	583	1,020	1,587	2,466
Speed, mi/hr				
Perigee	17,820	18,300	18,360	18,410
Apogee	16,100	15,070	13,930	12,500
e	0.0510	0.0969	0.141	0.191

Since the injection of Vanguard I into orbit, many other successful space launchings have been accomplished by the American and Russian scientists in their space exploration programs. To date, the United States has on record about fifty-five successful earth satellites of which about thirty-four are still in orbit, and the U.S.S.R. has on record about twenty satellites of which about five are in orbit. In addition, both groups of scientists have launched several interplanetary probes, among which are several sun-orbiting satellites and lunar probes. On August 27, 1962, a Venus probe, called Mariner 2 and weighing 447 pounds force, was launched by the United States, and on December 14, after a 109-day, 182,000,000-mile journey, it scanned the planet Venus (then 36,000,000 miles from the earth) for 42 minutes at a distance of 21,100 miles from it. Mariner 2 has gathered and supplied us with information, by radio waves, concerning magnetic fields, radiation, cosmic rays, cosmic dust, temperature, and the constitution of the surrounding clouds associated with the planet Venus. Some of the earth satellites have been put into orbit to establish effective meteorological spacecraft and orbiting observatories for the investigation of magnetic fields, radiation belts, and radiation and solar influences on manned spacecraft.

On July 10, 1962, the United States, in association with the Bell Telephone Laboratories, placed into orbit the first communications satellite Telstar, thus establishing the beginnings of a worldwide television and radio communications system. Telstar, weighing 170 pounds force and having a diameter of thirty-four inches, orbits the earth every 157.8 minutes with perigee and apogee values of 593 miles and 3,502 miles above the earth's surface. Its electronic equipment enabled it to receive television and radio signals from one point of the earth, amplify them several billion times and relay them to other parts of the earth. Successful broadcasts between the United States and different parts of Europe were accomplished. A photograph of Telstar is shown in the frontispiece of this text. On December 14, 1962, the successor to Telstar, called Relay, was placed into orbit by the United States in cooperation with the Radio Corporation of America. Relay has a period of 185.1 minutes per revolution and perigee and apogee values of 820 miles and 4,612 miles respectively above the earth's surface, thus permitting intercontinental communications for longer time intervals each day. The launchings of such additional communications satellites are being planned.

Of special significance in the exploration of space are the successful launchings of manned spacecraft which have been recovered after orbiting the earth. The U.S.S.R. astronaut Yuri Gagarin on April 12, 1961, returned safely to earth with his spacecraft Vostok I after orbiting once around the earth, and the astronaut Gherman Titov landed safely on earth with his spacecraft Vostok II after orbiting seventeen times August 6–7, 1961. In the United States, astronaut John H. Glenn brought his spacecraft Friendship 7 safely to earth after orbiting three times on February 20, 1962, and astronaut John Scott Carpenter on May 24, 1962, likewise orbited three times and returned safely in his spaceship Aurora 7. More recently the Russians on August 11, 1962, placed in orbit their astronaut Andrian G. Nikolayev in the spacecraft Vostok III, and on August 12, 1962, they placed into the identical orbit their astronaut Pavel R. Popovich in his spacecraft Vostok IV; these astronauts made radio and visual contact while orbiting and were both brought safely to earth six minutes apart four days after Nikolayev was placed in orbit. On October 3, 1962, the American astronaut Walter M. Schirra, Jr. made six orbits in his space capsule Sigma 7 before returning safely to earth. At the time of this writing there are plans for lunar landings and interplanetary exploration.

An orbiting spacecraft and its occupants are continuously in a state of weightlessness. This is a consequence of Newton's laws. Thus in the case of an orbiting astronaut, he exerts an inertial reaction which is equal in magnitude and opposite in direction to the gravitational accelerating force. Hence it is as though no gravitational field were present, resulting in a state of weightlessness. Another way of stating this is to indicate that the weight of a body manifests itself as the force exerted by the body on its support or the equal and opposite reaction of the support on the body. For an orbiting astronaut, we have the equation $mg - P = ma$, where mg is the earth's gravitational force, P is the reaction force of the space ship, and ma is the centripetal force, all acting on the astronaut. Since the astronaut is continuously in free fall, $a = g$ and $P = 0$, resulting in the weightless condition. This is analogous to the weightless state that a person in an elevator would experience if the elevator were in free fall, resulting in a zero apparent weight of the person, as manifested by no upward push of the elevator floor on the individual, and hence no downward force exerted by the person on the elevator floor.   (See Example 5.6 and Problems 5.6, 5.7, 5.10 and 5.20.)

Example 16.1.   Two spherical lead bodies whose masses are 3.25×10^3 gm and 1.45×10^3 gm are placed with their centers separated by 25.0 cm. Find the force of attraction.

Solution.   Employing Equation 16.9:

$$F = \frac{Gm_1m_2}{r^2} = \frac{(6.67 \times 10^{-8} \text{ cm}^3/\text{gm} \cdot \text{sec}^2)(3.25 \times 10^3 \text{ gm} \times 1.45 \times 10^3 \text{ gm})}{(25.0)^2 \text{ cm}^2}$$

$$= 5.03 \times 10^{-4} \text{ dyne}$$

Example 16.2.   A person weighing 150 pounds force on the surface of the earth would have what gravitational acceleration and weight on the surface of the moon?   The mass and radius of the moon are 1/81.5 and 0.273, respectively, times those of the earth.   Use 32.2 feet/sec² as the acceleration of gravity on the earth.

Solution.   The acceleration of gravity on the moon g_m is given by

$$g_m = \frac{32.2(1/81.5)}{(0.273)^2} = 5.30 \text{ ft/sec}^2$$

and the weight on the moon, w_m, is

$$w_m = 150 \frac{1}{(81.5)(0.273)^2} = 24.7 \text{ pf}$$

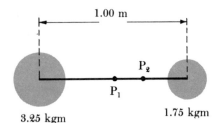

1.00 m

P_2

P_1

3.25 kgm

1.75 kgm

Figure 16.9.

Example 16.3.   Figure 16.9 shows two spherical masses of 3.25 kgm and 1.75 kgm with their centers placed 1.00 m apart.   Find (a) the intensity of the gravitational field at a point P_1 midway between the centers of the masses, (b) the gravitational potential at P_1, and (c) the work necessary to move a small mass of 10.0 gm through a distance of 20.0 cm from P_1 to P_2.

Solution.   (a) The resultant force that would act on a unit mass if it were placed at P_1 is the gravitational field strength at P_1.   Hence, applying Equation 16.10 and considering a force action to the right as positive and to the left as negative, we have

$$I = 6.67 \times 10^{-11} \frac{\text{nt} \cdot \text{m}^2}{\text{kgm}^2} \left(-\frac{3.25 \text{ kgm}}{(0.500)^2 \text{ m}^2} + \frac{1.75 \text{ kgm}}{(0.500)^2 \text{ m}^2} \right)$$

$$= -40.0 \times 10^{-11} \text{ nt/kgm}$$

The negative sign indicates that the resultant field acts to the left.

(b) Applying Equation 16.15 gives, for the potential at P_1,

$$V_{P1} = -6.67 \times 10^{-11} \frac{nt \cdot m^2}{kgm^2} \left(\frac{3.25\ kgm}{0.500\ m} + \frac{1.75\ kgm}{0.500\ m} \right)$$

$$= -6.67 \times 10^{-10}\ nt \cdot m/kgm$$

(c) The potential at point P_2 is

$$V_{P2} = -6.67 \times 10^{-11} \left(\frac{3.25}{0.700} + \frac{1.75}{0.300} \right) = -7.00 \times 10^{-10}\ nt \cdot m/kgm$$

Hence, from Equation 16.14,

$$\Delta V = V_{P1} - V_{P2} = 0.33 \times 10^{-10}\ nt \cdot m/kgm$$

and the work done is

$$W = 10 \times 10^{-3}\ kgm \times 0.33 \times 10^{-10}\ nt \cdot m/kgm$$
$$= 3.3 \times 10^{-13}\ joule$$

Problems

16.1. Two lead balls, one of mass 2.55 kgm and the other of mass 4.80 kgm, are placed with their centers 0.250 m apart. Find the mutual force of attraction.

16.2. The force of attraction between a large sphere of 2.00×10^3 gm and a small sphere is 1.45×10^{-5} dyne when their centers are 5.76 cm apart. What is the mass of the small sphere?

16.3. Given that the acceleration of gravity on the surface of Mars is 363 cm/sec² and that its radius is 2,100 miles, find its mass.

16.4. The ratios of the sun's and moon's masses to that of the earth are 3.32×10^5 and 1.23×10^{-2} respectively. The distances of the sun and moon from the earth are 1.50×10^{13} cm and 3.84×10^{10} cm respectively. How many times the force exerted by the moon on the earth is the force exerted by the sun on the earth?

16.5. The period of the moon is 27.3 days/revolution and its mean radius from the earth is 23.9×10^4 miles. At what distance from the earth would a moon have a period of 4.55 days/revolution?

16.6. Given that the moon revolves around the earth at an average distance of 3.84×10^{10} cm, or 60.3 times the earth's radius, calculate by Newton's law of gravitation the central acceleration of the moon. Check your result by making an independent calculation of the moon's centripetal acceleration, using for the period of the moon 27.3 days/revolution and for the acceleration of gravity on the earth 982 cm/sec². Can you account for the discrepancy?

16.7. Assuming that the earth moves in a circular orbit of radius 1.50×10^{13} cm with a period of 365 days/revolution, find the mass of the sun.

16.8. The electric force of attraction between an electron of mass 9.11×10^{-28} gm and a proton of mass 1.67×10^{-24} gm separated a distance of 0.530×10^{-8} cm is 8.20×10^{-3} dyne. How many times the gravitational force of attraction is this?

16.9. Show that the gravitational force of attraction of a solid homogeneous sphere on a point-mass located in its interior is directly proportional to the distance of the mass from the center of the sphere.

16.10. Show that the acceleration of gravity g_h at a height h above the surface of the earth is given by $g_h = g/(1 + h/r)^2$ where g is the value of the gravitational acceleration on the earth's surface and r is the radius of the earth assumed to be spherical.

16.11. An artificial earth satellite revolves in a circular orbit with a period of 1.50 hours/revolution. Find (**a**) the height of the satellite above the earth's surface and (**b**) the orbital speed. Solve the problem by employing the equation given in Problem 16.10 for the variation of g with altitude. Use 4.00×10^3 miles for the earth's radius.

16.12. An artificial earth satellite revolves in a circular orbit at a distance of 5.00×10^3 miles from the earth's center. Taking the radius of the earth as 4.00×10^3 miles, find the angular speed of the satellite. To solve the problem employ the equation given in Problem 16.10. Use 32.0 feet/sec² for the gravitational acceleration at the earth's surface.

16.13. The value of g at sea level and any latitude θ on the surface of the earth is given by the approximate equation $g = (9.83 - 0.0519 \cos^2 \theta)$ m/sec². What is the acceleration of gravity at an altitude of 500 miles above sea level and latitude 45.0°? Take the earth's radius as 4.00×10^3 miles.

16.14. A body falls from rest from a height h above the surface of the earth assumed to be spherical, of radius R. Taking into consideration the variation of the acceleration of gravity with altitude show that the body strikes the ground with a speed v given by $v^2 = 2gRh/(R + h)$ where g is the value of the acceleration on the earth's surface. Neglect the effect of air resistance. (*Hint:* Use the principle of the conservation of mechanical energy $\frac{1}{2}mv^2 - (GMm/r) = $ constant, where m is the mass of the body, M is the mass of the earth, and r is the distance out from the center of the earth. Evaluate the constant, subject to the initial condition that $v = 0$ when $r = R + h$ and then use Equation 16.11.)

16.15. (**a**) Show that the result given in Problem 16.14 reduces to the familiar result for the speed of a freely falling body, under the assumption of constant acceleration. (**b**) Using the result of Problem 16.14 find the speed with which the freely falling body strikes the ground when released from a height large compared with the radius of the earth. Assume $g = 32.0$ feet/sec² and take $R = 4.00 \times 10^3$ miles.

16.16. With what minimum initial velocity must a body be projected vertically from the surface of the earth so that it will escape from the earth's gravitational influence and never return? (*Hint:* Evaluate the total energy constant in Problem 16.14, subject to the condition that, when $r = \infty$, $v = 0$. This leads to the solution that the escape velocity is equal to $\sqrt{2gR}$ where R is the radius of the earth.) Neglect air resistance and use $g = 32.0$ feet/sec² and $R = 4.00 \times 10^3$ miles in the computation.

16.17. Find the velocity of escape from the surface of the moon. Take the mass of the moon as 7.34×10^{25} gm and its radius as 1.74×10^8 cm. See Problem 16.16 for the solution.

16.18. Show that Equation 16.14, modified for the choice that the position of zero gravitational potential is at the surface of the earth, leads to the familiar result *mgh* for the gravitational potential energy of a body elevated a distance h above the earth's surface where h is small compared with the radius of the earth.

16.19. Three mass points of 250 gm, 500 gm, and 750 gm are situated on the x axis. The 500 gm body is at the origin, the 250 gm body is 10.0 cm to the left of the origin, and the 750 gm body is 20.0 cm to the right of the origin. Find the resultant gravitational force action on the 500 gm body.

16.20. Solve for the force action on the 250 gm body in Problem 16.19.

16.21. In Problem 16.19, what is the gravitational potential at a point 10.0 cm to the right of the origin?

16.22. In Figure 16.9, Example 16.3, find (**a**) where the gravitational field intensity is zero and (**b**) the gravitational potential at this point.

16.23. Two equal mass points, each of 500 gm, are situated at two adjacent corners of a square 10.0 cm on a side. Find (**a**) the intensity of the gravitational field at the center of the square and (**b**) the work necessary to move a small mass of 5.00 gm from the center of the square to one of the other unoccupied corners.

16.24. The equation of an elliptic orbit in polar coordinates is given by $r^2 = b^2/(1 - e^2 \cos^2 \theta)$ where r and θ are the polar (radius and angle) coordinates of a point on the orbit relative to a fixed focus, b is the semiminor elliptic axis, and e is the eccentricity. The magnitude of the resultant velocity v of a satellite in an elliptic orbit is $v^2 = (dr/dt)^2 + r^2(d\theta/dt)^2$ where dr/dt and $d\theta/dt$ are the time derivatives of r and θ respectively. Show that the speeds of a satellite at perigee and apogee are given by $2\pi ab/r_1 T$ and $2\pi ab/r_2 T$ respectively, where a is the semimajor axis, b is the semiminor axis, T is the period of the satellite, and r_1 and r_2 are the minimum and maximum values of r respectively.

16.25. Using as knowns the values of T, perigee, and apogee in Table 16.1, compute the values of a, b, and e, and the maximum and minimum speeds of each of the first four earth satellites. Use 3,960 miles for the average radius of the earth and the expressions $2\pi ab/r_1 T$ and $2\pi ab/r_2 T$ for the speeds of a satellite at perigee and apogee respectively (see Problem 16.24).

Statics of Fluids

*S*O FAR WE HAVE CONFINED our discussion to the mechanics of mass points and solid bodies. Besides the solid state, matter may exist in two other physical states, the liquid and the gaseous. We shall now extend our development to include the liquid and the gas, each of which is termed a *fluid* because it is a substance that does not have a definite shape and can exhibit the phenomenon of flow. Of the three states of matter, the solid form has both definite volume and definite shape. A liquid, on the other hand, has a definite volume but no definite shape since it adapts its shape to the containing vessel. A gas, at the other extreme, has neither a definite volume nor a definite shape since it fills completely any container.

The chief distinguishing physical property of an *idealized perfect fluid* is that it possesses no rigidity and is therefore incapable of sustaining a permanent shearing stress. Most fluids exhibit this feature to a high degree but, as we have seen in Section 6.4, real fluids possess viscosity and therefore do exert some, although very little, shearing stress. Nevertheless, in our study of fluid states we shall consider that the fluid is ideal, i.e., that it possesses no viscosity and therefore supports no shearing stress. Under this assumption the laws and principles governing the behavior of ideal fluids may be derived simply and then the effects of viscosity may be brought in as a modification when necessary.

Liquids, on the one hand, are practically incompressible, possessing large bulk moduli comparable to those of solids while gases, on the other hand, are easily compressed. A liquid that is not completely confined forms a free surface at the top when in an open vessel. However, liquids and gases possess many properties in common and in general the same basic laws govern their behavior. The mechanical principles which we have developed for solids also apply to fluids but, as we shall see, because of the differences in the states additional principles come into play.

Fluid mechanics is divided into the subjects of *hydrostatics* and *hydrodynamics*. Hydrostatics deals with fluids at rest while hydrodynamics deals with fluids in motion, the prefix "hydro" referring to the most common and significant fluid, water. In this chapter we shall confine our study to the behavior of fluids at rest; the dynamic behavior of fluids we take up in the next chapter. As we have already indicated, in our discussions of hydrostatics we shall consider that the fluid is ideal, supporting no shearing stress, and in the case of liquids we shall neglect the small volume changes under pressure.

17.1.   Density and Specific Gravity.   A quantity which defines a property characteristic of all materials, and one which enters quite naturally into the descriptions of fluid behavior, is density.   The student is aware of the fact that equal volumes of different materials possess different masses. *Density* is defined as the *mass per unit volume* of a substance or

$$\rho = m/V \qquad\qquad (17.1)$$

where ρ is the density, m is the mass, and V is the volume of a given sample of material.   It is clear from Equation 17.1 that density has the units grams mass per cubic centimeter (gm/cm^3) in the cgs absolute system, kilograms mass per cubic meter (kgm/m^3) in the mks absolute system, and slugs per cubic foot ($slugs/ft^3$) in the English gravitational system.   In engineering practice it is frequently convenient to express the density in pounds force per cubic foot and refer to the quantity as the weight-density.   For example, the density of water at a temperature of 4°C, which is practically 1 gm/cm^3 in the cgs system and 1.94 slugs/cubic-foot in the English gravitational system, may also be given as 62.4 pounds-force/cubic-foot, which is its "weight-density." The densities of some solids, liquids, and gases are listed in Table 17.1.

Table 17.1.   *Densities of some solids, liquids, and gases.*

Solids	Density, gm/cm^3	Liquids at temp. in °C		Density, gm/cm^3	Gases (at 0°C, 76 cm Hg)	Density, gm/cm^3
Aluminum	2.70	Alcohol (ethyl)	0°	0.81	Air	1.293×10^{-3}
Balsa wood	0.13	Benzene	0°	0.90	Ammonia	0.771×10^{-3}
Copper	8.89	Chloroform	20°	1.49	Chlorine	3.214×10^{-3}
Cork	0.24	Ether	0°	0.74	Helium	0.178×10^{-3}
Glass	2.60	Gasoline	20°	0.67	Hydrogen	0.0899×10^{-3}
Gold	19.3	Mercury	0°	13.60	Neon	0.900×10^{-3}
Ice	0.917	Water, pure	4°	1.00	Nitrogen	1.250×10^{-3}
Iron	7.86	Water, sea	15°	1.03	Oxygen	1.429×10^{-3}
Lead	11.34					
Osmium	22.5					
Platinum	21.37					
Silver	10.5					
Tungsten	19.3					
Uranium	18.7					
Zinc	7.04					

The *specific gravity* of a substance is defined as the ratio of the density of the substance to the density of some other substance considered as a standard. For solids and liquids the standard commonly adopted is water at a temperature of 4°C, the value being 1 gm/cm³ or 62.4 pm/ft³. For gases the density of air or oxygen is used as a standard. Thus, with ρ for the density of the substance and ρ_w for the density of water, the specific gravity of a solid or liquid is

$$\text{specific gravity} = \rho/\rho_w \qquad (17.2)$$

Since the densities forming the ratio in Equation 17.2 each have the same unit, the specific gravity is a pure numeric, being the same in any system of units. In the metric cgs system ρ_w has the value of unity, with the result that the specific gravity is numerically equal to the density expressed in cgs units. In any other system of units ρ_w is not unity and the density is not equal numerically to the specific gravity. It is frequently more convenient to use a table of specific gravities rather than a table of densities because the specific gravity may then be employed to compute the density of a substance in any system of units. For example, by knowing that the density of water in the English system is 62.4 pounds-mass/cubic-foot the density of any substance in this system is conveniently obtained by multiplying the specific gravity by 62.4, as shown by Equation 17.2.

17.2. Pressure. A fluid confined in a container exerts forces on all portions of the container in contact with the fluid and on any object immersed in the fluid. The molecules of the fluid, being constantly in motion, collide with and rebound from the walls of the vessel and the surface of an immersed object. We shall have more to say about this detailed molecular motion later but for the present it should be realized that it is this molecular bombardment that results in a time rate of change in momentum or a force. In the study of fluids, rather than to concentrate on the force itself, it is convenient to employ the concept of pressure, which we shall now define. The term *pressure* is introduced to represent the *normal force per unit area*. Thus

$$p = F/A \qquad (17.3)$$

where F is the force which is normal to the area A and p is the pressure. If we choose the area A as that within a fluid, then the fluid on one side of A exerts a force F on the fluid on the other side of A. Equation 17.3 actually defines the *average pressure* over the area A, and if the force is uniformly distributed over the area the pressure is constant. If the force is not uniformly distributed over a surface the pressure in the fluid varies from point to point, necessitating the use of the more general concept of the *pressure at a point*. In what follows the left-hand column presents this concept in a more elementary fashion while the right-hand column contains the calculus development.

Consider a normal force ΔF nonuniformly distributed over a small area ΔA of a fluid or in contact with the fluid. The ratio of ΔF to ΔA defines the average pressure of this area. If we now allow ΔA to become smaller and smaller, the force ΔF likewise becomes smaller but the ratio $\Delta F/\Delta A$ remains finite and represents the average pressure over ΔA. The limit of this ratio as we permit ΔA to shrink to zero is defined as the pressure at this point, or

$$p = \lim_{\Delta A \to 0} \frac{\Delta F}{\Delta A} \qquad (17.4a)$$

where p is the pressure at the point. The student will notice that this definition is similar to that for velocity at a point or acceleration at a point.

Consider a normal force ΔF nonuniformly distributed over a small area ΔA of a fluid. Then the pressure at a point contained in the area is given by the expression $\lim_{\Delta A \to 0} \dfrac{\Delta F}{\Delta A}$ or

$$p = \lim_{\Delta A \to 0} \frac{\Delta F}{\Delta A} = \frac{dF}{dA} \qquad (17.4A)$$

where dF/dA is the derivative of F with respect to A. Hence when the pressure varies from one point to another over a surface the total force on the surface is given by the integral

$$F = \int p \, dA \qquad (17.4B)$$

the integration being taken over the whole surface. In the special case in which the pressure is constant, Equation 17.4B reduces to $F = pA$ as given by Equation 17.3.

Since pressure has the dimensions of force per unit area, the units of pressure in the cgs absolute, mks absolute, and English gravitational systems are respectively dynes per square centimeter (dynes/cm²), newtons per square meter (nt/m²), and pounds force per square inch (pf/in²). Sometimes pressures are expressed in other convenient units such as *atmospheres* (atm), one atmosphere representing the pressure exerted by the air at standard conditions, or *centimeters of mercury* (cm Hg), one centimeter of mercury representing the pressure exerted by a mercury column 1 cm high, or *bars*, one bar being defined as 10^6 dynes/cm². Some useful numerical equivalences are:

$$1 \text{ atm} = 14.7 \text{ pf/in}^2 = 1.013 \times 10^6 \text{ dynes/cm}^2$$
$$1 \text{ bar} = 10^6 \text{ dynes/cm}^2 = 10^5 \text{ nt/m}^2$$

17.3. Significant Properties of Hydrostatic Pressure. There are two significant properties of fluid pressure.

(1) *The force exerted on any area by a fluid at rest is always directed perpendicularly to the area.*

This principle is a consequence of the definition of an ideal fluid, in accordance with which there can be no shearing stress. If the force were not normal to the area in contact with the fluid there would be a component of force parallel to the area and, since the fluid cannot support a shearing stress, there would result a fluid motion in this component direction, which is contrary to the assumption that the fluid is at rest.

(2) *The pressure at any point in a fluid at rest is the same in all directions.*

This principle in effect states that the pressure at a point is independent of the orientation of the surface on which it acts, and it is readily proved by applying the conditions of equilibrium to any small volume of fluid.   Figure 17.1 shows a vessel containing a liquid and a triangular cross section of a prism of the liquid whose density is ρ.

Let the slant face of the prism have a length a and make any angle θ with the horizontal.   The dimension of the prism perpendicular to the plane of the figure is b.   Then the area of the slant face is ab, that of the vertical face is $ab \sin \theta$, and that of the horizontal face is $ab \cos \theta$.   The liquid surrounding the prism exerts the normal forces F_1, F_2, and F_3 on these faces.   Since the liquid prism is in translational equilibrium we have, applying the first condition of equilibrium,

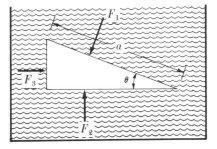

$$F_1 \sin \theta = F_2$$

and

$$F_1 \cos \theta + \tfrac{1}{2}\rho g a^2 b \sin \theta \cos \theta = F_3$$

Figure 17.1.   *Diagram used to show that pressure at a point in a fluid at rest is independent of the direction of the surface on which it acts.*

where $\tfrac{1}{2}\rho g a^2 b \sin \theta \cos \theta$ represents the force (vector not shown) due to the weight of the prism.   Observing that $F_1 = P_1 ab$, $F_2 = P_2 ab \sin \theta$, and $F_3 = P_3 ab \cos \theta$, where P_1, P_2, and P_3 are the average pressures on the slant, the vertical, and the horizontal faces respectively, we have

$$P_1 = P_2 \tag{17.5}$$

and

$$P_3 = P_1 + \tfrac{1}{2}\rho g a \sin \theta \tag{17.6}$$

Equations 17.5 and 17.6 are true for any prism and if we permit the size of the prism to shrink so that a approaches zero, then P_1, P_2, and P_3 approach the pressures at a point.   In the limit when $a = 0$ we thus have $P_1 = P_2 = P_3$ which proves the principle.

Since the pressure at a point in a fluid at rest is independent of direction it is not a vector quantity.   Pressure is ordinarily considered a scalar function of position.

17.4.   Variation of Pressure with Depth in a Fluid.   We shall here derive the law that describes the effect of gravity on the pressure of a fluid at rest.   To do this let us consider a vertical fluid cylinder of height h with horizontal faces and uniform cross-sectional area A in the interior of the fluid contained in the vessel, as shown in Figure 17.2.   The pressure at the upper surface of the fluid cylinder is p_1 and that at the lower surface is p_2.   Hence the downward force at the top is $p_1 A$ and the upward force at the bottom is p_2A. The weight of the fluid cylinder is mg and its density ρ is assumed to be constant throughout. This in turn assumes that the fluid is incompressible, a condition which is true of most liquids. Since the fluid cylinder is in translational equilibrium we have

$$p_1A + mg = p_2A$$

$$p_2 - p_1 = \frac{m}{A}g$$

and using $m = \rho Ah$ for the mass of the fluid cylinder leads to

$$p_2 - p_1 = \rho gh \tag{17.7}$$

Since the horizontal forces acting laterally on the fluid cylinder are balanced and have no vertical components, Equation 17.7 is the required result. This equation states that the pressure increases as we go downward into the fluid, the increase in pressure relative to a point in the fluid a distance h above being directly proportional to h. The pressure p_2 at a depth h below the surface of an incompressible fluid is therefore equal to the pressure p_1 at the surface plus the product of the density of the fluid, the acceleration due to gravity, and the depth. Equation 17.7 also states that the pressure is the same at all points in the same horizontal plane since this corresponds to a constant value for h. Notice that the pressure in the interior of a fluid at some depth h below the surface does not depend upon the area or the shape of the containing vessel but only upon the depth below the fluid surface.

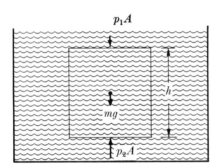

Figure 17.2. *Increase of pressure with depth in a fluid.*

With ρ in grams mass per cubic centimeter (gm/cm³), g in centimeters per square second (cm/sec²), and h in centimeters, the pressure in Equation 17.7 will come out in dynes per square centimeter (dynes/cm²); with ρ in kilograms mass per cubic meter (kgm/m³), g in meters per square second (m/sec²), and h in meters the pressure will come out in newtons per square meter (nt/m²). In the English gravitational system, if ρ is in slugs per cubic foot (slugs/ft³), g in feet per square second (ft/sec²), and h in feet, then the pressure will be in pounds force per square foot (pf/ft²).

For a gas, which is a compressible fluid, Equation 17.7 does not apply since the density ρ is not a constant but varies with the pressure and the temperature of the gas. With the assumption that the temperature remains reasonably constant analysis shows that the atmospheric pressure decreases exponentially with altitude.

17.5. Pascal's Principle. We have seen from Equation 17.7 that the pressure difference between two points in a fluid at rest depends only upon the vertical separation of the points and the density of the fluid. Therefore, if the pressure is increased at any point of a fluid there must be an equal increase in pressure at all other points in the fluid, provided the density remains unaltered, i.e., provided the fluid is incompressible. This is known as *Pascal's principle* which states that *an increase in pressure at any point in a confined incompressible fluid is transmitted in an equal increase in pressure at every other point of the fluid.* Since liquids are practically incompressible the principle is closely obeyed by them.

Pascal's principle of the transmission of pressure has many useful applications. The hydraulic press affords a striking example of its application. Figure 17.3 shows the essentials of this machine which consists of a vessel

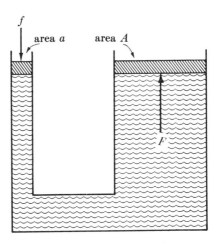

Figure 17.3. *The hydraulic press.*

containing a liquid such as oil and equipped with two pistons, a small one of area a and a large one of area A. When a small force f is exerted on the small piston the pressure f/a is transmitted undiminished to the large piston, and in accordance with Pascal's principle the force F acting on the large piston is given by

$$f/a = F/A$$

or

$$F = \frac{A}{a} f \tag{17.8}$$

Since $A/a > 1$ the hydraulic press is a force-multiplying machine and, in fact, the theoretical mechanical advantage is given by A/a. The actual mechanical advantage is somewhat less, owing to leakage or some energy dissipation due to friction. Nevertheless, the efficiency of hydraulic devices is 90% or more. Hydraulic presses of large sizes and high mechanical advantages are used to compress materials into bales and to press sheet metal against steel forms and dies.

There are many other applications of Pascal's principle, such as in the hydraulic jack, the hydraulic elevator, and hydraulic brakes. Automobiles containing hydraulic brakes are equipped with tubes that connect a master cylinder located near the brake pedal with the cylinders at the wheel brakes. The system is filled with a light oil, and when the foot pressure is applied to the brake pedal there is introduced an increase in fluid pressure which is transmitted through the tubes to the pistons of the cylinders at the wheel brakes.

17.6.   Pressure-Measuring Devices: Manometers and Barometers.

Instruments for measuring pressures are called manometers, gauges, or barometers.   We shall here describe several of the more common types.

In Figure 17.4a is shown a manometer of the open-tube type.   It consists of a U-shaped tube which contains a liquid, one end of the tube being con-

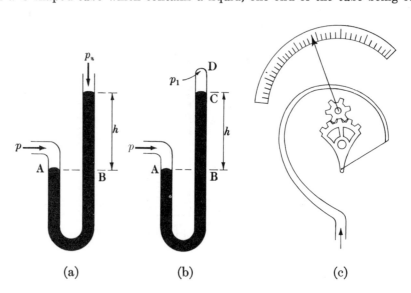

| (a) | (b) | (c) |

Figure 17.4.   (a) *The open-tube manometer*.   (b) *The closed-tube manometer*.   (c) *The Bourdon gauge*.

nected to the space in which the pressure p is to be determined and the other end being open to the pressure of the atmosphere, p_a.   The pressure at A is equal to the pressure at B so that $p = p_a + \rho g h$ where ρ is the density of the liquid.   Hence the difference $p - p_a$ between the absolute pressure and the atmospheric pressure, known as the *gauge pressure*, is proportional to the difference in the levels of the liquid h.   This type of manometer, which uses mercury, oil, or water as the liquid, is employed for measuring moderate pressures greater or less than atmospheric.   If the right-hand tube is closed and the tube is initially filled with the liquid, the portion CD in Figure 17.4b contains only some vapor of the liquid and the gauge is called a closed-tube manometer.   Here the absolute pressure is given by $p = \rho g h + p_1$ where p_1 is the pressure of the gas above the liquid.   Mercury or oil with a low vapor pressure is a suitable liquid for this type of manometer, which is also employed for measuring moderate pressures.

For measuring pressures of several pounds to several thousand pounds per square inch, as water pressure or steam pressure in boilers, a Bourdon pressure gauge, Figure 17.4c, may be employed.   The fluid under test enters a metal spring tube of variable cross section, the other end of which is closed.   Pressure causes the tube to straighten out and this motion is communicated by a lever or gear system to a pointer which sweeps over a calibrated scale.

For very low pressures used in high-vacuum techniques it is convenient to use a McLeod gauge which also employs mercury columns that yield pressure differences. For this and other high-vacuum gauges, such as the ionization gauge which depends for its action upon the electrical conductivity of a sample of gas whose molecules have become ionized, the student is referred to suitable texts or laboratory manuals.

In the measurement of atmospheric pressure one employs a barometer of either the mercurial or the aneroid type. The *mercurial barometer* is constructed by inserting in a dish of mercury a glass tube (longer than 76 cm) which is closed at the top and has previously been filled with mercury. The mercury then falls down somewhat from the closed end of the tube, remaining at a height h above the mercury level of the reservoir, as shown in Figure 17.5.

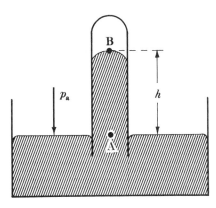

Figure 17.5. *The mercurial barometer.*

The pressure of the atmosphere, p_a, acting on the surface of the mercury is equal to the pressure at A which is at the same horizontal level as the mercury surface. This pressure at A is also equal to the pressure of the mercury column in the tube if the pressure of the mercury vapor in the space above B is neglected. Hence:

$$p_a = \rho g h \qquad (17.9)$$

where ρ is the density of mercury. At sea level and 0°C the atmosphere supports a column of mercury 76 cm high and the pressure in absolute units is

$$p_a = (13.6 \text{ gm/cm}^3)(980 \text{ cm/sec}^2)(76.0 \text{ cm})$$
$$= 1.013 \times 10^6 \text{ dynes/cm}^2 = 1.013 \times 10^5 \text{ nt/m}^2$$

This amount of pressure is known as an atmosphere and may also be expressed as 14.7 pounds-force/square-inch. At any one place the atmospheric pressure varies slightly throughout the day and from day to day, and as the pressure varies the mercury in the tube rises or falls. For greatest accuracy, the observed height of a mercurial barometer must be corrected for several effects such as the pressure exerted by the mercury vapor, the temperature, the local value of g, and the convex surface of the top of the mercury in the tube. When all significant corrections have been included the mercurial barometer yields the most accurate determination of atmospheric pressure. Since the pressure is proportional to the height h, it is common practice to express atmospheric pressure as well as other pressures in centimeters of mercury, written "cm Hg," or in inches of mercury, written "in. Hg." Thus a pressure of 1.00 cm Hg is taken to represent an absolute pressure of $1.00 \times 13.6 \times 980 = 13.3 \times 10^3$ dynes/cm^2.

A dry type of barometer, known as an *aneroid barometer*, is also used to indicate the pressure of the atmosphere. It consists of a partially evacuated metal cylindrical box one end of which is sealed with a thin corrugated metal membrane. When the atmospheric pressure changes the membrane deforms inward or outward and this motion, amplified by an attached system of levers and gears, is transmitted to a pointer which traverses a circular scale graduated in centimeters of mercury or in inches of mercury. This instrument is more convenient to use and quite sensitive to pressure changes. However, it must be calibrated against a mercury barometer.

17.7. Archimedes' Principle.   It is a common experience that it is easier to support and lift a body in water than in air. This indicates that when an object is lowered in water it apparently loses weight and, in fact, any fluid exerts an upward buoyant force upon a body immersed in it. It was Archimedes (287–212 B.C.), the Greek mathematician, who discovered the amount of this buoyancy. The principle bears his name and is stated as follows: *A body partially or wholly immersed in a fluid is buoyed vertically upward by a force that is equal in magnitude to the weight of the amount of fluid displaced.*

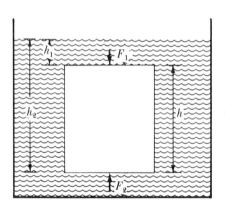

Figure 17.6. *Diagram used in showing that the buoyant force on a right circular cylinder equals the weight of displaced fluid.*

To show the truth of Archimedes' principle let us consider a right cylinder of height h and cross section A submerged in a fluid of density ρ as shown in Figure 17.6. The top and bottom of the cylinder respectively are at distances h_1 and h_2 below the fluid surface. The horizontal forces acting on the cylinder are in equilibrium and add up to zero. At the top of the cylinder where the pressure is p_1 the fluid exerts a downward force $F_1 = p_1A$ and at the bottom of the cylinder where the pressure is p_2 the fluid exerts an upward force $F_2 = p_2A$. The difference is the buoyant force F_B or

$$F_B = F_2 - F_1 = (p_2 - p_1)A$$

But $p_1 = \rho g h_1$ and $p_2 = \rho g h_2$. Therefore

$$F_B = \rho g A(h_2 - h_1) = \rho g A h \qquad (17.10)$$

Now, Ah is the volume of the cylinder and hence the volume of the displaced fluid; the buoyant force F_B is therefore equal to $\rho g A h$ which is the weight of the displaced fluid as given by Archimedes' principle.

Although the above proof is given for a specially shaped body, Archimedes' principle can be shown to be valid for any irregularly shaped body, as depicted in Figure 17.7.   As before, since the situation is one of static equilibrium, there is no resultant horizontal force on the body.   Now, the pressures on the body depend only upon the conditions that prevail on the surfaces bounding the body and not at all on what is contained inside this boundary.   Hence we may consider that the body is replaced by the surrounding fluid having the same surface boundary S without altering the forces exerted by the surrounding fluid.   The mass of fluid considered inside S is in static equilibrium so that the surrounding fluid exerts a resultant upward vertical force equal in magnitude to the weight of the fluid in S.   Hence any immersed body having the bounding surface S must be buoyed up by a resultant upward force equal in magnitude to the weight of the fluid displaced.   Furthermore, since the buoyant force is equal and opposite to the gravitational force acting on the fluid filling S before its displacement, the buoyant force acts through the center of gravity of the displaced fluid.

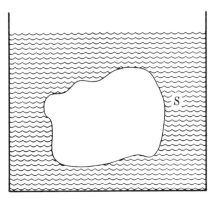

Figure 17.7. *Diagram used to prove Archimedes' principle for an irregularly shaped body.*

It is clear that if a body is only partially immersed in a fluid the buoyant force is equal to the weight of the volume of fluid displaced by only the submerged portion of the body.   When a body not completely submerged displaces an amount of fluid equal exactly to its weight, it will float.   When, completely submerged, the displaced fluid has a weight less than the weight of the body, the body will sink.

In very accurate determinations of the weight of a body made with the use of an analytical balance and standard masses a correction must be made when the density of the sample is different from that of the standard masses. Both the sample and the standards are buoyed up by the air and, since the volume of the sample is different from that of the standard masses, the corresponding amounts of displaced air are different so that the buoyant effects on the two sides of the balance are different.

17.8.   Archimedes' Principle and Density Determinations.   There are many useful and advantageous applications of Archimedes' principle such as in the design of stable ships, submarines, and balloon aircraft.   Here we shall see how Archimedes' principle makes it possible to determine the density and volume of irregularly shaped bodies.

Suppose we wish to determine the density ρ_s and volume V of an irregularly shaped, solid sample of material. Let the available liquid for the determination have a density ρ_l. First consider the case of $\rho_s > \rho_l$ in which the sample sinks in the liquid. The object is first weighed in air and its value w_a is recorded. It is then completely submerged in a container of the liquid and found to have a weight w_l. The buoyant force is given by the loss of weight and this must be equal to the weight of the liquid displaced. Therefore

$$w_a - w_l = V\rho_l g$$

or

$$V = (w_a - w_l)/\rho_l g \tag{17.11}$$

which gives the volume of the sample in terms of the observed values w_a and w_l and the known values ρ_l and g. Also, $\rho_s = w_a/Vg$ so that

$$\rho_s = \frac{w_a}{w_a - w_l}\rho_l \tag{17.12}$$

which yields the density of the sample. If water is used as the liquid, 1 gm/cm³ is used for ρ_l and Equation 17.12 yields a value numerically equal to the specific gravity.

In the case of $\rho_s < \rho_l$ in which the sample floats on the liquid, an object of any sort is attached by a string to act as a sinker for the sample. First the sample alone is weighed in air; second, the sample and sinker together are weighed, only the sinker being submerged; and third, the weight of both sample and sinker submerged is obtained. The student should show that the ratio ρ_s/ρ_l is now given by w_a divided by the difference between the values obtained in the second and third weighings.

For determining the density of a liquid there are several methods available. Equation 17.12 may be employed with a body of known density. A convenient and rapid method that yields fairly precise values is that of using a specially made, thin-walled glass bottle known as a *pycnometer*. The bottle has a snugly fitting, ground-glass stopper. A fine capillary hole running centrally from the bottom to the top of the stopper makes it possible to observe when the bottle is filled with a known volume of liquid. By weighing the bottle and its stopper before and after it is filled the mass of the liquid is readily obtained. A simple but less accurate means is the use of an *hydrometer*, which is a sealed cylindrical glass tube terminating at one end in a bulb, inside of which is some lead shot. The hydrometer, weighted at the bottom in this way, floats upright at some definite level when placed in water. When the hydrometer is placed in a liquid of greater density it rises to a higher level and when placed in a liquid of lesser density it sinks to a lower level. If the hydrometer is calibrated so that the water level is marked unity its readings will be specific gravity values. For very precise determinations of specific gravity, the Mohr-Westphal balance is employed; the student should get a laboratory manual and read a description of its use. Other methods for density determinations of liquids are revealed in the problems at the end of the chapter.

Gases have relatively low density values and require special methods for their determinations. These will be discussed in a later section.

17.9. Surface Tension. In addition to the properties associated with the body of a liquid there are interesting and significant properties that are displayed by the free surface of a liquid. The student is perhaps familiar with the fact that a steel needle when placed very carefully on the surface of a liquid floats in apparent contradiction to the principle of buoyancy, or that when a capillary tube is placed in a liquid the liquid rises into the tube above the free-liquid surface, or that a drop of mercury on a flat surface tends to a spherical shape rather than to a thin layer under gravitational action, or that the free surface of water in a glass container is horizontal except at the region of contact with the glass where it is concave upward. These and many other examples illustrate the unique behavior of the surface of a liquid and find their explanation and description in the phenomenon known as surface tension.

To understand the behavior of the surface of a liquid we consider that the liquid is composed of a vast number of molecules that attract each other with intense forces. Although the molecules of a liquid are continuously in motion, each molecule on a time average is surrounded by a certain number of neighbors, the average distance between molecular centers being of the order of 10^{-8} cm. That the nature of the intermolecular force which operates to keep the liquid molecules together within a few molecular diameters of one another is not gravitational is brought out by the calculation that the gravitational attraction between two molecules separated by 10^{-8} cm is of the order of 10^{-45} dynes while the requisite intermolecular force is of the order of 10^{-6} dynes. The significant attractive forces that act between molecules are so-called *short-range forces* which appear to be electrical in nature and due to the electric fields that surround the atoms out of which molecules are composed. Whereas gravitational force varies inversely as the square of the separation distance, intermolecular forces vary inversely as a much higher power of the separation distance, as high as the sixth and seventh power. The presence of such short-range intermolecular forces can be demonstrated by taking two blocks of steel especially prepared with surfaces that are clean, polished, and accurately plane and placing them with their faces in very good contact; it will be found that they cling together so securely that a very large force is required to pull them apart. In solids the molecules are very close together and the forces of cohesion are great. Only when the two blocks of steel are ground and polished to a sufficient flatness is it possible to bring their faces into near enough contact to enable the cohesive forces to become manifest. The intermolecular force of attraction between molecules of the same kind is called *cohesion*. When the intermolecular force of attraction is between molecules that are unlike it is called *adhesion*. Glue adheres to wood, and water adheres to glass. When the force of adhesion between a liquid and its container is greater than the force of cohesion in the liquid the liquid clings to the container and wets it, as in the case of water or oil and glass.   On the other hand, when the force of cohesion between the liquid molecules is greater than the force of adhesion between the liquid molecules and the molecules of the container, the liquid does not wet the solid, as in the case of mercury and glass.

Let us now see the effect that these short-range intermolecular forces have on the free surface of a liquid.   In Figure 17.8 are shown in cross section three

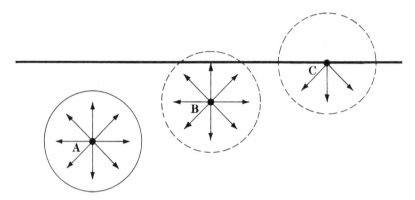

Figure 17.8.   *Effect of neighboring molecules on a liquid molecule.*

liquid molecules: molecule A well within the liquid interior, molecule B near the surface of the liquid, and molecule C at the free surface of the liquid. The intermolecular force of attraction is effective over a short range, of the order of, say, 10^{-7} cm, and it is convenient to consider a so-called sphere of action of this radius around each molecule and to suppose that only the liquid molecules within this spherical volume exert attractive forces on the central molecule.   For molecule A there are equal numbers of neighboring molecules in all radial directions at any one instant and there is no resultant inter- molecular effect on A.   Molecule B, having more liquid molecules in the lower half of its sphere of action, experiences a resultant downward force.   Such a resultant downward force is greatest on a surface molecule C which has no liquid molecules in the upper half of its sphere of action.   There is thus a very strong tendency of all surface molecules to be pulled into the interior of the liquid, an effect which causes the surface of the liquid to contract and act like a stretched membrane.   It is this contractile tendency that gives the surface of a liquid its unique properties and results in the phenomenon of surface tension.   When a liquid surface is in equilibrium the inward pull due to the cohesive forces of attraction are balanced by an enormous interior inter- molecular pressure, which has been estimated to be about 10,000 atmospheres. The presence of this hydrostatic pressure cannot be directly observed since a liquid is bounded on all sides by a surface and the forces due to this intermo- lecular pressure cancel out in hydrostatic measurements.

It is clear that when molecules from the interior of a liquid are brought to the surface, work must be done against the downward attractive intermolecular forces so that surface molecules possess a greater potential energy than interior ones. Furthermore, work must be done in increasing the free surface of a liquid. This then leads to the definition of the *surface tension σ* of a liquid: *the work done per unit area in extending the surface of a liquid*, or

$$\sigma = \text{work/area} \qquad (17.13)$$

We shall now apply Equation 17.13 to a rectangular film formed by dipping the wire frame ABCD shown in Figure 17.9 into a soap solution. The

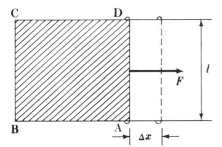

Figure 17.9. *Illustrating the work done in extending the surface of a liquid.*

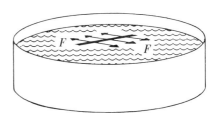

Figure 17.10. *Surface tension considered from the viewpoint of tangential contractile force per unit length.*

crosspiece AD is free to slide horizontally and it is found that it is necessary to apply a constant force F to prevent it from moving to the left because of the tendency of the film to shrink. Now consider increasing the surface area of the film by moving AD a distance Δx to the right. The work expended is $F \Delta x$ and the increase in surface area of the soap film is $2l \Delta x$, where l is the length AD, the factor 2 being necessary because there are two sides to the film. Equation 17.13 yields

$$\sigma = F \Delta x / 2l \Delta x$$
or
$$\sigma = F/2l \qquad (17.14)$$

Although Equation 17.14 was obtained for the wire frame shown in Figure 17.9 it is true that for a film of any shape σ comes out equal to a ratio of force to length. Accordingly, the surface tension may be thought of as the force per unit length, the denominator of Equation 17.14 being the total length of film each element of which is perpendicular to the line of action of the force. This definition follows as a consequence of the mathematical equivalence of the definition, given by Equation 17.13, and leads to the useful concept that the surface tension is equal to the tangential contractile force acting normal to any imaginary line of unit length on the liquid surface; see Figure 17.10.

We have seen that the effect of the downward intermolecular attraction on the molecules at the surface makes the surface behave as if it were under tension with a tangential pull in the surface in all directions. If a line is imagined to be drawn in the surface of the liquid as depicted in Figure 17.10, this line experiences a force F on one side, produced by the surface on that side, and an equal and opposite force F on the opposite side, produced by the surface on that side. Consider that the imaginary line is one unit in length; then the surface tension σ is numerically equal to F. It must be emphasized that the force on a surface molecule actually acts normal to the surface but is manifested as a tangential effect. It was indicated that the surface of a liquid, because of surface tension, behaves similarly to a stretched rubber membrane. However, the analogy cannot be pushed very far because the laws of force in the two cases are different. For a liquid surface the law is such that the force F is directly proportional to the length l and independent of the area of the film. When the liquid surface in Figure 17.9 is stretched the increase in the surface area is due to the fact that molecules leave the region between the two surfaces and become surface molecules which are subjected to the same intermolecular forces as all the other surface molecules. For a stretched elastic membrane the force depends not only upon l but also upon the area of the membrane: the larger the area the larger the force.

The contractile force in the surface of a liquid results in the liquid's contracting to a shape that makes the surface area, and hence the potential energy, the smallest possible consistent with a given volume. The shape satisfying such a condition is spherical and any volume of liquid under the action of surface tension alone assumes a spherical form. Raindrops, soap bubbles, and drops of mercury are familiar examples of spherical formations.

Either Equation 17.13 or 17.14 may be employed to compute the surface tension which, for a given liquid surface in contact with a given gas or other nonmiscible liquid, is a constant only at a given temperature. As would be expected, the surface tension decreases with increasing temperature. The metric units for σ, in accordance with Equation 17.13, are ergs per square centimeter (ergs/cm²) or joules per square meter (joules/m²) but are ordi-

Table 17.2. *Surface tension of some liquids in contact with air.*

Liquid	Temperature, °C	Surface tension σ, dyne/cm
Acetone	20	23.7
Benzene	20	28.9
Ethyl alcohol	20	22.3
Mercury	20	465
Soap solution	20	25
Water	0	75.6
Water	25	72.8
Water	100	58.9

narily stated, in accordance with Equation 17.14, as dynes per centimeter (dyne/cm) or newtons per meter (nt/m).   Table 17.2 lists some typical values of surface tension.

17.10.   Pressure beneath Convex and Concave Liquid Surfaces.
That the magnitude of the intermolecular pressure beneath a liquid surface depends on the curvature of the surface may be seen with the aid of Figure 17.11.   In each of the diagrams M is a molecule near the surface of a liquid,

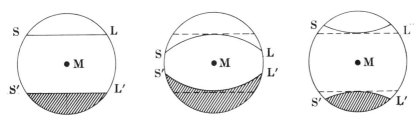

Figure 17.11 *Effect of the curvature of the liquid surface on inter-molecular pressure.*

the circles around them indicating the spheres of action within which neighboring molecules produce cohesive force actions on M.   The surface of the liquid, SL, is flat in (a), convex upward in (b), and concave upward in (c). The boundaries S'L' in the liquid are symmetrical with SL.   It is clear that the resultant downward unbalanced force acting on M is due in each case to only the molecules lying within the segment of the sphere below S'L', since there is no liquid above the surface SL.   Now, the volume and hence the number of molecular neighbors in the region below S'L' is greater in (b) and less in (c) than it is in (a). Therefore the intermolecular pressure with respect to that existing beneath a plane surface is greater beneath a convex liquid surface and less beneath a concave liquid surface.   It is also true that, regardless of which side the liquid may be on, the pressure on the concave side of a liquid surface is greater than that on the convex.

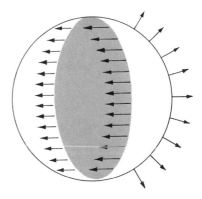

Figure 17.12. *Pressure inside a liquid spherical drop.*

Thus, within a liquid spherical drop the pressure is greater than it is outside, and we can find an expression for the difference in pressure in terms of the surface tension and the radius of the drop.   In Figure 17.12 the drop of radius r and surface tension σ is shown divided into two halves by the shaded vertical plane. Now consider the forces acting on the right-hand hemisphere which is in static equilibrium. Let Δp be the excess pressure inside the drop. This excess pressure gives rise to an outward force which is directed normal to each surface element of the hemisphere, and the resultant of these forces is a force directed to the right and perpendicular to the shaded plane having the magnitude $\pi r^2 \Delta p$. For equilibrium this force is balanced by the resultant force due to surface tension $2\pi r\sigma$ which acts to the left and is supplied by the film around the periphery of the vertical plane. Hence

$$\pi r^2 \Delta p = 2\pi r\sigma$$

or
$$\Delta p = 2\sigma/r \tag{17.15}$$

which states that the amount by which the pressure within a spherical drop is greater than the outside pressure is inversely proportional to the radius of the drop. Equation 17.15 also represents the amount by which the pressure in a gas bubble in a liquid is greater than the pressure in the surrounding liquid. It is readily seen that inside a hollow spherical soap bubble, which possesses two surfaces giving nearly equal radii, the excess pressure is

$$\Delta p = 4\sigma/r \tag{17.16}$$

In accordance with the fact that a smaller bubble has the larger pressure it is found that when a small soap bubble is placed in contact with a larger one the larger bubble keeps increasing in size while the smaller bubble decreases and finally disappears.

17.11. Angle of Contact and Capillarity. A molecule at the boundary of the surface of a liquid in a vessel which contains it is under the action of the resultant force of cohesion of the molecules of the liquid and the resultant force of adhesion of the molecules of the solid vessel. In general, the liquid surface near the point of contact is curved, the sense and amount of curvature depending upon the relative magnitudes of the forces of cohesion and adhesion. For the liquid surface to be in equilibrium it assumes a curvature such that the resultant between the cohesive and adhesive forces is perpendicular to the liquid surface. This is illustrated in Figure 17.13 where the resulting curvature is shown for a liquid that wets the wall of the container and a liquid that does not. In each diagram F_a, the resultant force of adhesion exerted by the wall, acts perpendicularly to the wall, and F_c, the resultant force of cohesion exerted by the liquid molecules, acts in some direction as indicated. In (a) the force of adhesion is greater than the force of cohesion and the liquid surface assumes a curvature so that F, the resultant between F_c and F_a, acts perpendicularly to the liquid surface. This requires that the liquid surface assume a curvature that is concave upward and the liquid creeps up on the solid wall. In (b) the cohesive force is greater than the adhesive force and the liquid surface, adjusting so that the resultant F is normal to it, curves so that it is convex upward. Figure 17.13a is representative of such combinations of substances as impure water and glass, while 17.13b exemplifies such combinations as mercury and glass or water and paraffin. For any pair of substances the liquid comes up to the surface at a definite angle θ, called the *angle of contact*, which is an indication of the relative values of the forces of adhesion and cohesion. If a tangent is drawn to the surface of the liquid at the point of contact with the wall, as shown in Figure 17.13, the

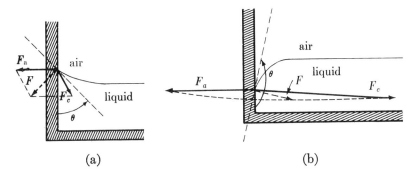

(a)   (b)

Figure 17.13. *Angle of contact for: (a) a liquid that wets the wall, and (b) a liquid that does not wet the wall.*

angle of contact is defined as the *angle measured within the liquid from the vertical wall to the tangent*. When the contact angle between a liquid surface and a wall is less than 90° the liquid wets the wall and when the contact angle is greater than 90° there is no wetting by the liquid. The angle of contact varies with the purity of the liquid and the cleanliness of the solid surface, but for clean and pure surfaces it is a characteristic reproducible constant. Table 17.3 lists some typical values of contact angles.

Table 17.3. *Angles of contact.*

Liquid	Solid	Contact angle θ, deg.
Alcohol	Glass	0
Glycerin	Glass	0
Mercury	Glass	140
Turpentine	Glass	17
Water (impure)	Glass	25 (approx.)
Water (pure)	Glass	0
Water	Paraffin	109

When a tube of fine bore, open at both ends, is placed in a liquid, the liquid, if it wets the tube walls, rises into the tube as shown in Figure 17.14a. If the liquid does not wet the tube walls, it is depressed in the tube as shown in Figure 17.14b. This phenomenon is known as *capillarity*, the tubes of small bore being called capillaries. The height to which the liquid rises or is depressed is a function of the contact angle, the radius of the tube, and the kind of liquid employed. We shall now derive this functional relationship. For this derivation consider Figure 17.14a, which shows a liquid that has

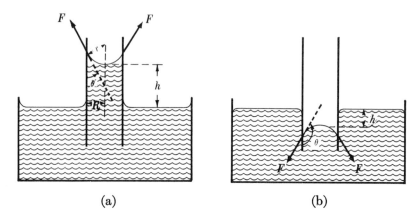

(a)   (b)

Figure 17.14. (a) *Capillary rise*: $\theta < 90°$. (b) *Capillary depression*: $\theta > 90°$.

risen in a tube of radius R to a height h above the liquid surface. The concave upper surface of the liquid in the tube, known as a *meniscus*, is here assumed to be spherical and of radius r. The liquid has the density ρ and it makes the contact angle θ with the tube. As we learned in Section 17.10, the pressure just below the liquid meniscus is less by $2\sigma/r$ than the atmospheric value just above, as given by Equation 17.15. Hence the liquid rises in the tube to just the appropriate height h to compensate for this change in pressure across the concave meniscus. Therefore:

$$2\sigma/r = \rho g h$$

or
$$h = 2\sigma/\rho g r \tag{17.17a}$$

and since $r \cos \theta = R$ we have

$$h = 2\sigma \cos \theta/\rho g R \tag{17.17b}$$

Equation 17.17a expresses h in terms of the radius of the meniscus while Equation 17.17b expresses the relation in terms of the radius of the capillary at the place where the concave meniscus is formed. We see that h varies inversely as R and directly as $\cos \theta$. For a liquid that does not wet the tube, such as mercury in glass, the contact angle is greater than 90° and Equation 17.17b yields a negative value which signifies that the liquid is depressed below the level in the container, as in Figure 17.14b. In this case the pressure just below the convex meniscus is greater than atmospheric by $2\sigma/r$.

Equation 17.17b may alternatively be derived by considering that the vertical component of the force of surface tension in Figure 17.14a, acting around the junction of the liquid and the tube, balances the weight of liquid in the tube. Thus $F \cos \theta = 2\pi R\sigma \cos \theta = \pi R^2 h\rho g$ which leads to Equation 17.17b. When a liquid of known σ, θ, and ρ is used, a measurement of h makes it possible to determine with relative ease the radius of a capillary tube. It is important to avoid holding to any concept of "capillary attraction." The liquid rises or is depressed in the capillary tube in order to equalize the pressure existing at any horizontal level in the container.

Capillary action is in part responsible for the rise of sap in trees, the rise of water through the pores of the soil, the rise of ink in a blotter, and many other phenomena.

Example 17.1. Find the pressure at the bottom of a barometric column of mercury 74.0 cm high.

Solution. The pressure at the bottom is given by Equation 17.7 with the pressure at the top of the column zero. Therefore:

$$p = \rho g h = 13.6 \, \frac{\text{gm}}{\text{cm}^3} \times 980 \, \frac{\text{cm}}{\text{sec}^2} \times 74.0 \text{ cm} = 9.86 \times 10^5 \text{ dynes/cm}^2$$

Example 17.2. A dam, impounding water in a reservoir, has a rectangular vertical cross section and is 50.0 feet long. The water in the dam stands 25.0 feet high. Find **(a)** the water pressure 15.0 feet below the water level and **(b)** the force of the water on the dam.

Solution. **(a)** The pressure is given by

$$p = \rho g h = \frac{62.4 \, \text{slugs}}{32.0 \, \text{ft}^3} \times 32.0 \, \frac{\text{ft}}{\text{sec}^2} \times 10.0 \text{ ft} = 624 \text{ pf/ft}^2$$

(b) Since the water pressure varies linearly with the depth below the surface, the average pressure is

$$p_{av} = \frac{0 + 62.4 \times 25.0}{2} = 780 \text{ pf/ft}^2$$

and the force is

$$F = p_{av} \times \text{area} = 780 \, \frac{\text{pf}}{\text{ft}^2} \times 25.0 \times 50.0 \text{ ft}^2$$

$$= 9.75 \times 10^5 \text{ pf} = 488 \text{ tons force}$$

Example 17.3. In Example 17.2 find the point of application of the resultant hydrostatic force acting on the dam. This point of application is called the *center of pressure.*

Solution. When the pressure is uniform over an area the center of pressure coincides with the center of gravity. However, when the pressure varies with the vertical distance below the surface of the liquid, as it does here, the center of pressure is most easily found by the use of the calculus. It will be more instructive to obtain the general solution in terms of the depth of liquid.

Figure 17.15 shows side and front views of the dam **AB**. The liquid has a depth l and F is the resultant hydrostatic force acting through the center of pressure C a distance h_c below the liquid surface. Let b be the length of the

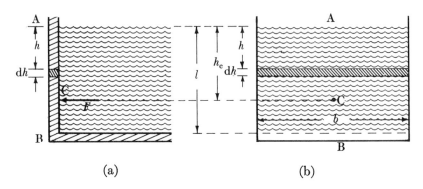

(a)   (b)

Figure 17.15. *The resultant hydrostatic force acts at the center of pressure* C: (a) *side view, and* (b) *front view, of dam* **AB.**

dam. To find h_c we choose a horizontal element of area $b\,dh$ a distance h below the liquid surface. The liquid force on this area is

$$dF = p\,dA = bp\,dh$$

and the total force on the entire wall is obtained by integration:

$$F = b \int_0^l p\,dh = b\rho g \int_0^l h\,dh = b\rho g l^2/2$$

The torque L of this force about an axis in the liquid surface is

$$L = Fh_c = b\rho g l^2 h_c/2$$

This torque may also be found by expressing the torque due to the force on the horizontal element, or

$$dL = h\,dF = b\rho g h^2\,dh$$

Integrating,

$$L = b\rho g \int_0^l h^2\,dh = b\rho g l^3/3$$

and equating the two equivalent expressions for torque,

$$b\rho g l^2 h_c/2 = b\rho g l^3/3$$

or
$$h_c = \tfrac{2}{3}l \qquad\qquad (17.18)$$

The result shows that the center of pressure is located two thirds of the way down from the liquid surface and, by symmetry, at the midpoint of b. This result holds for any plane rectangular surface whose top edge is not below the liquid surface. When the upper edge of the wall is submerged below the liquid surface, a more general expression must be derived (see Problem 17.44). These results are employed in the design of dams and other structures used to confine liquids.

Example 17.4. The areas of the small and large pistons of an hydraulic press are 1.25 and 100 square inches respectively. If an input force of 5.00 pounds force is required to lift a load of 300 pounds force, what is the efficiency of the device?

Solution. The ideal mechanical advantage is the ratio of the areas, or $100/1.25 = 80.0$. The actual mechanical advantage is the ratio of the output to the input force, or $300/5.00 = 60.0$. Therefore the efficiency in per cent is $60.0 \times 100/80.0 = 75.0\%$.

Example 17.5. An open-tube manometer is used to measure the absolute pressure of a gas. When the manometer is connected the mercury in the open tube is at a height of 35.5 cm above that in the connecting tube. Find the gas pressure when the barometer stands at 75.8 cm Hg.

Solution. The pressure of the gas is

$$p = 75.8 + 35.5 = 111 \text{ cm Hg}$$
$$= 111 \times 980 \times 13.6 = 1.48 \times 10^6 \text{ dynes/cm}^2$$

Example 17.6. A homogeneous body of specific gravity 0.748 floats with 1/3 its volume in water and 1/2 its volume in oil, as shown in Figure 17.16. Find the density of the oil.

Solution. Since the body is in equilibrium, its weight w is equal to the buoyant force F_B, or

$$w = F_B$$

If we let V represent the total volume of the body and ρ_0 the density of the oil, then the equilibrium equation is

$$V \times 0.748 \times g =$$
$$\tfrac{1}{3}V \times 1.00 \times g + \tfrac{1}{2}V \times \rho_0 \times g$$

which yields the value

$$\rho_0 = 0.830 \text{ gm/cm}^3$$

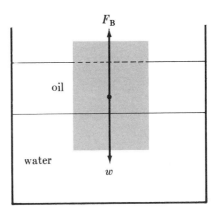

Figure 17.16.

Example 17.7. Find the increase in the submerged depth of a rectangular barge 20.0 feet by 15.0 feet when loaded with 3.00×10^3 pounds force.

Solution. By Archimedes' principle the weight of the additional volume of water displaced is equal to the load. Therefore the additional depth y is given by

$$20.0 \times 15.0y \times 62.4 = 3000$$
$$y = 0.160 \text{ ft} = 1.92 \text{ in}$$

Example 17.8. A clean wire ring 1.85 cm in diameter is used to measure the surface tension of a liquid. As the ring, supported horizontally, is carefully raised from the liquid the formed film breaks when the withdrawing force is 311 dynes. What is the surface tension of the liquid?

Solution. Apply Equation 17.14 and, since the ring forms two surface films,

$$\sigma = \frac{F}{2l} = \frac{311}{2 \times 1.85 \times 3.14} = 26.8 \text{ dynes/cm}$$

Problems

Wherever necessary employ for g the values 980 cm/sec² = 9.80 m/sec² = 32.0 ft/sec².

17.1. A solid metal cylindrical ring with inside and outside diameters of 2.26 cm and 3.58 cm, respectively, has a length of 8.00 cm and a mass of 547 gm. Find its specific gravity and identify the metal in accordance with Table 17.1.

17.2. The frustum of a right copper cone of original altitude 10.5 inches has top and base radii of 1.00 inch and 5.75 inches respectively. What is the mass of the frustum?

17.3. Find the pressure required to support a column of mercury 60.0 cm high. Express the answer in pounds force per square inch and in bars.

17.4. A column of oil, specific gravity 0.825, is 0.755 cm high. What is the pressure in newtons per square meter at the bottom of the column?

17.5. How high a column of water will 1.00 atmosphere support?

17.6. Find the pressure exerted by a column of water 2.00 m in height. Express your answer in dynes per square centimeter and in centimeters of mercury.

17.7. A vertical cylindrical tank 20.0 feet in diameter contains water to a height of 3.75 feet. Find (**a**) the hydrostatic pressure and (**b**) the hydrostatic force on the bottom.

17.8. The total hydrostatic force produced by water on the flat bottom of a tank of equilateral triangular cross section of side 2.55 feet is 304 pounds force. Find the depth of water.

17.9. A pipe, open at the top and rising at an angle of 25.0° with the level ground, contains water which is subjected to a pressure from below of 5.00 pounds force per square inch. How much of the pipe contains water?

17.10. A rectangular swimming pool 30.0 feet by 22.5 feet contains water to a depth of 3.00 feet at one end of the long dimension and 8.00 feet at the other end. Find the hydrostatic force on the bottom.

17.11. The vertical wall of a dam is 50.0 feet long and the surface of the water is 27.0 feet high. Find (**a**) the hydrostatic force on the wall and (**b**) the torque tending to overturn the dam.

17.12. A rectangular vessel of length 20.0 cm and width 15.0 cm contains the following: a 12.0 cm layer of mercury at the bottom, an 8.00 cm layer of water in the middle, and a 5.00 cm layer of oil (specific gravity 0.850) on top. Find the resultant force on each wall.

17.13. The small and large pistons of Figure 17.3 are 0.500 inch and 3.00 inches in diameter, respectively. Find the force exerted on the larger piston when a force of 100 pounds is exerted on the smaller piston.

17.14. Solve Problem 17.13 in which the smaller piston is elevated 20.0 feet above the larger piston and the hydraulic fluid is water.

17.15. The large piston of an hydraulic press exerts a force of 3.00×10^3 kgf when a force of 5.00 kgf is applied to the small piston whose diameter is 1.50 cm. If the efficiency of the device is 80.0% what is the diameter of the large piston?

17.16. The levels of mercury in an open-tube manometer connected for pressure measurement differ by 25.6 inches, the mercury in the open tube being higher. What is (**a**) the gauge pressure and (**b**) the absolute pressure?

17.17. The open-tube manometer shown in Figure 17.4a is used to measure gas pressure. If the level of mercury in the open tube stands 55.5 cm below that in the connecting tube what is the pressure of the gas? The barometric pressure is 75.5 cm Hg.

17.18. A closed-tube manometer containing oil of specific gravity 0.850 and negligible vapor pressure is connected to a gas supply which is under a pressure of 0.812 pounds force per square inch. What is the difference between the levels of oil in the arms of the manometer?

17.19. In the measurement of the density of a liquid a U-tube is employed as follows. Mercury of known density 13.6 gm/cm³ is poured into the tube and enough of the unknown liquid, not miscible in mercury, is added until it stands 50.5 cm above the mercury level in one arm, whereupon the mercury level in the other arm stands 2.50 cm above the liquid–mercury interface. Find the density of the liquid.

17.20. The two open ends of an inverted U-tube are placed in two beakers of liquid, one containing turpentine and the other a liquid whose density is to be determined. The top of the inverted tube has an opening which is con-
nected to an evacuation pump. After
some evacuation the turpentine has
risen a distance of 23.8 cm and the
other liquid a distance of 31.0 cm in the
tubes. Taking the density of turpentine as 0.870 gm/cm³ find the density
of the other liquid. Assume equal surface levels in the beakers.

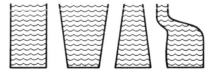

Figure 17.17. *Pascal's hydrostatic paradox, Problem 17.21.*

17.21. Figure 17.17 shows four differently shaped vessels all having the same area of base and filled with the same liquid to the same vertical height. Explain the paradox that even though each vessel contains a different volume of the liquid the pressure at the base of each is the same. Include in your explanation the analysis of the forces exerted by the walls of the vessels on the liquid.

17.22. An object has a weight of 315 gf in air and 225 gf when totally immersed in water. What is its specific gravity?

17.23. A stone with a specific gravity of 2.85 weighs 305 gf in air and 214 gf when totally immersed in a liquid. What is the density of the liquid?

17.24. A stone weighs 0.603 pounds force when totally immersed in water and 0.670 pounds force when totally immersed in oil of specific gravity 0.800. Find the specific gravity of the stone.

17.25. A body weighs 540 gf in air, 420 gf when submerged in water, and 435 gf when submerged in another liquid. Find the specific gravities of (**a**) the body and (**b**) the liquid.

17.26. A sample of white pine wood has a mass of 6.00 gm in air. A metal sinker is attached to it, and the weight of the combination when only the sinker is totally immersed in water is 23.5 gf, and the combined weight of wood and sinker when both are totally immersed in water is 8.50 gf. Find the density of the wood. Derive any formula you employ in the solution.

17.27. Find the pressure that is necessary to increase the density of aluminum by 0.250%. Use Table 14.1.

17.28. A piece of steel, dropped into the ocean, sinks to a depth where the pressure is 1.35×10^3 bars. Find the percentage change in the density of the steel. Use Table 14.1.

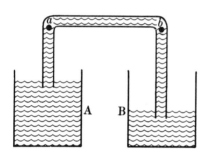

Figure 17.18. *The siphon, Problem 17.29.*

17.29. Show that the operation of the siphon in Figure 17.18 results in liquid's being discharged from vessel A into vessel B. (*Hint:* Show that the pressure at *b* is less than that at *a*.) Indicate the conditions under which the siphon will operate and under what conditions it will cease operating.

17.30. An hydrometer with a stem whose cross-sectional area is 0.500 cm² floats in pure water, displacing 80.0 cm³. Find the additional length of stem which becomes submerged when the hydrometer is placed in a liquid whose density is 0.850 gm/cm³.

17.31. A barge 20.5 feet by 32.2 feet is used to carry 200 people whose average weight is 148 pounds. How much does the barge sink in fresh water when loaded?

17.32. A block of wood has a mass of 180 gm and a specific gravity of 0.600. A hole is to be drilled into the wood and refilled with lead so that the composite body just floats in fresh water and none of the volume is above the surface. Find the volume of lead to be used.

17.33. An open vessel containing water is placed on a spring scale and found to have a weight W. A metal object of weight w is attached to a string and held so that the object is completely submerged in the water without touching the sides or bottom of the vessel. Show that the scale reading now is $W + F_B$ and the tension in the string is given by $w - F_B$ where F_B is the buoyant force on the object.

17.34. Using the arrangement outlined in Problem 17.33 solve the following. The vessel and water have a weight of 750 gf and when the object is suspended in the water the scale reads 850 gf. When the object is lowered so that it rests on the bottom of the vessel the scale registers 1.00×10^3 gf. Find (**a**) the weight of the object, (**b**) the density of the object, and (**c**) the tension in the string.

17.35. A pycnometer bottle weighs 51.32 gf when empty, 115.85 gf when filled with a liquid A, and 95.64 gf when filled with a liquid B whose specific gravity is 0.855. Find the specific gravity of liquid A.

17.36. A block of matter floats with 1/6 its volume in mercury and the remainder in water, as in Figure 17.16 except that the top surface of the block is at the surface of the water. Find the density of the block.

17.37. A brass alloy is 85.0% by weight copper and 15.0% by weight zinc. Taking the specific gravities of copper and zinc as 8.89 and 7.10 respectively, find the specific gravity of the alloy. Assume that the combined volumes of copper and zinc equal the volume of the alloy.

17.38. An alloy made of gold and silver weighs 800 gf in air and 745 gf when totally immersed in water. Find the masses of gold and silver, assuming that their combined volumes equal the volume of the alloy.

17.39. What fraction of the volume of an iceberg floating on sea water is above the water?

17.40. A balloon contains 5.00×10^5 m³ of hydrogen. Find the weight of added material that this balloon is capable of lifting in air.

17.41. In the determination of the true mass of a body with the use of an equal-arm sensitive analytical balance and standard masses, correction must be made for the buoyant force of the air if the densities of the body and standard masses are different. Show that if m_s and ρ_s are the mass and density of the standard respectively, ρ_b the density of the body, and ρ_a the density of air, the true mass is given by $m_s[1 - (\rho_a/\rho_s)] + \rho_a V_b$ where V_b is the volume of the body, or by $m_s [\rho_b(\rho_s - \rho_a)/\rho_s(\rho_b - \rho_a)]$. Show also that the true mass is approximately given by $m_s + m_s\rho_a[(1/\rho_b) - (1/\rho_s)]$.

17.42. A block of cork is placed on one pan of a sensitive equal-arm balance and the amount of counterpoising brass masses is observed to be 10.432 gm. The density of the brass is 8.40 gm/cm³. Find the true mass of the cork block (see Problem 17.41 and use the approximate solution).

17.43. A concrete dam of rectangular cross section is 8.00 feet thick, 20.0 feet high, and l feet long. How far below the top of the dam is the water level if the torque tending to keep the dam from overturning (torque due to the dam's weight) is 50.0% greater than that tending to overturn the dam (torque due to the water pressure)? Use 150 pounds force per cubic foot for the density of concrete and neglect the forces at the ends of the dam that tend to hold the dam upright.

17.44. A vertical wall of height h is under a liquid with its upper end a distance c below the liquid surface. Show that the distance from the liquid surface to the center of pressure below is given by $2(3c^2 + 3ch + h^2)/3(2c + h)$.

17.45. The level of water above the top of a rectangular water gate 8.50 feet high by 3.75 feet wide is 4.00 feet. Find (**a**) the hydrostatic force acting on the gate and (**b**) the depth of the center of pressure (see Problem 17.44).

17.46. A wire frame in the form of an inverted U of width 2.86 cm is withdrawn vertically from a soap solution at the rate of 0.125 mm/sec. Find (**a**) the force required in addition to gravity and (**b**) the power expended in overcoming surface tension. The temperature of the solution is 20°C.

17.47. A thin circular wire of 1.12 cm radius is supported horizontally in a liquid and withdrawn slowly by applying a steady upward force of 553 dynes. If the surface tension of the liquid is 35.8 dynes/cm what is the mass of the wire?

17.48. The rectangular frame shown in Figure 17.9 contains a liquid film of surface tension 31.8 dynes/cm. Find (**a**) the force exerted by the film on the crosspiece AD of length 1.95 cm and (**b**) the work done when AD moves through a distance of 2.64 cm.

17.49. A ring of thickness 0.150 cm is held at rest horizontally in a liquid whose surface tension is 30.4 dynes/cm. In pulling the ring free from the liquid surface it is found that a force of 996 dynes is required to break the film. Find the internal and external diameters of the ring.

17.50. To demonstrate surface tension a steel needle may be "floated" on the surface of water. Assuming a cylindrical needle, what is the greatest diameter that can be employed? Take the specific gravity of steel as 7.83 and the temperature of the water as 25°C.

17.51. A matchstick of length 1.56 cm floats in water. When a drop of ether is permitted to fall on one side of the stick the surface tension on that side is reduced by 12.5 dynes/cm. Find the magnitude and direction of the unbalanced force acting on the stick.

17.52. The pressure inside a bubble below the surface of water at 25°C is 50.0% more than atmospheric pressure. If the bubble has a diameter of 0.250 mm how far is it below the surface?

17.53. Find the height to which alcohol will rise in a glass capillary tube of 0.485 mm radius. Take the surface tension of alcohol as 22.3 dynes/cm. The specific gravity of the alcohol is 0.810.

17.54. The internal diameter of a mercury barometer is 4.50 mm. By how much must the barometric reading be corrected for surface tension?

17.55. What is the height of the mercury column in a barometer tube of inside diameter 1.00 mm on a day when the atmospheric pressure is 1.00 bar?

17.56. Two vertical glass plates are held 1.25 mm apart in water at 25°C. (a) To what height would the water rise between the plates? (b) To what height would the water rise in a cylindrical tube of radius equal to the distance between the plates?

17.57. A spherical drop of mercury at 20°C has a diameter of 1.60 mm. How much is the excess pressure inside the drop?

17.58. The excess pressure inside a soap bubble is 50.0 dynes/cm². What is the diameter of the bubble?

17.59. Two plane glass plates are held together at one pair of edges and separated slightly at the opposite edges, forming a wedge of small angle. The plates are partially immersed in a liquid, the line common to the edges in contact being vertical. Due to capillary action, the liquid rises into the space between the plates, the edge of the liquid on the plates forming a curve. Show that this curve is a rectangular hyperbola.

17.60. Find the work done in blowing a soap bubble of 10.0 cm diameter.

Dynamics of Fluids

WE HAVE WITNESSED IN rigid-body mechanics that when we pass over from the study of statics to the study of dynamics additional properties manifest themselves and our analysis is widened to include concepts of inertia, moment of inertia, kinetic energy, etc. Similarly, whereas in hydrostatics the principles of Pascal and Archimedes afford an explanation and description of the behavior of a fluid at rest, in hydrodynamics we must also deal with the inertial properties of the fluid. In applying Newton's laws of motion to a fluid we soon realize that the situation is rather complicated and to obtain a detailed description of the motion of each constituent molecule is an unfeasible task. However, we shall see that when we deal with the continuous aspect of fluid flow we can formulate generalized principles in accordance with which the behavior of a fluid is describable. A knowledge of these principles is necessary in order that we may thoroughly understand and be able to predict what happens when a fluid moves with respect to a stationary obstacle, or when a body moves through a stationary fluid, or when both body and fluid move relative to one another. These principles have direct application in the flight of aircraft, in the operation of aircraft instruments, and in the flight of missiles and satellites. As with rigid-body dynamics it will become apparent that the application of the energy principle to fluid flow leads directly to a useful mathematical formulation.

18.1. Steady, or Stationary or Streamline Flow. Consider that a fluid is flowing in a pipe as shown in Figure 18.1a. The path followed by a particle of the fluid is represented by the line 1-2-3, the velocity of the particle at position 1 being v_1, at position 2 being v_2, and at position 3 being v_3. As time goes on different particles of the fluid will occupy positions 1, 2, and 3. If, as time goes on, any succeeding particle travels the same path 1-2-3 and has the same velocities v_1 at 1, v_2 at 2, and v_3 at 3, then the motion is said to be *steady*, or *stationary*, and the path 1-2-3 followed by any and all succeeding particles is called a *streamline*. In streamline flow, a particle that passes through position 1 with velocity v_1 must also pass through positions 2 and 3 with the respective velocities v_2 and v_3. It is as if the particle's motion were confined to a small tube through which the particles are streaming and in fact a bundle of such similar streamlines is called a *tube of flow*. By the nature of a streamline it is clear that streamlines or lines of flow give the direction of the velocity of fluid flow at every point. By the definition of a streamline it follows that particles of a fluid cannot flow from one streamline to another, the motion being confined to tubes of flow. If the neighboring tubes of flow are identical, then it is convenient to consider that the fluid is flowing in one large tube as in the case of Figure 18.1a.

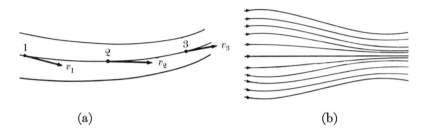

(a)   (b)

Figure 18.1. *Steady, or stationary or streamline flow.*

Figure 18.1b shows some streamlines of fluid flowing from an open region to a more constricted region of a pipe. In the constricted region the velocity of flow is increased.

18.2. The Equation of Continuity. In Figure 18.2 is shown a tube of flow of varying cross-sectional area. The liquid is shown passing areas A_1 and A_2 with normal velocities v_1 and v_2 respectively. We shall now assume that the fluid is incompressible, an assumption which as we have already seen is quite valid for liquids. It now follows, if there are no sources or sinks, that the quantity of liquid crossing area A_1 must be equal to that crossing area A_2 in any given time interval. Thus, with ρ as the constant density of the incompressible fluid and t the time interval, the volume of liquid passing any area A with a normal velocity v in the time interval t is $Av\rho t$ and

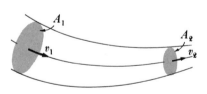

Figure 18.2. *Equation of continuity.*

$$A_1 v_1 \rho t = A_2 v_2 \rho t$$

or

$$A_1 v_1 = A_2 v_2 \tag{18.1}$$

Equation 18.1 is one form of the *equation of continuity* as applied to an incompressible fluid.* It expresses that the mass of fluid is "continuous" across all planes normal to the streamline flow and shows that where the area is small the velocity is large or vice versa. Furthermore, since v_2 is greater than v_1 in Figure 18.2, the liquid accelerates in the direction of v_2, the accelerating force being due to the presence of a larger pressure at A_1 and a smaller pressure at A_2. Hence, in the steady flow of an incompressible fluid, the pressure is greatest where the velocity is least and vice versa. This inverse relationship between pressure and velocity is quantitatively expressed by the Bernoulli equation which is derived in the following section.

18.3. Bernoulli's Equation. The basic equation in hydrodynamics is the Bernoulli equation which is named after its discoverer Daniel Bernoulli (1700–1782). The equation gives the relationship between the velocity, the pressure, and the elevation at points in a line of flow. It may be derived in two ways, by applying the energy theorem to a flow stream of fluid or by applying Newton's second law of motion to a fluid flowing in a tube of flow.

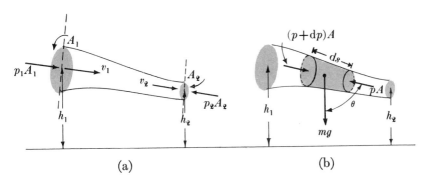

Figure 18.3. *Diagrams used in deriving Bernoulli's equation: (a) by energy considerations, and (b) by application of Newton's second law.*

The left column below contains the energy method and the right column contains the application of Newton's law by means of the calculus.

Consider the tube of flow shown in Figure 18.3a and assume that there is a steady state of flow of an incompressible frictionless fluid of density ρ. The flow is considered to take place from area A_1 to area A_2 under the action of a difference in pressure $p_1 - p_2$ and under the

Consider the portion of fluid indicated by the shaded section in the tube of flow in Figure 18.3b. This volume element has an infinitesimal length ds, a cross-sectional area A, and a mass m. Assume that the flow is steady and the fluid incompressible and frictionless.

---

* The density of a compressible fluid is not constant throughout a tube of flow, and the equation of continuity must be extended to take into account that a unit volume of fluid may contain different fluid masses.

action of a gravitational field as indicated by the elevation difference $h_1 - h_2$. Since the flow is steady it is characterized by the fact that in any time interval the mass of fluid passing through A_1 is the same as the mass of fluid passing through A_2. By the work-energy theorem the work done by the force due to pressure and by the gravitational force is equal to the change in kinetic energy. Applying this theorem to a mass m of fluid for a time interval t we have:

Work done by force due to pressure difference $= p_1 A_1 v_1 t - p_2 A_2 v_2 t$

Work done by gravity $= mg(h_1 - h_2)$
Change in kinetic energy $= \frac{1}{2}m(v_2{}^2 - v_1{}^2)$

Hence:

$$p_1 A_1 v_1 t - p_2 A_2 v_2 t + mg(h_1 - h_2)$$
$$= \frac{1}{2}m(v_2{}^2 - v_1{}^2)$$

But, by the continuity principle,

$$A_1 v_1 t = A_2 v_2 t = m/\rho$$

Therefore:

$$m(p_1 - p_2) + mg(h_1 - h_2) = \frac{1}{2}m(v_2{}^2 - v_1{}^2)$$

or:

$$p_1 + \rho g h_1 + \frac{1}{2}\rho v_1{}^2$$
$$= p_2 + \rho g h_2 + \frac{1}{2}\rho v_2{}^2 \quad (18.2)$$

The pressure on the right face of the fluid element is p, that on the left face is $p + dp$, and the fluid element is under the action of a force due to this difference in pressure as well as a gravitational force due to a difference in elevation along the direction of flow. Applying Newton's second law to this element of fluid we have

$$pA - (p + dp)A - mg\cos\theta = m(dv/dt)$$

where the downward direction of the acceleration of gravity has been taken as negative, θ is the angle that the flow direction makes with the vertical, and the acceleration dv/dt is in the direction of decreasing pressure. Now $m = \rho A\, ds$ where ρ is the density of the fluid mass and

$$(dv/dt) = v(dv/ds)$$

so that

$$-A\, dp - \rho A g\cos\theta\, ds = \rho A v\, dv$$

Observing that $ds\cos\theta = dh$ where dh is the vertical component of the displacement ds, we have

$$-dp - \rho g\, dh = \rho v\, dv$$

and remembering that ρ is constant,

$$-\int_{p_1}^{p_2} dp - \rho g \int_{h_1}^{h_2} dh = \rho \int_{v_1}^{v_2} v\, dv$$

where the limits are indicated in Figure 18.3b. Integrating,

$$p_1 - p_2 + \rho g(h_1 - h_2) = \frac{\rho}{2}(v_2{}^2 - v_1{}^2)$$

or:

$$p_1 + \rho g h_1 + \frac{1}{2}\rho v_1{}^2$$
$$= p_2 + \rho g h_2 + \frac{1}{2}\rho v_2{}^2 \quad (18.2)$$

Equation 18.2 is Bernoulli's equation and expresses the conservation of energy principle as applied to an incompressible fluid in steady motion without friction along a tube of flow. A convenient form of the equation is obtained by dividing Equation 18.2 by the density ρ:

$$\frac{p_1}{\rho} + gh_1 + \frac{1}{2}v_1{}^2 = \frac{p_2}{\rho} + gh_2 + \frac{1}{2}v_2{}^2 \quad (18.3)$$

Here on either side of the equation the first term represents the potential energy per unit mass of fluid due to pressure, the second term is the gravitational potential energy per unit mass of the fluid, and the last term is the kinetic energy per unit mass of the fluid. The principle states that the sum of these at any point in the fluid is equal to their sum at any other point, or, in general, that

$$\frac{p}{\rho} + gh + \frac{1}{2}v^2 = \text{constant} \tag{18.4}$$

Equation 18.4, stated in terms of the pressure p, height h, and velocity v at any point in the fluid, is a form that is often employed by engineers. The constant, of course, is different for different streamlines. When Equation 18.4 is divided by g there results another useful form of Bernoulli's equation:

$$\frac{p}{\rho g} + h + \frac{v^2}{2g} = \text{constant} \tag{18.5}$$

Engineers refer to h as the *elevation head*, $p/\rho g$ as the *pressure head*, and $v^2/2g$ as the *velocity head*. In this form the Bernoulli principle states that the total head remains unchanged in the steady flow of an incompressible frictionless fluid. The constant of Equation 18.5, which is different from that of Equation 18.4, is correspondingly referred to as the *total head*. When the fluid flow is along a horizontal tube, h does not vary and Bernoulli's equation reduces to the simpler form

$$\frac{p}{\rho g} + \frac{v^2}{2g} = \text{constant} \tag{18.6}$$

Notice that this equation clearly shows that the pressure is greatest where the velocity is least and vice versa, as already stated in the last section.

In applying Bernoulli's principle one may with equal effectiveness apply Equation 18.2, 18.4, or 18.5, but it must be remembered that the equations are applicable only under the condition that the fluid is incompressible, frictionless, and moving with streamline flow. When friction is considered to be present, a part of the mechanical energy of the flowing fluid is converted into heat energy and there results a gradual reduction of pressure along the flow line. It is then convenient to represent this pressure reduction by a term which is labeled the *friction head* (described in Section 18.4).

In applying the Equations 18.2–18.6, the units to be employed are as follows. In the cgs absolute system p is in dynes per square centimeter (dynes/cm²), ρ is in grams mass per cubic centimeter (gm/cm³), v is in centimeters per second (cm/sec), h is in centimeters, and g is in centimeters per square second (cm/sec²). In the mks absolute system p is in newtons per square meter (nt/m²), ρ is in kilograms mass per cubic meter (kgm/m³), v is in meters per second (m/sec), h is in meters, and g is in meters per square second (m/sec²). In the English gravitational system p is in pounds force per square foot (pf/ft²), ρ is in slugs per cubic foot (slugs/ft³), v is in feet per second (ft/sec), h is in feet, and g is in feet per square second (ft/sec²).

18.4. Applications and Illustrations of Bernoulli's Principle. The Bernoulli equation is one of the most important in the field of the hydrodynamics of ideal fluids. There are many illustrations and examples of the

Bernoulli principle and we shall here discuss some of the more significant applications.

Efflux Velocity of a Liquid from a Small Orifice. In Figure 18.4 is shown a tank containing a liquid which is flowing from an orifice located at a depth h below the liquid surface. To obtain an expression for the velocity of efflux from the orifice we apply Bernoulli's equation to two points in the liquid that are connected by streamline flow, a point 1 at the top of the liquid and a point 2 at the orifice. Equation 18.2 applied to these two points yields

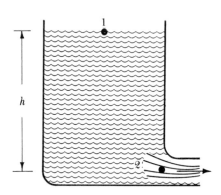

Figure 18.4. *Efflux of liquid from an orifice.*

$$p_1 + \rho g h_1 + \tfrac{1}{2}\rho v_1^2 = p_2 + \rho g h_2 + \tfrac{1}{2}\rho v_2^2$$

where the subscripts 1 and 2 refer to the corresponding points indicated in the figure. Since the pressure at 1 and 2 is atmospheric, $p_1 = p_2$. Also, if elevations are measured from the orifice level, taken as the middle of the orifice in the figure, then $h_2 = 0$ and $h_1 = h$. Therefore,

$$\rho g h + \tfrac{1}{2}\rho v_1^2 = \tfrac{1}{2}\rho v_2^2$$

and

$$v_2^2 = v_1^2 + 2gh \tag{18.7}$$

Now consider that the tank and orifice behave as one large tube of flow, the area at the top being A_1 and that at the orifice being A_2. From the equation of continuity $v_1 = (A_2/A_1)v_2$ and substituting into Equation 18.7 gives the velocity of efflux from the orifice:

$$v_2 = \sqrt{2gh}\,[1 - (A_2/A_1)^2]^{-1/2} \tag{18.8}$$

We see then that the velocity of efflux depends not only on the elevation head h but also on the ratio of the area of the orifice to that of the free surface. If this ratio is small enough so that $(A_2/A_1) \ll 1$, then $(A_2/A_1)^2$ may be neglected and we have the approximate result

$$v_2 = \sqrt{2gh} \tag{18.9}$$

which is precisely the value obtained if we consider that each particle of liquid falls freely from rest through a vertical height h. This, of course, is equivalent to considering that v_1 is approximately zero and the liquid flows out of the tank with constant elevation h, as shown by Equation 18.7. The result shown by Equation 18.9 is known as the theorem of Torricelli, who first discovered it in 1641.

It should be realized that in general the results here indicated are never really exact since the streamlines from all parts of the tank crowd together at the orifice and not every tube of flow that starts at a height h above the orifice goes on into the stream at the discharge opening. Some flow lines are broken up at the hole opening and eddies are formed. Furthermore, the cross section of the emitted stream contracts after leaving the orifice and then spreads out again, the contraction taking place because of the liquid's speed-up as it goes through the orifice. Due to this contraction phenomenon, known as the *vena contracta*, the time rate of discharge is a function of the geometry of the orifice, and Torricelli's theorem applies where the cross section of the stream is the least and the streamlines are all parallel. For a sharp-edged circular orifice, the contracted area is about 61% of the area of the opening. If the walls of the orifice are curved to fit the streamlines, contraction may be minimized.

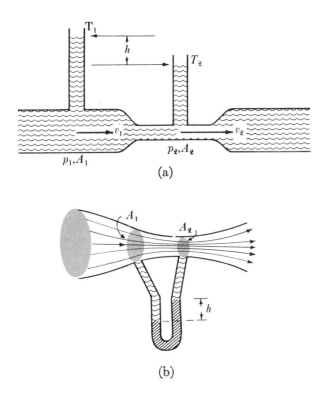

Figure 18.5. (a) *Liquid flow through a constriction.*
(b) *The Venturi flow meter.*

The Venturi Flow Meter. The measurement of the rate of flow of a gas or liquid through a pipe is a significant application of Bernoulli's principle. Figure 18.5a shows a liquid flowing through a constricted tube which is horizontal. Assuming no losses due to friction we can apply Bernoulli's equation to determine the pressure changes that take place along the tube. Let v_1, p_1, and A_1 represent the velocity, pressure, and cross-sectional area in the wide portion of the pipe, and v_2, p_2, and A_2 the corresponding quantities in the constricted portion. In the illustration, $A_2 < A_1$. Applying Bernoulli's equation, and remembering that the elevation is constant here, we have

$$p_1 + \tfrac{1}{2}\rho v_1^2 = p_2 + \tfrac{1}{2}\rho v_2^2$$

Combining this with the continuity equation $A_1 v_1 = A_2 v_2$ leads to the result

$$p_1 - p_2 = \frac{\rho v_1^2}{2}\left[\left(\frac{A_1}{A_2}\right)^2 - 1\right] \tag{18.10}$$

Since $A_1 > A_2$, then $p_1 > p_2$, and $v_2 > v_1$. There is therefore an increase in velocity and a decrease in pressure at the constricted portion of the pipe. The pressure difference in Equation 18.10 may be measured from the observed difference between heights of the liquid in the vertical tubes T_1 and T_2. From this and A_1 and A_2 the rate of liquid flow Q is obtained:

$$Q = A_1 v_1 = A_1 A_2 \sqrt{2(p_1 - p_2)/\rho(A_1^2 - A_2^2)} \tag{18.11}$$

where Q is the volume per second of liquid flowing.

These principles are embodied in the Venturi flow meter shown in Figure 18.5b. It consists of a tube having a constricted section to which is attached a manometer tube. When the meter is in use, $p_1 - p_2 = \rho'gh$ where ρ' is the density of the liquid in the manometer, such as mercury, and h is the difference in levels shown in the figure. The manometer may be calibrated, by means of Equation 18.11, to give the volume of fluid transported per second.

The Pitot Tube. The stream velocity of a flowing liquid or of a gas is measurable with a device called a Pitot tube, depicted in Figure 18.6. It

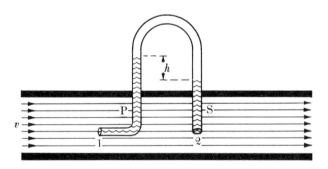

Figure 18.6. *The Pitot tube.*

consists of a straight section S called the static tube and a curved section P called the Pitot tube inserted as shown in a liquid which is assumed to flow uniformly from left to right. The tubes may be joined as shown or they each may be open to the atmosphere. The device is inserted so that the opening in the curved tube is at right angles to the direction of liquid flow while the opening in the static tube is parallel to the flow direction. At the opening 1 the liquid comes to rest and the streamlines divide around the opening; hence

$v_1 = 0$ and the pressure p_1 here is partly hydrostatic and partly due to the moving liquid. At the opening 2 the velocity v_2 is the stream velocity v and the pressure is the hydrostatic pressure p_2. Applying Bernoulli's equation to points 1 and 2 we have

$$p_1 + 0 = p_2 + \tfrac{1}{2}\rho v^2$$

and the stream velocity is given by

$$v = \sqrt{2(p_1 - p_2)/\rho} \tag{18.12}$$

The pressure difference in the tubes is given by $p_1 - p_2 = \rho g h$ where h is as indicated in the figure, so that

$$v = \sqrt{2gh} \tag{18.13}$$

The velocity of flow is therefore directly measured by observing h in the vertical tubes. Unless the sections of tubing that are inserted in the stream are so small that they do not appreciably disturb the flow lines it is necessary in practice to modify Equation 18.13 by a suitable empirical factor.

To adapt the Pitot tube to the measurement of the stream velocity of a gas one inverts the Pitot tube and employs a manometric liquid such as mercury to indicate the pressure difference (see Problem 18.7). The Pitot tube principle is employed on aircraft in air-speed indicators.

Flow along a Horizontal Tube with Friction. When friction is present some of the mechanical energy of a flowing stream is converted into heat with a consequent reduction of pressure along the tube. To see how this comes about consider Figure 18.7 which shows liquid flowing along a constant-

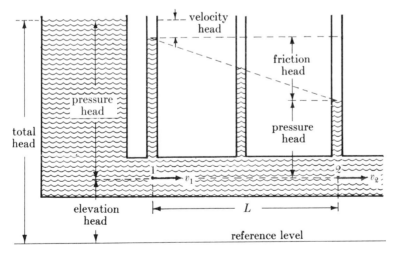

Figure 18.7. *Effect of friction on liquid flow in a horizontal tube.*

diameter horizontal pipe that joins the lower end of a tank in which the liquid is assumed to be kept at a fixed height. With respect to an arbitrary reference level the total head in the tank is composed of the elevation head plus the pressure head, as indicated. Since the cross-sectional area of the pipe is constant the velocity of flow is the same all along the pipe, and if there were no friction the velocity head would be the same at all points of the pipe and the liquid would stand at the same height in the vertical tubes, producing the same pressure head all along. However, with friction the pressure head gradually decreases along the pipe and the amount by which it decreases is represented by the *friction head*. Thus, if W is the work per unit mass of liquid per unit length of flow necessary to overcome friction, then Equation 18.3, applied to points 1 and 2 distant L apart (Figure 18.7) and modified to include energy loss due to friction, yields

$$\frac{p_1}{\rho} + gh_1 + \frac{1}{2}v_1{}^2 - \left(\frac{p_2}{\rho} + gh_2 + \frac{1}{2}v_2{}^2\right) = WL \qquad (18.14)$$

Here $v_1 = v_2$ and $h_1 = h_2$ so that

$$p_2 = p_1 - W\rho L \qquad (18.15)$$

Hence, the pressure at any point down the pipe decreases linearly with the distance along the pipe. This means that the friction head increases and the pressure head decreases along the direction of flow, resulting in a reduced speed of efflux from the pipe. This linear variation is indicated in Figure 18.7.

Examples Explained by Qualitative Application of Bernoulli's Principle. There are many examples of the use of Bernoulli's principle, some of which are commercial, laboratory, or household devices, others a part of our everyday experiences, and some even in the form of ingenious toys. For most of these the application of the qualitative statement of Bernoulli's principle, that *in a region where the velocity of flow is increased the fluid pressure is decreased with respect to that in the surrounding fluid and vice versa*, is sufficient to explain the action or phenomenon. We shall here review a few of the more familiar examples.

The student has perhaps seen, if not in a window display then in a laboratory or lecture demonstration, that a light ball such as a ping-pong ball or a jacks ball, can be supported on a rapidly moving jet of water or blast of air. The ball stays aloft even when the direction of the high-velocity jet makes an appreciable angle with the vertical. In the neighborhood of the jet or air blast the high velocity of the fluid is accompanied by a reduction of pressure below the surrounding atmospheric pressure and this results in a force that always pushes the ball toward the jet or air blast. Also, the vertical component of the forward force of the jet in part supports the ball against gravity.

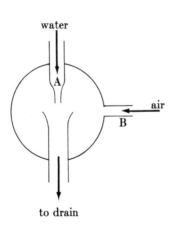

water

air

B

to drain

Figure 18.8. *The water aspirator.*

The water *aspirator* is employed in the laboratory as a vacuum pump. Its operation is illustrated in Figure 18.8. A stream of running water is directed through a constricted nozzle at A and then passes out through a wider opening to the drain. In the vicinity of A there exists a region of reduced pressure which draws in air through the side tube B to which is connected the vessel to be evacuated. The air is driven by the water stream through the outlet to the drain. An aspirator can reduce the pressure to about 1 cm Hg.

The *atomizer* or *spray jet* is shown in Figure 18.9. A high-speed stream of air is blown across the vertical tube that connects with the liquid in the bottle. The pressure in the vicinity of the top of the vertical tube is reduced below atmospheric pressure and the liquid is forced up into the air stream with the result that small droplets are formed, producing the spray.

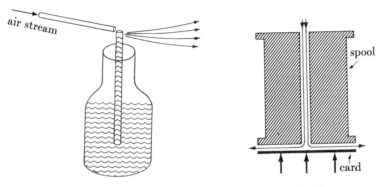

Figure 18.9. *The atomizer.*   **Figure 18.10.**

An impressive demonstration is to hold a spool vertically as shown in Figure 18.10 and to support a card with a finger against the lower face of the spool. When air is blown down through the hole the supporting finger can be removed and the card will not only remain in position but will be pressed more closely to the spool the harder one blows. The air, emerging from the hole, streams with a high velocity parallel to the card and radially from the center of the hole, and makes the pressure between the card and spool lower than atmospheric.

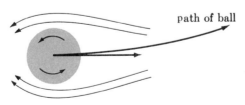

Figure 18.11. *Curved path of a spinning ball.*

In Figure 18.11 is shown how a pitched ball is made to move in a curve. If the pitcher in throwing the ball imparts a spin motion to it, the ball will follow a curved path. Suppose the ball is projected from left to right, as in the figure, and is spinning about a horizontal axis (perpendicular to the plane of the figure) with its top rotating in the direction of the pitcher. The spinning ball always drags a thin layer of air around it and the effect of the motion of the ball through the relatively still air is the same as if the ball were stationary and the air were moving past the ball from right to left. The velocity of the air at any point close to the ball is the resultant of the effect of the spin and of the effect of the translatory motion of the ball. Therefore, above the ball these two effects add while below the ball they subtract, producing a greater fluid velocity above the ball than below it. Hence the pressure below the ball is greater than that above it and this produces an unbalanced upward force which causes the ball to curve upward.

Still another example is afforded by the fact that when two ships are moving parallel they must avoid getting very close to one another, or they will collide. Between the ships, when they are close enough to form an effective constriction, the velocity of the water is greater than on their far sides where the pressure is greater, so that the ships are forced together.

As a last example we shall illustrate how the lift on an airfoil is explained by Bernoulli's principle. Figure 18.12a shows the streamlines around an airplane wing or airfoil moving from left to right. Because of the shape of the airfoil the streamlines are crowded together in the region above the foil very much as they are between the walls of a Venturi tube when the walls of the constricted region are considered separated. The streamlines above follow the curvature of the surface closely and at increasing distances from the foil they become less and less curved. Above the foil there is a high fluid velocity with a decreased pressure relative to that in the region below the foil, producing an upward force or lift. In addition, the air that strikes the lower

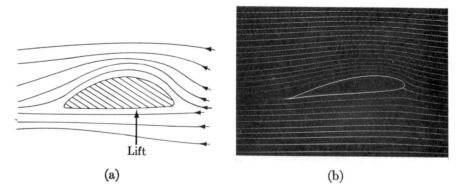

(a)   (b)

Figure 18.12. (a) *Streamlines around an airfoil showing the phenomenon of lift as explained by Bernoulli's principle.* (b) *Characteristics of streamline flow around an airfoil.* (c) *Effect of the angle of attack on the streamlines around an airfoil.* (*All photographs by courtesy of Dr. A. M. Lippisch, Collins Radio Company.*)

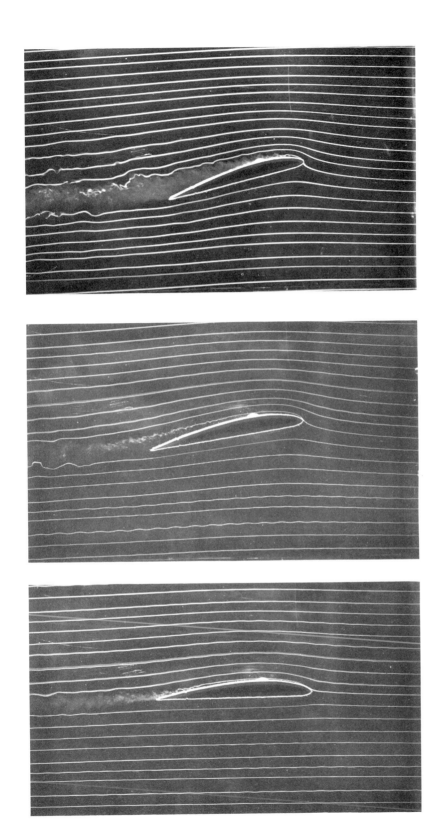

Figure 18.12(c).

part of the airfoil is deflected downward, producing by reaction an upward thrust. Both of these effects combine to produce the lifting force. The photograph Figure 18.12b, taken in a smoke tunnel, reveals these streamline characteristics around an airfoil section. Figure 18.12c are photographs of streamline flow around an airfoil section when there is an increase in the angle of attack, that is, the angle that the airfoil makes with the line of flight. Notice how, when the angle of attack increases, the streamlines above the airfoil must change direction more sharply, to follow the contour of the airfoil, and then smoothly join with the streamlines from below. When the angle is too large, as in the topmost photograph of (c), the streamline flow above and behind the airfoil breaks down and turbulence sets in, accompanied by whirls and eddies. When this happens Bernoulli's equation is inapplicable: the pressure above the airfoil rises, there is a marked reduction in the lift force, and the plane stalls.

18.5. Viscosity. In Section 6.4 we discussed the subject of viscous friction and the nature of the viscosity of liquids and gases. The student is urged at this time to review the treatment there given. It was there explained that the internal friction of a fluid, which gives rise to the phenomenon of viscosity, necessitates that a force be exerted to cause one layer of fluid to slide past a neighboring layer. For this type of flow we introduced the term *laminar* flow. This is also a streamline flow, the streams being parallel owing to the fact that the fluid moves in parallel layers or lamina. However, it is to be distinguished from what we have thus far considered in this chapter by the fact that in the motion of viscous fluid the magnitude of the velocity of the fluid changes as we move in a direction perpendicular to the streamlines (see Figure 6.4). Actually, no fluid is really a "perfect fluid," which is what we have been considering, and a real fluid will more or less support or transmit some shearing stress resulting in the property of viscosity.

From Equation 6.4 we have that the coefficient of viscosity of a fluid may be determined by performing an experiment in which the other quantities in the equation may be observed. However, it is much more convenient to permit the fluid to flow through a cylindrical tube at a relatively low speed: the flow will be laminar in type with sheets of fluid as cylindrical tubes sliding over each other. By observing the time rate of discharge of the fluid its coefficient of viscosity may be determined. This is made possible by the fact that when Equation 6.4 is applied to the flow of a viscous fluid through a cylindrical pipe an equation may be derived that states the following (see Problem 6.21):

$$Q = \pi R^4 (p_1 - p_2)/8\eta L \tag{18.16}$$

where Q is the quantity of fluid that flows out per unit time, R is the tube radius, $p_1 - p_2$ is the difference in fluid pressure existing at the ends of the tube, L is the length of the tube, and η is the coefficient of viscosity.

If R is in centimeters, $p_1 - p_2$ in dynes per square centimeter (dynes/cm²),
L in centimeters, and η in poises or dyne-second per square centimeter
(dyne·sec/cm²), then Q will be in cubic centimeters per second (cm³/sec).
This relation is known as Poiseuille's law, named after L. M. Poiseuille who
first discovered it and in whose honor the unit for viscosity (the poise) has
been named. By observing Q, R, $p_1 - p_2$, and L, η may be determined and
applied to speeds of flow that are small (to insure laminar flow and avoid the
formation of eddies or whirlpools). The equation provides an excellent means
of determining the coefficient of viscosity for liquids, and it may also be employed for gases and inviscid liquids. The velocity of flow is controlled by
the choice of a tube with a suitable radius for a given fluid.

Another method of determining the coefficient of viscosity of a fluid is
based on the fact that, when a sphere is moved with constant slow speed
through a medium, the fluid flow relative to the sphere is laminar in type.
Here the propelling force is equal to the viscous friction force and a mathematical analysis, which is beyond the scope of this treatment, yields the
relation

$$F = 6\pi\eta v r \tag{18.17}$$

where F is the viscous resistance force exerted on the sphere, η is the coefficient
of viscosity, v is the velocity of the sphere, and r is the sphere's radius. The
student can verify that when η is in poises, v in centimeters per second, and
r in centimeters, then F is in dynes. Equation 18.17 is called Stokes' law
after its discoverer. It is conveniently applied to a sphere that falls under
the action of gravity through a viscous medium and attains a terminal velocity v. When the sphere falls from rest with constant acceleration, the medium
exerts a small viscous frictional drag which increases as the velocity of the
sphere increases until it is equal to the accelerating force. Thereafter the
sphere falls with constant terminal speed v. We then have that

$$F = \tfrac{4}{3}\pi r^3 (\rho - \rho_0) g$$

where ρ is the density of the sphere and ρ_0 is the density of the viscous fluid.
Equation 18.17 now becomes

$$\tfrac{4}{3}\pi r^3 (\rho - \rho_0) g = 6\pi r \eta v$$

or

$$\eta = 2r^2(\rho - \rho_0)g/9v \tag{18.18}$$

By measuring the terminal velocity v of the sphere and knowing the other
quantities in the equation, η can be determined. This affords a convenient
method for the determination of the coefficients of viscosity of gases.

18.6. Turbulent Flow. So far we have been concerned with only
one of the two distinguishable types of fluid motion, the kind in which the
fluid particles move in smooth paths called streamlines and, when viscous
friction is present, is better described as laminar flow. We have indicated

that this kind of motion will take place only when the velocity of flow is relatively small. However, if the velocity of the fluid moving past a stream-lined body, or the velocity with which the body is dragged through a fluid, is gradually increased it happens that at a certain critical velocity the motion of the fluid changes its character rather abruptly and becomes the second kind, called *turbulent flow*. In turbulent flow there are no streamlines; instead, eddies, whirls, and fluctuations of a random nature are formed (See Figure 18.13). It can be shown that, for turbulent flow, the resistance to

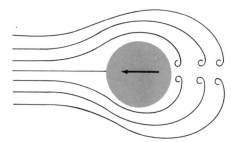

Figure 18.13. *The motion of a body through a fluid, causing turbulence in its wake.*

the motion of a fluid around an obstacle is proportional to the square of the velocity, whereas in laminar flow, as we have seen, the resistance to fluid motion is proportional to the first power of the velocity. Stokes' law and Poiseuille's law, true for laminar flow, are not valid for turbulent flow. The change in the force that opposes the motion of a body through a medium when the velocity changes from a value below critical to the critical value is due to the formation of vortices behind the body, as shown in Figure 18.13, resulting in a large pressure resistance to motion in addition to the smaller viscous resistance.

The circumstances that determine the critical velocity are those that indicate when turbulent motion will take place. When a body is dragged through a fluid the critical velocity is a function of both the kind of fluid and the shape of the body. Turbulence occurs also when a fluid streams through a pipe, and in the case of a cylindrical tube the critical velocity v_c is given by

$$v_c = \frac{\Re\eta}{\rho D} \tag{18.19}$$

where η and ρ are the coefficient of viscosity and the density of the fluid, respectively, D is the diameter of the tube, and $\Re$ is a dimensionless number called *Reynolds' number*, named after Osborne Reynolds who first discovered (1883) the conditions governing the change-over from streamline to turbulent flow. With laminar flow one always has small values of $\Re$, while with turbulent flow there are associated large values of $\Re$. For a given situation, that value of ℛ for which turbulence sets in may be found empirically since the pressure necessary to maintain a flow of fluid through a pipe at increasing velocities changes abruptly as the flow changes from the laminar to the turbulent type. Objects that have sharp edges and whose curvature changes abruptly produce turbulence, their motion through a fluid being greatly impeded owing to increased resistance. Hence objects such as airplanes, cars, and certain seacraft, which are to move rapidly through air or water, are shaped in a streamlined fashion to prevent turbulence as much as possible.

Problems

Where necessary use for g the values 980 cm/sec² = 9.80 m/sec² = 32.0 ft/sec².

18.1. A pipe 20.0 cm in diameter is discharging water at the rate of 100 cubic-inches/sec. At some point along the pipe there is a constriction of radius 6.00 cm. Considering water as incompressible and neglecting friction, find the speed of the water (**a**) through the pipe and (**b**) through the constriction.

18.2. A pipe 6.25 inches in diameter has at one point a constriction 4.75 inches in diameter. If the speed of an incompressible liquid at the wider section is 50.0 cubic-feet/min what is the speed at the constricted region?

18.3. A cylindrical water tank has a diameter of 6.00 feet. Nine feet below the water level a circular hole of diameter 0.400 inch is drilled through the side of the tank. Find the rate of flow of water from the orifice, neglecting the contraction phenomenon and the formation of eddies at the opening.

18.4. Solve Problem 18.3 for a tank diameter of 1.00 inch.

18.5. In Problem 18.1 find the difference in pressure between the wide and constricted portions of the pipe which is assumed to be horizontal.

18.6. A Venturi meter indicates a difference in water pressure of 10.5 pounds-force/square-inch between its normal section 3.55 inches in diameter and a constricted section 1.35 inches in diameter. How many cubic feet does it pass per minute?

18.7. An inverted Pitot tube is used as an air speed indicator. Show that the speed of the air relative to the device is given by $v = \sqrt{2\rho'gh/\rho}$ where ρ is the density of the air, ρ' is the density of the manometric liquid, h is the difference of level of the manometric liquid in the tube, and g is the gravitational acceleration.

18.8. An air speed indicator (see Problem 18.7) in an airplane is moving with a speed of 300 miles/hour. Find the difference of pressure in the two arms of the indicator. The density of air is 1.29×10^{-3} gm/cm³.

18.9. Water is pumped through city mains to a hill 80.5 feet above the station where the pressure is maintained at 55.0 pounds-force/square-inch. Assuming no losses due to friction, find the pressure at the top.

18.10. The wide section of a pipe is 14.3 square inches in cross-sectional area and a constricted section, 10.0 feet below, is 3.25 square inches in area. The water pressure at the constricted region is 8.50 pounds-force/square-inch. Find the pressure at the wide region if the water is flowing at the rate of 3.00 cubic-feet/sec.

18.11. In Problem 18.3 find the rate of flow, assuming the stream cross section contracts to 0.61 of the area of the circular orifice.

18.12. The level of water in a tank is maintained 1.75 inches above an orifice in the wall of the tank. The orifice has a diameter of 2.00 cm and the stream contracts to three fifths of the diameter as it emerges. Find the rate at which liquid discharges from the orifice.

18.13. A vertical standpipe has a small hole 5.00 feet above its base which rests on level ground. The stream of water issuing from the orifice strikes the ground at a horizontal distance of 30.0 feet. At what height above the hole is the water level maintained?

18.14. Explain the action of a siphon by an application of the Bernoulli equation.

18.15. Show that the equations of hydrostatics, expressing Pascal's principle, may be derived from the Bernoulli equation.

18.16. Show that the force F acting upward on the card in Figure 18.10 is given by $F = \rho v^2 A/2$ where ρ is the density of the air, v is the average speed of the air flowing between spool and card, and A is the effective area of the card.

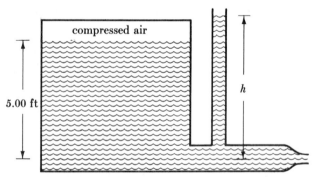

Figure 18.14. *Problem 18.17.*

18.17. Figure 18.14 shows a large-diameter tank containing water to a height of 5.00 feet and compressed air at a pressure of 20.7 pounds-force/square-inch. The horizontal pipe has a cross-sectional area of 3.00 square inches and an outlet section of 1.50 square inches. Find **(a)** the rate of discharge from the outlet and **(b)** the height h of water in the vertical pipe.

18.18. Solve Problem 18.17 for the case where the top of the tank is open to the atmosphere.

18.19. An elevated water tank supplies water to a house through a pipe which terminates in a faucet opening of effective diameter 0.300 inch. If the level of the water in the tank is 80.0 feet above the ground and the faucet is 30.0 feet above the ground, what is the time required for the open faucet to fill a tub of 15.0-cubic-foot capacity?

18.20. A liquid is forced through a capillary tube 15.0 cm in length and 1.50 mm in internal diameter under a pressure difference of 5.88×10^4 dynes/cm². If 105 cm³ of liquid is forced through in 30.0 sec what is the coefficient of viscosity of the liquid?

18.21. A capillary tube 15.0 cm long is to be used to permit 60.0 cm³/sec of alcohol to flow through it under a pressure difference of 4.90×10^4 dynes/cm² between its ends. Find the diameter of the tube. The coefficient of viscosity of alcohol is 0.0120 poise.

18.22. An apparatus for measuring the coefficient of viscosity of a liquid consists of an open-top container from whose bottom there extends downward a vertical tube. The container is kept full of the liquid under test while the discharge rate from the bottom of the vertical tube is observed. The container has a height of 15.0 cm, the vertical tube has a length of 7.50 cm and a diameter of 1.50 mm, the liquid has a specific gravity of 1.45, and the discharge rate is 3.50 cm³/sec. Find the coefficient of viscosity of the liquid.

18.23. A spherical metal ball of specific gravity 8.00 falls vertically with a terminal speed of 24.5 cm/sec in a viscous liquid whose density is 1.25 gm/cm³. The diameter of the ball is 3.08 mm. Find the viscosity of the liquid.

18.24. A droplet of oil, whose density is 0.885 gm/cm³, falls vertically in air with a terminal speed of 2.55 cm/sec. What is the mass of the drop? The coefficient of viscosity of the air is 1.81×10^{-8} poise. The density of air is 1.29×10^{-3} gm/cm³.

18.25. Two spherical metal balls, A and B, of specific gravities 8.50 and 5.75 respectively, fall with the same terminal velocity in glycerin of density 1.26 gm/cm³. Find the ratio of the diameters of the spheres.

Heat, Temperature, and Thermal Expansion

*H*EAT IS A FORM OF ENERGY and as such may be converted directly or indirectly into other forms of energy. Experience shows that when heat is applied to a body it may produce various effects: there may be a change in temperature of the body, there may be a change in the dimensions of the body, the magnetic and electrical properties of the body may change, the elastic properties of the body may be altered, the body may be induced to emit light, and the body may experience certain chemical changes. The physicist and engineer are concerned with these effects and we shall be elaborating on them in the appropriate sections of this book. In this chapter we shall briefly discuss the concept of heat, develop the meaning of temperature and temperature scales, and study the laws governing the phenomenon of thermal expansion. We shall then be in a position to study in subsequent chapters heat quantities and the methods of calorimetry, methods of heat transfer, thermal properties of solids, liquids, and gases, kinetic theory, and the generalized laws of thermodynamics.

19.1. The Meaning of Heat. We need only call upon our experience to realize that when bodies at different degrees of hotness or coldness are placed in an enclosure that is ideally free from any external effects, the hotter bodies become cooler, the colder bodies become warmer, and all the bodies and the enclosure itself eventually attain the same degree of warmth or coolness. We then say that all the bodies have reached a state of *thermal equilibrium.* Obviously, something has been transferred from the bodies which were initially hotter to those which were initially colder: we call that which has been transferred *heat.* Early in the development of theories concerning the nature of heat it was thought that heat was a kind of weightless fluid, called caloric, which all bodies possessed in varying amounts. The caloric theory explained the transfer of heat from one body to another by the flow of caloric fluid from the hotter to the colder body. The present concept of the nature of heat had its inception near the beginning of the nineteenth century when Count Rumford (Benjamin Thompson, 1735–1814) noticed the inexhaustible supply of heat attending the boring of cannon with a dull drill. Although the drill and cannon during the boring process got very hot, nothing cooled and he concluded that the caloric theory was incorrect and that the amount of heat developed was related to the mechanical work performed during the boring. In suggesting that there was a mechanical equivalent of the heat produced Count Rumford laid the foundation that heat was a form of energy. The more exacting and convincing evidence that heat is a form of energy came in 1845 when James Prescott Joule experimentally determined the amount of mechanical work required to produce a given amount of heat (See Section 20.5).

From the above we see that heat is energy in the process of transfer from a hotter body, or portion of a body, to a colder body or portion of a body. To understand more fully this dynamic concept of heat we shall for the moment consider some of the consequences of the present-day kinetic theory of matter. We shall later concern ourselves in greater detail with this theory (Chapter 22) but for the present it is necessary to realize that the atoms and molecules which compose a body are in continual motion. In a gas the molecules possess random translatory and rotatory motions that cause repeated collisions between themselves and with the walls of their container; in a solid state the atoms, although relatively fixed in some spacial interlocked arrangement, are free to oscillate about their mean positions of equilibrium; in a liquid the atoms have mobilities which are intermediate between those of the gas and the solid. There is thus present in every body internal mechanical energy in the form of kinetic and potential energy associated with these random motions of the atoms or molecules, and we say that a body possesses *internal energy*. This internal energy may be increased either by doing mechanical work on the body, as when a confined gas is compressed, or by adding heat to the body. In either case the thermal effects are manifest inside the body in the form of increased kinetic and potential energy associated with the random motions of the atoms or molecules of the body, and we detect this thermal energy increase by an indication that the body is hotter. It should be clear that the word *random*, describing the internal thermal motions of the atoms, means something separate and distinct from their motions when the body moves as a whole. In random internal motions the time average of these individual motions is zero so that the vector sum of all of the motions of all of the atoms or molecules averages out to zero. In accordance with the generalized principle of conservation of energy we can see that *the heat added to a body plus the work done upon the body is equal to the increase in the internal energy of the body.* We shall later elaborate on this statement.

Since heat is thermal energy in transit it is best to reserve the use of the word "heat" for this dynamic concept and to avoid talking about the heat *in* a body.

19.2. Temperature and Thermometry. Temperature is a term that is used to express how hot or cold a body is. Therefore, temperature is a property of a body or system that determines whether the body or system is in thermal equilibrium with other bodies or systems.   When two bodies of different degrees of hotness, or different temperatures, are placed in an insulated container, there is a flow of heat from the hotter body (higher temperature) to the colder body (lower temperature) until the bodies are in thermal equilibrium and have come to the same degree of hotness or the same temperature.   Only when two systems have the same temperature are they in thermal equilibrium, and when they are at different temperatures heat will always flow from the system of higher temperature to the system of lower temperature.

Consider a temperature-indicating device such as a sealed glass capillary tube containing a liquid that expands as its temperature increases.   After such a device is placed in contact with a system and enough time is allowed for the system and the device to reach a state of thermal equilibrium, the length of the liquid column in the capillary remains constant and we know that the device and the system have the same temperature.   If now this same device is placed in contact with another system and the length of the liquid column is the same as before we know that both systems are at the same temperature.   To have the device indicate a numerical value of a temperature we must calibrate it and thus define a scale of temperature.   When this is done the device becomes a *thermometer* which is capable of indicating numerical measures of temperature.

The first step in making a thermometer is to choose a property of a body that both changes with temperature and can be measured.   The thermometric properties commonly employed are the length of a mercury column in a glass capillary tube terminating in a bulb, the electrical resistance of a wire, the electromotive force of a device known as a thermocouple (Section 27.3), and the pressure of a gas kept at constant volume.   The next step is to define a temperature scale and this may be done by selecting two easily reproduced temperatures called *fixed points.** The lower fixed point, called the *ice point*, is the temperature of a mixture of ice and air-saturated water at standard atmospheric pressure.   The upper fixed point, called the *steam point*, is the temperature of steam in equilibrium with pure water at standard atmospheric pressure.   The last step is to assign arbitrary numbers to these fixed-point temperatures and divide the interval between them into an appropriate number of parts, thereby producing a thermometric scale that may be extended above and below the fixed points.

The two temperature scales most commonly employed are the *Celsius* scale and the *Fahrenheit* scale.   The Celsius scale, also known as the *centigrade* scale, was devised by Anders Celsius (1701–1744), its ice point numbered zero and its steam point numbered 100.   The Fahrenheit scale, devised by Gabriel Fahrenheit (1686–1736), has its ice point numbered 32 and its steam point numbered 212.   These numberings are indicated in Figure 19.1.   For con-

---

* In 1954 a temperature scale based on only one fixed point was adopted by international agreement (See Sections 22.8 and 22.9).

venience the interval between the ice and steam points is divided into 100 equal parts on the Celsius scale and into 180 equal parts on the Fahrenheit scale.   Each of these parts is called a degree (°) and written Celsius or centi-

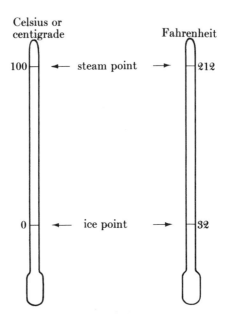

Celsius or
centigrade   Fahrenheit

100 ⊢   ◄—   steam point   —►   ⊢ 212

0 ⊢   ◄—   ice point   —►   ⊢ 32

Figure 19.1.   *The Celsius, or centi-grade,   and   Fahrenheit   temperature scales.*

grade degree (C°) or Fahrenheit degree (F°).   When either of these thermometers is used to measure temperature the indicated reading is expressed in degrees Celsius or centigrade (°C) or degrees Fahrenheit (°F).   Notice here the distinction between indicating the size of the degree or temperature interval, C°, and the actual temperature, °C.

Since there are 100 C° corresponding to 180 F° the size of one F° must be 5/9 times the size of one C°, or

$$5 \ C° = 9 \ F°$$

When both thermometers are indicating the same temperature, let us say between the ice and steam points, then the thermometric liquid has risen above the ice point to a height which is the same fraction of the interval between the ice and steam points.   Hence, if t_C represents the temperature in degrees Celsius and t_F represents the corresponding temperature in degrees Fahrenheit, then

$$\frac{t_C}{100} = \frac{t_F - 32}{180} \qquad (19.1)$$

Equation 19.1 gives the relation between the degrees Celsius and the degrees

Fahrenheit and is employed to convert a temperature expressed on one scale to the corresponding value on the other scale.   One may solve the equation for t_C or t_F but rather than attempting to remember these two resulting expressions it is best to use Equation 19.1 which can more readily be recalled because of the equality of the fractional rise.

Temperature scales may be numbered also above the steam point and below the ice point.   Although there is no limit to how high a temperature there may be attained, there is, as we shall see later, theoretically and experimentally a lowest temperature that can ever be attained.   This lowest possible temperature is called *absolute zero*.   (See Section 22.8). The temperature of absolute zero on the Celsius, or centigrade, scale is $-273.15°C$ and on the Fahrenheit scale it is $-459.67°F$.   For most purposes these values are taken to be $-273°C$ and $-460°F$.   Furthermore, it is often convenient to take this lowest possible temperature as the zero of the temperature scale and eliminate the use of negative numbers for temperature indications.   On such a transformed scale the temperatures are called absolute temperatures.   This gives rise to two more temperature scales: a Celsius, or centigrade, absolute scale, also called the Kelvin scale after Lord Kelvin who introduced it, and a Fahrenheit absolute scale, also called the Rankine scale. Thus the ice and steam points are respectively written on the Kelvin scale as $273°K$ and $373°K$ and on the Rankine scale as $492°R$ and $672°R$.   The centigrade and Kelvin scales are universally employed for scientific work, the Fahrenheit scale is generally used in the home and in industry, and the Rankine scale is often employed in engineering.

Although mercury-in-glass thermometers are convenient and extensively used as temperature-measuring devices, they are limited to a temperature range that extends from about $-39°C$ to about $357°C$, respectively the freezing and boiling points of mercury.   The useful range is actually less because of the excessive vapor pressure of mercury at the higher temperatures. Other liquids, such as alcohol (freezing point $-130°C$), may be employed as thermometric liquids to extend the range downward.   To increase the temperature-measuring range in both directions one may use a *resistance thermometer* which employs the electrical resistance (Section 26.4) of a metal as the thermometric property.   Since the electrical resistance of a wire may be measured with a high degree of precision, and since this resistance changes with change in temperature, resistance thermometry affords a means of measuring very small temperature changes.   A platinum resistance thermometer can operate in the range of about $-260°C$ to near the melting temperature of platinum, about $1,770°C$.   Another device which is often employed to measure small changes in temperature is a *thermocouple thermometer*, which consists of two wires of different metals joined together to form two junctions (Section 27.3).   When the junctions are at different temperatures there results an electromotive force whose magnitude depends upon the temperature difference of the junctions.   The electromotive force developed for a given temperature difference depends upon the kinds of metals employed.   Calibration data for commonly used thermocouples are readily available in engineer-

ing and physics handbooks. A thermocouple made of platinum and an alloy
containing 90% platinum and 10% rhodium can be used for measuring
temperatures as high as about 1,700°C. For measuring much higher temperatures an *optical pyrometer* may be used. The thermometric property here
is the character of the light emitted by an incandescent body such as the
filament of a lamp. The color and brightness of the light emitted depends
on the temperature of the incandescent filament through which a regulated
amount of electrical current is made to flow. The temperature of a furnace
may be determined by comparing the quality of the light emitted from the
lamp filament with that emitted from the hot furnace. An optical pyrometer
must, of course, have been calibrated in terms of known temperatures, usually as high as 3,000°C. Now, it is a fact that different thermometric substances give somewhat different values of the same temperature and the scales
of the different temperature-measuring devices discussed above are not in
perfect agreement. The *constant-volume gas thermometer* provides the most
accurate measurement of temperature. The thermometric property here is
the pressure of a gas at constant volume. The gas, usually hydrogen or
helium, is contained in a bulb of fixed volume and its pressure under varying
degrees of temperature may be measured by an open-tube mercury manometer, adjusted to keep the gas volume constant. The gas thermometer,
depending upon the general properties of gases, is usually used as a basic
standard for the calibration of other thermometers. A significant fact is
that the temperature scale of an ideal gas thermometer agrees with the Kelvin
temperature scale. (See Section 22.8.)

19.3. Thermal Expansion of Solids. In general, a solid substance
expands when heated. The increase in dimensions depends upon the material of the solid, its initial dimensions, and the change in temperature. We
shall now see what quantitative rela-
tionships there are for describing the
changes in the linear dimensions, the
area, and the volume of a solid which
has experienced a temperature increase.

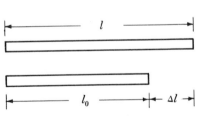

First consider a rod or wire of metal
which has been uniformly heated. Let
l_0 be the length of the rod at the tem-
Figure 19.2. *Linear expansion.*   perature t_0, l its length at the temperature t, and Δl the increase in length,
as shown in Figure 19.2. Experimen-
tally it is found that Δl is proportional both to l_0 and, to a high degree of
approximation, to the temperature increase $\Delta t = t - t_0$. Therefore

$$\Delta l = \alpha l_0 \Delta t \qquad\qquad (19.2)$$

where α, the proportionality factor, is called the *coefficient of linear expansion*. It is helpful to solve for α,

$$\alpha = \frac{\Delta l}{l_0} \times \frac{1}{\Delta t} \qquad (19.3)$$

and to describe the coefficient of linear expansion as the *fractional change in length per degree change in temperature*. The length of the rod after expansion is given by $l_0 + \Delta l$ or

$$l = l_0(1 + \alpha \Delta t) \qquad (19.4)$$

The value of the coefficient of linear expansion is different for different materials. Since l_0, l, and Δl are expressed in the same unit, the units of α are reciprocal Celsius or Fahrenheit degrees, written $/C° = (C°)^{-1}$ or $/F° = (F°)^{-1}$. When the linear expansion coefficient of steel is given as $12.0 \times 10^{-6}/C°$ it indicates that a specimen of any length expands by $12 \times 10^{-4}\%$ of that length. Since $1 F° = 5/9 C°$, the coefficient of expansion per Fahrenheit degree is $5/9$ of the value indicated per Celsius degree. Thus, for steel the linear coefficient of expansion is $6.67 \times 10^{-6}/F°$.

It is important to realize that Equations 19.2, 19.3, and 19.4 hold under the assumption that Δl is directly proportional to Δt. Actually, the expansion of a solid is not exactly proportional to the temperature change, and the coefficient of linear expansion for a given substance varies somewhat over different temperature intervals. In fact, in lieu of the linear function stated in Equation 19.4, the length L as a function of temperature t is given empirically by the infinite series $L = L_0(1 + \alpha_1 t + \alpha_2 t^2 + \alpha_3 t^3 + \ldots)$. Here L_0 is the length at the temperature $t = 0°C$ and the coefficients $\alpha_1, \alpha_2, \alpha_3, \ldots$ are constants which must be experimentally determined for a given material. For small temperature differences, of the order of 100 C°, the quadratic and higher terms may be neglected and we have $L = L_0(1 + \alpha_1 t)$, which has the same linear form as Equation 19.4 but in which L_0 represents the length at $0°C$. If the initial length is not at $0°C$, it can be shown (see Problem 19.17) that Equation 19.4 follows by the application of $L = L_0(1 + \alpha_1 t)$ for small temperature differences over which α_1 is the mean coefficient of linear expansion. It proves to be true that α and α_1 differ by a relatively negligible amount for small temperature differences, and Equations 19.2, 19.3, and 19.4 yield results which are sufficiently accurate for most computations.

Representative coefficients of linear expansion are shown in Table 19.1. Engineers and physicists must resort to more extensive tables in handbooks when dealing with thermal expansion. A significant fact is that different substances not only possess different coefficients of linear expansion but may exhibit different rates of expansion in different temperature ranges. Structures which are composed of different adjacent materials are less subject to becoming weak when the different materials possess rates of expansion, over wide temperature ranges, that are approximately equal. When structure sections that are joined possess significantly different expansion coefficients, very large forces of separation arise when the temperature changes, and the

Table 19.1. *Coefficients of linear expansion.*

Substance	α, $10^{-6}(C°)^{-1}$
Aluminum	23.8
Brass	19.3
Chromium	6.8
Copper	14.1
Glass (plate)	8.9
Glass (Pyrex)	3.6
Steel	12.0
Marble	11.7
Platinum	9.0
Tin	26.9
Tungsten	4.3
Zinc	26.3

resulting stresses must be allowed for. Certain metals, such as platinum and tungsten, have expansions that are similar to those of various kinds of glass, and this makes it possible to seal electrodes through glass, as in electric bulbs and x-ray electronic tubes, without the occurrence of breakage during the heating and cooling processes. The principles of linear expansion are also employed in *bimetallic* elements, temperature-compensated linear and torsional pendula, electrical thermostatic control switches, and in the design of expansion loops for use in steam lines and in the construction of bridges and rails. Details concerning these and other devices are covered in the examples and problems at the end of the chapter.

When the expanding specimen is a plate or a sheet of material, each dimension increases approximately linearly in accordance with Equations 19.2, 19.3, and 19.4. For an isotropic rectangular plate whose dimensions are l_{01} and l_{02} at an initial temperature t_0 the original area is $A_0 = l_{01}l_{02}$ and the expanded area due to a temperature increase $\Delta t = t - t_0$ is

$$A = l_{01}(1 + \alpha \Delta t)l_{02}(1 + \alpha \Delta t)$$
$$= l_{01}l_{02}[1 + 2\alpha \Delta t + (\alpha \Delta t)^2]$$

Since α is relatively small we may neglect the term $(\alpha \Delta t)^2$ for moderate intervals of temperature and obtain

$$A = A_0(1 + 2\alpha \Delta t) \tag{19.5}$$

Setting $\gamma = 2\alpha$ we see that

$$A = A_0(1 + \gamma \Delta t) \tag{19.6}$$

with

$$\gamma = \frac{\Delta A}{A_0} \times \frac{1}{\Delta t} \tag{19.7}$$

where $\Delta A = A - A_0$ and γ is the *fractional change in surface area per degree change in temperature*. Hence γ is the *coefficient of surface expansion* and is given by twice the coefficient of linear expansion. Although a rectangular shape was used to derive the expressions for area expansion, the results hold for any shape of area. Also, a little thought will make it clear that a plate with a hole in it will expand as if the plate were continuous, so that Equation 19.6 holds for the area expansion of a hole in a plate or disk that is heated.

It is left as an exercise in the problems to show by the same kind of development that the volume V at temperature t of a solid whose volume is V_0 at temperature t_0 is

$$V = V_0(1 + \beta \, \Delta t) \tag{19.8}$$

where $\Delta t = t - t_0$ and β, *the fractional change in volume per degree change in temperature*, is the *coefficient of volume expansion*, here given by

$$\beta = \frac{\Delta V}{V} \times \frac{1}{\Delta t} = 3\alpha \tag{19.9}$$

To the same approximation of relatively small changes in temperature the volume coefficient is three times the linear coefficient. Equations 19.8 and 19.9 hold for any shape of solid. It should be clear that the volume of a spherical cavity enclosed by a solid sphere-shaped shell expands on heating as if the spherical cavity were homogeneously filled with the material of the shell.

19.4. Thermal Expansion of Liquids. With few exceptions, liquids expand when subjected to an increase in temperature. Since a liquid takes the shape of its container, it does not have a fixed length or surface area and we are not concerned with its linear and area coefficients of expansion. As in the case of a solid, we define the coefficient of volume expansion of a liquid as the fractional change in volume per degree change in temperature and use Equation 19.8 to compute the expansion of the liquid. When applied to a liquid, β in Equation 19.8 is not computed from the linear coefficient; in fact, the coefficient of volume expansion for a liquid is, in general, about ten times the coefficient of volume expansion, 3α, for a solid. Nevertheless, the magnitudes of the coefficients of volume expansion of solids and liquids as a group are thought of as being small compared with the volume expansion of gases. In observing the volume change that occurs when a liquid in a container is heated, the expansion of the container must be taken into account. The observed increase in the volume expansion of the liquid is the difference between the expansion of the liquid and that of the container and is therefore a relative or apparent change in volume. An experimental method that does not depend on the expansion of the container and yields the absolute expansion of a liquid is described in Problem 19.34.

Although most liquids expand when heated, water exhibits an anomalous behavior in the vicinity of 4°C. When the temperature is raised from 0°C to 4°C the water contracts, and as the temperature is increased above 4°C the water expands. Thus water has a negative coefficient of volume expansion from 0°C to 4°C. At 4°C the volume of a given mass of water is a minimum and the density is a maximum. This behavior of water explains why the surfaces of ponds and lakes may freeze but the water at greater depths remains at 4°C.

19.5. Thermal Expansion of Gases. When we examine the behavior of a gas as a function of its temperature it is advisable to do so in two parts; the expansion of the gas as a function of the temperature is observed first under the condition that the gas is maintained at constant volume and then under the condition that the gas is maintained at constant pressure. The resulting experimental facts are simple and quite significant. They are shown in the plot of Figure 19.3 where V_0 and p_0 are respectively the volume

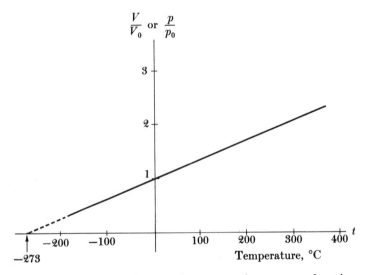

Figure 19.3. *The volume and pressure of a gas as a function of the temperature.*

and pressure of a given mass of gas at 0°C, and V and p are respectively the volume and pressure of the gas at temperature t°C. When the pressure of the gas is maintained at a constant value, the ratio V/V_0 as a function of t follows the straight line shown. On the other hand, when the volume of the gas is maintained at a constant value the ratio p/p_0 as a function of t follows the same straight line. Hence the equation of this straight-line variation is expressible as $V/V_0 = 1 + \beta t$ and $p/p_0 = 1 + \beta t$, or

$$V = V_0(1 + \beta t) \qquad \text{at constant pressure} \qquad (19.10)$$

and

$$p = p_0(1 + \beta t) \qquad \text{at constant volume} \qquad (19.11)$$

where β is the slope of the line. When the experimental data are extrapolated to the temperature axis the corresponding intercept is $-273°C$ (more precisely, $-273.15°C$). Therefore,

$$\beta = \frac{1}{273} \, /C° \qquad (19.12)$$

and Equations 19.10 and 19.11 become

$$V = V_0 \left(1 + \frac{t}{273}\right) \qquad \text{for } p = \text{constant} \qquad (19.13)$$

$$p = p_0 \left(1 + \frac{t}{273}\right) \qquad \text{for } V = \text{constant} \qquad (19.14)$$

Equation 19.13 is referred to as Charles' law and the law expressed by Equation 19.14 is credited to Gay-Lussac. Actually, Charles in 1787 discovered that all gases have the same expansion coefficients and Gay-Lussac in 1802 first published accurately the law giving the volume change of a gas as a function of temperature. It is perhaps more appropriate to refer to these laws jointly as the laws of Charles and Gay-Lussac. These laws indicate not only that the volume and pressure of a given mass of gas are linear functions of the temperature but also that the coefficient of volume expansion is identical with the coefficient of pressure change. In fact, the temperature intercept $-273°C$ is the same for all gases provided the pressure is not too large and the gas is not near its liquefaction temperature. By Equation 19.12, the volume of a gas at constant pressure increases by 1/273 of its value at 0°C for each centigrade degree rise in temperature. Likewise, the pressure of any gas at constant volume increases by 1/273 of its pressure at 0°C for each centigrade degree rise in temperature. Equations 19.10 and 19.11 show that β is the fractional change in volume, or the fractional change in pressure at 0°C, per degree change in temperature.

A significant consequence of these experimental facts concerning the behavior of gases is the indication that there is an absolute gas scale of temperature with a lowest possible temperature of $-273°C$, the absolute zero of temperature. Figure 19.3 suggests that this is the temperature at which a gas occupies zero volume and zero pressure. It is clear that this is an idealized concept, and when gases are cooled to the vicinity of absolute zero the results must be extrapolated as shown by the dotted portion of Figure 19.3, since all gases near $-273.15°C$ liquefy and do not then follow Equations 19.10 and 19.11.

The centigrade absolute temperature scale is readily introduced into Equations 19.13 and 19.14 by the substitution

$$T = t + 273 \qquad (19.15)$$

where the temperature T, termed centigrade absolute temperature, has as its zero the temperature $-273°C$, and the size of the degree on this scale is the same as the centigrade degree. In terms of this absolute temperature scale Equations 19.13 and 19.14 become:

$$V = \frac{V_0}{273} T \qquad \text{at constant pressure} \tag{19.16}$$

and

$$p = \frac{p_0}{273} T \qquad \text{at constant volume} \tag{19.17}$$

Notice that mathematically this has the effect of shifting the straight line in Figure 19.3 so that it passes through the origin of a coordinate system whose ordinate is V/V_0 or p/p_0 and whose abscissa is T. This arrangement, in which both V and p are directly proportional to T, is manipulatively more simple.

As our discussion has already indicated, Equations 19.16 and 19.17 do not hold for gases that are close to the temperature at which they become liquids. At temperatures somewhat above the indicated value of absolute zero all substances become liquids and it is not possible on the basis of the behavior of gases alone to say that there is an attainable absolute zero of temperature. Temperature scales based on the characteristic behavior of gases, such as the constant-volume thermometer mentioned in Section 19.2, are dependent upon the properties of a particular substance. A temperature scale which is independent of the properties of any substance is known as the *absolute thermodynamic scale* or the *Kelvin scale* (see Chapter 22). Temperatures on this theoretically ideal scale are identical with temperatures on the absolute gas scale, which employs a perfect gas, and are in rather close agreement with a constant-volume gas thermometer employing hydrogen.

As already stated in Section 19.2, the temperatures on the centigrade absolute, or Kelvin, scale are designated °K and those on the Fahrenheit absolute, or Rankine, scale are designated °R. Thus

$$T_R = \tfrac{9}{5} T_K \tag{19.18}$$

and

$$T_R = 460 + t_F \tag{19.19}$$

where T_R is the Fahrenheit absolute temperature in degrees Rankine, T_K is the centigrade absolute temperature in degrees Kelvin, and t_F is the Fahrenheit temperature in degrees Fahrenheit.

19.6. Boyle's Law and the Ideal Gas. In addition to the two gas laws embodied in Equations 19.16 and 19.17 there is a law that describes the relation between the pressure and volume of a given mass of gas when the temperature remains constant. This is known as *Boyle's law* which states that *for a fixed mass of gas, at constant temperature, the pressure exerted by the gas when its volume is changed varies in such a way that the product of pressure and volume remains constant.* Expressed in equation form we have

$$pV = \text{constant}, \quad \text{at constant temperature} \tag{19.20}$$

Although the product pV remains essentially constant when the volume is varied over wide limits it varies with the pressure, the deviations from the

law being more pronounced for the higher pressures.   It is useful to introduce
and employ the concept of an *ideal gas*, which by definition is an imaginary
gas that obeys Boyle's law for all pressures.   A real gas, such as hydrogen,
at low pressures behaves very nearly like an ideal gas.   A plot of Equation
19.20 for an ideal gas, with p as ordinate and V as abscissa, yields an equilateral hyperbola, as shown by the curves in Figure 19.4.   The different

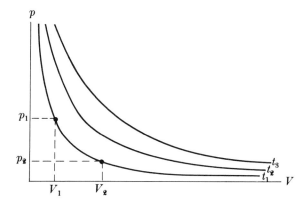

Figure 19.4.   *Boyle's law: for an ideal gas $pV =$
constant at constant temperature t; $t_3 > t_2 > t_1$.*

curves show the pressure-volume variation for different constant temperatures t.   In the figure, $t_3 > t_2 > t_1$ and so the constant in Equation 19.20 is
higher the higher the temperature.   At temperature t_1 for two different states
of the gas, p_1, V_1 and p_2, V_2, Boyle's law requires that $p_1V_1 = p_2V_2$ and the
areas of the corresponding rectangles indicated in Figure 19.4 are equal.
Each curve in the figure represents a process in which the temperature is
maintained the same and is therefore called an *isothermal*.

19.7.   The General Gas Law: Equation of State of an Ideal Gas.
The laws of Charles, Gay-Lussac, and Boyle can be combined into a single
equation that describes the behavior of an ideal gas even when all of the
three variables—volume, pressure, and temperature—change simultaneously.
This combined relation is known as the equation of state of an ideal gas or,
more commonly, the general gas law.   It can be readily derived by considering that a confined mass of gas with initial pressure, volume, and temperature
values is constrained at constant volume to acquire a higher pressure at a
higher temperature and is then expanded isothermally to the final volume
and pressure.   The details of this derivation are left as an exercise in the
problems.   The result is

$$pV = \frac{p_0V_0}{273} T \qquad\qquad (19.21)$$

The product p_0V_0 depends upon the kind of gas and the amount or mass of gas involved. Equation 19.21 is one form of the general gas law but it is more convenient to express the equation in such a way that it contains a universal gas constant that is the same for all gases. This can be done by utilizing the *Avogadro* law which states that *equal volumes of different gases at the same pressure and temperature contain the same number of molecules.* In accordance with this law for an ideal gas one gram-mole, that is, a mass in grams equal numerically to the molecular weight, occupies a volume of approximately 22.4×10^3 cm^3 at a temperature of 0°C and a pressure of 1 atmosphere (1.013×10^6 dynes/cm²). Hence for 1 gm-mole of any ideal gas at standard conditions (1 atmosphere and 0°C) the constant $p_0V_0/273$, designated by the symbol R, is the same for all gases. If the mass of gas represents an amount equal to n gm-moles, then the volume occupied at 0°C and 1 atmosphere is $22.4 \times 10^3 n$ cm^3 and the general gas law is

$$pV = nRT \tag{19.22}$$

where R, the *universal gas constant*, has a numerical value that depends upon the units employed in computing it. The number of gram-moles represented by m grams of a gas that has a molecular weight of M grams per gram-mole (gm/gm-mole) is

$$n = m/M \tag{19.23}$$

For the gas constant R we have

$$R = \frac{p_0V_0}{273} = \frac{(1.013 \times 10^6 \text{ dynes/cm}^2)(22.4 \times 10^3 \text{ cm}^3/\text{gm-mole})}{273 \text{ K}°}$$

$$\left.\begin{aligned} &= 8.31 \times 10^7 \text{ ergs/gm-mole} \cdot \text{K}° \\ &= 8.31 \times 10^3 \text{ nt} \cdot \text{m/kgm-mole} \cdot \text{K}° \end{aligned}\right\} \tag{19.24}$$

Sometimes pressure is expressed in atmospheres and the volume in liters; then

$$R = \frac{1.00 \text{ atm} \times 22.4 \text{ liters/gm-mole}}{273 \text{ K}°}$$

$$= 8.21 \times 10^{-2} \text{ liter} \cdot \text{atm/gm-mole} \cdot \text{K}° \tag{19.25}$$

In the English system the gas constant can be expressed in a variety of ways. For instance, using in Equation 19.24 the values 10^7 ergs = 0.7376 foot–pound-force, 453.6 gm = 1 pound mass, and 5/9 K° = R° yields

$$\left.\begin{aligned} R &= 1.545 \times 10^3 \text{ ft} \cdot \text{pf/pm-mole} \cdot \text{R}° \\ &= 4.97 \times 10^4 \text{ ft} \cdot \text{pf/slug-mole} \cdot \text{R}° \end{aligned}\right\} \tag{19.26}$$

where a pound-mole is the mass in pounds equal numerically to the molecular weight of the gas. Whenever one of the above gas constants is employed in Equation 19.22 its units, which must be carefully noted, will determine the units of p, V, and T and also the appropriate number of moles as given by Equation 19.25. For example, in employing $R = 1.545 \times 10^3$ ft·pf/pm-mole·R°, the units are pounds force per square foot (pf/ft²) for p, cubic feet for V, R° for T, and pounds mass for m.

In the usual applications of Equation 19.22 a fixed mass of gas is being dealt with, and then it is simpler to apply the equation

$$\frac{p_1 V_1}{T_1} = \frac{p_2 V_2}{T_2} \qquad (19.27)$$

where the two different subscripts represent any two states of the gas. In this equation mixed units for the pressures and for the volumes may be employed, but it must be remembered that the pressure is the actual pressure—not the gauge pressure, which is the difference between the actual and atmospheric pressure.

Two other convenient forms of the general gas law may be obtained by substituting the value for n in Equation 19.23 into Equation 19.22. This gives the equation

$$pV = \frac{m}{M} RT \qquad (19.28)$$

If the mass of gas is different for two states of the same gas, we have the equation

$$\frac{p_1 V_1}{m_1 T_1} = \frac{p_2 V_2}{m_2 T_2} \qquad (19.29)$$

Also, since the density ρ of a gas is given by m/V, Equation 19.29 in terms of densities is

$$\frac{p_1}{\rho_1 T_1} = \frac{p_2}{\rho_2 T_2} \qquad (19.30)$$

Another form of the gas law that is particularly useful is obtained by setting $N = n N_0$ where N_0, equal to 6.02×10^{23} molecules/gm-mole, is the *Avogadro number* or the *number of molecules in a gram-mole* and N is the number of molecules contained in n gm-moles of the gas. Equation 19.22 becomes

$$pV = NkT \qquad (19.31)$$

where

$$k = R/N_0 \qquad (19.32)$$

In Equation 19.31 the universal constant k is a ratio of two other universal constants. The constant k represents the gas constant per molecule and is called *Boltzmann's constant*. In the metric cgs system k has the value

$$k = \frac{8.31 \times 10^7 \text{ ergs/gm-mole} \cdot \text{K}^\circ}{6.02 \times 10^{23} \text{ molecules/gm-mole}}$$

$$= 1.38 \times 10^{-16} \text{ ergs/molecule} \cdot \text{K}^\circ \qquad (19.33)$$

The value of k in other systems of units may likewise readily be obtained.

Example 19.1. At 25.2°C the length of a brass rod is 98.58 cm and that of a steel rod is 98.60 cm. At what temperature will the rods be the same length?

Solution. Applying Equation 19.4 and using the coefficients of linear expansion in Table 19.1:

$$98.58[1 + 19.3 \times 10^{-6}(t - 25.2)] = 98.60[1 + 12.0 \times 10^{-6}(t - 25.2)]$$

$$t - 25.2 = \frac{(98.60 - 98.58) \times 10^6}{98.58 \times 19.3 - 12.0 \times 98.60} = 27.8°C$$

and the required temperature is $t = 53.0°C$.

Example 19.2. An aluminum plate at 68.5°F has an 8.00-inch-diameter hole in it. What is the diameter of the hole when the plate is heated to a temperature of 150°F?

Solution. The area of the hole expands as if the hole were an aluminum disk. Hence, applying Equation 19.5,

$$D^2 = D_0^2(1 + 2\alpha \, \Delta t)$$

where D_0 and D are respectively the initial and expanded diameters of the hole. Here we have

$$\alpha = (23.8 \times 10^{-6}/C°) \times \tfrac{5}{9}C°/F° = 13.2 \times 10^{-6}/F°$$

and

$$D^2 = 64.0[1 + 2 \times 13.2 \times 10^{-6}(150 - 68.5)]$$
$$D = 8.01 \text{ in}$$

Example 19.3. The cross-sectional area of a steel bar is 1.75 square inches. What force will just prevent the bar from expanding while it is heated from 20.0°C to 200°C?

Solution. When a rod is heated or cooled while its ends are confined or otherwise prevented from changing its dimensions, it is put into a condition of internal thermal stress. If the rod is free to expand or contract, the fractional change in length is, from Equation 19.2,

$$\Delta l/l_0 = \alpha \, \Delta t$$

If the rod is not free to change its dimensions, the strain is, from Equation 14.4,

$$\Delta l/l_0 = F/EA$$

where F/A is the stress and E is Young's modulus. Hence

$$F = EA\alpha \, \Delta t$$

Here $E = 29 \times 10^6$ pounds-force/square-inch, $A = 1.75$ square inches, $\alpha = 12 \times 10^{-6}/C°$ and $\Delta t = 180$ C°. Therefore, the force of compression is

$$F = \left(29 \times 10^6 \frac{pf}{in^2} \times 1.75 \ in^2 \times 12 \times 10^{-6}/C°\right) \times 180 \ C°$$
$$= 1.1 \times 10^5 \ pf$$

Example 19.4. A glass cylindrical tube is filled with 12.5 cm³ of mercury when the temperature is 39.0°F. What volume of mercury will overflow when the temperature is raised to 120.0°F? The linear coefficient of expansion of the glass is $3.60 \times 10^{-6}/C°$ and the volume coefficient of expansion of the mercury is $182 \times 10^{-6}/C°$.

Solution. If we let V_g be the volume of the tube and V_m the volume of the mercury after expansion, then

$$V_g = 12.5(1 + 3 \times 3.60 \times 10^{-6} \times 81.0 \times \tfrac{5}{9})$$

and

$$V_m = 12.5(1 + 182 \times 10^{-6} \times 81.0 \times \tfrac{5}{9})$$

The difference between these gives the overflow, the result being $V_m - V_g = 9.63 \times 10^{-2}$ cm³ of mercury. The apparent or differential volume coefficient of expansion here is $(182 - 10.8) \times 10^{-6}/\text{C}° = 171 \times 10^{-6}/\text{C}°$.

Example 19.5. The volume of a tire is 1.50×10^3 cubic inches at a gauge pressure of 26.3 pounds-force/square-inch and a temperature of 27.0°C. What is the gauge pressure of the enclosed air if the volume is 1.60×10^3 cubic inches and the temperature is 47.0°C? Take the atmospheric pressure as 14.7 pounds-force/square-inch.
Solution. Apply Equation 19.27:

$$\frac{p_1 V_1}{T_1} = \frac{p_2 V_2}{T_2} \qquad \begin{aligned} p_1 &= 26.3 + 14.7 = 41.0 \text{ pf/in}^2 \\ V_1 &= 1.50 \times 10^3 \text{ in}^3 \\ T_1 &= 27.0 + 273 = 300°\text{K} \\ V_2 &= 1.60 \times 10^3 \text{ in}^3 \\ T_2 &= 67.0 + 273 = 340°\text{K} \end{aligned}$$

Then,

$$p_2 = \frac{(41.0 \text{ pf/in}^2) \times 1.50 \times \cancel{10^3 \text{ in}^3} \times 340°\cancel{\text{K}}}{1.60 \times \cancel{10^3 \text{ in}^3} \times 300°\cancel{\text{K}}}$$

$$= 43.6 \text{ pf/in}^2 \text{ absolute pressure}$$

$$= 43.6 - 14.7 = 28.9 \text{ pf/in}^2 \text{ gauge pressure}$$

Example 19.6. A tank contains 2.50 cubic feet of oxygen at a gauge pressure of 450 pounds-force/square-inch and a temperature of 27.0°C. **(a)** Find the mass of oxygen in the tank. **(b)** If the tank valve is opened until the gauge pressure is 200 pounds-force/square-inch, what volume of oxygen, calculated at atmospheric pressure, will escape from the tank if the temperature does not change?
Solution. **(a)** We shall obtain the solution by employing R in two ways: by using Equation 19.24 and by using Equation 19.26. The number of gram-moles is n.

$$n = \frac{pV}{RT}$$

$$n = \frac{3.20 \times 10^7 \times 7.075 \times 10^4}{8.31 \times 10^7 \times 300}$$

$$= 90.8 \text{ gm-moles}$$

$$p = 450 \frac{\text{pf}}{\text{in}^2} + 14.7 \frac{\text{pf}}{\text{in}^2} = 464.7 \frac{\text{pf}}{\text{in}^2}$$

$$= 464.7 \frac{\cancel{\text{pf}}}{\cancel{\text{in}^2}} \times 6.89 \times 10^4 \frac{\text{dynes/cm}^2}{\cancel{\text{pf/in}^2}}$$

$$= 3.20 \times 10^7 \text{ dynes/cm}^2$$

$$V = 2.50 \cancel{\text{ft}^3} \times \frac{2.83 \times 10^4 \text{ cm}^3}{\cancel{\text{ft}^3}}$$

$$= 7.075 \times 10^4 \text{ cm}^3$$

$$T = 273 + 27 = 300°\text{K}$$

$$R = 8.31 \times 10^7 \text{ ergs/gm-mole} \cdot \text{K}°$$

The molecular weight of oxygen is 32.0 gm/gm-mole. Therefore the mass of oxygen is

$$m = 90.8 \text{ gm-moles} \times 32.0 \text{ gm/gm-mole} = 2.91 \times 10^3 \text{ gm}$$

To use Equation 19.26 the number of pound-moles is

$$n = \frac{pV}{RT} \qquad\qquad p = 464.7 \frac{\text{pf}}{\text{in}^2} \times \frac{144 \text{ in}^2}{\text{ft}^2} = 6.69 \times 10^4 \frac{\text{pf}}{\text{ft}^2}$$

$$n = \frac{6.69 \times 10^4 \times 2.50}{1.545 \times 10^3 \times 540} \qquad\qquad \begin{aligned} V &= 2.50 \text{ ft}^3 \\ T_R &= \tfrac{9}{5}T_K = \tfrac{9}{5} \times 300 = 540°R \\ R &= 1.545 \times 10^3 \text{ ft} \cdot \text{pf/pm-mole} \end{aligned}$$

$$= 0.200 \text{ pm-mole}$$

Using for the molecular weight of oxygen 32.0 pm/pm-mole

$$m = 0.200 \text{ pm-mole} \times 32.0 \text{ pm/pm-mole}$$
$$= 6.40 \text{ pm} = 2.91 \times 10^3 \text{ gm}$$

which agrees with the previous result.

(b) First obtain the volume that the 2.50 cubic feet of oxygen would occupy at a gauge pressure of 200 pounds-force/square-inch at constant temperature, applying Boyle's law. Thus:

$$\begin{aligned} V_1 p_1 &= V_2 p_2 \\ 2.50 \times 465 &= V_2 \times 215 \\ V_2 &= 5.41 \text{ ft}^3 \end{aligned} \qquad\qquad \begin{aligned} V_1 &= 2.50 \text{ ft}^3 \\ p_1 &= 465 \text{ pf/in}^2 \\ p_2 &= 215 \text{ pf/in}^2 \end{aligned}$$

Since 2.50 cubic feet of oxygen will remain in the tank, 2.91 cubic feet will escape, and at atmospheric pressure the volume V of escaped oxygen is given by

$$2.91 \times 215 = V \times 14.7$$
$$V = 42.4 \text{ ft}^3$$

Problems

19.1. Lead melts at 327°C. Express this on the Fahrenheit, Kelvin, and Rankine scales.

19.2. The boiling point of sulphur is 831°F. Express this on the centigrade, Kelvin, and Rankine scales.

19.3. Convert the following temperatures to Fahrenheit degrees: 75.2°C, −32.0°C, 500°R.

19.4. Convert the following temperatures to centigrade degrees: −200°F, 200°F, 50.0°R.

19.5. At what temperature are the centigrade and Fahrenheit temperatures the same?

19.6. Convert the coefficient of linear expansion $30.0 \times 10^{-6}(C°)^{-1}$ to $(F°)^{-1}$.

19.7. Two temperature scales A and B are arbitrarily assigned the following fixed points: ice points 50.0° on A and −50.0° on B; steam points 150° on A and 200° on B. (a) Convert a reading of 20.0° on A to the corresponding degrees on B. (b) Find the temperature which is the same for both scales.

19.8. Figure 19.5 illustrates a constant-volume gas thermometer. The volume of gas in the bulb B is kept constant by adjusting the mercury reservoir R to maintain the mercury level at the index point I. When the gas is cooled to a temperature of 0°C, the level of mercury in the reservoir is 5.60 cm below I. When the gas is heated to the steam point, the level of mercury in the reservoir is 20.20 cm above I. The observed barometric pressure is 76.00 cm Hg. Find the absolute zero of temperature in degrees centigrade.

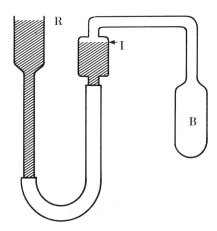

Figure 19.5. *Problem 19.8.*

19.9. A copper rod has a length of 99.5 cm at 25.6°C. Find its increase in length when it is heated to a temperature of 98.7°C.

19.10. An aluminum rod 1.00 m in length is observed to increase its length by 0.0135 mm. By how much has the temperature increased?

19.11. A steel tape, calibrated to read correctly at 0°C, is used for measuring the length of a room at 26.3°C. If the reading of the tape is 28.50 feet what is the length of the room?

19.12. The ratio of the length of a chromium wire to that of a copper wire is 1.001 at 0°C. At what temperature will the ratio of the length of the copper wire to that of the chromium wire be 1.001?

19.13. Steel railroad rails 40.0 feet in length are laid when the temperature is 50.0°F. What gap must be allowed between adjacent rail sections if the rails just touch when the temperature is 105°F?

19.14. A clock with a temperature-uncompensated brass pendulum beats seconds when the temperature is 25.0°C. How many seconds per day will the clock gain or lose when the temperature is 30.0°C? Assume the clock is a simple pendulum.

19.15. Find the fractional change in the period of a temperature-uncompensated brass pendulum clock when the temperature changes by 8.55 C°. Assume the clock is a simple pendulum.

19.16. At 0°C a rod of aluminum and a rod of copper have the same length, 1.25 m. To what temperature must they be heated to differ in length by 0.0750 mm?

19.17. Show that for relatively small temperature t the expression $L = L_0(1 + \alpha_1 t + \alpha_2 t^2 + \ldots)$, where L_0 is the length at 0°C, reduces to Equation 19.4, namely, $l = l_0(1 + \alpha_1 \Delta t)$ where α_1 is the mean coefficient of linear expansion over the temperature range $t - t_0$.

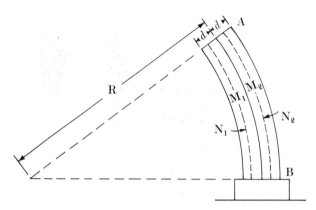

Figure 19.6. *The bimetallic strip, Problem 19.25.*

19.18. A steel rod has a length of 100 cm at 40°C. Find its length at 90°C. Do this in two ways, by using $L = L_0(1 + \alpha_1 t)$ where L_0 is the length at 0°C and by using Equation 19.4. What is the percentage difference in the computed results? Assume the data given to sufficient numbers of significant figures to yield a difference.

19.19. Using the data given for $(1/L_0)(dL/dt)$ as a function of t for aluminum, find the values of α_1 and α_2 assuming that $L = L_0(1 + \alpha_1 t + \alpha_2 t^2)$.

$t, C°$	10.00	20.00	30.00	40.00	50.00	60.00	70.00	80.00	90.00
$\left(\dfrac{1}{L_0}\right)\left(\dfrac{dL}{dt}\right)$ $\times 10^6 (C°)^{-1}$	22.32	22.44	22.55	22.67	22.78	22.89	23.01	23.12	23.24

19.20. A steel rim is to be fitted onto a wooden wheel 50.0 inches in diameter. To what temperature must we heat the rim, whose diameter is 49.9 inches at 70.0°F, in order to just position it over the wheel?

19.21. An aluminum plate at 20.0°C and a steel plate at 30.0°C have the same area. Find the common temperature at which both will again have the same area.

19.22. A copper plate has a 3.000-inch-diameter hole in it at 20.0°C and a steel ball is 3.001 inches in diameter at the same temperature. To what temperature must both be raised so that the ball just fits the hole?

19.23. The initial diameter of a round hole in a plate, whose coefficient of linear expansion is α, is D_0. Show that when D and D_0 are sufficiently close together, where D is the diameter of the hole when the temperature of the plate has been changed by an amount Δt, then $D = D_0(1 + \alpha \,\Delta t)$.

19.24. A glass sphere has a radius of 10.50 cm at 0°C. Find its radius, surface area, and volume at 500.0°C. The coefficient of linear expansion of the glass is $9.000 \times 10^{-6}/\text{C}°$.

19.25. Figure 19.6 shows the principle of the bimetallic strip. Two straight dissimilar metals M_1 and M_2, with respective linear expansion coefficients α_1 and α_2 (where $\alpha_2 > \alpha_1$), are riveted together side by side, their ends A and B coinciding at some given temperature. When the temperature is increased by an amount Δt, M_2 becomes longer than M_1 and the compound strip curves, as indicated, in the form of a circular arc. Show that the radius is given by $R = d/(\alpha_2 - \alpha_1)\Delta t$ where d is the thickness of either metal. (*Hint:* The central neutral lines N_1 and N_2 are neither under tension nor under compression, and expand as if each strip were free.)

19.26. Derive Equation 19.8.

19.27. A wire which is 3.00 m long at 25.0°C increases its length by 1.55 cm when its temperature is raised to 500°C. (**a**) Find the coefficient of linear expansion. (**b**) If the heated wire is clamped between two fixed supports, what is the force exerted on each support when the wire cools to its original temperature? The diameter of the wire is 5.00 mm and its Young's modulus is 200×10^9 nt/m². Neglect the expansion of the supports.

19.28. A brass bar 0.500 square inch in cross section acts as a cross-member between two fixed supports. When the bar is increased in temperature from 10.0°C to 100°C what force is exerted on the supports? Neglect the expansion of the supports. The Young modulus of the brass is 11.0×10^6 pounds-force/square-inch.

19.29. How much longer must a copper rod be than an aluminum rod if the copper rod is to expand three times as much as the aluminum rod when both are raised through the same temperature?

19.30. Figure 19.7 shows a cylindrical aluminum pendulum bob A supported by a glass pendulum rod G running lengthwise through the bob axis. The rod and bob rest on a crosspiece at the lower end as shown. Find what the lengths of G and A must be to keep the center of gravity of both at a distance of 100 cm below the point of support S during temperature changes. Neglect the effect of the crosspiece. Use for the coefficients of linear expansion of glass and aluminum $4.00 \times 10^{-6}/\text{C}°$ and $24.0 \times 10^{-6}/\text{C}°$ respectively.

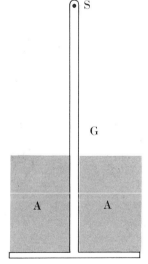

Figure 19.7. *Problem 19.30.*

19.31. The gridiron pendulum shown in Figure 19.8 is temperature compensated by virtue of the fact that one set of rods A, say of iron, expand to lower the bob, while another set B, say of zinc, expand to raise the bob. Show that, in keeping the center of gravity of the bob at a constant distance c below the point of support, the lengths of the rods B are given by $\dfrac{c\alpha_A}{\alpha_B - \alpha_A}$ where α_A and α_B are the coefficients of linear expansion of A and B respectively.

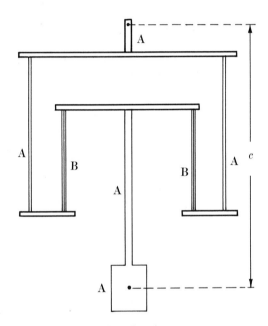

Figure 19.8. *Problem 19.31.*

19.32. A glass tube is filled with 12.5 cm³ of mercury at 20.0°C. How much mercury will overflow when the system is heated to 120°C? The coefficients of volume expansion are $182 \times 10^{-6}/C°$ for the mercury and $25.0 \times 10^{-6}/C°$ for the glass.

19.33. A glass bulb whose capacity is 10.0 cm³ is filled with mercury at 25.0°C. When the bulb and mercury are heated to 110°C, 1.85 gm of mercury overflow. Using $18.2 \times 10^{-5}/C°$ for the cubical coefficient of expansion of mercury find the coefficient of linear expansion of the glass.

19.34. In Figure 19.9 is shown an apparatus for making an absolute determination of the coefficient of volume expansion of a liquid. The arms of the U-tube that contains the liquid are surrounded by temperature jackets, the left and right arms being kept at temperatures t_1 and t_2 respectively. With $t_1 > t_2$, the heights of the liquid in the tubes are h_1 and h_2 as shown. Show that the coefficient of volume expansion is given by

$$\beta = (h_1 - h_2)/(h_2 t_1 - h_1 t_2).$$

19.35. Plot the following data for the volume of water as a function of the temperature. What essential features are revealed by the resulting graph?

Temp., °C	−20	−10	0	4	10	20	30
Volume, cm³	1.0020	1.0008	1.0001	1.0000	1.0003	1.0018	1.0043
Temp., °C	40	50	60	70	80	90	100
Volume, cm³	1.0078	1.0121	1.0171	1.0228	1.0290	1.0359	1.0434

19.36. Show four vertical temperature scales corresponding to the scales °K, °C, °F, and °R. On each indicate the steam point, the ice point, and the absolute zero value. Now show the truth of Equations 19.18 and 19.19.

19.37. A gas thermometer like that shown in Figure 19.5 is calibrated, with the pressure at the ice point 70.4 cm Hg and the pressure at the steam point 96.2 cm Hg. **(a)** Find the coefficient of pressure change of the gas. **(b)** When the bulb is placed in a warm bath the gas pressure is observed to be 90.5 cm Hg; find the temperature of the bath.

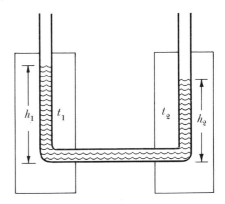

Figure 19.9. *Problem 19.34.*

19.38. A steel tank contains 2.55 cubic feet of oxygen at a gauge pressure of 210 pounds-force/square-inch. What volume will this gas occupy at 30.2 pounds-force/square-inch and the same temperature? The pressure of the atmosphere is 14.7 pounds-force/square-inch.

19.39. Derive Equation 19.21 for an ideal gas with the aid of Figure 19.10. Consider a confined mass of gas initially at volume V_0, pressure p_0 and temperature 0°C. At constant volume V_0, increase the temperature and pressure of the gas to the values t°C and p_1 respectively. Finally, expand the gas isothermally to the volume V and pressure p.

19.40. Find the volume occupied by a mass of 5.76 pounds of air at 150°F and a pressure of 3.00 atmospheres. Consider that air is composed of 21.0% oxygen and 78.0% nitrogen, whose molecular weights are respectively 32.0 and 28.0, and of 1.00% argon, whose atomic weight is 39.9.

19.41. A volume of 60.0 cm³ of hydrogen is collected in a test tube whose open end is immersed in a dish of mercury. With the barometer at 73.5 cm Hg and the temperature at 20.0°C, the mercury in the test tube stands 25.0 cm above the mercury level in the dish. Find the mass of hydrogen in the tube. The density of the hydrogen at standard conditions (0°C and 76.0 cm Hg) is 0.0899 gm/liter.

19.42. Given that oxygen has a density of 1.429 gm/liter at 0°C and a pressure of 76.0 cm Hg, find what volume would be occupied by 5.00 gm of carbon dioxide (CO_2) at a temperature of 27.0°C and a pressure of 100 cm Hg. The atomic weights of carbon and oxygen are respectively 12.0 and 16.0.

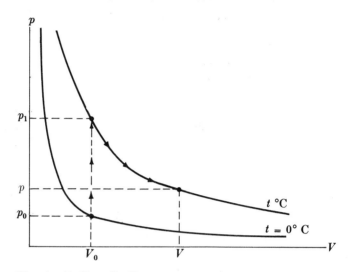

Figure 19.10.   *Problem 19.39.*

19.43. A tank holds 6.00 liters of oxygen at a pressure of 25.0 atmospheres and a temperature of 68.0°F. Some oxygen is withdrawn and the pressure and temperature are 15.0 atmospheres and 50.0°F. Find (**a**) the mass of oxygen originally in the tank and (**b**) the volume of oxygen withdrawn.

19.44. A barometer, made of an inverted tube in a dish of mercury, has some air trapped in the tube. When the mercury in the tube stands at a height h cm the air space is l cm long. The tube is now pushed down into the mercury reservoir until the mercury stands at a height h' cm and the air space is l' cm long. Show that the pressure of the atmosphere in centimeters of mercury is given by $(hl - h'l')/(l - l')$. Assume no temperature change.

19.45. Using the values given in Table A.2 of the Appendix, find the masses of the hydrogen, nitrogen, and oxygen molecules.

19.46. In a later chapter it is shown that for an ideal gas the average kinetic energy of a molecule is given by $\frac{3}{2}kT$ where k is Boltzmann's constant and T is the absolute temperature. Find the root-mean-square speeds of the oxygen and hydrogen molecules at 20°C. (*Hint:* The average kinetic energy of a molecule is $\frac{1}{2}m\overline{v^2}$ where $\overline{v^2}$ is the average of the square speed of a molecule of mass m.)

Heat Quantities

SINCE HEAT IS A FORM OF energy, any mechanical-energy unit can be used to measure heat and thermal energy, such as the erg, the joule, the foot–pound-force. However, units based on the amount of energy required to change the temperature of a definite amount of water have been developed and are universally used. In this chapter we shall define these specific units and other thermal quantities based upon them, indicate their relationship to the ordinary mechanical units, and show how the general expression for the quantity of heat is employed in the formulation of the principle of the conservation of energy as applied to heat exchange between bodies and their surroundings. We shall see that in the *calorimeter* we have a means of making measurements of quantities of heat. It will also be emphasized that a *change of state*, from the solid (or liquid) to the liquid (or solid) phase or from the liquid (or gaseous) to the gaseous (or liquid) phase, is not accompanied by a change in temperature, and that the amount of heat energy involved in a change of state is associated with the work involved in changing the distances between the molecules. Finally, the concepts of vaporization, the triple point, and the critical point will be introduced.

20.1. Units of Heat. Several units of heat are in use, each being designated the quantity of heat required to raise the temperature of a unit mass of water through one degree. In the metric cgs system the unit is called the *calorie* (cal) and is defined as the *quantity of heat required to raise the temperature of one gram of water from 14.5°C to 15.5°C*. Actually, the quantity of heat necessary to increase the temperature of 1 gm of water through 1 C° varies somewhat between 0°C and 100°C and the value at 14.5°C to 15.5°C is very nearly one hundredth of the heat needed to raise 1 gm of water from 0°C to 100°C. In the metric mks system the unit is the *kilogram calorie* (or kilocalorie, kcal) which is defined as 1,000 calories. In biology, physiology, and cook book terminology this unit is called a calorie also, but is written *Calorie*, capitalized, to distinguish it from the calorie. When a nutritionist refers to the fact that there are 136 Calories in a doughnut it means that approximately 136 kcal will be liberated when a dried doughnut is completely burned in an atmosphere of pure oxygen.

In the English system the unit of heat is called the *British thermal unit* (Btu) which is defined as the *quantity of heat required to raise the temperature of one pound mass of water from 58.5°F to 59.5°F*. To relate the British thermal unit and the calorie we recall that 453.6 gm = 1 pm and 1 F° = $\frac{5}{9}$ C° so that 1 Btu represents the quantity of heat necessary to raise 252 gm ($=\frac{5}{9} \times 453.6$) of water through 1 C°, or

$$1 \text{ Btu} = 252 \text{ cal}$$

20.2. Heat Capacity and Specific Heat. The *heat capacity* or *thermal capacity* of a body is defined as the *quantity of heat required to raise the temperature of the entire body through one degree*. Thus, different masses of a homogeneous body have proportionately different heat capacities. These are expressed in the units of calories per centigrade degree (cal/C°) or British thermal units per Fahrenheit degree (Btu/F°).

To obtain a quantity which is characteristic of the material composing a body, we introduce the quantity called *specific heat*. *The specific heat is defined as the quantity of heat required to raise the temperature of a unit mass of a substance through one degree*. The specific heat of a material is, then, the heat capacity per unit mass of a body composed of the material and has the units calorie per gram-mass–centigrade-degree (cal/gm·C°) or British thermal unit per pound-mass–Fahrenheit-degree (Btu/pm·F°).* Table 20.1 lists the spe-

Table 20.1. *Specific heats.*

Substance	Specific heat, cal/gm·C° or Btu/pm·F°
Aluminum (20°C)	0.214
Brass (15–100°C)	0.094
Copper (15–100°C)	0.0931
Glass (20–100°C)	0.199
Ice (−20°C)	0.480
Iron (20°C)	0.107
Lead (20°C)	0.0305
Mercury (20°C)	0.0333
Silver (20°C)	0.0558
Steam (1 atm; 110°C)	0.481
Tin (20°C)	0.0543
Zinc (20°C)	0.0925

cific heats of some common substances, where it is to be noticed that 1 cal/gm·C° = 1 Btu/pm·F°. The specific heat is ordinarily not constant and changes somewhat with the temperature.

---

* One may consider the specific heat of a substance to be the ratio of the heat capacity of the body composed of the substance to the heat capacity of the same mass of water and may treat the specific heat as a numeric which bears the same relation to heat capacity as specific gravity bears to density.

With c as the specific heat, the heat Q necessary to increase the temperature of a body of mass m by an amount $\Delta t = t_f - t_i$ is

$$Q = cm\,\Delta t = cm(t_f - t_i) \tag{20.1}$$

where t_f and t_i are the final, or resultant, and the initial temperatures, respectively. The units for m and Δt are chosen to correspond to the units used to express c. When $t_f < t_i$ an amount of heat, Q, is given up by the body when it cools.

20.3. Change of Phase and Latent Heats. Matter exists in solid, liquid, or gaseous phases and, under suitable conditions of temperature and pressure and by the application of heat, a solid may change into the liquid phase and a liquid into the gaseous phase. To illustrate the temperature variation when heat is continuously applied to a solid which can go into the liquid and gaseous phases, let us consider starting with a mass of 1 gm of ice at $-20°C$ and atmospheric pressure. Suppose a known amount of heat is supplied to the ice continuously and no heat is permitted to escape. The

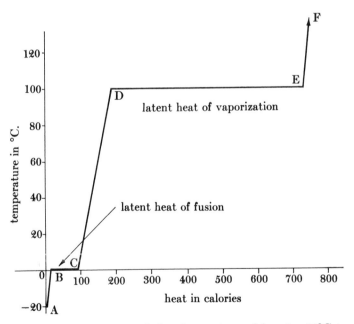

Figure 20.1. *Heat needed to change 1 gm of ice at $-20°C$ to steam above 120°C.*

temperature–heat variation is shown in Figure 20.1. From A to B the added heat increases the temperature of the ice, the temperature increasing 1 C° for each 0.48 cal added, or a total of 9.6 cal needed to arrive at point

B which corresponds to the 1 gm of ice at 0°C. From B to C all the heat that is added goes toward changing the ice to water, a melting process that involves a change of phase with no change in temperature. Even when heat is continuously supplied the temperature remains at 0°C until all of the ice is melted, so point C also corresponds to 1 gm of water at 0°C. During the melting process, from B to C, ice and water coexist, and the heat required to change 1 gm of ice to water is known as the *latent heat of fusion* of ice, which is 79.7 cal/gm. From C the water increases in temperature by 1 C° for each calorie absorbed until point D is reached, where the water is at 100°C. Again a change of phase takes place upon the addition of heat, the water changing into the vapor phase from D to E with no change in temperature, as is shown. The heat required to change 1 gm of water to steam is known as the *latent heat of vaporization* of water, which is 539 cal/gm. At E the water vapor is at 100°C; the addition of more heat superheats the steam and its temperature rises 1 C° for each 0.48 cal absorbed, as shown by EF.

Similar changes of phase occur with many other substances which change states at definite temperatures and do not decompose as the melting or boiling points are approached. The temperature at which a phase change occurs depends upon the pressure, and so the latent heat associated with a phase change depends upon the temperature and pressure attending the change. In general, the latent heat of fusion of a material is the *heat required to change a unit mass of the material from the solid at its melting point to the liquid phase at the same temperature and pressure.* The latent heat of vaporization of a material is the *heat required to change a unit mass of the material from the liquid at its boiling point to the gaseous phase at the same temperature and pressure.*

When heat is removed from a liquid, its temperature decreases and the substance freezes or returns to the solid phase when cooled to the temperature at which it melted. In solidifying, the liquid gives up an amount of heat equal exactly to the latent heat of fusion. Similarly, when a gas is cooled to the temperature at which the substance boiled, it returns to the liquid phase and, in condensing, gives up an amount of heat equal to the latent heat of vaporization. When proper conditions of temperature and pressure obtain, a substance can change from the solid to the gaseous phase directly, absorbing an amount of heat per unit mass known as the *heat of sublimation.* In the reverse process this same amount of heat is liberated. At atmospheric pressure, solid carbon dioxide (CO_2) and moth balls *sublime.*

Table 20.2 lists the melting points, the latent heats of fusion, the boiling points, and the latent heats of vaporization of some substances at atmospheric pressure. Latent heats are expressed in calories per gram mass or British thermal units per pound mass. They are generally represented by the symbol L; the heat absorbed or liberated when a mass m changes phase is then given by Lm. The table shows that for some substances relatively large amounts of energy are required to separate the molecules when the solid changes to the liquid, and that much larger amounts are needed to do the work of separation and external work against the atmosphere when the liquid changes to gas.

Table 20.2.   *Latent heats at atmospheric pressure.*

Substance	Melting point, °C	Latent heat of fusion, cal/gm	Boiling point, °C	Latent heat of vaporization, cal/gm
Aluminum	660	93.0	2056	2000
Copper	1083	43.3	2300	1750
Hydrogen	−259	14.0	−253	108
Iron	1535	5.50	3000	1620
Lead	327	5.86	1620	200
Nitrogen	−210	6.09	−196	47.6
Oxygen	−219	3.30	−183	50.9
Platinum	1774	27.2	4300	640
Silver	960	21.1	1950	550
Ice	0	79.7	100	539

For crystalline substances such as ice and the metals listed in Table 20.2 there is a definite transition or melt temperature.   On the other hand, amorphous substances such as glass do not exhibit a definite melting temperature and are considered supercooled liquids.

20.4.   Calorimetry and Method of Mixtures.   The measurement of quantities of heat is called *calorimetry*; it is ordinarily done with a thermally insulated container called a *calorimeter*.   When a heat experiment is carried out in a calorimeter it is ideally desirable that no heat flows to or from the insulated vessel.   Since it is not possible to prevent such leakage entirely, procedures that make it possible to correct for such heat transfer must be employed.   In considering the *method of mixtures* for the determination of a heat quantity, such as specific heat, we shall assume that heat losses due to leakage are negligible.

We have already indicated that when two or more objects, initially at different temperatures, are placed in contact, heat flows from the hotter to the cooler bodies until thermal equilibrium is established and all bodies are at the same temperature.   In this method of mixtures the conservation of energy dictates that the heat lost by the bodies whose temperatures are initially above the equilibrium temperature is equal to that gained by the bodies whose temperatures are initially below the equilibrium temperature.   Consider, then, a calorimeter of mass m_c containing a mass m_w of water, both at a temperature t_0.   Into the water is introduced a hot metal at a temperature t. If m is the mass of the metal, c its specific heat, and t_f the final, or resultant, temperature of the mixture, then, assuming that no heat escapes from or enters into the calorimeter system, we have:

heat lost = heat gained

$$cm(t - t_f) = 1 \times m_w(t_f - t_0) + c_c m_c(t_f - t_0)$$

or

$$cm(t - t_f) = (m_w + c_c m_c)(t_f - t_0) \tag{20.2}$$

where c_c is the specific heat of the calorimeter.

In Equation 20.2 we see that the effect of the calorimeter is simply equivalent to considering that the mass of water, increased by an amount $c_c m_c$, gains all the heat lost by the hot metal. For this reason the product $c_c m_c$ is called the *water equivalent* of the calorimeter. Usually a stirrer and thermometer are employed in carrying out a calorimeter experiment, and then their water equivalents also enter into the heat equation. Obviously, if all terms but one are known or measurable in Equation 20.2, the method of mixtures makes it possible to determine one quantity. Thus, the water calorimeter may be used to determine the specific heat of a metal, when a calorimeter of known specific heat is employed and the remaining quantities are either measured or observed. The method then yields the average specific heat over the temperature range $t_f - t$. When a substance in a method-of-mixtures experiment undergoes a change of phase the appropriate heat of fusion or heat of vaporization terms must be additionally included in the equation that expresses the heat interchange. For example, the heat of fusion of ice and the heat of vaporization of water are thus determined; examples of these are taken up in the problems at the end of the chapter.

20.5. Relation between Mechanical and Heat-Energy Units. In Section 19.1 we indicated that when mechanical energy is expended upon a system the energy which disappears is precisely equivalent to the quantity of heat produced. The ratio between the magnitude of the mechanical units and that of the heat units was first determined by Joule who used falling weights in a system of pulleys to rotate a set of paddles in a water calorimeter. The mechanical energy expended was known from the weights and their distance of fall, while the heat units were obtained by observing the temperature rise of the masses of water and calorimeter. Experiments of this kind, as well as the more precise methods of converting electrical energy to heat, yield the following relationships:

$$4.185 \text{ joules} = 1 \text{ cal}$$

or

$$778 \text{ ft} \cdot \text{pf} = 1 \text{ Btu}$$

These relationships are often referred to as the *mechanical equivalent of heat,* which is ordinarily assigned the symbol $J = 4.185$ joules/cal $= 778$ ft·pf/Btu.

20.6. Vaporization. When a substance changes to the vapor, or gaseous, phase the process is referred to as *vaporization.* It has been indicated that in sublimation there is a conversion from the solid to the gaseous phase without a passage through the liquid phase; this is one of the three ways in which vaporization may occur. The two remaining ways are *evaporation* and *boiling*.

In evaporation there is a conversion from the liquid to the vapor phase which occurs at the liquid surface. The liquids that are left open to the atmosphere generally disappear by evaporation, the molecules escaping from the surface of the liquid. The rate of evaporation per unit area of liquid surface depends upon the temperature of the liquid and the pressure exerted upon it. Since it is the most energetic molecules of the liquid surface that escape, the liquid remaining possesses a smaller average molecular speed. Hence, evaporation cools the liquid; the reader has noticed the cooling of his skin by evaporation of perspiration and the use of an alcohol sponge to cool a feverish person. When a liquid is confined in a closed vessel the molecules that accumulate by evaporation above the liquid surface are in motion and some re-enter the liquid. As evaporation continues more molecules re-enter until a state of equilibrium is reached when the rate at which the molecules leave the surface is equal to the rate at which they re-enter the liquid; the vapor is then said to be *saturated* and exerts a maximum pressure known as the *saturated-vapor pressure*. This pressure depends upon the temperature's being, for water, for example, 1.75, 9.25, and 76.0 cm Hg at 20, 50, and 100°C, respectively. The pressure of a saturated vapor is independent of its volume, so that Boyle's law is not obeyed. If the volume of a saturated vapor is increased, more liquid vaporizes, while if the volume is decreased, some vapor condenses to the liquid phase, the saturated-vapor pressure remaining the same at the same temperature.

Boiling is similar to evaporation but takes place throughout the liquid interior, bubbles forming in the interior of the liquid as well as at the liquid surface. These bubbles of saturated vapor rise, expand, and break at the surface. They form only when the saturated-vapor pressure of the liquid at the existing temperature is equal to the external pressure on the liquid. Thus for water at 90°C the saturated-vapor pressure is 52.6 cm Hg and, if the atmospheric pressure is 76.0 cm Hg, any bubble in the liquid interior collapses and disappears. However, if the temperature is increased to 100°C, the saturated-vapor pressure is 76.0 cm Hg and bubbles of saturated vapor form. When heat is further continuously supplied, the bubbles keep forming, the liquid vaporizes, and the heat supplied goes into producing a change of phase without a change in temperature. Thus, boiling can be made to occur either by increasing the temperature of the liquid until the saturated-vapor pressure is equal to the external pressure or by reducing the pressure on the liquid to the value of the saturated-vapor pressure at the existing temperature. Water at 20°C may be made to boil by decreasing the pressure upon it to 1.75 cm Hg. At this temperature not much cooking or sterilizing could be accomplished!

20.7. The Triple Point. We have seen that increasing the pressure upon a liquid elevates the temperature at which boiling occurs. Likewise, the temperature at which freezing takes place depends upon the external pressure. For substances which expand when changing from the liquid to the solid phase, such as water, an increase in pressure lowers the freezing point. For example, during ice-skating the pressure of the blade on a small amount of ice lowers the freezing point and melting takes place. The water film acts as a lubricant and refreezes as soon as the pressure is reduced. This phenomenon of refreezing when the external increase in pressure has been removed is called *regelation*. In the case of substances that contract on solidifying, an increase in pressure elevates the freezing point.

The saturated-vapor pressure of a liquid as a function of temperature may be exhibited by a curve which represents the pressure and temperature at which a change of phase from liquid to gas occurs. This curve also signifies the pressure and temperature at which the liquid and vapor phases can exist in equilibrium with each other. Equilibrium curves may also be drawn for the solid and liquid phases and for the solid and vapor phases. When these three curves are plotted, as in Figure 20.2, they intersect in a common point O,

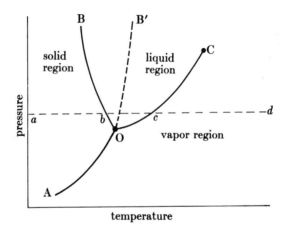

Figure 20.2.   *Triple-point diagram.*

called the *triple point*, where all three phases may exist in equilibrium. Curve OA represents the pressure and temperature at which the solid and the vapor can remain in equilibrium with each other; curve OB, for substances like water, which expand on freezing, and the dashed curve OB', for substances like carbon dioxide which contract on freezing, represent the equilibrium values of pressure and temperature between the solid and liquid; curve OC represents the equilibrium values of pressure and temperature between the liquid and the vapor. These equilibrium curves—the sublimation curve, the melting curve, and the vaporization curve—intersect in the triple point O where all three phases coexist.

In the region between OA and OB (or OB') only the solid phase can exist, between OB (or OB') and OC only the liquid phase can exist, and between OA and OC only the vapor phase can exist. Consider a solid substance whose melting curve slopes in the direction OB and whose temperature is increased at constant pressure along the path between a and d. The substance remains solid until the melting temperature b is reached, when it is in equilibrium with the liquid phase. In the region between b and c the substance is in the liquid phase, and at the temperature c, the boiling point, it is in equilibrium with the vapor phase. At temperatures greater than c the vapor becomes super-heated. If the pressure is constant below the triple point and the temperature is increased, the solid sublimates into the vapor phase without ever passing through the liquid phase. For water, the triple point occurs at a temperature of 0.0098°C and a pressure of 4.6 mm Hg. Hence, at atmospheric pressure H_2O can exist as a solid, liquid, or vapor. The triple point for CO_2 occurs at a temperature of -56.6°C and a pressure of 5.11 atmospheres, so at atmospheric pressure CO_2 can exist only as a solid or a vapor and, open to the atmosphere, CO_2 sublimates to the vapor phase. The lowest pressure at which CO_2 can exist as a liquid is 5.11 atmospheres, and the tanks which store CO_2 in liquid-vapor form are under a vapor pressure of about 56 atmospheres at a room temperature of about 20°C.

20.8. The Critical Point. In Figure 20.2 the vaporization curve terminates at a point C, called the critical point, which is a condition of pressure and temperature of a real gas at which its liquid and vapor densities are equal. Below this critical temperature a real gas can be liquefied by the application of pressure alone, but above it the gas cannot. This behavior of real gases is further illustrated by Figure 20.3, which shows the pressure-volume curves of a gas at the critical temperature T_c, at temperatures T_1, T_2, T_3 (less than T_c), and at temperatures T_4, T_5, T_6 (greater than T_c). Consider a confined gas initially at the pressure and volume corresponding to the point a on the isothermal T_3. As the volume is decreased the pressure increases along the curves from a to b, following approximately Boyle's law. At b there is a break in the curve and the gas begins to condense or liquefy. With further reduction in volume the isothermal follows the horizontal line from point b to point c, the quantity of gas decreasing and the quantity of liquid increasing, until at point c all of the gas has changed to the liquid phase. The steep rise from c to d represents the very large increase in pressure necessary to reduce further the volume of liquid, which is relatively incompressible. For the isothermals $T_2 > T_3$ and $T_1 > T_2$ the behavior is similar, the horizontal portion, representing the saturated-vapor region, decreasing in extent as shown. Thus, at higher temperatures greater pressures must be applied to initiate the formation of the liquid, and at the critical temperature T_c the extremities of the horizontal liquid-vapor line have approached and coincided at C where there is an inflection point and the densities of the liquid and vapor phase are equal. When the temperature of the gas is greater than the critical temperature (T_4, T_5, and T_6) the gas cannot be liquefied no matter how great a pressure is applied. It is clear that only when a real gas is well above its critical temperature will it obey Boyle's law, and it then must be cooled to below its critical temperature before it can be liquefied by the application of pressure. It is customary to refer to a gaseous substance below its critical temperature as a vapor and one above its critical temperature as a gas.   The pressure and volume corresponding to the critical temperature are called the critical pressure and critical volume.   The critical temperature, pressure, and volume per gram of water are 374°C, 218 atmospheres, and 3.14 cm³/gm.   For CO_2 they are 31.1°C, 73.0 atmospheres, and 2.17 cm³/gm.   All real gases show the general behavior described above.   An ideal gas, of course, would obey Boyle's law at all times and could never be liquefied!   (Why?)

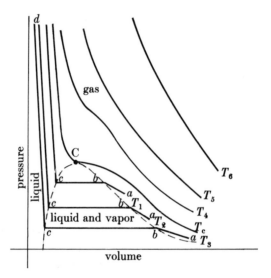

Figure 20.3. *Isothermal curves of a real gas, illustrating the critical temperature, pressure and volume.*

The horizontal portions (*b* to *c*) in Figure 20.3 indicate that the pressure of a saturated vapor of a given substance is independent of the volume occupied by the vapor and depends only upon the temperature.   If the volume of a saturated vapor is increased more liquid will evaporate, and if the volume is reduced some of the vapor will condense.

20.9.   Humidity.   The atmosphere, composed chiefly of nitrogen, oxygen, carbon dioxide, and other gases, contains some moisture in the form of water vapor.   The mass of water vapor present in the atmosphere per unit volume of air is called the *absolute humidity*.   The amount of this invisible vapor present in the atmosphere varies over wide limits and seldom is enough to produce saturation. A more useful index of the degree of saturation of the atmosphere is the *relative humidity*, which is the ratio of the amount of water vapor present per unit volume of air at a given temperature to the amount per unit volume that would be present if the air were saturated at that temperature. This ratio multiplied by 100 expresses the relative humidity in per cent. Since the *dew point* is that temperature at which the vapor in the atmosphere begins to condense, it is clear that at the dew point the relative humidity is 100%. Relative humidity may also be expressed as the ratio of the pressure of the water vapor present in the atmosphere to the saturated-vapor pressure of water at the existing temperature. Hence, by knowing the dew point and by referring to a table which lists the saturated-vapor pressure of water as a function of the temperature one may compute the relative humidity.

Problems

Unless otherwise indicated, the specific heat is to be considered constant and given by the values listed in Table 20.1 where applicable.

20.1. Find the quantity of heat required to increase the temperature of 1.55 pounds of aluminum from 40.0°F to 225°F.

20.2. A 500-pound iron ball cools from 300°F to 68.0°F. How much heat is given up?

20.3. A glass container whose mass is 150 gm contains 50.0 cm³ of water at 15.5°C. How many calories are required to heat the water to 85.0°C?

20.4. Solve Problem 20.3 where initially 50.0 gm of ice at 0°C are added to the water in the container.

20.5. Find the heat required to change 450 gm of ice at −25.0°C to steam at 115°C under atmospheric pressure.

20.6. An aluminum calorimeter has a mass of 105 gm and contains 250 gm of water at 25.0°C. Find the temperature of the mixture resulting when a mass of 600 gm of copper at 98.0°C is placed in the water.

20.7. Consider that the calorimeter in Problem 20.6 is made of 105 gm of copper and that 600 gm of aluminum heated to 98.0°C are added. Find the resulting temperature.

20.8. A copper calorimeter, whose mass is 150 gm, contains 375 gm of water at 20.0°C. Into this are placed 250 gm of lead at 95.0°C and 100 gm of aluminum at 50.0°C. Find the final temperature of the mixture.

20.9. A copper calorimeter whose mass is 0.750 pounds contains 1.75 pounds mass of water at 68.0°F. When 0.500 pounds mass of a metal at 190°F is added, the resulting temperature is 76.0°F. Find the specific heat of the metal.

20.10. When 0.550 kgm of a metal is heated to 100°C and placed on a large cake of ice, 0.105 kgm of ice is melted. What is the specific heat of the metal?

20.11. An aluminum calorimeter, whose mass is 225 gm, contains 300 gm of water at 20.0°C. Into this are placed 250 gm of iron at 150°C and 20.0 gm of ice at −10.0°C. Find the resulting temperature.

20.12. A copper calorimeter of 150 gm contains 250 gm of water at 25.0°C. Into the water are placed 100 gm of ice at 0°C. Find the resulting temperature.

20.13. A mass of lead cools from 342°C to 327°C in 1.95 minutes, after which the temperature remains constant for 21.1 minutes while the mass solidifies. Considering that the rate of heat loss is uniform, find the latent heat of fusion of lead. Take the specific heat of lead above its melting point as 0.0360.

20.14. Find the mass of steam at 100°C that will condense on a mass of 90.0 gm of iron whose initial temperature is 25.0°C.

20.15. Into an aluminum calorimeter having a mass of 200 gm and containing 500 gm of water at 20.0°C are added 150 gm of ice at −20.0°C and 10.0 gm of steam at 120°C. Find the resulting temperature of the mixture.

20.16. In determining the heat of fusion of ice a mass of ice m_i at 0°C is dropped into a calorimeter of mass m_c and specific heat c_c containing a mass of water m_w at a temperature t_0. When all of the ice has melted the resulting temperature of the mixture is t_f. Show that the latent heat of fusion of the ice is $[(t_0 - t_f)(m_w + m_c c_c) - m_i t_f]/m_i$. What is the effect on the measurement of the latent heat if the ice is not carefully dried before being dropped into the calorimeter?

20.17. Devise an experiment whereby the latent heat of vaporization of water may be determined, and derive the working equation.

20.18. The product of the specific heat and the molecular, or atomic, weight is known as the *molar*, or *atomic*, *heat capacity*. Calculate the atomic heat capacity of the pure elements listed in Table 20.1 and observe that the results are very nearly equal to 6 cal/gm·atomic-wt·C°. This fact is known as the *law of Dulong and Petit* and holds experimentally for temperatures that are not very low. At low temperatures the specific heat approaches zero as the temperature approaches absolute zero, and the law is not followed. What is the significance of the Dulong and Petit law?

20.19. A *continuous-flow* calorimeter is used for measuring the mechanical equivalent of heat. A stream of water flows through a tube along whose center is a heating element which adds heat at a known rate. When the inlet and outlet temperatures have reached a steady state, the rate at which heat is carried away by the water is equal to that developed by the heater. The heater supplying heat at the rate of 550 watts and a steady-state temperature difference of 26.8 C° existing between the inlet and outlet points, 440 gm of water are collected at the outlet in 1.50 minutes. Find the mechanical equivalent of heat.

20.20. Water falls a distance of 150 feet and comes to rest in a pool at the bottom. Assuming that all of the kinetic energy is transformed into heating the water, find the rise in temperature of the water.

20.21. With what speed must a lead bullet at 10.0°C strike a wooden block so that upon being brought to rest a temperature equal to the melting point of lead will be developed? Assume that 50.0% of the kinetic energy of the bullet goes into heat.

20.22. X-rays are produced by having high-speed electrons strike a metal target. If 12.6×10^{16} electrons strike a copper target each second with a speed of 10^{10} cm/sec what is the increase in the temperature of a 300 gm copper target after 3 minutes of electron bombardment? Consider that 98.0% of the electron energy goes into heating the target. The rest mass of an electron is 9.11×10^{-28} gm. Use the relativistic mass.

20.23. The following table gives the pressure p of saturated water vapor as a function of the temperature t. Plot p against t. Find an equation that will approximately represent this curve.

t, °C	0	5	10	15	20	40	50	60	80	100	120	140
p, mm Hg	4.6	6.5	8.9	12.7	17.5	55.1	92.5	149	355	760	1490	2710

20.24. When a loop of fine wire is passed over a block of ice and weights of several pounds force are hung from each end of the wire, the wire melts its way through, leaving a solid block of ice above it. Explain this.

20.25. The critical temperatures of the gases ammonia, argon, carbon dioxide, oxygen, and sulphur dioxide are respectively 132, -122, 31, -119, and 157°C. Which of these gases can be liquefied at room temperature (20°C) without precooling? Explain.

20.26. On a day that the temperature is 68.0°F the dew point is 55.0°F. Using the information given in Problem 20.23, find the relative humidity.

20.27. The relative humidity in a room is 70.0% at 20.0°C. The temperature drops to 15.0°C. Find (**a**) the relative humidity and (**b**) the dew point. Use the information given in Problem 20.23.

20.28. A glass bottle, containing some water and dry air at 76.0 cm Hg, is sealed at 27.0°C and placed in a pot of water which is kept boiling. Assuming that the volume occupied by the air remains unchanged, find the pressure in the bottle. (*Hint:* Dalton's law of partial pressures states that the pressure exerted by a mixture of gases which do not react chemically is equal to the sum of the pressures which each gas would exert separately if each were allowed to occupy the entire space alone.)

Transfer of Heat

I_N *THIS CHAPTER WE CONSIDER* the methods by which heat may be transmitted from one point to another. The following facts are familiar to all of us. When one end of a metal rod is heated the other end of the rod becomes hot; when heat is supplied to one portion of a liquid, as to the bottom of a kettle containing some water, the liquid throughout becomes hot; the transfer of heat from the sun to the earth takes place through space which contains no material medium. These illustrations exemplify the three ways in which heat is transferred: by *conduction*, by *convection*, and by *radiation*. We shall here consider some of the fundamental principles which pertain to these three modes of heat transfer.

21.1. Conduction. Conduction of heat through a body will occur when the different parts of the body are of different temperatures. In Figure 21.1 a slab of material of cross-sectional area A and thickness L has one of its faces kept at a temperature T_1 and the other face kept at a temperature $T_2 < T_1$. Heat will flow in the direction shown, and we consider that a steady state has been reached: at any point of the slab the temperature is steady or unchanging with time. The quantity of heat ΔQ through any element Δs whose faces have a temperature difference ΔT is experimentally found to be directly proportional to A, ΔT, and the elapsed time Δt, and inversely proportional to Δs. Therefore,

$$\Delta Q = kA \,\Delta t \,\frac{\Delta T}{\Delta s} \tag{21.1}$$

where k, the proportionality constant, depends on the nature of the slab material and is called the *coefficient of thermal conductivity*. The time rate of flow of heat H is given by

$$H = \frac{\Delta Q}{\Delta t} = kA \frac{\Delta T}{\Delta s} \tag{21.2}$$

and is seen to be directly proportional to $\Delta T/\Delta s$ which is called the *temperature gradient* in the region Δs. For a geometric body like that in Figure 21.1 the temperature at points within the slab decreases from left to right uniformly so that the temperature gradient is constant, and we may write Equation 21.2 as

$$H = kA \frac{T_1 - T_2}{L} \qquad (21.3)$$

When the temperature does not decrease at a constant displacement rate, such as in the direction of the radial heat flow through a cylindrical pipe, Equation 21.2 is used in a differential form, illustrated in Example 21.2.

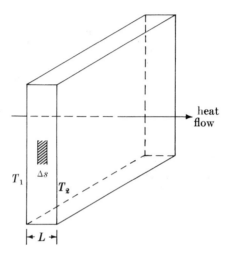

Figure 21.1.

The above equations express the law of heat conduction and Equation 21.3 may be used for computing the quantity of heat per unit time flowing through a parallel-faced slab of material and for similar problems. The numerical value of the thermal conductivity coefficient depends on the units used for the other quantities in the conduction equation. Thus, if in Equation 21.3 A is in square centimeters, L is in centimeters, ΔT is in centigrade degrees, and H is in calories per second, then k is in calorie-centimeters, per second–square-centimeter–centigrade-degree (cal·cm/sec·cm²·C°). In British units it is usual to express H in British thermal units per hour, A in square feet, L in inches, and ΔT in Fahrenheit degrees, with k in British thermal units times inches, per hour–square-foot–Fahrenheit-degree (Btu·in/hr·ft²·F°). Sometimes it is convenient to use other combinations of units for A, ΔT, and L; then k takes on the corresponding units in Equation 21.3.

The transfer of heat by conduction is explained, on the one hand, by the fact that molecules in the vicinity of the heat source acquire large thermal vibrations which are communicated to neighboring molecules by collision and, on the other hand, by the motions of free electrons that may exist in the material. In this connection it is significant to realize that metals, which have high thermal conductivities, also have high electrical conductivities, and nonmetals, which have low thermal conductivities, also in general have low electrical conductivities. The successive communications of the thermal vibrations in nonmetals account for the process of conduction, while in metals the process of heat conduction is additionally effected by the movements of the free electrons which have become detached from their molecules. These free electrons, which are responsible for a metal's high electrical conductivity, also share in the process of heat conduction from hotter to colder portions of a material.

The conduction equation shows that the higher the coefficient of thermal conductivity the larger the time rate of heat flow. Table 21.1, listing some

Table 21.1. *Thermal conductivities (near 20°C).*

Substance	k, cal·cm/sec·cm²·C°	k, Btu·in/hr·ft²·F°
Metals		
Aluminum	0.49	1.4×10^3
Brass	0.26	0.75×10^3
Copper	0.92	2.7×10^3
Gold	0.70	2.0×10^3
Lead	0.083	0.24×10^3
Nickel	0.22	0.64×10^3
Silver	1.0	2.9×10^3
Steel	0.11	0.32×10^3
Nonmetals		
Brick	1.7×10^{-3}	5.0
Concrete	4.1×10^{-3}	12
Cork	0.10×10^{-3}	0.30
Glass	2.5×10^{-3}	7.2
Glass wool	0.090×10^{-3}	0.27
Wood	0.25×10^{-3}	0.72
Liquids		
Benzene	0.33×10^{-3}	0.096
Ethyl alcohol	0.42×10^{-3}	1.2
Water	1.5×10^{-3}	4.3
Gases		
Air	0.056×10^{-3}	0.16
Hydrogen	0.38×10^{-3}	1.1
Oxygen	0.056×10^{-3}	0.16

typical values of thermal conductivity coefficients, shows that silver and copper, which have relatively high electrical conductivities, also have high thermal conductivities. In general, nonmetals, liquids, and gases have much smaller thermal conductivities. Air that cannot circulate because of being trapped in such materials as wool, textiles, corkboard, and other porous substances serves to make these materials good heat insulators.

21.2.   Convection.   In convection we have a mode of heat transfer that involves the actual motion of a fluid (gas or liquid).   The water in a container under which there is a gas flame, and the air in a room which contains a hot stove, are heated by convection.   The air molecules near the heat source acquire a greater amount of kinetic energy.   In consequence, the density of these fluid molecules decreases.   These rarefied hot fluid regions rise owing to buoyancy, and cooler layers of molecules come in and are heated. The rising warm air gives up its heat to the cooler layers above and to the walls of the container or room.   These cool layers, now being more dense, fall to the bottom of the container or room and a continuous circulation of convection currents sets in, the fluid gradually becoming heated throughout. The reader may be familiar with the fact of land and sea breezes that are due to convection currents in the atmosphere.   In the daytime the land becomes hotter than the sea and the air above the land rises and is replaced by the cooler sea air, in a circulation pattern.   At night the land cools more rapidly than the sea, the cooler air over the land replaces the warmer air which rises over the sea, and again a circulation of convection current sets in.

The occurrence of such convection currents, due to changes in fluid density because of their expansion when heated, is known as *natural convection*.   The fluid may also be made to move by means of a pump or blower, and then the heat transfer is termed *forced convection*.

21.3.   Radiation.   The third way in which heat may be transmitted from a body does not require a material medium and is called *radiation*. Radiant energy is continually emitted from all bodies in the form of electromagnetic waves, and so it travels with the speed of light.   Radiant heat waves traverse a vacuum more readily than a material medium such as air, where they are somewhat absorbed.   Radiant heat comes from the heated filament inside an evacuated lamp, our sun which provides the earth with energy so necessary to life, the glowing logs in a fireplace, a room radiator, a flatiron and, in fact, the surfaces of all hot bodies.   When radiant heat waves are absorbed by a substance the energy is converted into heat, and the motions of the molecules of the absorbing body are increased.   As in the case of other wave motions such as light or sound, when radiant energy falls upon an object part of the energy is reflected, part is absorbed, and part is transmitted.   Some substances, such as a very black solution of iodine in carbon disulphide, or hard rubber, are very easily penetrated by radiant heat, while ordinary glass is a good absorber of heat waves.

It is an experimental fact that when a small object is suspended in the center of a large evacuated enclosure whose inside walls are maintained at a constant temperature, the temperature of the body, regardless of its initial temperature, eventually becomes equal to that of the enclosure.   Furthermore, if several objects are placed within the enclosure, some with highly polished surfaces, some with dull rough surfaces, and some with blackened surfaces, they all acquire the temperature of the enclosure, indicating a state of thermal equilibrium. Even though the objects are at the same temperature they are continuously emitting radiant energy and therefore each body must be absorbing radiant energy at a rate equal to its emission rate. This follows from *Prevost's law of exchange* which states that *when an object is in a state of thermal equilibrium the rate at which it radiates energy is equal to the rate at which it absorbs energy from its surroundings.* Now, the body with the polished surface reflects most of the radiant waves while the body with the dull rough surface absorbs a large proportion of the radiation and the body with the blackened surface absorbs most of the radiation falling upon it. Since all of the bodies attain the same temperature, it follows that good absorbers of radiant energy are also good emitters of radiation and poor emitters are poor absorbers. Blackened or rough-surfaced bodies emit and absorb more radiant energy per unit time than white or polished bodies. The thermos bottle acts as an effective heat insulator because it consists of two glass flasks, a smaller one inside a larger one, sealed together at the top with the space between their walls evacuated so that heat flow by conduction or convection is eliminated. Radiation is effectively minimized by silvering the inside surface of the outer flask and the outside surface of the inner flask. The highly reflecting silvered surfaces are poor emitters and poor absorbers so that any hot food placed inside the bottle well stoppered will remain hot for a long time, there being very little loss of heat through the top to the outside.

An absorber which ideally absorbs all of the radiant energy that is incident upon it is called a *black body*. Such an ideal absorber and, hence, emitter of all radiations cannot be found but there are substances, such as lampblack, which absorb more than 99% of all incident radiant energy. However, a black body may be closely approximated by an enclosure equipped with a very small opening. When radiant energy enters the opening it is very nearly entirely "trapped" because of repeated reflection and absorption on the walls of the enclosure, and the opening has the characteristics of a black body. Such a hot body emits radiation of all wavelengths (see Section 36.2) and these have an energy distribution that exhibits a maximum at a wavelength that depends on the temperature of the body. The energy falls on each side of the maximum, being more steep on the short-wavelength side.

21.4. The Stefan-Boltzmann Law of Radiation. The rate of emission of radiant energy per unit area from the surface of a body depends upon the nature of the surface and upon its temperature. The equation that expresses this relationship, known as the Stefan-Boltzmann law, is

$$\mathfrak{R} = e\sigma T^4 \tag{21.4}$$

where $\mathfrak{R}$ is the rate at which energy is radiated from unit area of a body, T is the absolute temperature of the body, e is a quantity characteristic of the surface, and σ is a universal constant equal to 5.670×10^{-5} ergs/sec·cm²·°K⁴ in cgs units or 5.670×10^{-8} joules/sec·m²·°K⁴ in mks units. The quantity e is called the *emissivity* or *emissive power* of the surface, which depends on the nature and temperature of the absorbing surface and has a value that ranges from 0, for a perfect reflector that absorbs no radiant energy, to 1 for a black body that absorbs all radiant energy falling upon it. From Equation 21.4 the emissivity may be defined as a ratio of the rate at which a body radiates energy per unit area to the rate at which a black body radiates energy per unit area at the same temperature. Since any body in thermal equilibrium with its surroundings absorbs exactly as much energy as it radiates, the emissivity of a body is equal to its *absorptivity* which represents the fraction of the incident radiation which is absorbed. The fact that $\Re$ varies directly as the fourth power of the absolute temperature of a body explains the large amount of radiant energy that proceeds from a hot body. Equation 21.4 also represents the rate of absorption of radiant energy per unit area by a body in an enclosure whose temperature is T, the energy that a body absorbs being equal to the energy it would radiate in the same time if it were at the temperature T.

For a body at temperature T_1 in an enclosure whose temperature is T_2, the rate of absorption of energy per unit area by the body is $e\sigma T_2{}^4$ and the rate of emission of energy per unit area from the body is $e\sigma T_1{}^4$, if e remains constant. The net loss of radiant energy per unit area is

$$\Re = e\sigma(T_1{}^4 - T_2{}^4) \tag{21.5}$$

where T_1 is considered greater than T_2. If the temperature of the enclosure is greater than that of the body, the body radiates less energy per unit time per unit area than it absorbs, and Equation 21.5 yields a negative value.

21.5.   Newton's Law of Cooling.

When a hot object at an initial temperature T loses heat to the surrounding air, it cools by conduction, convection, and radiation. An empirical law known as Newton's law of cooling states that the rate of loss of heat per unit area is proportional to the difference in temperature between the object and the ambient temperature T_a or

$$\Re = b(T - T_a) \tag{21.6}$$

where b is the proportionality constant which depends on the material and character of the surface of the cooling object. Newton's law of cooling holds only approximately, being fairly valid for differences in temperature $(T - T_a)$ of the order of a few degrees.

Example 21.1.   A household electric refrigerator is well insulated except for the door, which is 5.00 inches thick, 2.50 feet wide, and 4.50 feet high. To keep the average inside temperature at 38.0°F when the room temperature is 85.0°F, the motor runs 10.0 minutes and rests for 15.0 minutes. How many British thermal units per hour must be removed from the interior while the motor is running? Take the average coefficient of thermal conductivity of the door as 0.200 Btu·in/hr·ft²·F°.

Solution. Applying Equation 21.3:

$$H = kA \frac{T_1 - T_2}{L} = 0.200 \frac{\text{Btu}\cdot\text{in}}{\text{hr}\cdot\text{ft}^2\cdot\text{F}°} \times 2.50 \times 4.50 \text{ ft}^2 \frac{(85.0 - 38.0) \text{ F}°}{5.00 \text{ in}}$$

$$H = 21.2 \text{ Btu/hr}$$

Hence, 21.2 Btu/hr is the rate of heat flow into the refrigerator. Since the motor runs 40.0% of the time, the rate of heat removal is $2.50 \times 21.2 = 53.0$ Btu/hr.

Example 21.2. A cylindrical steam pipe of length l is surrounded by a closely fitting cylindrical insulating jacket of thermal heat conductivity k and inner and outer radii r_i and r_o respectively. Find the rate of the radial flow of heat from the inside to the outside of the jacket when steam at a temperature T_i is passing through the pipe and the temperature of the outer surface of the jacket is T_o.

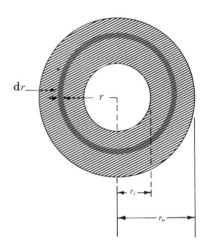

Figure 21.2.

Solution. Figure 21.2 shows in cross section the pipe and insulating jacket. Considering a thin insulating cylindrical shell of radius r and thickness dr, Equation 21.2 for the rate of heat flow in the radial direction becomes, in differential form,

$$H = -kA \frac{dT}{dr}$$

where the minus sign indicates that the heat flow is in the direction of decreasing temperature. Here $A = 2\pi rl$ so that

$$H \frac{dr}{r} = -2\pi kl \, dT$$

At thermal equilibrium the rate of flow of heat through each cylindrical section of insulating jacket is the same and equal to H. Hence,

$$H \int_{r_i}^{r_o} \frac{dr}{r} = -2\pi kl \int_{T_i}^{T_o} dT$$

Integrating,

$$H \ln \frac{r_o}{r_i} = -2\pi kl(T_o - T_i)$$

and

$$H = \frac{2\pi kl(T_i - T_o)}{\ln \frac{r_o}{r_i}}$$

where ln is the natural, or Napierian, logarithm.

Example 21.3. How much power is radiated from a heated cylindrical metal filament 15.0 cm in length and 0.0250 mm in diameter maintained at 2.70×10^3 °C in an evacuated container? The emissivity of the filament at this temperature is 0.300. Neglect losses due to conduction.

Solution. Applying Equation 21.4:

$$\Re = e\sigma T^4$$

$$\Re = (0.300)\left(5.67 \times 10^{-5} \frac{\text{erg}}{\text{sec} \cdot \text{cm}^2 \cdot °\text{K}^4}\right)(2.97 \times 10^3)^4(°\text{K}^4)$$

$$= 132 \text{ watts/cm}^2$$

and power radiated $= (132 \text{ watts/cm}^2)(\pi \times 0.00250 \times 15.0) \text{ cm}^2 = 15.6$ watts.

Problems

21.1. A glass plate 5.00 mm thick, 10.5 cm wide, and 30.0 cm long is placed with its large area on a hot plate which is maintained at 200°C. Find the amount of heat conducted per hour through the glass if the upper surface is at 20.0°C.

21.2. A cylindrical copper rod 0.500 inch in diameter and 1.00 foot in length is thermally insulated except for its ends, which are kept at temperatures of 68.0°F and 128°F. What is the rate of heat conduction along the rod?

21.3. In an experiment for determining the coefficient of thermal conductivity, one end of a rod 15.0 cm² in cross section is heated until a steady rate of heat flow is established. Two temperature-measuring contacts on the rod, separated by 10.0 cm, indicate a temperature difference of 15.8 C° while the unheated end of the rod raises the temperature of 142 gm of water through 4.80 C° in 40.0 sec. What is the thermal conductivity of the rod?

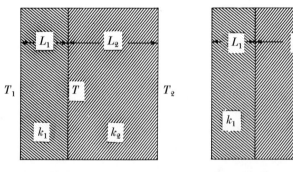

Figure 21.3.   **Figure 21.4.**

21.4. Figure 21.3 shows in cross section a wall composed of two different materials in contact. If T_1 and T_2 are the temperatures of the outside surfaces, show that, when thermal equilibrium is established, $T = (aT_1 + bT_2)/$ $(a + b)$ where $a = k_1/L_1$, $b = k_2/L_2$, and T is the temperature of the common surface.

21.5. Figure 21.4 shows in cross section a wall composed of three different materials in contact. Show that, when the outside surfaces are maintained at a difference in temperature, ΔT, at thermal equilibrium the rate of flow of heat per unit area of surface is given by $H = \Delta T/(a + b + c)$ where $a = L_1/k_1$, $b = L_2/k_2$, and $c = L_3/k_3$.

21.6. A spherical shell of inner radius r_i and outer radius r_o has its inner and outer surfaces maintained at the temperatures T_i and T_o respectively. A steady flow of heat takes place radially outward from the inner to the outer surface. Show that the rate of heat flow is given by $4\pi k(T_i - T_o)/(1/r_i - 1/r_o)$ where k is the coefficient of thermal conductivity.

21.7. A cylindrical steam pipe is surrounded by an asbestos insulator of inside diameter 0.750 inch and thickness 0.250 inch. When the pipe is carrying steam at a temperature of 220°F and the temperature of the outside surface is 80.0°F, what is the amount of heat conducted through the asbestos per hour for a 10.0-foot length of pipe? The thermal conductivity of the asbestos is 0.500 Btu·in/hr·ft²·F°.

21.8. One end of a copper rod 10.0 cm long is in thermal contact with one end of an aluminum rod 15.0 cm long, the cross sections of both rods being 5.00 cm². The free end of the copper rod is maintained at a temperature of 170°C and the free end of the aluminum rod is maintained at 20.0°C. The sides of the bars are thermally insulated. Find (a) the temperature of the junction and (b) the steady rate of heat flow.

21.9. Referring to Problem 21.6, plot a graph of the temperature gradient as a function of the distance out from the center of the spherical surfaces.

21.10. Plot a graph of the temperature gradient as a function of the distance out from the center of the cylindrical pipe in Example 21.2. Compare this with the graph in Problem 21.9.

21.11. A metal ball of radius r is first coated uniformly with insulating material of thermal conductivity k_1 and thickness t_1 and then with another insulating coating of thermal conductivity k_2 and thickness t_2. The surface in contact with the metal ball is maintained at a temperature T_1 and the outside surface is maintained at a temperature T_2 ($<T_1$). Show that when there is a steady radial flow of heat the temperature T of the surface common to both insulators is

$$T = \frac{r(aT_1 + bT_2) + b(t_1 + t_2)T_2}{r(a + b) + b(t_1 + t_2)}$$

where $a = k_1/t_1$ and $b = k_2/t_2$.

21.12. A cylindrical metal rod of radius r and length l is first coated uniformly with insulating material of thermal conductivity k_1 and then with an insulating coating of inner and outer radii r_1 and r_2 and thermal conductivity k_2. The surface in contact with the metal is held at a temperature T_1 and the outside surface is maintained at a temperature T_2 ($<T_1$). Show

that when there is a steady radial flow of heat the temperature T of the surface common to both insulators is

$$T = \frac{aT_1 + bT_2}{a + b}$$

where $a = \ln (r_2/r_1)^{k_1}$ and $b = \ln (r_1/r_2)^{k_2}$.

21.13. A steel rod whose cross-sectional area is 2.25 cm² has a length of 55.6 cm. One end of the rod is in a cake of ice at 0°C and the other end is maintained at a temperature of 300°C. If 50.0% of the heat escapes, how much ice will be melted in 1.25 hours?

21.14. A cubical box for storing solid carbon dioxide measures 2.0 feet on an edge on the outside. Its 1.0-inch walls are made of 0.50-inch cork on the outside adjacent to a layer of 0.50-inch glass wool. With the temperature on the outside of the box 70°F and that on the inside −97°F, how much heat is conducted into the box in 12 hours? (*Hint:* See Problem 21.4.)

21.15. At what rate is energy radiated from a tungsten ribbon filament 8.50 mm long and 2.15 mm wide when it is maintained at a temperature of 2527°C? Use for the emissivity of the filament 0.330 and neglect losses due to conduction.

21.16. A fire brick whose emissivity is 0.750 is radiating at the rate of 50.0 watts/cm². What is its temperature?

21.17. Assuming the sun to radiate as a black body, find the rate at which it loses energy when its surface temperature is 5.80×10^3 °K and its radius is 7.00×10^5 km.

21.18. Using the result of Problem 21.17, find the *solar constant*, i.e., the energy received on the earth per unit area per unit time on a surface perpendicular to the sun's rays. The radius of the earth's orbit is 1.49×10^{11} m.

21.19. A blackened metal sphere of radius 1.00 cm is in an evacuated chamber whose inside surface is maintained at a temperature of 300°K. How many watts must be supplied to the sphere to maintain its temperature at 400°K? Consider the sphere a black body.

21.20. A cup of tea cools from 90.0°C to 86.5°C in 120 sec when the ambient temperature is 20.0°C. In what time will it cool from 68.0°C to 66.0°C?

21.21. Show that Newton's law of cooling follows from the Stefan-Boltzmann law when the temperature of the body is close to the ambient temperature.

21.22. A body of mass m and specific heat c cools from an initial temperature T_0 in a room whose temperature is T_a. Show that the temperature T of the body at any time t after it begins to cool is given by $T = T_a + (T_0 - T_a) e^{-(b/mc)t}$ where e is the base of the natural logarithm and b is the constant in Equation 21.6.

Kinetic Theory
and Thermodynamics

*I*N CHAPTER 19 WE HAVE SEEN that the laws governing the thermal behavior of gases are relatively simple. These ideal gas laws are obeyed very closely by such gases as hydrogen, helium, oxygen, and nitrogen except under the conditions of very low temperature and very high pressure. In fact, any gas at low pressure and well above its liquefaction point exhibits a close approach to an ideal gas and the ideal-gas laws furnish a good approximation to the behavior of most gases. These simple gas laws may be described by a theory based upon a simple model. In this chapter we present some of the significant aspects of this theory, called the *kinetic theory of gases*, which was developed during the latter half of the nineteenth century. In this same century there was also developed the science of thermodynamics which deals with the interconversion between heat and mechanical work or other forms of energy. The discipline of thermodynamics, which is an experimental science, is governed by two general laws of nature called *the first law of thermodynamics* and *the second law of thermodynamics*. In this chapter we give a brief introduction to these laws and show how their application leads to the development of the absolute thermodynamic temperature scale. We shall see that the first law of thermodynamics is merely the principle of the conservation of energy as it applies to the relation between heat and mechanical energy. We shall also see that the second law of thermodynamics is a principle based upon experience and indicates that there are many kinds of processes involving a conversion of heat into mechanical energy which do not happen and cannot be made to happen even though their occurrence would not violate the first law of thermodynamics.

22.1. Kinetic Theory of Gases. We have seen that gases possess certain properties that are not possessed by liquids and solids. For example, in Section 19.5 it was shown that all gases have very nearly the same coefficient of volume expansion whereas solids and liquids exhibit different coefficients of volume expansion. Gases possess no definite shape or volume and completely fill whatever it is that contains them. The elastic properties of gases are different from those of liquids and solids. Gases are observed to exert very large pressures on the walls of containers.

Since the beginning of the eighteenth century there evolved a theory of an ideal gas aimed at describing the characteristic behavior of ideal gases and known as the *kinetic theory of gases*. In accordance with this theory, it is assumed that a gas is composed of individual molecules which (*1*) are on an average so far apart in relation to their small size that there are no interacting forces between them except during collision, (*2*) are in continuous rapid straight-line random motion, and (*3*) strike each other and the walls of a container with impacts that are perfectly elastic. Such assumptions are reasonable and valid in the light of the observed behavior and physical properties of gases, liquids, and solids. In a monatomic gas, for example, the molecules have diameters of the order of 10^{-8} cm, behave as hard rigid spheres, have average speeds of the order of 10^5 cm/sec, and have a *mean free path* (that is, travel an average distance between intermolecular impacts) of the order of 10^{-5} cm at normal pressures. According to the theory, the pressure exerted by a gas in a container is due to continual collisions of the gas molecules on the walls of the container. We shall now see not only how this comes about but also how, in the application of this theory, we are able to correlate the temperature of a gas with the molecular speed.

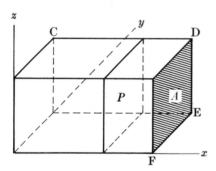

Figure 22.1. *Pressure of a gas is due to molecular bombardment.*

Let the rectangular container of length CD, height ED, and width FE shown in Figure 22.1 have a volume V and contain a total of N molecules of mass m each. Consider the molecules that are between the imaginary plane P and the container wall of area A. If the distance between P and this right-hand wall is small compared with the mean free path of the molecules, all the molecules in this region having a component of velocity toward the right will collide with the wall without encountering any other molecules. In this region suppose that there are $\mathfrak{N}_1$ molecules per unit volume possessing a velocity component v_{1x} in the x direction. Then, since the molecules possess completely random motions, the number of molecules that collide with the wall in the time t is $\mathfrak{N}_1 A v_{1x} t / 2$. Each of these molecules striking the wall with an x component of momentum $m v_{1x}$ rebounds with an x component of momentum $-m v_{1x}$. Hence the change in momentum per molecule per collision is $2m v_{1x}$ and the time rate of change in momentum of these molecules is

$$\frac{\mathfrak{N}_1 A v_{1x} t \times 2 m v_{1x}}{2t} = \mathfrak{N}_1 A m v_{1x}^2$$

which, by Newton's laws, represents the force exerted by the molecules on the wall. Hence the pressure p_1 exerted by these molecules on the wall of area A is

$$p_1 = \mathfrak{N}_1 m v_{1x}^2$$

Now, not all molecules of a gas have the same speed. In fact, Maxwell showed—and it has been experimentally verified—that they possess a distribution of speeds called the *Maxwellian distribution*, shown in Figure 22.2.

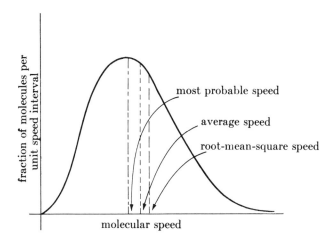

Figure 22.2. *Maxwellian distribution of molecular speeds.*

The ordinate is the relative number of molecules in a unit speed interval and the abscissa represents the molecular speed. It is seen that, for completely random molecular motions, relatively small numbers of molecules have small and large speeds, most having intermediate speeds. The curve shows that the number of molecules in a given speed interval increases from zero to a maximum value, which corresponds to the most probable speed, then decreases exponentially, passing through a value corresponding to the arithmetic mean, or average, value of the speeds and, at somewhat higher speed, through a value corresponding to the root-mean-square speed (described below). The mathematical expression for the Maxwellian distribution contains the absolute temperature as a parameter, so Figure 22.2 represents the distribution at some one temperature. For a higher temperature the peak of the curve drops and shifts to the right. That the molecules of a gas do have random motions and exhibit a Maxwellian distribution of speeds has been experimentally verified in several ways, one of which is by direct observation of *Brownian motions* in liquids and gases. In 1827 Robert Brown observed that very fine dust or smoke particles suspended in air execute random motions due to the random impacts of the air molecules. The motions of the suspended particles may be observed with a microscope and it is found that they follow the Maxwellian distribution curve.

Returning now to the region in Figure 22.1 where $\mathfrak{N}_1$ molecules per unit volume with a velocity component v_{1x} are considered, there are also per unit volume $\mathfrak{N}_2$, $\mathfrak{N}_3$, . . . , molecules with respective velocity components v_{2x}, v_{3x}, . . . Collisions of these groups of molecules with the wall give rise to the pressures

$$p_2 = \mathfrak{N}_2 m v_{2x}{}^2, \quad p_3 = \mathfrak{N}_3 m v_{3x}{}^2, \quad \cdots ,$$

and the total pressure due to all molecular groups is

$$p = m(\mathfrak{N}_1 v_{1x}{}^2 + \mathfrak{N}_2 v_{2x}{}^2 + \mathfrak{N}_3 v_{3x}{}^2 + \cdots +) \tag{22.1}$$

Representing the total number of molecules per unit volume by $\mathfrak{N}$ we may define the average of the squares of the x components of velocity, $\overline{v_x{}^2}$, by

$$\overline{v_x{}^2} = \frac{\mathfrak{N}_1 v_{1x}{}^2 + \mathfrak{N}_2 v_{2x}{}^2 + \mathfrak{N}_3 v_{3x}{}^2 + \cdots +}{\mathfrak{N}}$$

and Equation 22.1 becomes

$$p = \mathfrak{N} m \overline{v_x{}^2} \tag{22.2}$$

Similar expressions are valid for the pressure exerted on the walls perpendicular to the y direction with $\overline{v_y{}^2}$ in place of $\overline{v_x{}^2}$ and perpendicular to the z direction with $\overline{v_z{}^2}$ in place of $\overline{v_x{}^2}$. The velocity v of any one molecule is, of course, given in terms of its components by $v^2 = v_x{}^2 + v_y{}^2 + v_z{}^2$. Averaging over all the molecules, we have $\overline{v^2} = \overline{v_x{}^2} + \overline{v_y{}^2} + \overline{v_z{}^2}$ and, since there is no preferred direction for the molecules, the average of the square of the velocity component in one direction is equal to that in any other direction. Hence $\overline{v_x{}^2} = \overline{v_y{}^2} = \overline{v_z{}^2} = \overline{v^2}/3$ so that

$$p = \tfrac{1}{3}\mathfrak{N} m \overline{v^2} \tag{22.3}$$

The $\sqrt{\overline{v^2}}$ is the square root of the average square of the speeds and is called the *root-mean-square* (rms) value of the speed, as indicated in Figure 22.2. Since $\mathfrak{N} = N/V$ where N is the total number of molecules in the container of volume V, we have

$$pV = \tfrac{1}{3} N m \overline{v^2} \tag{22.4}$$

The translational kinetic energy of a molecule, it may be recalled, is $\tfrac{1}{2}mv^2$. Then the average translational kinetic energy per molecule is $\tfrac{1}{2}m\overline{v^2}$ and Equation 22.4 may be written

$$pV = \tfrac{2}{3} N (\tfrac{1}{2} m \overline{v^2}) \tag{22.5}$$

Equation 22.5, derived theoretically, states that the product of the pressure and the volume of an ideal gas is equal to two thirds of the total translational kinetic energy of the molecules. If it is assumed that the molecular kinetic energy remains constant at constant temperature, the equation is Boyle's law with the proportionality constant evaluated as shown. Furthermore, if we compare Equation 22.5 with the empirical equation of state, Equation 19.31, we see that

$$\tfrac{1}{2} m \overline{v^2} = \tfrac{3}{2} k T \tag{22.6}$$

where k is the Boltzmann constant. This equation affords a physical meaning of temperature and states that the mean translational kinetic energy per molecule of an ideal gas is directly proportional to the absolute temperature.

If the development of the kinetic theory is to lead to a description of the equation of state for an ideal gas, this deduction of the dependence of the average molecular kinetic energy on temperature is a consequence. From Equation 22.6 it also follows that the internal energy of an ideal gas depends only upon its temperature, since for an ideal gas there is no potential energy because there are no attractive forces. The implications associated with Equation 22.6 hold only under the conditions of the kinetic theory, which assumes rigid-sphere molecules that travel only in straight lines and possess no rotational or vibrational motions. Would you expect Equation 22.6 to hold when the pressure of the gas is high or when the temperature of the gas is high?

There is another inference that can be made from Equation 22.6. We have used the fact that there are three independent directions of motion of translation (the x, y, and z directions) and, since there is no preference for any one direction, the translational kinetic energy associated with each component of velocity is $\frac{1}{2}kT$. We have considered our molecules in the kinetic theory development to be point-masses. Hence, three coordinates are required to specify the position of a molecule at any instant and we say that the molecule has three *degrees of freedom*, by which is meant the number of independent coordinates necessary to describe the motion. Therefore, the translational kinetic energy is equally divided among the three degrees of freedom, and each degree of freedom per molecule has associated with it an amount of energy equal to $\frac{1}{2}kT$. This is in accordance with the principle known as the *equipartition of energy* or equal division of energy among the number of degrees of freedom. Experimental observations on monatomic gases show that the total energy is "partitioned" equally among the three degrees of freedom, but the disagreement shown by some diatomic and polyatomic gases indicates that the classic principle is not universally applicable. We should not expect, in fact, agreement from more complicated molecules, which do not behave as hard point-mass spheres. We shall return to this when we discuss the specific heats, which are best described by the modern quantum theory.

22.2. The First Law of Thermodynamics.

The study of thermodynamics concerns itself with the relations between heat as a form of energy and work, and the energy changes that are due to the flow of heat and the accomplishment of work. Its development is based on the first and second laws of thermodynamics. As will become evident, the first law of thermodynamics is nothing more than the principle of the conservation of energy restated to include heat.

In Section 19.1 it was asserted that the internal energy of a body may be increased by adding heat to the body or doing work upon it. Suppose we consider heating a gas which is free to expand. Of the amount of heat absorbed, part goes into increasing the internal energy of the gas and part goes into performing external work on the surroundings. If ΔQ is the heat absorbed, ΔU the increase in internal energy, and ΔW the work done by the gas, then

$$\Delta U = \Delta Q - \Delta W \qquad (22.7)$$

Equation 22.7 expresses the *first law of thermodynamics* where Δ represents a small change in the quantities U, Q, and W. It is clear that all quantities in the equation must be expressed in the same units—ergs, joules, or calories. To examine more closely some significant facts concerning this equation, consider that a gas which is in a cylindrical container equipped with a movable piston expands when heat is applied and does work against the surroundings. In general, the pressure and volume of the gas are represented by the curve CD shown in Figure 22.3. Consider an initial state of the system (the gas)

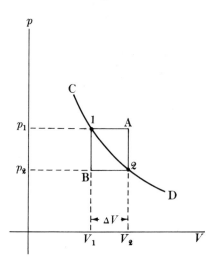

Figure 22.3. *Work done by an expanding gas.*

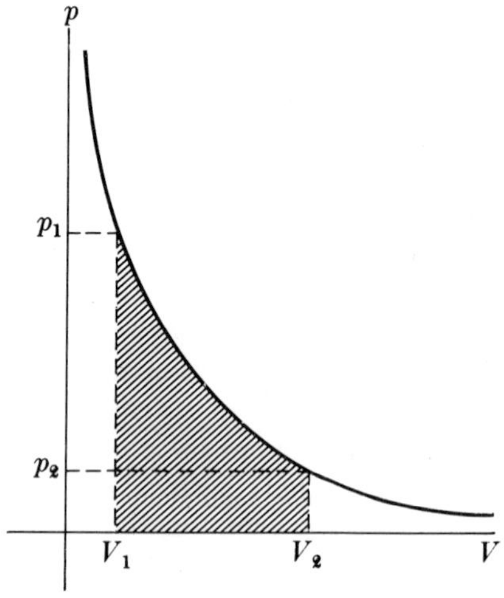

Figure 22.4. *Work done in isothermal expansion of an ideal gas.*

characterized by the pressure p_1 and volume V_1, and a closely neighboring state characterized by the pressure p_2 and volume V_2. Heat can flow into or out of the system through the walls. There are numerous ways in which the system can be brought from state 1 to state 2. In particular, if the pressure is constant at the value p_1 the gas may be permitted to expand from 1 to A, and then the gas is permitted to change from A to 2 at constant volume V_2. Only during the expansion from 1 to A does the system do work against the piston, and if the area of the piston is A and it moves a distance Δs, the work is $\Delta W = p_1 A \, \Delta s = p_1 \, \Delta V = p_1(V_2 - V_1)$ which is the area under the line 1A. Likewise, if the path from state 1 to state 2 is by way of the path from 1 to B at constant volume V_1 and then from B to 2 at constant pressure p_2 the work is $\Delta W_2 = p_2 \, \Delta V$ which is the smaller area under the line B2. In general, if the path is along the curved line from 1 to 2 the work done is the intermediate area under this curve. It is clear, then, that the *work done by this kind of system depends not only on the initial and final states but also on the path.*

When we consider the flow of heat in relation to the different ways of achieving a change from state 1 to state 2 we obtain a similar result.   State 1 is characterized by the pressure p_1 and a temperature T_1 and state 2 is characterized by the pressure p_2 and temperature T_2.   The system may be heated at constant pressure p_1 until the temperature T_1 is attained, and then the pressure may be changed to the value p_2 at constant temperature T_2.   On the other hand, the pressure may be changed from p_1 to p_2 at constant temperature T_1 and then the system may be heated at constant pressure p_2 until the temperature T_2 is obtained.   The quantity of heat flowing into the system is different for each of these paths as well as for any intermediate path.

Unlike the gravitational potential-energy change which, as we recall, is independent of the path and depends only upon the potential levels, the ΔQ and the ΔW in Equation 22.7 are each a function of the intermediate states or of the path involved.   However, if ΔQ and ΔW are measured when a system is made to change from some initial state 1 to some final state 2 by any path whatsoever, it is found that the difference $\Delta Q - \Delta W$ is the same for all paths connecting 1 and 2.   Since ΔQ is the energy that has been added to the system by heat transfer and ΔW is the work performed by the system, $\Delta Q - \Delta W$ represents the internal-energy change of the system.   Thus ΔU in Equation 22.7 is independent of the path and depends only upon the initial and final states.   In applying the first law of thermodynamics, ΔQ is considered positive when heat enters the system, and ΔW positive when work is performed by the system.

22.3.   Applications of the First Law of Thermodynamics.   As a first example, consider that a substance is subjected to an *isovolumic* process, one in which the volume remains constant.   Obviously, with no change in volume there can be no work performed, $\Delta W = 0$, and Equation 22.7 indicates that $\Delta U = \Delta Q$, which is to say that all of the heat added to the system goes into increasing its internal energy.

As a second example, consider an *isobaric* process, one taking place at constant pressure, while the volume changes by an amount ΔV.   Here, as we have seen, $W = p\,\Delta V$ and $\Delta U = \Delta Q - p\,\Delta V$.   For example, in a steam engine water is brought to the boiling point in the boiler and vaporized to steam which in turn is superheated, all changes occurring at constant pressure.

As a third example, consider a process that takes place *isothermally*, or at constant temperature.   For an ideal gas, the pressure-volume curve at constant temperature, called an isotherm, is given by Boyle's law.   In Figure 22.4 the work done by the gas in expanding from a volume V_1 to a volume V_2 is given by the shaded area.   When this area is accurately computed the result is

$$W = nRT \ln \frac{V_2}{V_1} = 2.30 \, nRT \log \frac{V_2}{V_1} \qquad (22.8)$$

where nRT are the quantities appearing in Equation 19.22 for the general gas law, ln is the natural logarithm, and log is the logarithm to the base 10. The calculus student will recognize that Equation 22.8 is readily obtained from $W = \int_{V_1}^{V_2} p\, dV = nRT \int_{V_1}^{V_2} dV/V$. For the temperature to be constant during the process, heat must enter the system on expansion and leave the system on compression.

Our fourth example deals with a process in which no heat enters or leaves the system; it is known as an *adiabatic* process. In the application of Equation 22.7 this means that $\Delta Q = 0$ so that $\Delta U = -\Delta W$, indicating that the work done on the system goes into increasing its internal energy. During an adiabatic compression of a gas the internal energy increases with an attendant increase in temperature; an adiabatic expansion entails a decrease in internal energy accompanied by a decrease in temperature. An adiabatic condition will prevail if the system is adequately thermally insulated. Since heat flow occurs comparatively slowly, an adiabatic condition can be made to take place if the process is performed quickly. For example, in an expansion cloud chamber, which makes visible the tracks of nuclear charged particles and other ions, confined water vapor is suddenly expanded adiabatically, its temperature is lowered sufficiently to produce a supersaturated condition, and water droplets condense on any particles serving as condensation nuclei.

22.4. Specific Heats of Ideal Gases. In Section 20.2 the specific heat was defined as the quantity of heat needed to raise the temperature of 1 gm of a substance through one degree. From the general gas law we see that the temperature of a gas may be altered by varying the pressure and making the volume constant, by varying the volume and making the pressure constant, or by varying both the pressure and the volume. We have seen that when a gas is heated at constant volume no external work is done, and the added heat goes into increasing the internal energy of the gas. However, when the gas is heated at constant pressure some of the heat is used in performing work against the surrounding pressure. Hence, for a given mass of gas it takes more heat to raise the temperature of the gas by one degree at constant pressure than it does at constant volume. Of the many specific heats possible for a gas the two specific heats—one at constant pressure and the other at constant volume—are the significant ones.

To derive the relationship between the two significant specific heats of a gas we shall use the symbols C_p and C_v to represent the *molar specific heats* at constant pressure and constant volume respectively. These represent the quantity of heat required to raise the temperature of 1 mole of a gas through one degree. Now, if n moles of a gas at constant volume are heated by an amount ΔQ and the temperature increases by an amount ΔT, we have, from the first law of thermodynamics,

$$\Delta U = \Delta Q = nC_v\,\Delta T \tag{22.9}$$

When the same amount of gas is heated at constant pressure until the same temperature rise occurs, the heat added is $nC_p \Delta T$ and the first law of thermodynamics yields

$$\Delta U = nC_p \Delta T - p \Delta V \tag{22.10}$$

where $p \Delta V$ is the work done by the expanding gas. Since the temperature change in both processes is the same and no internal work is done by an ideal gas on expansion, the change in internal energy is the same, and we may substitute the value ΔU from Equation 22.9 into Equation 22.10. Therefore,

$$n(C_p - C_v)\Delta T = p \Delta V \tag{22.11}$$

The work done by the expanding gas may be evaluated by using the general gas law. If V_1 and V_2 are the initial and final values of the volume and T_1 and T_2 are the corresponding temperatures, then $pV_1 = nRT_1$, $pV_2 = nRT_2$, and $p(V_2 - V_1) = nR(T_2 - T_1)$ or $p \Delta V = nR \Delta T$. Equation 22.11 now becomes

$$n(C_p - C_v)\Delta T = nR \Delta T$$

or

$$C_p - C_v = R \tag{22.12}$$

which shows that $C_p > C_v$ and the difference between the molar specific heats at constant pressure and at constant volume is equal to the universal gas constant R. It must be remembered that Equation 22.12 is strictly valid for an ideal gas; however, it agrees with the experimental values for some real gases which are composed of molecules of simple type and are at low pressures. For example, $R = 8.31$ joules/gm-mole$\cdot$C$^\circ$ $= 1.99$ cal/gm-mole$\cdot$C$^\circ$ and the measured differences between the specific heats in these same thermal units for some gases are as follows: 1.99 for A, He, H_2, N_2, O_2, CO, and 2.00 for NO, H_2O, CH_4. The more complex types of molecule show deviations from these values, e.g., 2.03 for CO_2, 2.04 for HCl, 2.15 for SO_2 and NH_3, and 2.4 for C_2H_5OH. The ratio of C_p to C_v is ordinarily represented by the symbol γ which has the experimental value 1.67 for monatomic gases and very nearly 1.40 for the diatomic. Polyatomic molecules usually cannot be grouped to show approximately the same values of γ.

The classical kinetic theory can go a good way toward explaining the specific heats of gases. In accordance with the equipartition of energy, each degree of freedom per molecule has associated with it an amount of energy equal to $\frac{1}{2}kT$. Of a monatomic gas, considered as point-mass molecules, there are only three translational degrees of freedom, and the total translational kinetic energy is $\frac{3}{2}NkT$ which is equal to $\frac{3}{2}RnT$; see Equation 19.32. The internal energy of a monatomic gas is entirely in the form of translational kinetic energy, so that $U = \frac{3}{2}RnT$ and $\Delta U = \frac{3}{2}Rn \Delta T$ which, combined with Equation 22.9, yields $C_v = \frac{3}{2}R$. Substitution into Equation 22.12 gives $C_p = \frac{5}{2}R$. This leads to the theoretical value $\gamma = C_p/C_v = 5/3 = 1.67$, in close agreement with the experimental values. For a diatomic molecule, considered rigid and dumbbell-shaped, there are five degrees of freedom: three translational coordinates which fix its center of mass and two rotational coordinates which fix its orientation. Here, then, $C_v = \frac{5}{2}R$, $C_p = \frac{7}{2}R$, and $\gamma = 7/5 = 1.40$, again in agreement with experiment. The molecules of polyatomic gases and of some diatomic gases, such as Cl_2, can absorb not only translational and rotational energy but also vibrational energy. This introduces more degrees of freedom and a consequent lowering of γ, as observed. However, the classical kinetic theory is not able to explain all the quantitative aspects of the specific heat measurements that are described adequately by the *quantum* theory of Planck. According to Planck's theory, a molecule can absorb or emit energy in discrete amounts only. These units of quanta, as they are called, are directly proportional to the frequency of the radiant energy. When the natural vibrational or rotational frequencies of a molecule are

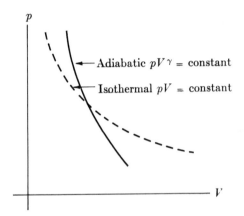

Figure 22.5. *Isothermal and adiabatic pressure-volume curves.*

small, these added degrees of freedom are present at the lower temperatures, but for molecules which require large quanta to match their natural frequencies the degrees of freedom are suppressed at the lower temperatures.

Although the internal energy of a gas depends only upon the temperature, that of a solid or a liquid depends upon volume as well. Since the expansion coefficients of solids and liquids are by comparison very small, there is negligible external work done. In the case of solids and liquids the quantity usually measured is C_p. Although the kinetic theory of gases is not valid for a solid we observe that in a solid each atom has six degrees of freedom: three vibrational degrees of freedom and three potential-energy degrees of freedom. If the equipartition principle is applied, the molar specific heat is predicted to be 6 cal/gm-mole·C°. Problem 20.18 shows that this is approximately true, in accordance with the Dulong and Petit law. As was pointed out in that problem, classical theory demands that the specific heat of a solid be independent of temperature. Actually, experiment shows that the specific heat of a solid drops to a value near zero at 0°K and approaches the Dulong and Petit value at high temperature.

22.5.   Adiabatic Expansion or Compression of an Ideal Gas.   We
have seen that when a gas is compressed adiabatically the work done on it
goes into increasing its internal energy and the temperature increases.   During an adiabatic expansion the temperature of the gas decreases.   Therefore,
Boyle's law cannot describe an adiabatic change and it can be shown (see
Problem 22.17) that the relation between p and V for an adiabatic process is

$$pV^\gamma = \text{constant} \tag{22.13}$$

where $\gamma = C_p/C_v$.   When a gas expands adiabatically it is cooled, with the
result that it undergoes a greater drop in pressure for a given volume change
than if it were expanded isothermally.   This is illustrated in Figure 22.5
where the dotted curve represents the isothermal at some constant temperature and the solid curve is the adiabatic.

The constant in Equation 22.13 depends upon the mass of gas.   If the
gas is initially characterized by the values p_1, V_1, T_1 and undergoes an adiabatic change so that the subsequent values are p_2, V_2, T_2, then the pressures
and the volumes are related by Equation 22.13 or $p_1 V_1^\gamma = p_2 V_2^\gamma$ and the
temperature after the adiabatic change is given by $p_1 V_1/T_1 = p_2 V_2/T_2$.

22.6.   The Second Law of Thermodynamics.   We have seen that
the law of the conservation of energy as expressed by the first law of thermodynamics embraces heat as a form of energy.   No exceptions to this law are
known and its truth is based on a large amount of experimental proof.   We
can imagine processes, however, which would not violate the first law of
thermodynamics, but which never occur.   For example, when a hot body is
in contact with a cold body and the two are thermally insulated from their
surroundings, it never happens that the cold body gets colder and the hot
body gets hotter; if such a process were to occur the total energy of the system
would remain constant.   When a body falls from a table top to the ground
its acquired kinetic energy is converted into heat and other forms of energy,
but the reverse process, in which a body at rest on the ground suddenly
springs up to the table top, with a consequent cooling of the ground, never
happens and yet such an occurrence would be in keeping with the first law
of thermodynamics.   The reader can supply other examples of reverse processes that never happen even though they would not violate the first law of
thermodynamics.   As long as energy is conserved, the first law lays no re-
striction on our imagining the complete conversion of heat into work as well
as the conversion of work into heat.   However, it is not in the nature of
things ever to be able to convert a given amount of heat energy completely
into work.   It is the second law of thermodynamics, a principle not derivable
from the first law, which governs the direction in which a thermodynamic
process can occur and affords an understanding of the loss of availability
of heat energy.

Before stating the second law of thermodynamics it is helpful to discriminate between *reversible* and *irreversible* processes. Consider changing the state of a system that is in thermodynamic equilibrium. Thermodynamic equilibrium postulates that thermodynamic coordinates such as temperature, pressure, and density are the same at all points of a system and that no unbalanced forces exist in the interior of the system or between the system and its surroundings. During the process of changing the state of the system, such as increasing the pressure, there is usually a departure from thermodynamic equilibrium. However, if the process is carried out in such a way that at each instant equilibrium conditions prevail, the process is called reversible. For example, if we reduce the volume of a given mass of gas by a succession of infinitesimal changes in pressure, allowing enough time for the new equilibrium states to be established, the system is never in a state differing more than infinitesimally from an equilibrium state, and the process is denoted reversible. An ideal reversible process may be achieved in practice by increasing the external pressure very slowly. If the conditions external to the system are changed very slowly in the reverse direction, then the gas will pass through the same series of equilibrium states in the reverse direction. On the other hand, if the process does not involve such infinitesimal changes, so that there is not present a uniform succession of equilibrium states, it is irreversible which does not, thermodynamically speaking, mean that the system cannot be returned to its original state. If a gas is compressed rapidly, eddies will develop in the gas and the attendant kinetic energy will be converted into heat, the process then being irreversible. An isothermal process, characterized by a constant temperature, is a reversible process and may be achieved by surrounding a system with a constant temperature and changing the other thermodynamic variables so slowly that at each stage turbulence does not set in and there is enough time for the temperature to be the same at all points. An adiabatic process may be reversible or irreversible and, if no heat is to enter or leave the system it should be surrounded by a perfect heat insulator. There are, however, no perfect heat insulators and the adiabatic process must be carried out with sufficient rapidity to prevent the system from gaining or losing heat. Actually, all processes are irreversible, since there is always some turbulence present. Nevertheless, the concept of an irreversible process is useful in the study of thermodynamics. A very significant ideal reversible cycle, in which a series of reversible processes returns the system to its original condition, is the Carnot cycle, which is discussed in the next section.

We shall now state the second law of thermodynamics in two equivalent ways; the first statement is due to Lord Kelvin and the second statement is due to Clausius.

It is not possible to have a process whereby the only result is the extraction of heat from a reservoir and the conversion of all of this heat into work.

It is not possible to have a process whereby heat is removed from a reservoir at one temperature and absorbed in equal quantity by a reservoir at a higher temperature.

The second law of thermodynamics may be expressed in a variety of ways and it leads to inferences and deductions that have far-reaching significance. In effect, the law states that it is impossible for a self-contained system to transfer heat indefinitely from a body of one temperature to a body of a higher temperature. To sustain such a process would involve work from an outside agent. Although work can be dissipated completely into heat, the second law stipulates that only a fraction of heat energy may be converted into work.

There are derivable from the second law, as applied to heat engines, important consequences. One is that it is not possible for a heat engine that is operating in cycles between two reservoirs at constant temperatures to have an efficiency greater than that of a reversible engine operating between the same two reservoirs. Another consequence is that all reversible engines operating between two constant-temperature reservoirs have the same efficiency.

22.7.   The Carnot Cycle.   In a heat engine about 30%, or less, of the heat energy is transformed into mechanical work and 70% or more of the heat intake is rejected into the exhaust. We have seen that the second law of thermodynamics indicates that it is impossible ever to construct an engine that will convert a given amount of heat completely into mechanical work. Carnot in 1824 studied the problem of the efficiency of a heat engine and derived a theoretically important reversible cycle, called the *Carnot cycle*, which indicates the upper limit of the efficiency of a real engine. The system consists of a working substance (gas, liquid, or solid) which is contained in a cylinder equipped with a heat-conducting base and thermally insulating walls and frictionless piston. The substance is imagined to be carried through a reversible cycle consisting of two isothermal and two adiabatic reversible processes. In order to accomplish this there is provided a heat reservoir at a temperature T_1, another reservoir at a lower temperature T_2, both reservoirs being of very large heat capacity, and a heat-insulating stand.

The Carnot cycle is shown in Figure 22.6 and we shall now indicate how a substance is carried through it. For simplicity we consider that the working substance is an ideal gas whose initial state is represented by p_1, V_1, T_1 corresponding to point A. With the cylinder on the heat reservoir at temperature T_1 the gas is allowed to expand very slowly isothermally until it reaches some point B characterized by p_2, V_2, T_1. From A to B an amount of heat Q_1 is absorbed by the gas through the base of the cylinder and the gas in moving the piston does the amount of work given by the area under AB. The cylinder is now placed on the insulating stand and the gas, permitted to expand adiabatically and reversibly to point C, does an amount of work represented by the area under BC, and the temperature falls to T_2. Point C is characterized by p_3, V_3, T_2. The cylinder is now placed on the reservoir whose temperature is T_2 and the gas is compressed very slowly and isothermally to the point D, an amount of work shown as the area under CD being performed on the gas and an amount of heat Q_2 leaving the gas. The point D is characterized by p_4, V_4, T_2. To complete the cycle, the cylinder is placed on the insulating stand and compressed adiabatically and reversibly to the point **A**, an amount of work done on the gas being represented by the area under **DA**, and the temperature, pressure, and volume of the gas returning to their initial values.

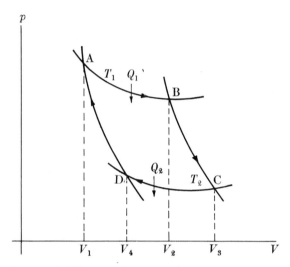

Figure 22.6.   *The Carnot cycle.*

From the diagram it is clear that the work done by the gas during expansion, from A to B to C, is greater than the work done on the gas during compression, from C to D to A. Hence the net work done by the gas is represented by the area enclosed by cyclic path ABCDA. Applying Equation 22.7 to the cycle and observing that $\Delta U = 0$, since the initial and final states are the same, we have the work done in the process:

$$\Delta W = \Delta Q = Q_1 - Q_2 \tag{22.14}$$

where $Q_1 - Q_2$ is the net heat absorbed by the gas. The efficiency of a heat engine, ε, is defined as the ratio of the work output to the heat input. Hence, for the Carnot engine,

$$\varepsilon = \frac{Q_1 - Q_2}{Q_1} = 1 - \frac{Q_2}{Q_1} \tag{22.15}$$

It is important to emphasize again that in the cycle of events heat is absorbed from a high-temperature source, only a part is converted into mechanical work, and the remainder is discharged as heat at a lower temperature. Since every heat engine exhausts an amount of heat Q_2 which is never zero, Equation 22.15 shows that the efficiency of a heat engine is less than 100%. The heat Q_2, although part of the output of the heat engine, represents the heat absorbed by the engine that is not converted into mechanical work and is therefore wasted. Real heat engines do not operate exactly on a reversible cycle, but the Carnot cycle gives significant information regarding any heat engine and indicates the upper limit of the efficiency of a real engine. Although an ideal gas was employed as the working substance it is clear that the result obtained is independent of the working substance.

If the Carnot cycle is performed in the reverse (counterclockwise) sense, an amount of heat Q_2 is removed from the low-temperature reservoir and an amount of heat Q_1 is delivered to the high-temperature reservoir. Work, of course, must be done on the system by an external agent in order that heat may be extracted from the low-temperature reservoir. By repeating such a cyclic process we have a system which is a *refrigerator* rather than a heat engine. In a refrigerator heat is transferred from a body at low temperature to a body at high temperature with the aid of external work.

Let us return to Figure 22.6 and consider that we have n moles of an ideal gas as the working substance. The isothermals yield, in accordance with Equation 22.8,

$$Q_1 = nRT_1 \ln \frac{V_2}{V_1} \qquad (22.16)$$

and

$$Q_2 = nRT_2 \ln \frac{V_3}{V_4} \qquad (22.17)$$

Now, $p_1V_1 = p_2V_2$, $p_3V_3 = p_4V_4$, $p_4V_4{}^\gamma = p_1V_1{}^\gamma$, and $p_2V_2{}^\gamma = p_3V_3{}^\gamma$, and these multiplied together yield $V_2/V_1 = V_3/V_4$. Hence, from Equations 22.16 and 22.17,

$$\frac{Q_1}{Q_2} = \frac{T_1}{T_2} \qquad (22.18)$$

and Equation 22.15 may be written

$$\mathcal{E} = \frac{T_1 - T_2}{T_1} \qquad (22.19)$$

where T_1 and T_2 are the temperatures as measured on the ideal gas thermometer scale. Although Equation 22.19 was obtained by employing an ideal gas as working substance, the second law of thermodynamics leads us to the conclusion that the efficiencies of all Carnot engines operating between the same two temperatures are the same, regardless of the working substance. The equation indicates that any real engine, such as a steam engine, must operate with an intake temperature T_1 as high as possible and an exhaust temperature T_2 as low as possible if it is to possess the greatest efficiency attainable.

22.8. The Kelvin Thermodynamic Temperature and Absolute Zero.
We have mentioned that the second law of thermodynamics leads to the conclusions that no engine operating between two temperatures can be more efficient than a Carnot engine operating between the same temperatures,

and that the efficiencies of all Carnot engines operating between the same two temperatures are the same, irrespective of the working substance. This indicates that the ratio Q_1/Q_2 depends only upon the two temperatures, and it was Lord Kelvin who accordingly proposed that Equation 22.18 be used to define a temperature scale which would be independent of the properties of any substance, unlike the liquid or gas thermometers which, as we have seen, depend on the kind of thermometric substance employed. The scale defines what is known as the absolute thermodynamic temperature scale. Since Equation 22.18 gives only the ratio between any two Kelvin temperatures T_1 and T_2, the scale may be completely defined by arbitrarily designating 100 Kelvin degrees as the difference between the ice point and the steam point, or by assigning an arbitrary Kelvin temperature to a body, such as the temperature of the triple point of water ($273.16°K$). The triple point of water is accurately reproducible and its use in the absolute scale makes the Kelvin thermodynamic scale agree with the centigrade scale defined in terms of the ice and steam points.

Now consider a series of Carnot engines all having the adiabatics AD and BC of Figure 22.6 where AB represents the steam point isothermal, DC represents the triple-point isothermal, and successive neighboring isothermals are in between. The topmost engine may be imagined to absorb heat from a source, do some work, and reject a smaller amount of heat at a lower temperature. The next engine may be thought of as absorbing the heat rejected by the first engine at its exhaust temperature, also doing an amount of work, and rejecting a smaller amount of heat to the next engine at a still lower temperature. All engines will be operating in a similar fashion, but the last one will reject no heat at a temperature of *absolute zero*. Absolute zero may therefore be defined as the temperature of a reservoir to which a Carnot engine exhausts no heat when it operates between this temperature and any higher temperature. Therefore at absolute zero an isothermal process and an adiabatic process are identical.

A gas thermometer employing an ideal gas gives temperatures on the absolute thermodynamic scale. In fact, if it were possible to have an ideal gas, its equation of state $T = pV/nR$ would afford a definition of absolute temperature. In accordance with the third law of thermodynamics, which we shall not discuss, it is accepted that the lowest temperature attainable is greater than absolute zero and a temperature of absolute zero is experimentally impossible. Temperatures as low as $0.001°K$ have been attained.

22.9. The International Temperature Scale.

The use of a single fixed point, the triple point of water, in the calibration of thermometers was adopted in 1954 at the Tenth Conference on Weights and Measures in Paris. The number chosen for this fixed point, as we have indicated, is $273.16°K$. With the constant-volume gas thermometer as the standard thermometer, the ideal gas temperatures are obtained in terms of the standard triple-point temperature. As discussed earlier, this scale is identical with the absolute thermodynamic Kelvin scale.

To provide reproducible fixed points that could be conveniently employed for calibration purposes, the International Temperature Scale was adopted; the fixed points of this scale are given in Table 22.1.

Table 22.1. *Fixed points of the International Temperature Scale (at standard atmospheric pressure).*

Substance	Specification	Temp., °C
Oxygen	Boiling point	−182.97
Ice	Melting point	0.00
Water	Boiling point	100.00
Sulphur	Boiling point	444.60
Antimony	Melting point	630.50
Silver	Melting point	960.80
Gold	Melting point	1,063.00

The international scale and the Celsius scale are in very close agreement, the differences being, in general, negligible.

Problems

22.1. Determine the root-mean-square speeds of hydrogen and oxygen molecules and helium and argon atoms at 0°C. Use Table A.2 of the Appendix for the known atomic weights of the elements and apply Equation 22.6.

22.2. Calculate the root-mean-square speed of steam molecules at 127°C.

22.3. Calculate the total translational kinetic energy of all the molecules of an ideal gas whose volume is 1.50 liters and whose pressure is 1.75 atmospheres.

22.4. Find the root-mean-square speed of air molecules at 0°C and 76.0 cm Hg pressure, assuming an ideal gas. The density of air at these conditions is 1.29 kgm/m³.

22.5. Figure 22.7 shows the variation of the force between two molecules as a function of their distance of separation r. The force is one of attraction and small at large r, increases with decreasing r, passes through a maximum, and decreases to zero at $r = r_0$. For $r < r_0$ the force becomes one of repulsion which rises steeply. In the light of this curve, what conclusions can you come to regarding some of the assumptions of the kinetic theory? The value of r_0 is of the order of a molecular diameter.

22.6. Calculate the gravitational attraction between two hydrogen molecules which are 30.0 diameters apart. The diameter of a hydrogen molecule is 2.33×10^{-8} cm. Of what significance is this force among the forces depicted in Figure 22.7?

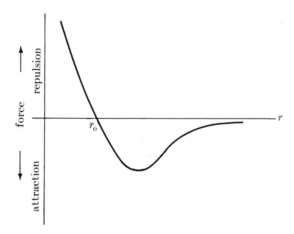

Figure 22.7. *Force between two molecules as a function of their separation, Problem 22.5.*

22.7. The Maxwellian distribution of speeds shown in Figure 22.2 is represented by the equation

$$\frac{\Delta N}{N} = 4\pi \left(\frac{m}{2\pi kT}\right)^{3/2} v^2 \, e^{-(mv^2/2kT)} \Delta v$$

where $\Delta N/N$ represents the fraction of the molecules in the interval Δv, v is the speed, and the other quantities have the meanings employed in the chapter. Show that the most probable speed is given by $\sqrt{2kT/m} = \sqrt{2/3} v_{rms}$ where v_{rms} is the root-mean-square speed.

22.8. The mean free path of a gas molecule among similar molecules is given by $(\pi\sqrt{2}nd^2)^{-1}$ where n is the number of molecules per unit volume and d is the molecular diameter. The molecules of a gas at standard conditions have a root-mean-square speed of 10^5 cm/sec and a diameter of 3×10^{-8} cm. Find (**a**) the mean free path and (**b**) the collision frequency.

22.9. Criticize the statement that Equation 22.6 indicates that at absolute zero temperature the average kinetic energy of the molecules is zero.

22.10. Calculate the translational kinetic energy of a gas molecule under standard conditions when it is moving with the most probable speed in a Maxwellian distribution. (See Problem 22.7).

22.11. When 1.000 gm of water is boiled at a pressure of 1.000 atmosphere, it becomes 1,671 cm³ of steam. Using the heat of vaporization of water, 538.7 cal/gm, find (**a**) the external work done in expanding against the constant-pressure surroundings and (**b**) the increase in internal energy of the system.

22.12. The volume of 1.50 gram-moles of an ideal gas is increased isothermally at 20.0°C from 3.25 liters to 18.5 liters. How much work is done?

22.13. What is the increase in internal energy of a system which absorbs 675 cal while 150 joules of work is done on it?

22.14. An ideal gas at 30.0 pounds-force/square-inch occupies 4.55 cubic feet. It is compressed isothermally to a pressure of 50.0 pounds-force/square-inch and then heated at constant pressure until it occupies the original volume. How much work is done by the gas?

22.15. A mass of an ideal gas ($\gamma = 1.40$) occupies a volume of 600 cm³ at atmospheric pressure and a temperature of 27.0°C. If it is compressed adiabatically to a volume of 200 cm³ what are the corresponding (**a**) pressure and (**b**) temperature?

22.16. A mass of a monatomic gas occupies a volume of 0.500 liter at a pressure of 1.25 atmospheres and a temperature of 325°K. The gas is compressed adiabatically until its pressure is 2.50 atmospheres. Find the corresponding (**a**) volume and (**b**) temperature.

22.17. Show that the relation between p and V for an adiabatic process is $pV^\gamma = $ constant. (*Hint:* Use Equation 22.7 with $\Delta Q = 0$, $\Delta U = nC_v \Delta T$, $\Delta W = p \Delta V$, and observe that $p \Delta V + V \Delta p = nR \Delta T$.)

22.18. Show from Equation 22.13 that, for an adiabatic, $TV^{\gamma-1} = C_1$ and

$$p^{\frac{1-\gamma}{\gamma}} T = C_2$$

where C_1 and C_2 are constants.

22.19. In Joule's free-expansion experiment an apparatus similar to that shown in the schematic of Figure 22.8 is employed. Two rigid containers A and B, connected by a stopcock, are immersed in water, and the system is carefully insulated to prevent any heat from entering or leaving the system. Initially, A is filled with gas and B is completely evacuated. After thermal equilibrium is established, the stopcock is opened and the gas is permitted to rush into B. After thermal equilibrium is re-established it is found that the temperature of the water remains unchanged throughout the experiment.

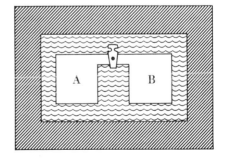

Figure 22.8. *Problem 22.19.*

What conclusions can you come to, on the basis of the observed result?

22.20. An equation of state that describes most nearly the behavior of a real gas was proposed by *van der Waals* and has the form, for 1 mole of a gas,

$$\left(p + \frac{a}{V^2}\right)(V - b) = RT$$

where a is very nearly a constant for a given mass of gas whose volume is V, and b is very nearly a constant and proportional to the volume occupied by the molecules in 1 mole of the gas. The quantities a and b are different for different gases, a/V^2 representing the correction due to the existence of intermolecular forces in real gases and b taking account of the finite dimensions of the molecules. Determine the general characteristics of the isotherms given by this equation and compare with those of the isotherms shown in Figure 20.3.

22.21. A steam engine takes in heat at 227°C and discharges its exhaust at 27.0°C. Calculate its maximum ideal efficiency.

22.22. A Carnot engine absorbs 95.0 cal of heat at 117°C and delivers 70.0 cal to the low-temperature reservoir. What is the temperature of the low-temperature reservoir?

22.23. The efficiency of a Carnot engine is to be increased from 30.0% to 40.0% by decreasing the exhaust temperature. If the high-temperature reservoir is 200°C, by how many degrees must the exhaust temperature be lowered?

22.24. A Carnot refrigerator extracts 0.250 cal from a body at 7.00°C and delivers energy to a body at 127°C. (a) How much energy is delivered? (b) How much mechanical energy is required?

Wave Motion

THE TWO PRINCIPAL MEANS by which energy may be trans-
ferred from one point to another point are the motion of particles or bodily
motion of matter between these points and a *wave motion* that involves no
physical transfer of material between the points. The transfer of the kinetic
energy of high-velocity jets of steam onto the rotating blades of a steam
turbine is an example of particle transmission. The transmission of sound
and all electromagnetic radiation such as light, radiant heat, and radio are
examples of wave motion. In fact, the phenomenon of wave motion is present
in every branch of physics and we shall devote this chapter to a study of some
of the significant properties of *mechanical waves*, which are waves in deformable
or elastic media. Sound, water waves, and waves on a string are examples
of mechanical waves. All waves have certain properties in common, and
some of the fundamental ideas that we shall develop in this chapter will aid
in the understanding of electromagnetic waves, which are not mechanical
in nature and are taken up in another part of this text. The wave concepts
we encounter in this and the following chapter are also useful in descriptions
of the properties and behavior of atomic and subatomic particles in connection
with the modern study known as wave mechanics (Section 36.4).

23.1. Mechanical Waves. Mechanical waves require for their production a moving or vibrating *source* and an *elastic medium*. The source
produces a displacement or disturbance of some portion of the elastic medium
which in turn enables the disturbance to be transmitted. The elastic medium
is to be thought of as consisting of particles which are connected, neighbor to
neighbor, by elastic forces. Each particle in such a succession occupies a
position of equilibrium, and when displaced is under the influence of a restoring
force due to the elastic forces of attraction and repulsion. If one of the particles is subjected to a displacement by an external source, the existing elastic
forces cause the neighboring particles to undergo a displacement which results
in a displacement of succeeding particles. In this manner there is propagated
a wave of displacements through the medium, the particles of the medium
more remote from the source experiencing the displacement at successively
later times and the disturbance proceeding at a definite speed. If the source

is a periodic oscillating device, such as the prong of a tuning fork in air or water or a violin string, all the particles of the medium execute the same kind of oscillatory motion, their relative displacements being progressively out of phase. It is to be noted that no part of the medium moves along in the direction of the wave motion, only a disturbance or configuration being propagated through the medium. For example, when water waves proceed outward from their source of origin, floating objects such as cork simply bob up and down and back and forth, and do not move in the direction of the ripples. The transmission of the wave motion, and energy, is a consequence of the fact that the medium possesses elasticity and inertia.

When the particles of a medium move or vibrate perpendicularly to the direction of propagation of the wave disturbance there is produced a *transverse wave*. Such a wave results when one end of a taut rope is vibrated in a direc-

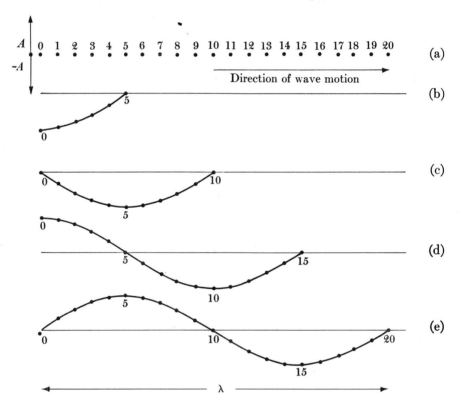

Figure 23.1. *Illustrating the mechanism of production of a transverse wave.*

tion at right angles to the length of the rope. In Figure 23.1a is shown a succession of equally spaced particles of a rope or other medium numbered 0, 1, 2, 3, . . . , the particles being elastically connected. Consider that particle 0 is subjected to a to-and-fro vertical motion by means of a vibrating source, as indicated by the double-pointed arrow. The shape of the wave disturbance is determined by the manner in which the source moves, and we shall assume that the source subjects particle 0 to a simple harmonic vibration of amplitude A as indicated. When particle 0 starts downward, its motion is transmitted successively to the neighboring particles, and in (b), where 0 is at its maximum negative displacement, it is assumed that the disturbance has reached particle 5 after a quarter-period, particles 1, 2, 3, and 4 being displaced as indicated. After the second quarter-period, particle 0 is at the equilibrium position, particle 5 has its maximum negative displacement, and the disturbance has reached particle 10, as shown in (c). In (d), after the third quarter-period, particle 0 is at its maximum upward displacement, particle 5 is at its equilibrium position, particle 10 has reached its maximum negative displacement, and the disturbance has advanced to particle 15. In (e) particle 0 has returned to its starting position, one period of vibration has been completed, and the disturbance has reached particle 20, which is the first particle in step or in phase with 0. The wave form shown in (e) is a sine curve, since the vibrating source is simple harmonic, and it is to be noted that each particle executes the same simple periodic motion as the source particle 0, there being present a constant progressive phase difference between neighboring particles. This simultaneous vibratory motion of all of the particles results in the transverse disturbance which is propagated through the medium with a definite speed. It is clear that if the source motion were of such a nature as to deliver only a sharp blow to the rope, only a single wave pulse would travel along the rope. Solids are suitable media for the transmission of transverse elastic waves. In gases the elastic forces between molecules are too small for a transverse wave to be transmitted.

When the particles of the medium move or vibrate parallel to the direction of propagation of the wave disturbance there is produced a *longitudinal wave*. We can again use a succession of particles, like those in Figure 23.1a, to show the characteristics of a longitudinal wave whose source particle 0 is subjected to a horizontal to-and-fro motion. The motion of 0 to the right is imparted to the neighboring particles and produces a compressional pulse; motion of 0 to the left produces a pulse of rarefaction. Both pulses travel outward to the right, and when 0 oscillates back and forth there is propagated a continuous train of compressions and rarefactions which gives rise to a traveling disturbance or configuration called a longitudinal wave, or a compressional wave. In the regions of compression the particles are closer together than is normal and are moving in the direction of wave propagation, while in the regions of rarefaction the particles are farther apart than is normal and are moving in the direction opposite to wave propagation. The regions of compression are also called regions of *condensation*. A longitudinal wave, then, is characterized by a series of alternating condensations and rarefactions and its wave form is plotted by laying off the horizontal displacements of the particles perpendicularly to the direction in which they actually occur. If the vibrating source is of the simple periodic type the wave form will again be represented by a sine curve. Sound waves are longitudinal waves, and we shall discuss them in greater detail in Chapter 24. Solids, liquids, and gases are able to transmit longitudinal waves.

There are also waves that are neither transverse nor longitudinal, but a combination of both. For example, in waves on the surface of water the particles of water trace out circular or elliptical paths.

23.2. Relation between Velocity, Frequency, and Wavelength.

We have seen that all the particles of an elastic medium which is transmitting a simple periodic wave disturbance vibrate with simple harmonic motion about their positions of equilibrium. All particles reach the same displacement in their paths, although at different times, and it is the relative displacement of any two particles that represents the phase between them. In Figure 23.1e particles 0 and 20 are in phase and we define the distance between any one particle and the very next one which is in phase with it as the *wavelength* λ. In the time that 0 (and each of the other particles) executes one complete vibration, called the *period T*, the wave disturbance has progressed a distance λ so that the velocity v of the wave propagation is given by

$$v = \frac{\lambda}{T} = f\lambda \qquad (23.1)$$

where f is the *frequency*, the number of complete vibrations per unit time. Equation 23.1, relating the velocity, frequency or period, and wavelength is quite general, holding for any sinusoidal wave motion. The velocity v is really to be thought of as the *phase velocity* of the wave, in contrast to what is known as the group velocity; this is significant when a wave disturbance is composed not of a single wavelength but of a group of waves of somewhat different wavelengths. Then there are a number of phase velocities that travel through the medium, and they combine and give rise to a group velocity which may be greater or less than the phase velocity. We shall be limiting our discussion to simple harmonic waves and phase velocity. In Equation 23.1, if f is in cycles or vibrations per second and λ is in centimeters (actually, centimeters per cycle or per vibration), then v is in centimeters per second.

23.3. Trigonometric Expression for a Simple Harmonic Wave.

It should be evident that for a simple harmonic wave the displacement of any particle of the medium, represented by the y coordinate of the sine curve in Figure 23.1e, is a function of both the position x of the particle measured horizontally from 0 and the time t. Let us now consider that at time $t = 0$ the shape of a rope which is transmitting a sinusoidal wave disturbance is given by the solid curve in Figure 23.2. Then the equation of this curve is $y = A \sin (2\pi x/\lambda)$ where y is the displacement, or ordinate value, of any point of the curve removed horizontally from 0 by an amount x. Thus,

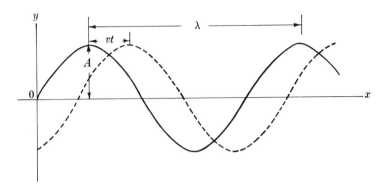

Figure 23.2. *Illustrating that y is a function of x and t.*

specifying x in terms of λ, when $x = \lambda/4$, then $y = A$, and when $x = 3\lambda/4$, then $y = -A$, etc. Consider that at some later time t the wave has advanced to the right a distance vt on the dashed curve. The y coordinate of any point on this displaced curve is given by

$$y = -A \sin \frac{2\pi}{\lambda} (x - vt) \qquad (23.2)$$

Equation 23.2 gives the relationship of the displacement y as a function of x and t. For example, when $x = 0$, $y = A \sin (2\pi t/T)$ and the particle at 0

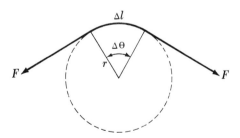

Figure 23.3. *Illustrating a wave pulse in a section of a stretched cord of length Δl.*

oscillates sinusoidally with time. For a wave traveling to the left, in the negative x direction, the same equation holds, vt being replaced by $-vt$.

23.4. **Velocity of a Transverse Wave in a Stretched Cord.** The speed with which a transverse wave moves through an elastic medium such as a cord depends upon how quickly a distorted portion of the cord transmits the disturbance to neighboring portions, and this will depend upon the tension of the cord and its inertia. To derive the expression that shows this depend-

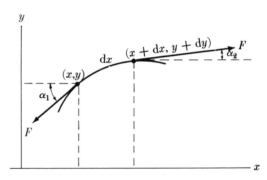

Figure 23.4. *The calculus derivation of the wave equation.*

ence consider a cord of mass per unit length, m_u, stretched horizontally under a uniform tension force F. We shall present the derivation in two ways: in the left column is given a noncalculus development while the right column contains a treatment with the calculus.

Consider that the stretched cord is given an impulsive blow which creates a transverse pulse that travels with a speed v from right to left. Imagine that, since the wave pulse is maintained as it advances, the string moves from left to right with the same speed v, as shown in Figure 23.3, so that the wave pulse remains fixed in space and the particles of the cord successively move around it. In the figure, Δl, the length of a small section of the pulse, is considered the arc of a circle of radius r and to be under the action of the tension F acting at its extremities. The centripetal force acting on the mass $m_u \Delta l$ is supplied by the vertical components of the tangential forces. Hence

$$2F \sin\left(\frac{\Delta\theta}{2}\right) = \frac{m_u \Delta l v^2}{r}$$

Since the angle $\Delta\theta$ is small we may substitute for $\sin\left(\frac{\Delta\theta}{2}\right)$ its radian measure

Consider a small length of cord dx distorted as in Figure 23.4, the ends subject to the uniform tension F acting in the directions α_1 and α_2 with the horizontal. Although the pulls on the ends of the element dx are equal in magnitude, their directions are not opposite and there is a resultant y component. Hence, equating this unbalanced force with the mass times the y component of acceleration we have

$$F(\sin \alpha_2 - \sin \alpha_1) = m_u \, dx \, \frac{\partial^2 y}{\partial t^2}$$

where the partial-derivative symbol $\partial/\partial t$ is employed to indicate that the time rate of change of the y displacement is to be computed when x is held constant. Since we are considering small transverse displacements we may replace the sines by tangents, or

$$\sin \alpha_1 \cong \tan \alpha_1 = \left(\frac{\partial y}{\partial x}\right)_x$$

and

$$\frac{\Delta\theta}{2} = \frac{\Delta l}{2r}.$$ Therefore,

$$v = \sqrt{F/m_u} \qquad (23.3)$$

$$\sin\alpha_2 = \tan\alpha_2 = \left(\frac{\partial y}{\partial x}\right)_{x+dx}$$

$$= \left(\frac{\partial y}{\partial x}\right)_x + \frac{\partial}{\partial x}\left(\frac{\partial y}{\partial x}\right)dx$$

where the partial derivatives with respect to x indicate that t is to be kept constant. Therefore

$$F\frac{\partial^2 y}{\partial x^2}\,dx = m_u\,dx\,\frac{\partial^2 y}{\partial t^2}$$

and

$$\frac{\partial^2 y}{\partial t^2} = \frac{F}{m_u}\left(\frac{\partial^2 y}{\partial x^2}\right) \qquad (23.3A)$$

This equation is the one-dimensional *wave equation*, and it can be shown that its most general solution is a function of $x - vt$. Equation 23.2 is one of its solutions and may be used to compute the derivatives in Equation 23.3A. Thus,

$$\frac{\partial^2 y}{\partial t^2} = -A\frac{2\pi}{\lambda}v^2\sin\frac{2\pi}{\lambda}(x - vt)$$

$$\frac{\partial^2 y}{\partial x^2} = -A\frac{2\pi}{\lambda}\sin\frac{2\pi}{\lambda}(x - vt)$$

and substituting into Equation 23.3A yields the relation

$$v = \sqrt{F/m_u} \qquad (23.3)$$

which shows that the velocity of a transverse wave in a cord is a function only of the tension F and the mass per unit length m_u. The student should verify the following. When F is in dynes and m_u is in grams mass per centimeter, v is in centimeters per second; when F is in newtons and m_u is in kilograms mass per meter, v is in meters per second; when F is in pounds force and m_u is in slugs per foot, v is in feet per second. It must be realized that Equation 23.3 holds under the condition that the amplitude of the pulse or transverse vibration is not so large as to make the substitution of θ for $\sin\theta$ invalid. Also, for large amplitudes the cord tension would not remain unchanged.

23.5. Velocity of a Longitudinal Wave in an Elastic Medium. Equation 23.3 is an example of the general result that the square of the velocity of a wave in an elastic medium is proportional to the ratio of an elasticity factor of the medium to an inertial factor of the medium. For a stretched cord or wire, the elastic restoring force is the tension of the cord or wire and its mass per unit length furnishes the inertial factor.

For the velocity of a longitudinal wave in a solid rod, the elasticity factor is Young's modulus of elasticity of the rod and the inertial factor is the rod's density.   Hence,

$$v = \sqrt{\frac{E}{\rho}} \tag{23.4}$$

where E is Young's modulus and ρ is the density.

For the velocity of a longitudinal wave in a liquid or gas, the elasticity factor is the bulk modulus of elasticity of the fluid and the inertial factor is the fluid's density.   The equation expressing this is

$$v = \sqrt{\frac{B}{\rho}} \tag{23.5}$$

where B is the bulk modulus.   In the case of a gas the value of the bulk modulus, which is the ratio of the change in pressure to the fractional change in volume, depends upon whether the process is isothermal or adiabatic. Hence there are two bulk moduli, the isothermal bulk modulus and the adiabatic bulk modulus.   It can be shown (see Problem 23.16) that the isothermal bulk modulus is the pressure of the gas p while the adiabatic bulk modulus is γp where γ is the ratio of the specific heat at constant pressure to that at constant volume.   When a longitudinal wave passes through a gas, the regions of compression are slightly heated and the regions of expansion are slightly cooled.   These changes occur at a rapid rate and the regions of heating and cooling are large compared with the mean free path of the gas, so there is very little time available between the heating and cooling periods for the temperature to become equalized by heat conduction.   Hence, the velocity of a longitudinal wave in a gas is given by

$$v = \sqrt{\frac{\gamma p}{\rho}} \tag{23.6}$$

23.6.   Energy Transmission by a Wave.   Each particle in a simple periodic wave executes a simple harmonic motion about an equilibrium position and possesses a total amount of energy which is equal to its maximum kinetic energy as it passes through the equilibrium position.   This energy is passed on to succeeding particles in the medium and travels in the direction of propagation with the speed v.   It will be remembered that in simple harmonic motion the energy of a vibrating body changes from kinetic to potential energy, the total energy remaining constant.   In a stretched string the transmitted energy is stored alternately in each section of the string as kinetic energy of motion and potential energy of elastic deformation.   This total energy W is obtained from Equation 15.14, which states that

$$W = 2\pi^2 m f^2 A^2 \tag{23.7}$$

where m is the mass of the body, f is the frequency, and A is the amplitude of vibration.   For a string that transmits a transverse wave, or for a spring that transmits a longitudinal wave, the energy W_u per unit length of string or spring is given by

$$W_u = 2\pi^2 m_u f^2 A^2 \tag{23.8}$$

where m_u is the mass per unit length of string or spring. The significant fact revealed by Equations 23.7 and 23.8 is that the energy of a wave is directly proportional to the square of the frequency of vibration and the square of the amplitude. When a wave passes through a medium the density of a unit cross section of the medium is simply the mass per unit length. Hence, the energy per unit volume is $2\pi^2\rho f^2 A^2$ where ρ is the density of the medium. The amount of energy that flows per unit time through each unit of area perpendicular to the direction of propagation, called the intensity I, is

$$I = 2\pi^2 \rho f^2 A^2 v \tag{23.9}$$

where v, the wave speed, is the speed with which the energy per unit volume is transmitted. Again we see that the intensity is directly proportional to the square of the frequency and the square of the amplitude.

When a wave is propagated from a point source, through a uniform medium, the flow of energy through any solid angle spreads out over increasing spherical surface areas perpendicular to the direction of flow. These surface areas increase in direct proportion to the square of their distances from the point source. Hence the intensity of a wave from a point source falls off inversely as the square of the distance from the source. From a line source of wave radiation the energy spreads out over cylindrical surface areas which are proportional to the perpendicular distances from the line source. Hence, from a line source the intensity decreases in inverse proportion to the first power of the perpendicular distance from the line source.

23.7.   Significant Properties of Wave Motion.   We have seen that transverse and longitudinal waves carry and transmit energy. They are also capable of exhibiting the phenomena of *reflection, refraction, interference,* and *diffraction.* In addition, transverse waves are able to demonstrate the phenomenon of *polarization.* Although we shall be discussing these phenomena in detail in the sections on sound and light we shall here give some introductory descriptions and indicate some significant aspects.

Whenever a wave, traveling in one medium, falls upon an interface that separates this medium from another whose ratio of elastic to inertial property is different, some of the energy reflects into the first medium and some of the energy enters the second medium. If the wave is obliquely incident on the interface, it shows a change in direction as it enters the second medium because its speed in the second medium is different from that in the first; this phenomenon is called *refraction.* Both reflection and refraction take place in accordance with established laws, which are dealt with in Chapter 32.

Although reflection and refraction may be adequately described in terms of a mechanism that involves a motion of particles in the direction of energy flow, the phenomena of interference and diffraction are best described by a wave motion. An essential principle in these explanations, known as the *superposition principle*, is the fact that, when two waves travel simultaneously through the same medium, each wave proceeds through the medium and produces its effect independently of the presence of the other wave. In accord-

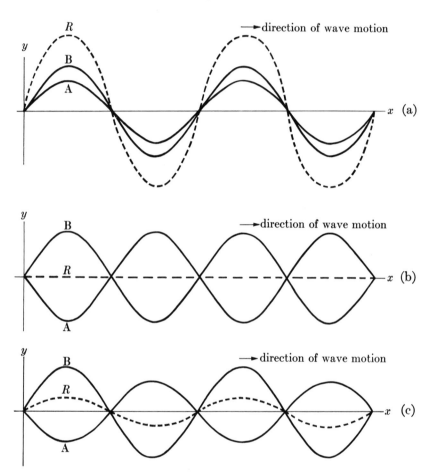

Figure 23.5. *Showing constructive and destructive interference of waves.*

ance with this principle the resulting disturbance due to the two waves is the vector sum of their individual disturbances. Thus, if one of the wave trains traveling alone through a medium produces a particle displacement y_1 at some point, and another wave traveling alone through the same medium produces a particle displacement y_2 at the same point, the displacement due to the simultaneous action of both waves is the resultant $y_1 + y_2$.

Three types of possible combinations of particle displacement, called *interference*, are illustrated in Figure 23.5. When y_1 and y_2 are in the same direction and equal or unequal in magnitude the resultant has a magnitude which is their sum; (a) shows two waves, A and B, of the same frequency, in phase, differing in amplitude, and moving in the same direction. The combined effect of both waves is obtained by adding the ordinates of each at every position x to obtain the resultant wave R, and illustrates reinforcement, or *constructive interference*. When y_1 and y_2 are in opposite directions and equal in magnitude the resultant disturbance is zero; (b) shows the two waves which meet 180°, or half a wavelength, out of phase at every position x and produce the resultant R which has a zero displacement at every point, illustrating *complete destructive interference*. When y_1 and y_2 are in opposite directions and unequal in magnitude the resultant disturbance is given by their difference; (c) shows the two waves which are 180° out of phase and differ in amplitude, producing the resultant R shown and illustrating *partial destructive interference*.

Another type of interference, which is particularly noticeable in sound, results when two waves of slightly differing frequencies travel in the same direction through the same medium at the same time and thus give rise to a kind of pulsating interference called *beats*. Here the beat frequency is easily shown to be equal to the difference in the two interfering frequencies.

Still another type of interference, which has basic application in all kinds of wave motion and is discussed in some detail in the next chapter, occurs when two waves of the same frequency and amplitude travel through the same medium at the same time but in opposite directions. This kind of wave combination sets up a system or pattern of *stationary*, or *standing*, waves exhibiting regions (points, lines, or surfaces) where some characteristic of the wave, such as displacement or pressure in a longitudinal sound wave, or current or voltage in an electromagnetic wave, is zero, and similar regions where this characteristic is a maximum. The regions of zero value are called *nodes* and those of maximum value are called *antinodes* or *loops*. For example, when one end of a cord is fastened to a rigid support and the other end is vibrated transversely, the outgoing waves and reflected waves at the wall interfere to form a standing-wave pattern of displacement nodes and loops. The characteristics of such a system of standing waves are depicted by the series of graphs in Figure 23.6. In (a) are shown two sinusoidal waves of equal frequency and amplitude traveling in opposite directions but coinciding momentarily at time $t = 0$. Their directions of travel are indicated by the arrows pointing to the right and the left and their resultant displacement is shown by the dashed curve. In (b) the wave traveling to the right and the wave traveling to the left have each advanced one eighth of a wavelength and their resultant has simply reduced in amplitude. One eighth of a period later, in (c), the resultant is instantaneously zero. Succeeding pictures correspond to successive eighth-periods, and we see in (d) and (e) that the resultant has the same amplitudes as in (b) and (a), respectively, but reversed 180°. In (f) the amplitude of the resultant again decreases, reaching a zero value in (g), and then increases again through (h) to a maximum value in the opposite direction in (i). We notice that the resultant wave crosses the axis always at the same points, which have zero displacement, and these are the nodes

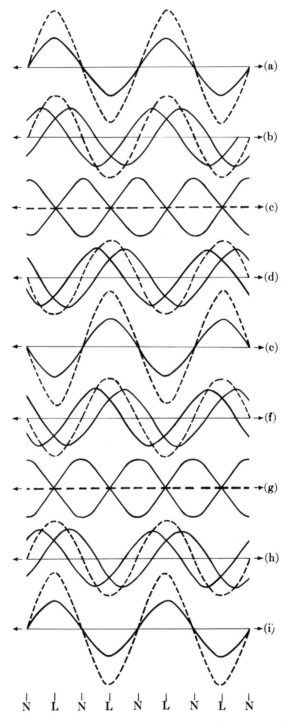

Figure 23.6. *Showing the characteristics of a standing wave. The two oppositely directed waves, coincident in phase in* (a), (e), *and* (i), *are solid curves. The resultant wave is dotted. Each graph differs by one eighth of a period.*

which are indicated by N at the bottom of the figure. Between any two adjacent nodes the particles of the medium execute simple harmonic motions up and down with the same frequency as the two interfering waves and with a maximum amplitude as shown. The points of maximum amplitude are the antinodes or loops and their positions are indicated by L in the lower part of the figure. It is clear that the nodes are spaced $\lambda/2$ apart and the loops are midway between the nodes. Notice that the maximum amplitude-changes in adjacent loops are in opposite directions. The standing wave on a cord stretched between two rigid supports is characterized by nodes at both ends, nodes every half-wavelength from each end, and loops midway between the nodes. If n is the total number of nodes on such a stretched string, the length of the string is clearly $(n-1)(\lambda/2)$.

In addition to interference, one other phenomenon that is employed as a criterion of wave motion is *diffraction*, which is the bending of a wave disturbance into the region behind an obstacle or the spreading of a wave disturbance after the wave has passed through an opening. In order that this bending or spreading of the waves may be observed or detected, the size of an obstacle or opening is made small in comparison with, or of the order of, the wavelength of the disturbance. When the size of the obstacle or opening is large compared with the wavelength, sharp shadows are cast and the disturbance appears to travel in straight lines. A person sitting in an auditorium behind a supporting pillar can hear sound waves originating from the stage but is not able to see the source unless he looks around the pillar. Audible sound waves have wavelengths that may be measured in feet while visible light waves have wavelengths of the order of 10^{-5} cm. From the same sound waves there would be cast a very sharp sound shadow by an extensive building or a hill. We shall be discussing diffraction in greater detail in our study of optics, where it enters in a significant fashion.

We have indicated that only transverse waves exhibit the phenomenon of polarization. In fact, polarization is a test of whether a wave is or is not transverse in character. When a string is passed through a slotted board and a transverse wave is sent along the string, the disturbance will not pass through if the slot is at right angles to the direction of vibration. We shall see that in the case of light there are transverse electric vibrations in two perpendicular planes, and when a light wave is sent through a slitlike electrical device one of the transverse vibrations may be transmitted while the other is quenched. The transmitted wave with vibrations in only one plane is said to be *polarized*. Since the vibrations in longitudinal waves are parallel to the direction of wave travel they are transmitted regardless of the orientation of any slitlike device, and a longitudinal wave cannot be polarized. The principles of polarization are dealt with in Chapter 35.

Example 23.1. What is the speed of a transverse wave traveling along a cord that has a linear density of 2.50×10^{-3} pounds-mass/foot and is under a tension of 15.0 pounds force?

Solution. Applying Equation 23.3,

$$v = \sqrt{F/m_u} \qquad\qquad F = 15.0 \text{ pf}$$

$$v = \sqrt{\frac{1.50 \times 32.0 \times 10^3 \text{ pf}}{2.50 \text{ slugs/ft.}}} \qquad m_u = \frac{2.50}{32.0} \times 10^{-3} \text{ slug/ft}$$

$$= 438 \text{ ft/sec}$$

Example 23.2. The equation of a transverse wave on a string is $y = 1.5 \sin \pi(0.55x - 90t)$. Find the wavelength, frequency, period, and speed of propagation when y and x are in centimeters and t is in seconds.

Solution. Comparing the equation with the form given by Equation 23.2,

$$\frac{2\pi}{\lambda} = 0.55\pi \quad \text{and} \quad \lambda = 3.6 \text{ cm}$$

$$\frac{2\pi}{\lambda} v = 90\pi \quad \text{and} \quad v = 1.6 \times 10^2 \text{ cm/sec}$$

Also,

$$f = \frac{v}{\lambda} = \frac{1.6 \times 10^2}{3.6} = 44 \text{ cycles/sec}$$

and

$$T = \frac{1}{f} = 2.3 \times 10^{-2} \text{ sec/cycle}$$

Example 23.3. Show by dimensional analysis that the speed of a wave in a string under tension is given by Equation 23.3.

Solution. Assume that v is given by the product of a function of the tension F and a function of the mass per unit length m_u. Thus

$$v = F^a m_u{}^b$$

where the exponents are determinable from the requirement that the dimensions on each side of the equation must be the same. Using l for length, m for mass, and t for time, we have

$$lt^{-1} = m^a l^a t^{-2a} m^b l^{-b}$$

or

$$lt^{-1} = m^{a+b} l^{a-b} t^{-2a}$$

Equating the exponents of the same dimensional quantities we obtain

$$2a = 1$$

$$a - b = 1$$

$$a + b = 0$$

and these yield the values $a = 1/2$ and $b = 1/2$, so that

$$v = \sqrt{F/m_u}$$

Problems

23.1. A tuning fork is vibrating with a frequency of 320 cycles/sec in air at 0°C. Calculate the wavelength of the sound.

23.2. A cord 100 cm long has a mass of 0.333 gm. The string is under a tension of 2.55 kgf. With what speed will a transverse wave travel along the cord?

23.3. Find the speed of a longitudinal wave in a glass rod whose Young modulus is 1.00×10^7 pounds-force/square-inch and whose specific gravity is 2.50.

23.4. The wavelength of a compressional wave in a metal rod is 50.5 feet. If the speed of the wave decreases from 1.65×10^4 feet/sec to 1.08×10^3 feet/sec as it emerges in the air, what is the wavelength in air?

23.5. A metal pipe 150 feet long is struck a blow at one end, and an observer at the other end records 0.127 sec as the time interval between the arrival of the wave disturbance through the pipe and that through the air. Taking 1.08×10^3 feet/sec as the speed of sound in air, find the Young modulus of the pipe whose density is 480 pounds-mass/cubic-foot.

23.6. From the same point two waves are emitted in phase with frequencies of 11.0 cycles/sec and 16.0 cycles/sec. What is their phase difference at the end of 1.25 sec?

23.7. A sinusoidal wave has a period of 0.025 sec/cycle and an amplitude of 0.75 cm. Find the displacement, speed, and acceleration of one of the particles 0.21 sec after it is at the midpoint of its vibration path.

23.8. The wavelength of a longitudinal wave in water is 2.92 m. Find the adiabatic bulk modulus of water. The frequency of the wave is 500 cycles/sec.

23.9. Obtain Equation 23.4 by dimensional analysis.

23.10. Two waves travel through the same medium with a speed of 340 m/sec. The waves have the frequencies 256 cycles/sec and 280 cycles/sec. What is the phase difference at a point 1.50 m distant from a point where the waves are in phase?

23.11. Show that the difference in phase between any two particles in a wave train traveling in the x direction is given by $(2\pi/\lambda)(x_2 - x_1)$ where x_1 and x_2 are the x coordinates of the particles.

23.12. Given two waves $y_1 = A_1 \sin(\omega t + \alpha_1)$ and $y_2 = A_2 \sin(\omega t + \alpha_2)$, and using the superposition principle, show that the displacement of the resultant wave is given by $y = A \sin(\omega t + \alpha)$ where ω is the angular velocity, α_1 and α_2 are the phase constants, and A and α are given by

$$A^2 = A_1^2 + A_2^2 + 2A_1A_2 \cos(\alpha_2 - \alpha_1)$$

$$\tan \alpha = \frac{A_1 \sin \alpha_1 + A_2 \sin \alpha_2}{A_1 \cos \alpha_1 + A_2 \cos \alpha_2}$$

23.13. At a time $t = 0$ a simple harmonic wave has the form $y = A \sin (\pi x/100)$ where y and x are in centimeters. The velocity of the wave is 50.0 cm/sec to the right. Find the equation for the wave at a time $t = 3.00$ sec.

23.14. Using the superposition principle, find the resultant displacement of the two oppositely directed waves $y_1 = A \sin [(2\pi/\lambda)(x - vt)]$ and $y_2 = A \sin [(2\pi/\lambda)(x + vt)]$ and observe that the displacement nodes occur at $x = 0, \lambda/2, \lambda, 3\lambda/2, 2\lambda, \ldots$, with antinodes midway between adjacent nodes.

23.15. A longitudinal wave with a frequency of 2.50×10^3 cycles/sec has a speed of 332 m/sec at standard temperature and pressure. If the amplitude of the wave is 2.85×10^{-3} cm, what is its intensity?

23.16. Show that for an ideal gas the isothermal bulk modulus is p and the adiabatic bulk modulus is γp, where p is the pressure and γ is the ratio of the specific heat at constant pressure to that at constant volume.

23.17. Show that for an ideal gas Equation 23.6 may be put into the form

$$v = \sqrt{\gamma RT/M}$$

where R is the gas constant per mole, T is the absolute temperature, and M is the molecular weight. What is the significance of this equation?

23.18. Obtain Equation 23.8 by calculating the sum of the kinetic and potential energy per unit length of a transverse wave in a stretched string. [*Hint:* Kinetic energy per unit length $= \frac{1}{2}m_u(\partial y/\partial t)^2$ and the restoring force per unit length is $m_u(\partial^2 y/\partial t^2)$.]

23.19. The characteristics of the interference giving rise to beats can be obtained by using the superposition principle and finding the resultant displacement of the two displacements $y_1 = A \sin 2\pi f_1 t$ and $y_2 = A \sin 2\pi f_2 t$ acting at any one point in the medium. Obtain the resultant and interpret the result. Make use of the trigonometric identity $\sin \theta + \sin \varphi = 2 \sin \frac{1}{2}(\theta + \varphi) \cos \frac{1}{2}(\theta - \varphi)$.

23.20. A string 96.0 cm in length and of total mass 0.600 gm is under tension, one end being fixed and the other end attached to a vibrator which is vibrating at 120 cycles/sec transverse to the length of the string. What must be the tension if the standing-wave pattern is to contain four nodes?

23.21. Show that the slope of a vibrating string at any point x is equal to the ratio of the speed of the particle at that point to the wave speed.

Sound

*T*HE SUBJECT OF SOUND may be pursued in either of two ways, according to the meaning assigned to it. The physiological and psychological, or subjective, approach is concerned with the sense of hearing and the sensations received by individuals from disturbances in the air and other media. The physical, or objective, approach is concerned with the disturbances themselves and their production, propagation, and mechanical reception. Although both aspects of sound are interrelated in an ultimate coverage of the subject, we shall devote our development in this book to the physical aspect. We shall accordingly define sound as *any vibrating disturbance in an elastic medium capable of producing an auditory sensation.* Our definition indicates the existence of sound waves regardless of the presence or absence of an ear to receive them.

Sound waves, which can be propagated in solids, liquids, and gases, have a large range of frequencies. The frequencies in the audible range, those to which the human ear is capable of responding, range from about 20 cycles/sec to about 20,000 cycles/sec. When longitudinal mechanical waves have a frequency below the audible range they are termed *infrasonic* waves and when they are above the audible range they are termed *ultrasonic* (or supersonic) waves. The properties of ultrasonic waves, which contain large amounts of energy, have increasingly attracted the attention of investigators, with the result that accelerated research is leading to fruitful developments. Ultrasonic frequencies between 10^8 and 10^9 cycles/sec can be produced and these are in the range of visible wavelengths.

A fertile field of application of sound waves and their properties is the production, reproduction, and transmission of musical sounds by musical instruments and other, less familiar, devices. Although we shall not devote much time in this book to the physics of music, which is more appropriate in special courses in acoustics or the physical theory of music, we shall develop some of the principles which are basic to all musical instruments and are derived from such phenomena as resonance and the vibrations of strings, air columns, plates, and diaphragms. We shall also see that the psychological characteristics of sound—*pitch, loudness,* and *quality* or *timbre*—are correlated with the physical characteristics *frequency, intensity,* and *wave form.* At the end of the chapter some of the significant aspects associated with moving sound sources are considered.

24.1.   Dependence of Sound Velocity in a Gas on Temperature.
Referring to Problem 23.17 and using the result there indicated, we see that, to the approximation that a gas obeys the ideal gas law, the velocity of sound is directly proportional to the square root of the absolute temperature.   Hence

$$\frac{v}{v_0} = \sqrt{\frac{273 + t_C}{273}} \tag{24.1}$$

where v_0 and v are the velocities of sound in the gas at $0°C$ and $t_C°C$ respectively, and the values shown under the radical are the corresponding absolute temperatures.   We thus have

$$v = v_0 \left(1 + \frac{t_C}{273}\right)^{1/2} = v_0(1 + 0.003366t_C)^{1/2} \tag{24.2}$$

Occasionally an approximate formula is obtained by using the binomial expansion and neglecting higher-order terms for values of t that are not too large.   Thus,

$$v = v_0 \left(1 + \frac{1}{2} \times \frac{t_C}{273}\right) = v_0(1 + 0.00183t_C)$$

For a sound wave in air, $v_0 = 332$ m/sec $= 1,088$ feet/sec, and the approximate equations are

$$v = (332 + 0.608t_C) \text{ m/sec} \tag{24.3a}$$

and

$$v = (1,053 + 1.15t_F) \text{ ft/sec} \tag{24.3b}$$

where the velocity of sound at $0°F$ is $1,053$ feet/sec and t_F is temperature in degrees Fahrenheit.   The velocity of sound in air increases approximately 0.608 m/sec for each centigrade degree rise in temperature, or 1.15 feet/sec per Fahrenheit degree rise.

The velocity of sound varies with the temperature of the transmitting medium.   However, in solids and liquids the amount by which the velocity changes with temperature is small and, in general, negligible.

24.2.   Reflection of Sound Waves at Boundaries.   In Section 23.7 we indicated that when two similar waves travel through the same medium at the same time but in opposite directions a standing-wave pattern, characterized by nodes and loops, is produced.   When standing waves occur on a string under tension or in an air column or on a rigid rod, the interfering waves are caused by reflections from the ends of the vibrating system, and the precise locations of the nodes depend upon whether a node or a loop occurs at the end of the system.   To see just what happens at the reflecting boundary we consider a sound wave reflected at the boundary of a more dense medium and a less dense medium, as shown in Figure 24.1.   It will be remembered that a compressional wave is a succession of condensations and rarefactions (C and R in the figure).   It will also be recalled that the particles of the medium in a condensation are moving in the same direction as the direction of wave travel, while in a rarefaction the particles of the medium are moving in a direction opposite to that of wave travel. In the figure the small arrows above and below the C's and R's represent the motions of the particles of the medium in the incident and reflected waves, which are shown separated one above the other for clarity.

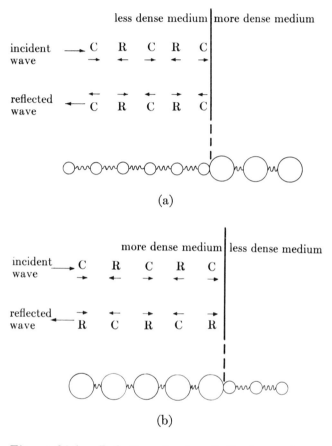

Figure 24.1. *Reflection of a longitudinal wave from:*
(a) *a more dense medium showing change in phase, and*
(b) *a less dense medium showing no change in phase.*

Consider first Figure 24.1a which shows the incident wave striking a more dense medium and a condensation striking the boundary at the instant depicted. When a compressional pulse strikes a medium that is more dense than the one in which it is traveling the case is analogous to one of an elastic direct central impact of one ball on another, more massive, ball. This analogous situation is depicted by the string of spheres shown at the lower part of the diagram, the smaller ones representing the less dense medium and the larger ones the more dense medium. A compressional pulse traveling from left to right and being transmitted from one small ball to the next through the elastic coupling represented by the springlike connectors between balls, like the elasticity of a medium, gets to be reflected as a compressional pulse when the last small ball strikes the first of the larger balls. Hence a pulse of condensation is reflected from a more dense medium as a pulse of condensation, and the displacement of a particle at the boundary undergoes a 180° change of phase upon reflection. The incident and reflected succession of condensations and rarefactions is shown in the upper part of Figure 24.1a. It is clear that, in the same way, a pulse of rarefaction striking a more dense medium is reflected as a pulse of rarefaction. We then arrive at the conclusion that the superposition of the incident and reflected waves at the reflecting boundary of a more dense medium gives rise to a displacement node at the reflecting surface and at every half-wavelength therefrom.

Now consider Figure 24.1b, depicting a condensation pulse which is incident on a medium less dense than the one in which it is traveling. By resorting to the analogy of elastic impact by a massive ball on a less massive ball it is seen that at the boundary a compressional pulse traveling from left to right through the balls causes a gap or rarefaction at the boundary, and this rarefaction reflects to the left. Hence, there is no change of phase on the displacement of the particles at the boundary of a less dense medium. The student should consider also the instant at which a rarefaction pulse strikes the less dense medium and see that this results in a reflected condensation pulse. Hence, at the boundary of a less dense medium a displacement antinode or loop is formed, and at every half-wavelength therefrom.

Similar results occur with transverse waves. When a transverse wave is sent along a cord toward an end which is fastened to a rigid support or attached to a more massive string, there is a reversal in phase at the boundary. If the end of the string is free or is attached to a less massive string, there is no change of phase at the boundary. (See Section 34.2.)

We shall now use these facts to determine the characteristics of some vibrating systems.

24.3. Vibrating Systems. *The Vibrating String.* When a string under tension is bowed, plucked, or struck, the transverse disturbance travels to both ends where reflections take place, forming stationary waves with displacement nodes at both ends and at every half-wavelength therefrom. In Figure 24.2 three of these nodes N originate from each end, and it is clear that a standing-wave pattern along the entire length of the string will obtain when the two systems of nodes coincide. This condition can be fulfilled in two ways: either the wavelength is adjusted so that an integral number of half-wavelengths fits into a fixed length of string or the string length is adjusted to accommodate an integral number of fixed half-wavelengths. For a vibrating string of a given length, sustained standing waves are possible in any one of a series of modes, the first four members of which are shown in Figure 24.3. In (a) is shown the standing-wave pattern for the simplest mode of vibration with a node at each end of the string and a loop in the center. This mode is called the *fundamental* or *first harmonic*. In this mode

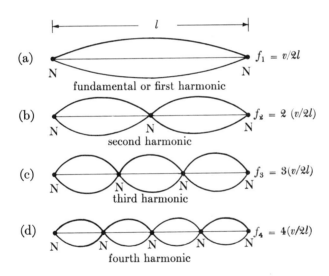

Figure 24.2.   *Illustrating the relation between wavelength and length of string for the formation of standing waves.*

the string vibrates in one segment, twice its length, $2l$, is equal to the wavelength, and the frequency is $f_1 = v/\lambda_1 = v/2l$ where v is the speed of the transverse wave and is fixed for a given string under a fixed tension. In (b) the next simplest mode contains three nodes, the wavelength is $\lambda_2 = l$,

(a) $f_1 = v/2l$
                    fundamental or first harmonic

(b) $f_2 = 2\,(v/2l)$
                         second harmonic

(c) $f_3 = 3(v/2l)$
                          third harmonic

(d) $f_4 = 4(v/2l)$
                         fourth harmonic

Figure 24.3.   *Modes of vibration of a string.   Both even and odd harmonics are possible.*

the string vibrates in two segments, and the frequency is $f_2 = v/l = 2(v/2l)$. This mode is known as the second harmonic, sometimes also called the first overtone. In (c) one more node has been added, the string vibrates in three segments, and the frequency is $f_3 = v/\lambda_3 = 3(v/2l)$. This mode is called the third harmonic or second overtone. The fourth harmonic, (d), corresponds to a vibration in four segments. Each succeeding harmonic corresponds to a standing-wave pattern containing one additional node. It is seen that both the even and the odd harmonics are possible in a vibrating string, the frequency of the nth harmonic being given by

$$f_n = \frac{nv}{2l} = \frac{n}{2l} \sqrt{\frac{F}{m_\mathrm{u}}} = nf_1 \qquad (24.4)$$

where F is the tension, m_u is the mass per unit length, and n is an integer. Such frequencies, in which the length of the string is an integer times a half-wavelength, are the so-called *free vibrations* of a string. These transverse vibrations of a string set up condensations and rarefactions in the surrounding medium (e.g., in air) and proceed away from the string as compressional sound waves. By adjusting the tension F, a string of mass per unit length m_u may be given a desired fundamental frequency. This is the method employed by violinists, violists, cellists, etc., to tune their instruments. In addition, the string may be shortened and its fundamental frequency increased by pressing the finger on the string against the finger-board. The different strings on an instrument such as the violin have different values of m_u, those of smaller linear density having a higher fundamental frequency in accordance with Equation 24.4.

A string is capable of vibrating in a number of modes simultaneously, the waves of different wavelengths, as they pass through one another, giving rise to a complex resultant wave shape in the string. Just which harmonics are present, and what their relative amplitudes are, depends upon the character of the excitation and upon the point at which the string is excited. The particular harmonics evoked and their relative intensity distributions are different from a struck, plucked, or bowed string. For example, in the case of the bowing of a string, the speed of the bow movement and its pressure, as well as its point of contact, have a pronounced effect on the harmonics produced and their relative intensities. Usually the striking or bowing of a string, as with the violin or piano hammer, is done at about one-eighth the effective length of the string from one end, in order to eliminate the seventh and ninth harmonics which are quite dissonant. We can see how the point of excitation on a string has this kind of effect by realizing that at the point where the string is excited a node cannot exist and there must be a loop; when a bow is moved across the string it drags the string for a short distance until the restoring force causes the string to slip back past its equilibrium position, and the cycle is repeated as the string is bowed. If we concentrate on the patterns shown in Figure 24.3 and extrapolate to the patterns of higher harmonics, we can see that if the string is pulled up at its center point and released the even harmonics will be absent, because they require the presence of a node at the midpoint, and the amplitudes of the odd harmonics will decrease with an increasing number of harmonics. Again, if the string is excited at a point one fourth of its length from one end the second harmonic will be present with a large amplitude, the third harmonic with a very small amplitude, and the fourth harmonic will be absent. In fact, each harmonic that is an integral multiple of the fourth harmonic will be absent.

The coexistence of harmonic waves on a string with frequencies that are

integral multiples of one fundamental frequency is an important illustration
of the superposition principle. We have seen that the several coincident
vibrations give rise at any point to a resultant effect which is obtained by
plotting the displacements of the component vibrations with their correct
amplitudes and phases as a function of the time, and adding the ordinates
for each value of the time. The reverse process, of analyzing or decomposing
a complex vibration into component harmonic vibrations, can be accomplished
by application of the Fourier theorem. This theorem states that any periodic
function may be represented as the sum of a number of sine and cosine functions with frequencies that are integral multiples of one fundamental frequency. In accordance with this theorem, the resultant displacement of any
particle in a medium through which a complex periodic wave is traveling is
given by the Fourier series

$$y = A_0/2 + A_1 \cos \omega t + A_2 \cos 2\omega t + A_3 \cos 3\omega t + \cdots +$$
$$+ B_1 \sin \omega t + B_2 \sin 2\omega t + B_3 \sin 3\omega t + \cdots + \qquad (24.5)$$

where $\omega \, (= 2\pi f)$ is the angular velocity of the fundamental whose frequency
is f. For some functions a small number of terms is sufficient to represent
the complex wave, for other functions a large number of terms, and even an
infinite number is required for an exact representation. The A's and the B's
in the Fourier series are constants which are determinable from the given
complex periodic function. We shall not go into the method used for such
determinations, but it is significant to point out that it affords a powerful
means of analyzing complex wave forms.

The Vibrating Air Column. When air or other gas has the form of a
column within a rigid pipe or tube of finite length, a disturbance produced
at one end is propagated along the column as a longitudinal wave and is
reflected from the ends of the tube in a manner similar to the reflections of
transverse waves in a stretched string. These waves, traveling in opposite
directions through the gaseous medium, give rise to standing waves. Such
vibrating columns may be of the open type, in which both ends are open, or
of the closed type in which one end is open and the other end is closed.
Organ pipes and wind instruments exemplify vibrating air columns that
exhibit series of harmonic modes of vibration; see Figure 24.4.

When a longitudinal disturbance reflects inside the tube at the open end
it effectively reflects at the boundary of a less dense medium, and a displacement loop is formed there. For example, a condensation reaching the open
end expands from a confined region into an open region and a rarefaction
reflects back into the pipe. The tube, of course, has to be small in the cross-
sectional dimension compared with the wavelength of the sound. Therefore,
the fundamental or first harmonic mode of the open air column has a displacement loop L at each end, the length of the tube l_o is equal to half a wavelength, and the frequency is $f_1 = v/2l_o$. The next member of the series
contains an additional loop in the standing-wave pattern, the length of the
tube is equal to one wavelength, the frequency is twice the fundamental
frequency, and we have as a possible mode of vibration the second harmonic.

Succeeding modes of vibration have frequencies that are integral multiples of the fundamental, as in the vibrating string, both the even and the odd harmonics being permissible, as shown in Figure 24.4a.

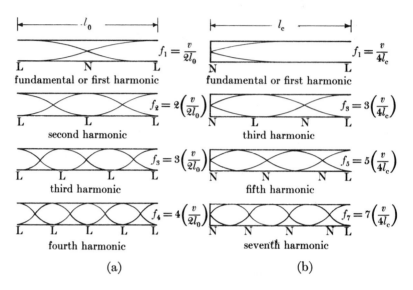

(a)   (b)

Figure 24.4. *Modes of vibration of open and closed air columns:* (a) *open air column,* (b) *closed air column.*

In the closed type of tube there must be a displacement node at the closed end and a displacement antinode, or loop, at the open end, as shown in Figure 24.4b. For the fundamental mode of vibration, $l_c = \lambda/4$, where l_c is the length of the tube, and the frequency is $f_1 = v/4l_c$. The second member of the series contains two displacement nodes and loops, $l_c = \frac{3}{4}\lambda$, and the frequency is $f_3 = 3(v/4l)$, the third harmonic, a frequency which is three times that of the fundamental. The third member of the series contains three displacement nodes, $l_c = \frac{5}{4}\lambda$, and the frequency is $f_5 = 5(v/4l_c)$, the fifth harmonic. Hence, the closed air column contains only the odd harmonics, the even harmonics being physically inadmissible. Here the third harmonic is called the first overtone, the fifth harmonic the second overtone, and so on.

Comparing the frequencies for the open and closed pipes it can be seen that odd harmonic frequencies of an open pipe of a given length can be obtained with a closed pipe of half the length. The harmonic vibrations of a closed pipe correspond to what is termed a quarter-wave system; those of an open pipe, as well as of a vibrating string, correspond to a half-wave system. An air jet directed against the open end of either pipe maintains a series of condensations and rarefactions down the tube and results in the standing-wave patterns corresponding to the characteristic modes of vibration illustrated in Figure 24.4. As in the case of a string, the fundamental and overtones of a vibrating air column exist at the same time.

The assumption was made that the displacement loop occurs exactly at the open end of a pipe. This is not strictly true, since reflection is a consequence of the expansion of the disturbance into the region beyond the open end. The loop actually occurs a short distance beyond the plane of the open end, and this distance is a function of the cross-sectional dimension of the tube. For a cylindrical pipe whose radius r is small compared with the wavelength, the distance that must be added to the open end to locate the center of the displacement loop is approximately $0.6r$. For an open pipe of cylindrical cross section, the end correction must be doubled to obtain the effective length of the pipe.

Vibrating Rods, Plates, and Membranes. To set a rod in longitudinal vibration one may clamp it at some point and stroke it lengthwise with a rosined cloth. The mode of vibration that is evoked depends upon where the rod is clamped. In Figure 24.5 are shown some of the modes of vibra-

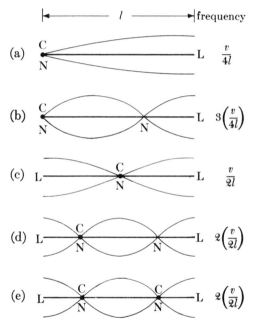

Figure 24.5. *Modes of vibration of a rod clamped at positions C.*

tion of a rod clamped at different positions C. In (a) the rod is clamped at one end and its fundamental mode has a node at the clamped end and a loop at the free end, so that $\lambda = 4l$ and the frequency is $v/4l$ as indicated. The next highest mode of vibration is shown in (b), with an additional node at $l/3$ from the free end and a frequency $3v/4l$, the third harmonic or first overtone. The rod clamped at one end therefore produces a series of standing-wave patterns and corresponding modes of vibration that resemble those of the closed pipe with the existence of only odd harmonics.   In (c) is shown the standing-wave pattern for the fundamental mode of longitudinal vibration of a rod clamped at its midpoint where a node exists with loops at the free ends.   Here the frequency is $v/2l$ and succeeding modes of vibration are obtained by adding nodes in pairs symmetrically placed on opposite sides of the clamped position, the frequencies being $3(v/2l)$, $5(v/2l)$, etc.   If the rod is clamped at a point $l/4$ from one end as in (d), or from both ends as in (e), the standing-wave pattern is as shown, and corresponds to a frequency v/l which is the second harmonic of the fundamental when the rod is clamped at its midpoint.

Rods may also be made to vibrate transversely if they are clamped and struck sharply.   For transverse vibrations the frequencies of the overtones are unharmonic; i.e., they do not bear an integral multiple relationship to the fundamental frequency.   In the marimba and xylophone, flat bars of metal or wood are supported at two locations, approximately one quarter of the length from each end (actually, $0.224l$).   When the bar is supported at these nodal points and struck in the middle, the fundamental mode of vibration is evoked.   A tuning fork is effectively such a vibrating bar, bent to form a U and having a short stem extending below the curved base.   The two nodal points are thus brought closer together and are located on either side of and close to the stem.   When one of the prongs is struck, a transverse vibration is set up, the prongs vibrating toward and away from each other. After a tuning fork is struck, any overtones that may be present are markedly transient and the tone that persists is a single frequency.   For this reason tuning forks are conveniently employed as frequency standards.   It must always be kept in mind that a mechanically vibrating body, whether transverse or longitudinal, always produces a compressional wave in air.

When a thin metal plate is clamped at its center and struck or bowed at some point on its edge, it will vibrate in a rather complicated fashion.   Likewise, when a plate or membrane is supported at its outer edge and struck a blow, the plate or membrane will break up into a series of vibrating segments, as in the case of vibrating strings, rods, or bars.   These are two-dimensional vibrators, and the two-dimensional waves, reflecting from the boundaries, set up standing-wave patterns characterized by nodal lines rather than points. The nodal-line patterns may be demonstrated by supporting a plate or membrane horizontally, sprinkling fine sand on the surface, and causing it to vibrate.   The sand particles move around and accumulate in the places of least motion, thus indicating the nodal lines.   Many modes of vibration are possible, depending on the manner in which the two-dimensional vibrator is supported and on the means of excitation.   In the case of a circular drumhead clamped around its edge, the circular edge is a nodal line.   The fundamental mode of vibration is given when the membrane surface oscillates as a whole, the center of the drumhead having the maximum displacement in a direction normal to its plane.   The overtones, which have nodal lines that are concentric circles, diameters, or combinations of circles and diameters, have frequencies that are not integral multiples of the fundamental.   For example, the mode of vibration just above the fundamental is characterized by a diametral nodal line in addition to the nodal line formed by the periphery of the membrane. The two semicircular sections oscillate with opposite displacements above and below the equilibrium plane of the drumhead, and the frequency is 1.593 times that of the fundamental. In the next highest mode of vibration there are two diametral nodal lines at right angles, dividing the surface into four right-angular vibrating segments. Adjacent segments have opposite displacements, and the frequency is 2.136 times that of the fundamental.

It should be clear from the above discussion that all elastic bodies can vibrate with a definite set of proper or characteristic frequencies corresponding to given boundary conditions, such as the end conditions of open or closed tubes or the circular boundary of a stretched membrane. In some systems the frequencies are related harmonically, while in other systems the frequencies are not integral multiples of the fundamental mode; in all cases, however, there are standing waves characterized by nodal points in one-dimensional vibrators, nodal lines in two-dimensional vibrators, and nodal surfaces in three-dimensional vibrators. For characterizing the behavior of atomic and nuclear systems, quantum mechanics provides methods of determining the characteristic, or *eigen*, frequencies, and the results are somewhat analogous to those of the classical mechanical vibrating systems described above.

24.4. Resonance. Whenever properly timed impulses are imparted to a system capable of vibrating and the frequency of the impulses is equal to one of the characteristic frequencies of the system, the system is set into vibration with a very large amplitude. This phenomenon is called *resonance.* In our discussion of the production of standing waves in an air column the persistence of the wave patterns shown in Figure 24.4 entails the supply of properly timed impulses so that the air column resonates with the applied impulses. Consider, for example, a train of compressional waves approaching from right to left the quarter-wavelength closed pipe in Figure 24.4b. A condensation that enters the pipe reflects as a condensation at the closed end and returns at the open end to reflect again as a rarefaction. If, at the instant that the rarefaction due to reflection starts down the tube, the rarefaction from the incoming train of waves just reaches the open end, the two rarefactions unite to produce a rarefaction of increased amplitude, and the air column resonates to its fundamental frequency. The incoming disturbances will be in step with the pulses due to reflections when the frequency of the incoming wave is equal to the natural frequency of the quarter-wave tube or when the wavelength is given by $\lambda = 4l_c$. This is the shortest possible resonant length, and the next length possible is one which permits an entering condensation to return, after reflection, to the open end of the pipe in time to unite with the incoming rarefaction which is three quarter-wavelengths removed from the incoming condensation. Under this condition, properly timed impulses again prevail and the length of the tube is given by $l_c = \frac{3}{4}\lambda$. Similarly, it is possible to obtain resonance when the tube length is an odd multiple of a quarter-wavelength. A resonant tube with a variable tube length is often employed in the laboratory to measure the wavelength of sound at a known frequency, as from a tuning fork or audio oscillator, and thereby to determine the speed of longitudinal sound waves in a gas. If the tube length is kept constant, as in Figure 24.4b, then when the wavelength of the incoming wave is varied the tube will resonate to the succession of frequencies shown in the figure. It is clear that the coincidence of the two systems of nodes due to reflections at the ends of the string shown in Figure 24.2 is again an illustration of resonance. Any resonant body or system in effect becomes a source of intense sound.

A significant way to describe resonance is from the viewpoint of a forced vibration. Whenever a vibrating source is coupled to a system which is capable of oscillating, the system is made to oscillate with the frequency of the vibrating source. The oscillations are called forced oscillations, and the degree to which the system responds depends upon the relation between the frequency of the source and the natural frequency of the system. The closer the frequency of the source to the natural frequency of the system, the greater the amplitude of the response by the system; when the frequency of the source is equal to the natural frequency of the system, resonance occurs, the source applies a greater amount of energy, and the oscillations of the system become quite vigorous.

There are many applications of the phenomenon of resonance in the fields of mechanics, musical instruments, electricity, light, nuclear physics, etc. A few are mentioned in the following.

To increase the amplitude of oscillation of a person on a swing it is necessary to supply properly timed impulses; either an external person supplies these impulses or the person on the swing pumps at the correct times. Tuning forks are effectively mounted on top of wooden resonant boxes closed at one end and open at the other; to produce resonance, the length of the box is made a quarter-wavelength of the sound emitted by the fork. To eliminate the possibility of introducing dangerously large amplitude vibrations in the members of a bridge structure, soldiers are instructed to break step when marching across the bridge. The tuning of a radio or video signal is accomplished by adjusting the natural frequency of the electrical receiving elements to equal or nearly equal the desired broadcast signal frequency. When light passes through certain dispersing media the absorption curve exhibits a resonant maximum, indicating, on the basis of a classical explanation, that the frequency of the oscillating electromagnetic field is equal to the frequency of oscillation of the electrons in the dispersing medium. In nuclear physics there are many examples of resonance: the resonance absorption of neutrons by elements such as uranium is significant in the design of nuclear reactors and in the phenomenon of fission (the splitting of a nucleus into two or more parts).

24.5. Pitch, Loudness, and Quality. Musical sounds may differ from one another in three distinct ways: in *pitch*, in *loudness*, and in *quality*. These are the three subjective characteristics of sound and we shall now discuss the corresponding three objective aspects.

Pitch has to do with the position of a sound in a musical scale. The judgment of an individual enters into its placement and it is therefore not possible to obtain an exact quantitative determination of any pitch. Usually, however, changes in the frequency of vibration correlate with changes in pitch, and the lower the frequency, for instance, the lower the pitch. Sometimes it is convenient to use the term "frequency" as synonymous with "pitch" but, although they are intimately related, they do not mean the same thing. It is a fact that the judgment of pitch is somewhat influenced by the loudness of the sound; in the case of pure sinusoidal sound waves in the low-frequency range, around 300 cycles/sec, the pitch appears to get lower as the loudness increases. It is also true that if a musical tone is composed of a group of components whose frequencies differ by a constant amount, such as 200, 300, or 400 cycles/sec, the ear may judge the pitch to be in the neighborhood of 100 cycles/sec. The ear, then, in effect creates a frequency which is not present in the objective stimulus, and this is known as a subjective tone. It may be explained by the fact that the diaphragm and other vibratile parts of the ear are nonlinear in their response to the sound waves that fall upon them. Hence there are passed on to the nerve impulses reaching the brain centers disturbances which are not exact replicas of the original sound waves. As the nonlinearity of the ear mechanism is a function of the loudness level of the sound in certain frequency ranges, overtones not originally present are introduced and difference tones produced by pairs of existing overtones subjectively give rise to a fundamental tone, as in the example cited.

Loudness has to do with the magnitude of an auditory sensation. Again, this being a subjective attribute of a sound wave, it is difficult to establish an exact quantitative measurement of it. Nevertheless it is desirable to establish a numerical scale of loudness. The physical quantity which is associated with loudness is intensity which, as we have seen, refers to the time rate of energy flow per unit area. Although there is this dependence of loudness upon intensity, a given percentage increase in intensity is not judged as the same increase in loudness. In fact, the relationship is not at all simple. Loudness depends also upon frequency, and the sensitivity of the ear is different in the various audiofrequency ranges. An approximate relationship known as the Weber-Fechner law states that the response of a sense organ is proportional to the logarithm of the magnitude of the stimulus. In accordance with this law as applied to sound we have

$$S = C \log I \qquad (24.6)$$

where S is the magnitude of the loudness sensation, C is a constant, log is the logarithm to base 10, and I is the intensity of the sound. I_0 is an arbitrary reference intensity, usually taken to be on the threshold of hearing, and S_0 is correspondingly the smallest sound that can be heard. Then

$$S_0 = C \log I_0 \qquad (24.7)$$

Letting $S - S_0 = \alpha$, where α is the *intensity level*, we have

$$\alpha = C \log \frac{I}{I_0} \qquad (24.8)$$

As stated above, this law is only approximate but gives a fair representation of the relation between loudness and intensity for pure tones. The use of the logarithmic scale is convenient, since the ear is sensitive over a large range of intensities. The intensity level α may be expressed in a unit called the *bel*, after Alexander Graham Bell, in which case $C = 1$. The bel is rather large and the more usual unit employed is the *decibel* (db), one tenth of a bel; hence α in decibels is

$$\alpha = 10 \log \frac{I}{I_0} \qquad (24.9)$$

The reference level I_0 is taken as 10^{-16} watt/cm² which is roughly the intensity of the threshold of audibility in the neighborhood of 1,000 cycles/sec. Thus, if $I = 10^{-16}$ watt/cm², its intensity level is zero. The ear can tolerate a maximum of about 10^{-4} watt/cm², known as the threshold of feeling, and this corresponds to an intensity level of $\alpha = 10 \log 10^{12} = 120$ db. By setting $\alpha = 1$ db in Equation 24.9, $I/I_0 = 1.26$ so that a 1 db rise in intensity level corresponds to a 26% increase in sound intensity.

It must be emphasized that Equation 24.9 will compare loudness levels of waves of the same type at differing intensities. When applied to waves of differing complexities it will not, in general, give correct loudness variations. For complex tones there is no simple relationship between loudness and intensity.

Quality is that characteristic of a particular sound that enables one to distinguish it from all other sounds of the same pitch and loudness. The French use the word *timbre* and the Germans the word *klang farbe* to mean what we call quality. Quality enables us to distinguish the sound of a violin from that of a clarinet or the sound of a piano from that of a trombone, even when the different instruments are producing the same note at the same intensity level. Sound waves are produced by bodies which vibrate. This vibration may be with a single frequency, such as the vibration of a tuning fork, but more generally the vibration contains many components and gives rise not to a simple sinusoidal wave but to a complex wave form. A complex wave form containing only a fundamental and its third harmonic, whose amplitude is half that of the fundamental, is shown in Figure 24.6 as the dashed curve. The complex wave is formed by the superposition principle described in Chapter 23, and its Fourier representation is given by $y = A \sin \omega t + (A/2) \sin 3\omega t$, where A is the amplitude of the fundamental. In the same way it is possible to produce a wave of any desired shape by combining simple waves in suitable proportions. Only waves with precisely the same shape contain the same number of simple waves with identical relative amplitude distributions. We have seen that when a string is bowed or a plate is struck or an air column is excited, and it is permitted to vibrate freely, it vibrates with a multitude of frequencies simultaneously. When a musical instrument is made to emit a note it usually emits a complex wave containing a fundamental and many harmonics. In general, different sound-producing instruments emit wave forms that are different by virtue of the fact that the vibrating elements oscillate in different complex ways. It was Helmholtz (1821–1894) who first made a thorough study of the quality of sound. He found that the *quality, or timbre, of a sound is determined by the number and relative intensities of the overtones that enter into its formation.*

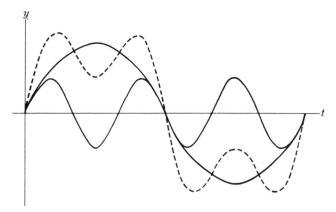

Figure 24.6.   *Complex wave form (dashed curve) formed by two simple waves.*

For example, when a cornet sounds the standard pitch $A = 440$ cycles/sec it contains the first five harmonics, with the third harmonic the strongest, the second harmonic about six tenths as strong, the first and fourth harmonics about four tenths as strong, and the fifth harmonic a little over one tenth as strong. A clarinet sounding the same frequency with the same intensity contains the first seven harmonics, with the third harmonic the strongest, the first harmonic about nine tenths as strong, the fifth harmonic about seven tenths as strong, the seventh harmonic about half as strong, the fourth and sixth harmonics about three tenths as strong, and the second harmonic about two tenths as strong. Both the number of harmonics present and their relative intensities are different and cause a different quality. It is also clear, from Figure 24.4, that an open and closed pipe sounding the same pitch with the same intensity have different qualities. The open pipe, containing both the even and the odd harmonics, is much richer in tonal quality.

24.6.   The Doppler Effect.   In our discussion of the subject of pitch and its relation to frequency we made no mention of the effect of the motion of a source of sound relative to the ear receiving the sound. The pitch of the sounding horn on an automobile appears higher when the automobile is approaching a stationary observer and appears lower when it is receding from the observer.   The same phenomenon occurs when the sound source is stationary and the observer is moving toward or away from the source. This apparent change in pitch as heard by an observer, when there is relative motion between source and observer, is known as the *Doppler effect*.   In obtaining an expression that shows the dependence of the observed pitch upon the speed of the source or observer we shall consider that the motion of the source or observer is along the line joining them and that the medium is at rest.   We shall employ the following notation:

$$f = \text{frequency of the source}$$
$$f' = \text{frequency of the sound as heard by the observer}$$
$$v = \text{speed of sound}$$
$$v_s = \text{speed of the source}$$
$$v_o = \text{speed of the observer}$$

Observer in Motion.   When an observer is moving *toward* a stationary source at a speed v_o, he receives each second more waves than when he is standing still.   During one second the observer moves a distance numerically equal to v_o.   If λ is the wavelength of the sound source, the number of additional waves received in one second is v_o/λ.   Since $\lambda = v/f$, the increase in the frequency is $f(v_o/v)$ and the pitch f' heard by the observer is

$$f' = f + f\left(\frac{v_o}{v}\right) = f\left(\frac{v + v_o}{v}\right) \tag{24.10}$$

If the observer is receding at speed v_o from the stationary source, the sign of v_o is negative and the apparent pitch is

$$f' = f\left(\frac{v - v_o}{v}\right) \tag{24.11}$$

In general, then, for an observer moving relative to a stationary source,

$$f' = f\left(\frac{v \pm v_o}{v}\right) \tag{24.12}$$

where the plus sign is to be used for the observer approaching the source and the minus sign for the observer receding from the source.

Source in Motion.   When the source is moving toward a stationary observer at a speed v_s there is an apparent decrease in wavelength because the source is moving in the direction in which the wave surfaces are approaching the observer.   This is illustrated in Figure 24.7 where O is the observer and the source is moving to the right with a speed v_s, covering the distances between the equally spaced points P_1, P_2, . . . , P_6 in one-second time intervals. The point source emits a spherical wave surface on which all vibrations are in phase, and the circles represent the positions of these surfaces which have originated from the source as it passed each point P.   Thus, when the source is at point P_6 the wave surface emitted one second earlier at P_5 has advanced the distance to surface 5 equal in radius to v_s drawn from the center P_5. The disturbance which was emitted at P_4 two seconds earlier is out a distance $2v_s$ from P_4, and so on to the outermost circle, which represents the position of the disturbance emitted five seconds earlier and which is out a distance

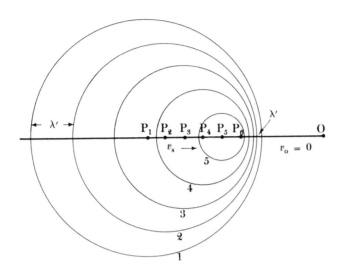

Figure 24.7.   *Doppler effect due to motion of a source relative to a stationary observer.*

$5v_s$ from P_1.   Since the period of the sound source is $(1/f)$ sec/cycle, during each cycle of vibration the source advances a distance v_s/f which is the amount by which the wavelength is shortened.   Therefore, the wavelength of the sound perceived by the observer is $\lambda' = v/f - v_s/f = (v - v_s)/f$ and the pitch as heard by the observer is

$$f' = \frac{v}{\lambda'} = f\left(\frac{v}{v - v_s}\right) \tag{24.13}$$

If the source is receding from the stationary observer at the speed v_s the sign of v_s is positive and

$$f' = f\left(\frac{v}{v + v_s}\right) \tag{24.14}$$

In general, for a source moving relative to a stationary observer,

$$f' = f\left(\frac{v}{v \mp v_s}\right) \tag{24.15}$$

where the minus sign is to be used for the source approaching the observer and the plus sign for the source receding from the observer.

When both source and observer are in motion the pitch as heard by the observer is given by

$$f' = f\frac{v \pm v_o}{v \mp v_s} \tag{24.16}$$

where the upper signs in numerator and denominator indicate motion of both toward each other and the lower signs indicate motion of both away from one another.

If the medium transmitting the sound waves is moving toward the observer with a speed v_m, then

$$f' = f \frac{v + v_m \pm v_o}{v + v_m \mp v_s} \qquad (24.17)$$

The Doppler effect has general application to all waves and is very significant in the study of light. Atoms emit light waves due to the transitions of the electrons associated with them and, when an atom is moving relative to a wavelength-measuring device, the measured wavelength of the radiation is subject to a Doppler shift. When light from a gas discharge tube is observed there are atoms moving at high speed toward and away from the observer and a spread in the frequencies or wavelengths is recorded, a fact known as *Doppler broadening*. As another example, it is found that the wavelengths of light emitted from elements on certain astronomical bodies such as stars are somewhat longer than those of the same elements on earth. Certain other astronomical bodies show the reverse. This means that some astronomical bodies are receding from the earth and others are approaching the earth. The student knows that radar waves are reflected from moving objects such as planes or automobiles. If the moving object is approaching the source of radar waves the frequency of the reflected waves is increased, and vice versa. Electromagnetic radiation detected from an earth satellite also undergoes a Doppler shift. In the field of nuclear physics, when a nucleus emits a gamma ray the total energy of production is shared by the gamma ray and the nucleus which recoils. There is thus a loss in energy of the gamma ray and this is interpretable as a Doppler effect due to the motion of the recoiling nucleus. Recently, Mössbauer discovered that in some tightly bound atoms in certain crystals the nuclei do not recoil, the crystal as a whole takes up the recoil momentum, and the gamma rays are emitted with a negligible Doppler shift. Significant research associated with the Mössbauer effect is at present being performed in the fields of nuclear physics, solid-state physics, gravitation, and relativity.

It is important to point out that the Doppler expressions here developed for sound do not apply to light. In sound the quantities v_o and v_s are measured relative to the medium which transmits the sound wave and determines its speed, and it makes a difference whether the source is at rest and the observer is moving or the observer is at rest and the source is moving, even though the relative separation speed of source and observer may be the same. Thus, when v_o in Equation 24.10 is set equal to v_s in Equation 24.13 the two expressions yield different values of f'. In the case of light or other electromagnetic radiation, a material medium for its transmission is not required and it makes no difference whether a source of light is moving with respect to a stationary observer or whether an observer is moving with respect to a stationary source: only the relative motion of source and observer leads to the correct Doppler expression. These facts are embodied in Einstein's theory of relativity. Equations 24.12 and 24.15 may be employed to give approximately the correct Doppler shift for light if the speed of the source or observer is small compared with the speed of light.

24.7. Supersonic Speeds and Shock Waves. Consider Figure 24.8, an extension of the diagram for the moving source in Figure 24.7. This shows the sound patterns around a moving source when the source is moving with the speed of sound and when the source is moving with a speed that exceeds that of sound. In each diagram the circles represent *wave fronts*, all points of whose surfaces vibrate in the same phase. For an assumed point source of sound these surfaces are spherical in an isotropic medium. In each diagram are shown the spherical wave fronts which have originated at the various positions P_1, P_2, . . . , P_5, corresponding to successive time intervals, of the source whose position is S at the instant depicted. The manner of diagramming the spherical wave surfaces is similar to that in Figure 24.7; for example, in the time it takes the source to traverse the distance P_1S, the wave emitted at P_1 has reached the outermost circle, marked 1.

First consider Figure 24.8a for a source moving with the speed of sound. Here the source is at all times coincident with the position of the wave front in the direction of motion and all the wave fronts superimpose at the source position, producing at S and its vicinity a vibrational energy of very high density. This is what constitutes the sonic barrier frequently encountered by high-speed aircraft, which experience a greatly increased resisting force at sonic speed. When an airplane traveling at sonic speed is not too far from the earth, the high-density vibrational energy arrives at the earth with the speed of sound before it is dissipated, and this energy is transferred to objects with great force.

Now consider Figure 24.8b for a source moving at supersonic speed. Here the source S is always ahead of the emitted sound and tangents to the wave fronts take the shape of a cone with the source at its apex, as shown. The high concentration of energy is now distributed along the lines of the V, forming what is termed a shock wave along the envelope to the wave fronts. No sound is heard from the source until the shock wave, thrown off from the sides, arrives on the earth at the speed of sound with a sudden crack. A familiar example of such a wave front is the bow wave of a ship moving through water. Another example, perhaps less familiar to the beginning student of physics, is the case of a fast-charged particle, such as an electron or proton, traveling through a transparent medium with a speed greater than the speed of light in the medium. Here an optical shock wave, known as *Čerenkov radiation*, is generated.

When a body such as an aircraft passes from a subsonic speed to a supersonic speed the drag resistance increases rather suddenly in the transonic region; this is characterized by the ratio of the speed of the body to the local

speed of sound. This ratio is called the Mach number in honor of Ernst
Mach (1838–1916) who performed basic experiments in this field. From
Figure 24.8b the reciprocal of the Mach number is given by

$$\sin \theta = \frac{P_1A}{P_1S} = \frac{v}{v_s}$$

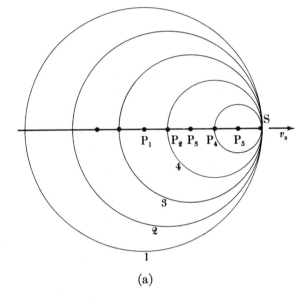

(a)

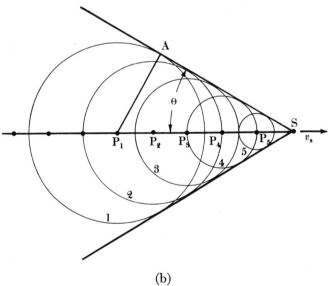

(b)

Figure 24.8. *Wave front from a source traveling: (a) at the
speed of sound, and (b) at a speed greater than sound.*

where P_1A is the distance from the center P_1 of the spherical wave front 1 to the tangent point A, P_1S is the distance from P_1 to the source S, v_s is the speed of the source, and v is the speed of sound. The figure is drawn for a Mach number of 2. When v_s becomes comparable to v the Doppler expressions obtained in the previous section do not hold and require modification.

Problems

24.1. Compute the per cent error incurred when Equation 24.3a rather than Equation 24.1 is employed to obtain the speed of sound in a gas at 30.0°C.

24.2. The A string of a violin, 31.8 cm long, has a mass of 0.230 gm. If it is tuned to its fundamental of 440 vibrations/sec, what is its tension?

24.3. A string is 1.15 feet long and has a mass of 8.25×10^{-4} pounds mass. It is under a tension of 15.0 pounds force. Compute the frequency of vibration of its first overtone.

24.4. One end of a horizontal stretched string is attached to a rigid support and the other end is fastened to the prong of a tuning fork which is vibrating 60.0 times a second at right angles to the string. When the tension is 500 gf the string vibrates in one segment. (**a**) For what tension will the string vibrate in five segments? (**b**) If the string is fastened to the prong so that the vibrations are parallel to the string direction, what must the tension be for the string to vibrate in one segment?

24.5. By what per cent must the tension be increased to raise the pitch of a violin string that is flat by 5%?

24.6. From the equation $y = A \sin (\omega x/v + \alpha)$ for the displacement y at any point along a string, where ω is the angular velocity, v is the wave velocity, and α is a constant, obtain Equation 24.4, giving the standing-wave frequencies $f_n = nv/2l$ for a stretched string of length l fastened at the ends.

24.7. A vertical glass tube open at the top and equipped with a constriction valve at the bottom is filled with water. When a tuning fork vibrating at 264 vib/sec is held above the tube and the water is permitted to flow slowly out through the valve, the first resonance in the air column occurs when the level of the water is 31.5 cm from the top, and the next resonance occurs 96.3 cm from the top. Find (**a**) the speed of sound in the air column and (**b**) the end correction.

24.8. The third harmonic of an open organ pipe has the same frequency as the fifth harmonic of a closed pipe 2.50 feet in length. What is the length of the open pipe?

24.9. An organ pipe has a pitch of 440 vibrations/sec at 68.0°F. What pitch will it have when the temperature is raised to 88.0°F?

24.10. The apparatus displayed in Figure 24.9 is employed for measuring the speed of sound in a gas or in a metal rod by the Kundt method. A metal rod of length l is clamped at its center as shown, one end of which terminates in a piston P_1 which is free to vibrate longitudinally in a glass cylindrical rod G. An adjustable plunger P_2 is at the other end of the resonant tube. When longitudinal vibrations are set up in the rod by its being stroked with a rosined

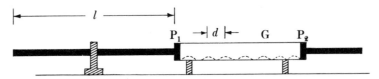

Figure 24.9. *Problem 24.10.*

cloth and the air column is adjusted in length by P_2 until resonance occurs, the standing-wave nodes and loops are detected by lycopodium powder or cork dust which has previously been spread over the interior of the tube. At resonance the powder becomes visibly agitated and its particles line up in detectable node and loop patterns. If the rod is 95.6 cm long and the measured average distance d between displacement loops in the dust pattern is 6.75 cm, what are (a) the speed of sound in the rod and (b) the frequency of vibration of the rod? The gas in the tube is air, at 25.5°C.

24.11. If the rod in Problem 24.10 is clamped at one-fourth the distance from the piston end and P_2 is adjusted for resonance, what is the distance between the heaps of powder in the tube?

24.12. Two closed organ pipes, vibrating in their fundamental mode, produce 36.0 beats in 30.0 sec. Neglecting the end correction, find the length of the longer pipe when that of the shorter is 2.50 feet. The temperature is 68.0°F.

24.13. A tuning fork with a frequency of 512 vibrations/sec is mounted on a wooden box, to increase the loudness. This resonant box is closed at one end only. If the end correction amounts to 1.00% of the wavelength of sound, how long should the box be for greatest effectiveness? Make the computation for 68.0°F.

24.14. Using the superposition principle, plot the resultant of the following component in-phase wave forms: (a) two sine waves with frequencies in the ratio 1:3 and amplitudes in the ratio $1:\frac{1}{3}$, (b) three sine waves with frequencies in the ratios 1:3:5 and amplitudes in the ratios $1:\frac{1}{3}:\frac{1}{5}$, and (c) four sine waves with frequencies in the ratios 1:3:5:7 and amplitudes in the ratios $1:\frac{1}{3}:\frac{1}{5}:\frac{1}{7}$. Note the approach to the representation of a square wave. Write the equation for the Fourier series representation of a square wave.

24.15. Plot the resultant wave form represented by the equation $y = \sin \omega t - \frac{1}{2} \sin 2\omega t + \frac{1}{3} \sin 3\omega t - \frac{1}{4} \sin 4\omega t$. If the series with positive odd harmonics and negative even harmonics is continued indefinitely, what wave does this Fourier series represent?

24.16. Two sound waves have intensity levels of 20.00 db and 40.00 db. When sounded together what are (**a**) the resultant sound intensity and (**b**) the corresponding intensity level? The reference intensity is 10^{-6} μwatt/m².

24.17. Find the pressure amplitude of the faintest sound that can be heard in air at 20.0°C and 76.0 cm Hg. The intensity I of a sound wave is related to the pressure amplitude p by the expression $I = p^2/2\rho v$ where ρ is the density of the air and v is the speed of the sound wave. Take 10^{-16} watt/cm² as the threshold of audibility.

24.18. Using Equation 23.9 find the amplitude of vibration of the particles of air transmitting ordinary conversation, which has an intensity level of about 60.0 db. The temperature and pressure of the air are 20.0°C and 76.0 cm Hg. Make the computation for 300 vibrations/sec.

24.19. The intensity level at a point from a steadily sounding point source of sound is 50.0 db. (**a**) What is the sound intensity at a point 2.50 times as far from the source? (**b**) What is the change in intensity level at this point?

24.20. The horn on an automobile moving at 60.0 miles/hour sounds steadily at 200 vibrations/sec. As the automobile passes close to a stationary observer, what is the apparent frequency he hears as the automobile (**a**) approaches and (**b**) recedes from him? Neglect the motion of the air and take the speed of sound as 1,100 feet/sec.

24.21. Do Problem 24.20 for the observer in motion and the source stationary.

24.22. A source of sound moving at 100 feet/sec and emitting a tone of 500 vibrations/sec is approaching an observer who is moving in the same direction at 60.0 feet/sec. What is the pitch of the source as heard by the observer? Take the speed of sound as 1,100 feet/sec and consider the air still.

24.23. Two identical sources, each emitting a sound of the same frequency, are stationed some distance apart. When an observer, between the two, moves toward one of the sources with a speed of 5.00 feet/sec, he hears 6.00 beats/sec. What is the frequency of the sources? Take the speed of sound as 1,100 feet/sec and consider the air still.

24.24. A source of sound and an observer are moving in opposite directions and separating, the source at 60.0 miles/hour and the observer at 30.0 miles/hour. A wind is blowing at 21.0 miles/hour in the direction of motion of the source. If the speed of sound in still air is 1,100 feet/sec and the sound emitted by the source is 400 vibrations/sec, what is the frequency as heard by the observer?

24.25. Show that if the speed of the observer and the speed of the source have the same value u, then Equation 24.15 becomes practically identical with Equation 24.12 for $u \ll v$.

24.26. A bullet traveling through the air forms a shock wave, the wave front being a cone of apex angle 67.0°. Taking the speed of sound as 1,100 feet/sec, find the speed of the bullet.

Appendix

Table A.1. *Significant physical constants.*

The values listed are based on the isotope $^{12}_6$C which is assigned the exact value 12 amu. The values based on $^{12}_6$C are 0.0318 per cent lower than the values based on $^{16}_8$O = 16 amu.

Name	Symbol used in text	Value
Speed of light	c	2.998×10^8 m/sec
Gravitational constant	G	6.673×10^{-11} nt$\cdot$m^2/kgm^2
Universal gas constant	R	8.314 joules/mole$\cdot$K$^\circ$
Boltzmann's constant	k	1.380×10^{-23} joule/K$^\circ$
Stefan-Boltzmann constant	σ	5.670×10^{-8} joule/m$^2\cdot$sec$\cdot^\circ$K^4
Avogadro's number	N_0	6.023×10^{23}/mole
Faraday constant	F	9.649×10^4 coul/mole
Planck's constant	h	6.625×10^{-34} joule$\cdot$sec
Rydberg constant for hydrogen	R_H	1.097×10^7/m
Mechanical equivalent of heat	J	4.185 joules/cal
Permittivity constant	ϵ_0	8.854×10^{-12} farad/m
Permeability constant	μ_0	1.257×10^{-6} henry/m
Atomic mass unit (1/12 mass of $^{12}_6$C)	amu	1.660×10^{-27} kgm
Energy equivalent of 1 amu		931.4 Mev
Electronic charge	e	1.602×10^{-19} coul
Electron rest mass	m_0	$\begin{cases} 9.108 \times 10^{-31} \text{ kgm} \\ 5.486 \times 10^{-4} \text{ amu} \end{cases}$
Energy equivalent of electron rest mass	m_0c^2	0.511 Mev
Proton rest mass	m_p	$\begin{cases} 1.672 \times 10^{-27} \text{ kgm} \\ 1.00728 \text{ amu} \end{cases}$
Neutron rest mass	m_n	$\begin{cases} 1.675 \times 10^{-27} \text{ kgm} \\ 1.00866 \text{ amu} \end{cases}$

Table A.2. *Atomic weights of the elements.*

The values listed are based on $^{12}_{6}C = 12$ amu (see notation in Table A.1 and Section 27.1). A value in parentheses is the mass number of the most stable (long-lived) of the known isotopes. To locate an element by its atomic number refer to Table A.3.

Element	Symbol	Atomic number Z	Average atomic weight	Element	Symbol	Atomic number Z	Average atomic weight
Actinium	Ac	89	(227)	Mercury	Hg	80	200.59
Aluminum	Al	13	26.98	Molybdenum	Mo	42	95.94
Americium	Am	95	(243)	Neodymium	Nd	60	144.24
Antimony	Sb	51	121.75	Neon	Ne	10	20.183
Argon	A	18	39.948	Neptunium	Np	93	(237)
Arsenic	As	33	74.92	Nickel	Ni	28	58.71
Astatine	At	85	(210)	Niobium	Nb	41	92.91
Barium	Ba	56	137.34	Nitrogen	N	7	14.007
Berkelium	Bk	97	(247)	Nobelium	No	102	(253)
Beryllium	Be	4	9.012	Osmium	Os	76	190.2
Bismuth	Bi	83	208.98	Oxygen	O	8	15.9994
Boron	B	5	10.81	Palladium	Pd	46	106.4
Bromine	Br	35	79.909	Phosphorus	P	15	30.974
Cadmium	Cd	48	112.40	Platinum	Pt	78	195.09
Calcium	Ca	20	40.08	Plutonium	Pu	94	(242)
Californium	Cf	98	(251)	Polonium	Po	84	(210)
Carbon	C	6	12.011	Potassium	K	19	39.102
Cerium	Ce	58	140.12	Praseodymium	Pr	59	140.91
Cesium	Cs	55	132.905	Promethium	Pm	61	(147)
Chlorine	Cl	17	35.453	Protactinium	Pa	91	(231)
Chromium	Cr	24	52.00	Radium	Ra	88	(226)
Cobalt	Co	27	58.93	Rhenium	Re	75	186.2
Copper	Cu	29	63.54	Rhodium	Rh	45	102.905
Curium	Cm	96	(247)	Rubidium	Rb	37	85.47
Dysprosium	Dy	66	162.50	Ruthenium	Ru	44	101.1
Einsteinium	E	99	(254)	Samarium	Sm	62	150.35
Emanation	Em	86	(222)	Scandium	Sc	21	44.96
Erbium	Er	68	167.26	Selenium	Se	34	78.96
Europium	Eu	63	152.0	Silicon	Si	14	28.09
Fermium	Fm	100	(253)	Silver	Ag	47	107.870
Fluorine	F	9	19.00	Sodium	Na	11	22.990
Francium	Fr	87	(223)	Strontium	Sr	38	87.62
Gadolinium	Gd	64	157.25	Sulfur	S	16	32.064
Gallium	Ga	31	69.72	Tantalum	Ta	73	180.95
Germanium	Ge	32	72.59	Technetium	Tc	43	(97)
Gold	Au	79	196.97	Tellurium	Te	52	127.60
Hafnium	Hf	72	178.49	Terbium	Tb	65	158.92
Helium	He	2	4.003	Thallium	Tl	81	204.37
Holmium	Ho	67	164.93	Thorium	Th	90	232.04
Hydrogen	H	1	1.00797	Thulium	Tm	69	168.93
Indium	In	49	114.82	Tin	Sn	50	118.69
Iodine	I	53	126.90	Titanium	Ti	22	47.90
Iridium	Ir	77	192.2	Tungsten	W	74	183.85
Iron	Fe	26	55.85	Uranium	U	92	238.03
Krypton	Kr	36	83.80	Vanadium	V	23	50.94
Lanthanum	La	57	138.91	Xenon	Xe	54	131.30
Lawrencium	Lw	103	(257)	Ytterbium	Yb	70	173.04
Lead	Pb	82	207.19	Yttrium	Y	39	88.905
Lithium	Li	3	6.939	Zinc	Zn	30	65.37
Lutetium	Lu	71	174.97	Zirconium	Zr	40	91.22
Magnesium	Mg	12	24.31				
Manganese	Mn	25	54.94				
Mendeleevium	Mv	101	(256)				

Table A.3. *Periodic table of the elements.*

The table may be used to locate an element by its atomic number, indicated above each symbol.

Period	I	II	III	IV	V	VI	VII	VIII	0
1	1 H								2 He
2	3 Li	4 Be	5 B	6 C	7 N	8 O	9 F		10 Ne
3	11 Na	12 Mg	13 Al	14 Si	15 P	16 S	17 Cl		18 A
4	19 K	20 Ca	21 Sc	22 Ti	23 V	24 Cr	25 Mn	26 Fe 27 Co 28 Ni	
4	29 Cu	30 Zn	31 Ga	32 Ge	33 As	34 Se	35 Br		36 Kr
5	37 Rb	38 Sr	39 Y	40 Zr	41 Nb	42 Mo	43 Te	44 Ru 45 Rh 46 Pd	
5	47 Ag	48 Cd	49 In	50 Sn	51 Sb	52 Te	53 I		54 Xe
6	55 Cs	56 Ba	57–71 Lanthanide series*	72 Hf	73 Ta	74 W	75 Re	76 Os 77 Ir 78 Pt	
6	79 Au	80 Hg	81 Ti	82 Pb	83 Bi	84 Po	85 At		86 Em
7	87 Fr	88 Ra	89–103 Actinide series†						

*Lanthanide, or rare earth, series

57 La	58 Ce	59 Pr	60 Nd	61 Pm	62 Sm	63 Eu	64 Gd
65 Tb	66 Dy	67 Ho	68 Er	69 Tm	70 Yb	71 Lu	

† Actinide series

89 Ac	90 Th	91 Pa	92 U	93 Np	94 Pu	95 Am	96 Cm
97 Bk	98 Cf	99 E	100 Fm	101 Md	102 No	103 Lw	

Table A.4. *Natural sines and cosines.*

	.0	.1	.2	.3	.4	.5	.6	.7	.8	.9	
0°	.0000	.0017	.0035	.0052	.0070	.0087	.0105	.0122	.0140	.0157	.0175	89°
1°	.0175	.0192	.0209	.0227	.0244	.0262	.0279	.0297	.0314	.0332	.0349	88°
2°	.0349	.0366	.0384	.0401	.0419	.0436	.0454	.0471	.0488	.0506	.0523	87°
3°	.0523	.0541	.0558	.0576	.0593	.0610	.0628	.0645	.0663	.0680	.0698	86°
4°	.0698	.0715	.0732	.0750	.0767	.0785	.0802	.0819	.0837	.0854	.0872	85°
5°	.0872	.0889	.0906	.0924	.0941	.0958	.0976	.0993	.1011	.1028	.1045	84°
6°	.1045	.1063	.1080	.1097	.1115	.1132	.1149	.1167	.1184	.1201	.1219	83°
7°	.1219	.1236	.1253	.1271	.1288	.1305	.1323	.1340	.1357	.1374	.1392	82°
8°	.1392	.1409	.1426	.1444	.1461	.1478	.1495	.1513	.1530	.1547	.1564	81°
9°	.1564	.1582	.1599	.1616	.1633	.1650	.1668	.1685	.1702	.1719	.1736	80°
10°	.1736	.1754	.1771	.1788	.1805	.1822	.1840	.1857	.1874	.1891	.1908	79°
11°	.1908	.1925	.1942	.1959	.1977	.1994	.2011	.2028	.2045	.2062	.2079	78°
12°	.2079	.2096	.2113	.2130	.2147	.2164	.2181	.2198	.2215	.2233	.2250	77°
13°	.2250	.2267	.2284	.2300	.2317	.2334	.2351	.2368	.2385	.2402	.2419	76°
14°	.2419	.2436	.2453	.2470	.2487	.2504	.2521	.2538	.2554	.2571	.2588	75°
15°	.2588	.2605	.2622	.2639	.2656	.2672	.2689	.2706	.2723	.2740	.2756	74°
16°	.2756	.2773	.2790	.2807	.2823	.2840	.2857	.2874	.2890	.2907	.2924	73°
17°	.2924	.2940	.2957	.2974	.2990	.3007	.3024	.3040	.3057	.3074	.3090	72°
18°	.3090	.3107	.3123	.3140	.3156	.3173	.3190	.3206	.3223	.3239	.3256	71°
19°	.3256	.3272	.3289	.3305	.3322	.3338	.3355	.3371	.3387	.3404	.3420	70°
20°	.3420	.3437	.3453	.3469	.3486	.3502	.3518	.3535	.3551	.3567	.3584	69°
21°	.3584	.3600	.3616	.3633	.3649	.3665	.3681	.3697	.3714	.3730	.3746	68°
22°	.3746	.3762	.3778	.3795	.3811	.3827	.3843	.3859	.3875	.3891	.3907	67°
23°	.3907	.3923	.3939	.3955	.3971	.3987	.4003	.4019	.4035	.4051	.4067	66°
24°	.4067	.4083	.4099	.4115	.4131	.4147	.4163	.4179	.4195	.4210	.4226	65°
25°	.4226	.4242	.4258	.4274	.4289	.4305	.4321	.4337	.4352	.4368	.4384	64°
26°	.4384	.4399	.4415	.4431	.4446	.4462	.4478	.4493	.4509	.4524	.4540	63°
27°	.4540	.4555	.4571	.4586	.4602	.4617	.4633	.4648	.4664	.4679	.4695	62°
28°	.4695	.4710	.4726	.4741	.4756	.4772	.4787	.4802	.4818	.4833	.4848	61°
29°	.4848	.4863	.4879	.4894	.4909	.4924	.4939	.4955	.4970	.4985	.5000	60°
30°	.5000	.5015	.5030	.5045	.5060	.5075	.5090	.5105	.5120	.5135	.5150	59°
31°	.5150	.5165	.5180	.5195	.5210	.5225	.5240	.5255	.5270	.5284	.5299	58°
32°	.5299	.5314	.5329	.5344	.5358	.5373	.5388	.5402	.5417	.5432	.5446	57°
33°	.5446	.5461	.5476	.5490	.5505	.5519	.5534	.5548	.5563	.5577	.5592	56°
34°	.5592	.5606	.5621	.5635	.5650	.5664	.5678	.5693	.5707	.5721	.5736	55°
35°	.5736	.5750	.5764	.5779	.5793	.5807	.5821	.5835	.5850	.5864	.5878	54°
36°	.5878	.5892	.5906	.5920	.5934	.5948	.5962	.5976	.5990	.6004	.6018	53°
37°	.6018	.6032	.6046	.6060	.6074	.6088	.6101	.6115	.6129	.6143	.6157	52°
38°	.6157	.6170	.6184	.6198	.6211	.6225	.6239	.6252	.6266	.6280	.6293	51°
39°	.6293	.6307	.6320	.6334	.6347	.6361	.6374	.6388	.6401	.6414	.6428	50°
40°	.6428	.6441	.6455	.6468	.6481	.6494	.6508	.6521	.6534	.6547	.6561	49°
41°	.6561	.6574	.6587	.6600	.6613	.6626	.6639	.6652	.6665	.6678	.6691	48°
42°	.6691	.6704	.6717	.6730	.6743	.6756	.6769	.6782	.6794	.6807	.6820	47°
43°	.6820	.6833	.6845	.6858	.6871	.6884	.6896	.6909	.6921	.6934	.6947	46°
44°	.6947	.6959	.6972	.6984	.6997	.7009	.7022	.7034	.7046	.7059	.7071	45°

	.9	.8	.7	.6	.5	.4	.3	.2	.1	.0	

Table A.4. *(Continued)*

Sines (read down)   Cosines (read up)

	.0	.1	.2	.3	.4	.5	.6	.7	.8	.9	
45°	.7071	.7083	.7096	.7108	.7120	.7133	.7145	.7157	.7169	.7181	.7193	44°
46°	.7193	.7206	.7218	.7230	.7242	.7254	.7266	.7278	.7290	.7302	.7314	43°
47°	.7314	.7325	.7337	.7349	.7361	.7373	.7385	.7396	.7408	.7420	.7431	42°
48°	.7431	.7443	.7455	.7466	.7478	.7490	.7501	.7513	.7524	.7536	.7547	41°
49°	.7547	.7559	.7570	.7581	.7593	.7604	.7615	.7627	.7638	.7649	.7660	40°
50°	.7660	.7672	.7683	.7694	.7705	.7716	.7727	.7738	.7749	.7760	.7771	**39°**
51°	.7771	.7782	.7793	.7804	.7815	.7826	.7837	.7848	.7859	.7869	.7880	38°
52°	.7880	.7891	.7902	.7912	.7923	.7934	.7944	.7955	.7965	.7976	.7986	37°
53°	.7986	.7997	.8007	.8018	.8028	.8039	.8049	.8059	.8070	.8080	.8090	36°
54°	.8090	.8100	.8111	.8121	.8131	.8141	.8151	.8161	.8171	.8181	.8192	35°
55°	.8192	.8202	.8211	.8221	.8231	.8241	.8251	.8261	.8271	.8281	.8290	**34°**
56°	.8290	.8300	.8310	.8320	.8329	.8339	.8348	.8358	.8368	.8377	.8387	33°
57°	.8387	.8396	.8406	.8415	.8425	.8434	.8443	.8453	.8462	.8471	.8480	32°
58°	.8480	.8490	.8499	.8508	.8517	.8526	.8536	.8545	.8554	.8563	.8572	31°
59°	.8572	.8581	.8590	.8599	.8607	.8616	.8625	.8634	.8643	.8652	.8660	30°
60°	.8660	.8669	.8678	.8686	.8695	.8704	.8712	.8721	.8729	.8738	.8746	**29°**
61°	.8746	.8755	.8763	.8771	.8780	.8788	.8796	.8805	.8813	.8821	.8829	28°
62°	.8829	.8838	.8846	.8854	.8862	.8870	.8878	.8886	.8894	.8902	.8910	27°
63°	.8910	.8918	.8926	.8934	.8942	.8949	.8957	.8965	.8973	.8980	.8988	26°
64°	.8988	.8996	.9003	.9011	.9018	.9026	.9033	.9041	.9048	.9056	.9063	25°
65°	.9063	.9070	.9078	.9085	.9092	.9100	.9107	.9114	.9121	.9128	.9135	**24°**
66°	.9135	.9143	.9150	.9157	.9164	.9171	.9178	.9184	.9191	.9198	.9205	23°
67°	.9205	.9212	.9219	.9225	.9232	.9239	.9245	.9252	.9259	.9265	.9272	22°
68°	.9272	.9278	.9285	.9291	.9298	.9304	.9311	.9317	.9323	.9330	.9336	21°
69°	.9336	.9342	.9348	.9354	.9361	.9367	.9373	.9379	.9385	.9391	.9397	20°
70°	.9397	.9403	.9409	.9415	.9421	.9426	.9432	.9438	.9444	.9449	.9455	**19°**
71°	.9455	.9461	.9466	.9472	.9478	.9483	.9489	.9494	.9500	.9505	.9511	18°
72°	.9511	.9516	.9521	.9527	.9532	.9537	.9542	.9548	.9553	.9558	.9563	17°
73°	.9563	.9568	.9573	.9578	.9583	.9588	.9593	.9598	.9603	.9608	.9613	16°
74°	.9613	.9617	.9622	.9627	.9632	.9636	.9641	.9646	.9650	.9655	.9659	15°
75°	.9659	.9664	.9668	.9673	.9677	.9681	.9686	.9690	.9694	.9699	.9703	**14°**
76°	.9703	.9707	.9711	.9715	.9720	.9724	.9728	.9732	.9736	.9740	.9744	13°
77°	.9744	.9748	.9751	.9755	.9759	.9763	.9767	.9770	.9774	.9778	.9781	12°
78°	.9781	.9785	.9789	.9792	.9796	.9799	.9803	.9806	.9810	.9813	.9816	11°
79°	.9816	.9820	.9823	.9826	.9829	.9833	.9836	.9839	.9842	.9845	.9848	10°
80°	.9848	.9851	.9854	.9857	.9860	.9863	.9866	.9869	.9871	.9874	.9877	**9°**
81°	.9877	.9880	.9882	.9885	.9888	.9890	.9893	.9895	.9898	.9900	.9903	8°
82°	.9903	.9905	.9907	.9910	.9912	.9914	.9917	.9919	.9921	.9923	.9925	7°
83°	.9925	.9928	.9930	.9932	.9934	.9936	.9938	.9940	.9942	.9943	.9945	6°
84°	.9945	.9947	.9949	.9951	.9952	.9954	.9956	.9957	.9959	.9960	.9962	5°
85°	.9962	.9963	.9965	.9966	.9968	.9969	.9971	.9972	.9973	.9974	.9976	**4°**
86°	.9976	.9977	.9978	.9979	.9980	.9981	.9982	.9983	.9984	.9985	.9986	3°
87°	.9986	.9987	.9988	.9989	.9990	.9990	.9991	.9992	.9993	.9993	.9994	2°
88°	.9994	.9995	.9995	.9996	.9996	.9997	.9997	.9997	.9998	.9998	.9998	1°
89°	.9998	.9999	.9999	.9999	.9999	1.0000	1.0000	1.0000	1.0000	1.0000	1.0000	0°

| | .9 | .8 | .7 | .6 | .5 | .4 | .3 | .2 | .1 | .0 | |

Table A.5. *Natural tangents and cotangents.*

Tangents (read down)   Cotangents (read up)

	.0	.1	.2	.3	.4	.5	.6	.7	.8	.9	
0°	.0000	.0017	.0035	.0052	.0070	.0087	.0105	.0122	.0140	.0157	.0175	89°
1°	.0175	.0192	.0209	.0227	.0244	.0262	.0279	.0297	.0314	.0332	.0349	88°
2°	.0349	.0367	.0384	.0402	.0419	.0437	.0454	.0472	.0489	.0507	.0524	87°
3°	.0524	.0542	.0559	.0577	.0594	.0612	.0629	.0647	.0664	.0682	.0699	86°
4°	.0699	.0717	.0734	.0752	.0769	.0787	.0805	.0822	.0840	.0857	.0875	85°
5°	.0875	.0892	.0910	.0928	.0945	.0963	.0981	.0998	.1016	.1033	.1051	84°
6°	.1051	.1069	.1086	.1104	.1122	.1139	.1157	.1175	.1192	.1210	.1228	83°
7°	.1228	.1246	.1263	.1281	.1299	.1317	.1334	.1352	.1370	.1388	.1405	82°
8°	.1405	.1423	.1441	.1459	.1477	.1495	.1512	.1530	.1548	.1566	.1584	81°
9°	.1584	.1602	.1620	.1638	.1655	.1673	.1691	.1709	.1727	.1745	.1763	80°
10°	.1763	.1781	.1799	.1817	.1835	.1853	.1871	.1890	.1908	.1926	.1944	79°
11°	.1944	.1962	.1980	.1998	.2016	.2035	.2053	.2071	.2089	.2107	.2126	78°
12°	.2126	.2144	.2162	.2180	.2199	.2217	.2235	.2254	.2272	.2290	.2309	77°
13°	.2309	.2327	.2345	.2364	.2382	.2401	.2419	.2438	.2456	.2475	.2493	76°
14°	.2493	.2512	.2530	.2549	.2568	.2586	.2605	.2623	.2642	.2661	.2679	75°
15°	.2679	.2698	.2717	.2736	.2754	.2773	.2792	.2811	.2830	.2849	.2867	74°
16°	.2867	.2886	.2905	.2924	.2943	.2962	.2981	.3000	.3019	.3038	.3057	73°
17°	.3057	.3076	.3096	.3115	.3134	.3153	.3172	.3191	.3211	.3230	.3249	72°
18°	.3249	.3269	.3288	.3307	.3327	.3346	.3365	.3385	.3404	.3424	.3443	71°
19°	.3443	.3463	.3482	.3502	.3522	.3541	.3561	.3581	.3600	.3620	.3640	70°
20°	.3640	.3659	.3679	.3699	.3719	.3739	.3759	.3779	.3799	.3819	.3839	69°
21°	.3839	.3859	.3879	.3899	.3919	.3939	.3959	.3979	.4000	.4020	.4040	68°
22°	.4040	.4061	.4081	.4101	.4122	.4142	.4163	.4183	.4204	.4224	.4245	67°
23°	.4245	.4265	.4286	.4307	.4327	.4348	.4369	.4390	.4411	.4431	.4452	66°
24°	.4452	.4473	.4494	.4515	.4536	.4557	.4578	.4599	.4621	.4642	.4663	65°
25°	.4663	.4684	.4706	.4727	.4748	.4770	.4791	.4813	.4834	.4856	.4877	64°
26°	.4877	.4899	.4921	.4942	.4964	.4986	.5008	.5029	.5051	.5073	.5095	63°
27°	.5095	.5117	.5139	.5161	.5184	.5206	.5228	.5250	.5272	.5295	.5317	62°
28°	.5317	.5340	.5362	.5384	.5407	.5430	.5452	.5475	.5498	.5520	.5543	61°
29°	.5543	.5566	.5589	.5612	.5635	.5658	.5681	.5704	.5727	.5750	.5774	60°
30°	.5774	.5797	.5820	.5844	.5867	.5890	.5914	.5938	.5961	.5985	.6009	59°
31°	.6009	.6032	.6056	.6080	.6104	.6128	.6152	.6176	.6200	.6224	.6249	58°
32°	.6249	.6273	.6297	.6322	.6346	.6371	.6395	.6420	.6445	.6469	.6494	57°
33°	.6494	.6519	.6544	.6569	.6594	.6619	.6644	.6669	.6694	.6720	.6745	56°
34°	.6745	.6771	.6796	.6822	.6847	.6873	.6899	.6924	.6950	.6976	.7002	55°
35°	.7002	.7028	.7054	.7080	.7107	.7133	.7159	.7186	.7212	.7239	.7265	54°
36°	.7265	.7292	.7319	.7346	.7373	.7400	.7427	.7454	.7481	.7508	.7536	53°
37°	.7536	.7563	.7590	.7618	.7646	.7673	.7701	.7729	.7757	.7785	.7813	52°
38°	.7813	.7841	.7869	.7898	.7926	.7954	.7983	.8012	.8040	.8069	.8098	51°
39°	.8098	.8127	.8156	.8185	.8214	.8243	.8273	.8302	.8332	.8361	.8391	50°
40°	.8391	.8421	.8451	.8481	.8511	.8541	.8571	.8601	.8632	.8662	.8693	49°
41°	.8693	.8724	.8754	.8785	.8816	.8847	.8878	.8910	.8941	.8972	.9004	48°
42°	.9004	.9036	.9067	.9099	.9131	.9163	.9195	.9228	.9260	.9293	.9325	47°
43°	.9325	.9358	.9391	.9424	.9457	.9490	.9523	.9556	.9590	.9623	.9657	46°
44°	.9657	.9691	.9725	.9759	.9793	.9827	.9861	.9896	.9930	.9965	1.000	45°
	.9	.8	.7	.6	.5	.4	.3	.2	.1	.0		

Table A.5. (Continued)

Tangents (read down)   Cotangents (read up)

	.0	.1	.2	.3	.4	.5	.6	.7	.8	.9	
45°	1.000	1.003	1.007	1.011	1.014	1.018	1.021	1.025	1.028	1.032	1.036	44°
46°	1.036	1.039	1.043	1.046	1.050	1.054	1.057	1.061	1.065	1.069	1.072	43°
47°	1.072	1.076	1.080	1.084	1.087	1.091	1.095	1.099	1.103	1.107	1.111	42°
48°	1.111	1.115	1.118	1.122	1.126	1.130	1.134	1.138	1.142	1.146	1.150	41°
49°	1.150	1.154	1.159	1.163	1.167	1.171	1.175	1.179	1.183	1.188	1.192	40°
50°	1.192	1.196	1.200	1.205	1.209	1.213	1.217	1.222	1.226	1.230	1.235	39°
51°	1.235	1.239	1.244	1.248	1.253	1.257	1.262	1.266	1.271	1.275	1.280	38°
52°	1.280	1.285	1.289	1.294	1.299	1.303	1.308	1.313	1.317	1.322	1.327	37°
53°	1.327	1.332	1.337	1.342	1.347	1.351	1.356	1.361	1.366	1.371	1.376	36°
54°	1.376	1.381	1.387	1.392	1.397	1.402	1.407	1.412	1.418	1.423	1.428	35°
55°	1.428	1.433	1.439	1.444	1.450	1.455	1.460	1.466	1.471	1.477	1.483	34°
56°	1.483	1.488	1.494	1.499	1.505	1.511	1.517	1.522	1.528	1.534	1.540	33°
57°	1.540	1.546	1.552	1.558	1.564	1.570	1.576	1.582	1.588	1.594	1.600	32°
58°	1.600	1.607	1.613	1.619	1.625	1.632	1.638	1.645	1.651	1.658	1.664	31°
59°	1.664	1.671	1.678	1.684	1.691	1.698	1.704	1.711	1.718	1.725	1.732	30°
60°	1.732	1.739	1.746	1.753	1.760	1.767	1.775	1.782	1.789	1.797	1.804	29°
61°	1.804	1.811	1.819	1.827	1.834	1.842	1.849	1.857	1.865	1.873	1.881	28°
62°	1.881	1.889	1.897	1.905	1.913	1.921	1.929	1.937	1.946	1.954	1.963	27°
63°	1.963	1.971	1.980	1.988	1.997	2.006	2.014	2.023	2.032	2.041	2.050	26°
64°	2.050	2.059	2.069	2.078	2.087	2.097	2.106	2.116	2.125	2.135	2.145	25°
65°	2.145	2.154	2.164	2.174	2.184	2.194	2.204	2.215	2.225	2.236	2.246	24°
66°	2.246	2.257	2.267	2.278	2.289	2.300	2.311	2.322	2.333	2.344	2.356	23°
67°	2.356	2.367	2.379	2.391	2.402	2.414	2.426	2.438	2.450	2.463	2.475	22°
68°	2.475	2.488	2.500	2.513	2.526	2.539	2.552	2.565	2.578	2.592	2.605	21°
69°	2.605	2.619	2.633	2.646	2.660	2.675	2.689	2.703	2.718	2.733	2.747	20°
70°	2.747	2.762	2.778	2.793	2.808	2.824	2.840	2.856	2.872	2.888	2.904	19°
71°	2.904	2.921	2.937	2.954	2.971	2.989	3.006	3.024	3.042	3.060	3.078	18°
72°	3.078	3.096	3.115	3.133	3.152	3.172	3.191	3.211	3.230	3.251	3.271	17°
73°	3.271	3.291	3.312	3.333	3.354	3.376	3.398	3.420	3.442	3.465	3.487	16°
74°	3.487	3.511	3.534	3.558	3.582	3.606	3.630	3.655	3.681	3.706	3.732	15°
75°	3.732	3.758	3.785	3.812	3.839	3.867	3.895	3.923	3.952	3.981	4.011	14°
76°	4.011	4.041	4.071	4.102	4.134	4.165	4.198	4.230	4.264	4.297	4.331	13°
77°	4.331	4.366	4.402	4.437	4.474	4.511	4.548	4.586	4.625	4.665	4.705	12°
78°	4.705	4.745	4.787	4.829	4.872	4.915	4.959	5.005	5.050	5.097	5.145	11°
79°	5.145	5.193	5.242	5.292	5.343	5.396	5.449	5.503	5.558	5.614	5.671	10°
80°	5.671	5.730	5.789	5.850	5.912	5.976	6.041	6.107	6.174	6.243	6.314	9°
81°	6.314	6.386	6.460	6.535	6.612	6.691	6.772	6.855	6.940	7.026	7.115	8°
82°	7.115	7.207	7.300	7.396	7.495	7.596	7.700	7.806	7.916	8.028	8.144	7°
83°	8.144	8.264	8.386	8.513	8.643	8.777	8.915	9.058	9.205	9.357	9.514	6°
84°	9.514	9.677	9.845	10.02	10.20	10.39	10.58	10.78	10.99	11.20	11.43	5°
85°	11.43	11.66	11.91	12.16	12.43	12.71	13.00	13.30	13.62	13.95	14.30	4°
86°	14.30	14.67	15.06	15.46	15.89	16.35	16.83	17.34	17.89	18.46	19.08	3°
87°	19.08	19.74	20.45	21.20	22.02	22.90	23.86	24.90	26.03	27.27	28.64	2°
88°	28.64	30.14	31.82	33.69	35.80	38.19	40.92	44.07	47.74	52.08	57.29	1°
89°	57.29	63.66	71.62	81.85	95.49	114.6	143.2	191.0	286.5	573.0	∞	0°

	.9	.8	.7	.6	.5	.4	.3	.2	.1	.0	

Table A.6. *Logarithms to base 10.*

N	0	1	2	3	4	5	6	7	8	9
10	0000	0043	0086	0128	0170	0212	0253	0294	0334	0374
11	0414	0453	0492	0531	0569	0607	0645	0682	0719	0755
12	0792	0828	0864	0899	0934	0969	1004	1038	1072	1106
13	1139	1173	1206	1239	1271	1303	1335	1367	1399	1430
14	1461	1492	1523	1553	1584	1614	1644	1673	1703	1732
15	1761	1790	1818	1847	1875	1903	1931	1959	1987	2014
16	2041	2068	2095	2122	2148	2175	2201	2227	2253	2279
17	2304	2330	2355	2380	2405	2430	2455	2480	2504	2529
18	2553	2577	2601	2625	2648	2672	2695	2718	2742	2765
19	2788	2810	2833	2856	2878	2900	2923	2945	2967	2989
20	3010	3032	3054	3075	3096	3118	3139	3160	3181	3201
21	3222	3243	3263	3284	3304	3324	3345	3365	3385	3404
22	3424	3444	3464	3483	3502	3522	3541	3560	3579	3598
23	3617	3636	3655	3674	3692	3711	3729	3747	3766	3784
24	3802	3820	3838	3856	3874	3892	3909	3927	3945	3962
25	3979	3997	4014	4031	4048	4065	4082	4099	4116	4133
26	4150	4166	4183	4200	4216	4232	4249	4265	4281	4298
27	4314	4330	4346	4362	4378	4393	4409	4425	4440	4456
28	4472	4487	4502	4518	4533	4548	4564	4579	4594	4609
29	4624	4639	4654	4669	4683	4698	4713	4728	4742	4757
30	4771	4786	4800	4814	4829	4843	4857	4871	4886	4900
31	4914	4928	4942	4955	4969	4983	4997	5011	5024	5038
32	5051	5065	5079	5092	5105	5119	5132	5145	5159	5172
33	5185	5198	5211	5224	5237	5250	5263	5276	5289	5302
34	5315	5328	5340	5353	5366	5378	5391	5403	5416	5428
35	5441	5453	5465	5478	5490	5502	5514	5527	5539	5551
36	5563	5575	5587	5599	5611	5623	5635	5647	5658	5670
37	5682	5694	5705	5717	5729	5740	5752	5763	5775	5786
38	5798	5809	5821	5832	5843	5855	5866	5877	5888	5899
39	5911	5922	5933	5944	5955	5966	5977	5988	5999	6010
40	6021	6031	6042	6053	6064	6075	6085	6096	6107	6117
41	6128	6138	6149	6160	6170	6180	6191	6201	6212	6222
42	6232	6243	6253	6263	6274	6284	6294	6304	6314	6325
43	6335	6345	6355	6365	6375	6385	6395	6405	6415	6424
44	6435	6444	6454	6464	6474	6484	6493	6503	6513	6522
45	6532	6542	6551	6561	6571	6580	6590	6599	6609	6618
46	6628	6637	6646	6656	6665	6675	6684	6693	6702	6712
47	6721	6730	6739	6749	6758	6767	6776	6785	6794	6803
48	6812	6821	6830	6839	6848	6857	6866	6875	6884	6893
49	6902	6911	6920	6928	6937	6946	6955	6964	6972	6981
50	6990	6998	7007	7016	7024	7033	7042	7050	7059	7067
51	7076	7084	7093	7101	7110	7118	7126	7135	7143	7152
52	7160	7168	7177	7185	7193	7202	7210	7218	7226	7235
53	7243	7251	7259	7267	7275	7284	7292	7300	7308	7316
54	7324	7332	7340	7348	7356	7364	7372	7380	7388	7396
	0	**1**	**2**	**3**	**4**	**5**	**6**	**7**	**8**	**9**

Table A.6. *(Continued)*

N	0	1	2	3	4	5	6	7	8	9
55	7404	7412	7419	7427	7435	7443	7451	7459	7466	7474
56	7482	7490	7497	7505	7513	7520	7528	7536	7543	7551
57	7559	7566	7574	7582	7589	7597	7604	7612	7619	7627
58	7634	7642	7649	7657	7664	7672	7679	7686	7694	7701
59	7709	7716	7723	7731	7738	7745	7752	7760	7767	7774
60	7782	7789	7796	7803	7810	7818	7825	7832	7839	7846
61	7853	7860	7868	7875	7882	7889	7896	7903	7910	7917
62	7924	7931	7938	7945	7952	7959	7966	7973	7980	7987
63	7993	8000	8007	8014	8021	8028	8035	8041	8048	8055
64	8062	8069	8075	8082	8089	8096	8102	8109	8116	8122
65	8129	8136	8142	8149	8156	8162	8169	8176	8182	8189
66	8195	8202	8209	8215	8222	8228	8235	8241	8248	8254
67	8261	8267	8274	8280	8287	8293	8299	8306	8312	8319
68	8325	8331	8338	8344	8351	8357	8363	8370	8376	8382
69	8388	8395	8401	8407	8414	8420	8426	8432	8439	8445
70	8451	8457	8463	8470	8476	8482	8488	8494	8500	8506
71	8513	8519	8525	8531	8537	8543	8549	8555	8561	8567
72	8573	8579	8585	8591	8597	8603	8609	8615	8621	8627
73	8633	8639	8645	8651	8657	8663	8669	8675	8681	8686
74	8692	8698	8704	8710	8716	8722	8727	8733	8739	8745
75	8751	8756	8762	8768	8774	8779	8785	8791	8797	8802
76	8808	8814	8820	8825	8831	8837	8842	8848	8854	8859
77	8865	8871	8876	8882	8887	8893	8899	8904	8910	8915
78	8921	8927	8932	8938	8943	8949	8954	8960	8965	8971
79	8976	8982	8987	8993	8998	9004	9009	9015	9020	9025
80	9031	9036	9042	9047	9053	9058	9063	9069	9074	9079
81	9085	9090	9096	9101	9106	9112	9117	9122	9128	9133
82	9138	9143	9149	9154	9159	9165	9170	9175	9180	9186
83	9191	9196	9201	9206	9212	9217	9222	9227	9232	9238
84	9243	9248	9253	9258	9263	9269	9274	9279	9284	9289
85	9294	9299	9304	9309	9315	9320	9325	9330	9335	9340
86	9345	9350	9355	9360	9365	9370	9375	9380	9385	9390
87	9395	9400	9405	9410	9415	9420	9425	9430	9435	9440
88	9445	9450	9455	9460	9465	9469	9474	9479	9484	9489
89	9494	9499	9504	9509	9513	9518	9523	9528	9533	9538
90	9542	9547	9552	9557	9562	9566	9571	9576	9581	9586
91	9590	9595	9600	9605	9609	9614	9619	9624	9628	9633
92	9638	9643	9647	9652	9657	9661	9666	9671	9675	9680
93	9685	9689	9694	9699	9703	9708	9713	9717	9722	9727
94	9731	9736	9741	9745	9750	9754	9759	9763	9768	9773
95	9777	9782	9786	9791	9795	9800	9805	9809	9814	9818
96	9823	9827	9832	9836	9841	9845	9850	9854	9859	9863
97	9868	9872	9877	9881	9886	9890	9894	9899	9903	9908
98	9912	9917	9921	9926	9930	9934	9939	9943	9948	9952
99	9956	9961	9965	9969	9974	9978	9983	9987	9991	9996
	0	1	2	3	4	5	6	7	8	9

Answers to Odd-Numbered Problems

Chapter 1

1.3. 1.28×10^{-3} km.
1.5. 3.16×10^{7} sec.
1.7. 2.54×10^{7} mμ.
1.13. 20.36, 20.32, 0.309, 134; 1.56, 1.52, 0.0268, 0.0113; 3.6, 3.2, 0.73, 15.9.
1.15. 2037 ft^2.

Chapter 2

2.1. x component $= -9.40$ cm, y component $= 3.42$ cm.
2.3. 13.0 ft at 67.4° north of west.
2.5. 280 units at 329.2° with positive extension of x axis.
2.9. 99.6°.
2.11. 9.59° east of north.
2.13. 120 units at 297.3° with positive extension of x axis.
2.15. $i\underline{/-23.0°}$ 160 m.

Chapter 3

3.1. East component $= 22.0$ ft/sec; north component $= 38.1$ ft/sec.
3.3. 14.6 mi/hr at 42.8° north of east.
3.5. (*a*) 62.8 ft/sec, (*b*) 55.0 ft/sec, (*c*) 57.8 ft/sec.
3.7. 40.0 cm/sec.
3.11. 4.40 ft/sec westward.
3.15. (*a*) 50.0 ft/sec, (*b*) 375 ft.
3.19. (*a*) 6.82 ft/sec^2, (*b*) 4.30 sec.
3.21. 5.83 sec.
3.23. (*a*) 100 ft, (*b*) 5.00 sec, (*c*) 224 ft below top of building, (*d*) 179 ft/sec, (*e*) 8.09 sec.
3.29. (*a*) 17.1 m/sec, (*b*) 3.48 sec, (*c*) 17.1 m/sec.
3.31. 94.5 ft above point of projection.
3.33. (*a*) 1.41 sec, (*b*) 1.27×10^{3} ft.
3.35. 178 ft.
3.37. 5.19×10^{3} ft horizontally from target.

3.39. (*a*) 3.19 × 10³ m, (*b*) 51.0 sec.
3.43. 270 ft/sec.
3.45. 11.9 mi/hr at 36.4° north of east.

Chapter 4

4.1. 1.23 × 10⁴ dynes.
4.3. 8.87 × 10⁻² slug or 2.86 pm.
4.7. 3.66 m/sec westward.
4.13. 32.2 pf.
4.15. 1.64 × 10⁻²² m/sec².

Chapter 5

5.1. 9.10 × 10⁻² poundal, 1.26 × 10³ dynes, 1.26 × 10⁻² nt, 2.84 × 10⁻³ pf.
5.3. 1.94 ft/sec², 2.18 × 10² pf.
5.5. 2.00 tons force.
5.7. (*a*) 71.0 pf, (*b*) 57.0 pf, (*c*) 0.
5.9. 150 ft.
5.11. 4.26 ft/sec² downward.
5.13. (*a*) $\theta_1 > \theta_2$, (*b*) $m_1 \sin \theta_1 = m_2 \sin \theta_2$.
5.15. 0.970 ft/sec², 4.12 pf.
5.17. 27.5 pf.
5.21. (*a*) 64/7 ft/sec², (*b*) 80/7 pf and 72/7 pf.
5.23. (*a*) 21.4 ft/sec, (*b*) 4.80 ft/sec², (*c*) 720 pf.
5.25. $a_A = 8.00$ ft/sec², $a_B = 4.00$ ft/sec².
5.27. (*a*) $a_A = 0$, $a_B = 16.0$ ft/sec², $a_C = 8.00$ ft/sec²; (*b*) $a_A = 224/17$ ft/sec²,
$a_B = 160/17$ ft/sec², $a_C = 32/17$ ft/sec².

Chapter 6

6.1. 0.0917.
6.3. (*a*) 0.689 sec, (*b*) 0.465 m.
6.5. 0.275.
6.7. (*a*) 204 pf, (*b*) 438 pf at 66.2° with the direction of friction (23.8° with the
direction of the normal reaction), (*c*) 126 pf.
6.9. 27.0 pf.
6.11. 0.433.
6.13. 0.600 sec.
6.15. 5.00 pf.
6.17. 0.0161.

6.19. (*a*) 0.156 mi, (*b*) 37.4 mi/hr.

6.21. 1.57×10^{-2} poise.

Chapter 7

7.1. 4.00 kgf in the shorter cord, 3.00 kgf in the longer.

7.3. Tension $= 3.46 \times 10^3$ pf, weight $= 1.73 \times 10^3$ pf.

7.5. $T_{AB} = 54.2$ pf, $T_{BC} = 42.3$ pf, $T_{CD} = 50.0$ pf, $w = 20.4$ pf.

7.7. $F_{CD} = 507$ pf, $F_{BC} = 953$ pf.

7.9. 900 pf.

7.11. 0.267.

7.13. 600 pf.

7.15. 1.00, independent of weight of ball.

7.17. 800 pf collinear with, and opposite in direction to, the 200 pf.

7.19. Left support 62.2 pf, right support 178 pf.

7.21. 1.25 ft from the first fulcrum location.

7.23. 150 pf, 150 pf, 250 pf.

7.25. Tension and horizontal component of the reaction at A equal 3.59×10^3 pf.

7.27. (*a*) 2.92×10^3 pf, (*b*) horizontal force $= 206$ pf, vertical force $= 3.29 \times 10^3$ pf.

7.31. Reaction of wall $= 172$ pf, horizontal component $= 172$ pf, vertical component $= 200$ pf.

7.33. 105 pf.

7.35. Tension $= 33.9$ pf, normal reaction of wall $= 38.7$ pf, normal reaction of ground $= 117$ pf.

7.37. 250 pf in same direction as original force and 625 pf·ft clockwise couple.

7.39. With base line as x axis, apex above, and from left corner as origin: $\bar{x} = 9.00$ ft, $\bar{y} = 24.0$ ft.

7.47. The following answers are in units of 10^3 pf: $F_1 = 4.00$, $F_2 = 3.00$,
$F_{AB} = 4.00\sqrt{2}$ (C), $F_{AG} = 4.00$ (T), $F_{BG} = 1.00$ (C), $F_{BC} = 4.00$ (C),
$F_{GE} = 3.00$ (T), $F_{GC} = 1.00\sqrt{2}$ (T), $F_{CE} = 1.00$ (C), $F_{CD} = 3.00$ (C),
$F_{ED} = 3.00\sqrt{2}$ (T).

Chapter 8

8.1. 2.86×10^5 degrees, 157 rad/sec, 2.87×10^4 rev/min^2, 7.28×10^{-5} rad/sec, 1.99×10^{-7} rad/sec.

8.3. (*a*) 13.1 ft/sec, (*b*) 1.31 ft/sec^2.

8.7. (*a*) 6.62×10^{15} rev/sec, (*b*) 22.0×10^7 cm/sec.

8.9. (*a*) 54.9 rad/sec, (*b*) 628 rad, (*c*) 10.7 sec.

8.11. (*a*) 16.0 rad/sec^2, (*b*) 20.0 rad/sec.

8.13. 16.36 min after 12 and 49.08 min after 12.

8.15. (*a*) 0.203 sec, (*b*) 0.126 rad.

Chapter 9

9.1. (*a*) 355 nt, (*b*) 47.1 rad.
9.3. (*a*) 9.13 × 10²⁴ cm/sec², (*b*) 8.31 × 10⁻³ dyne.
9.5. 8.64 rev/min.
9.7. (*a*) 8.56 nt, (*b*) 8.56 nt.
9.9. (*a*) 16.0 ft/sec, (*b*) 22.6 ft/sec, (*c*) 19.6 ft/sec.
9.11. (*a*) 0.112 ft/sec², (*b*) 16.9 rev/day.
9.13. (*a*) 1.57 rad/sec, (*b*) 31.4 cm/sec, (*c*) 70.3 cm/sec².
9.15. (*a*) 1.92 rad, (*b*) 90.1 cm/sec² at 69.0° with the radial acceleration direction.
9.17. (*a*) Car will skid, since $\mu g < v^2/r$, (*b*) 65.6°.
9.19. (*a*) 76.8°, (*b*) 33.2 pf.
9.21. (*a*) 1.68°, (*b*) 9.80 nt.
9.23. (*a*) 68.4°, (*b*) 1.33 × 10⁵ nt, (*c*) 27.9 cm.
9.25. 194 ft.
9.27. (*a*) $\varphi = \sin^{-1}(1/4)$, (*b*) $r/2$.
9.29. 17.4 cm.

Chapter 10

10.1. 1.78 × 10⁻² kgm·m².
10.3. 7 ml^2/48.
10.7. $2mr^2/3$.
10.9. 7.40 × 10⁻² kgm·m².
10.11. 9.42 × 10⁻⁴ slug·ft².
10.13. $8mr^2$.
10.15. 10.4 pf·ft.
10.17. 62.8 pf·ft.
10.19. 3.92 × 10³ nt.
10.21. (*a*) 1.78 × 10² cm/sec², (*b*) 9.26 × 10⁵ dynes, 9.62 × 10⁵ dynes, (*c*) 45.0 rad/sec².
10.23. (*a*) 9.30 × 10³ dynes, (*b*) 7.44 gm·cm², (*c*) 1.86 × 10³ gm·cm²/sec.
10.27. (*a*) 4.78 rad/sec², (*b*) 140 pf, 247 pf.
10.29. 2.29 ft/sec².
10.31. (*a*) 3.60 ft/sec² in the direction of the 10 pf, (*b*) 6.40 pf opposite to the direction of the 10 pf.

Chapter 11

11.1. (*a*) 6.00 × 10³ ft·pf, (*b*) 5.88 × 10⁶ ergs, (*c*) 5.88 × 10⁴ joules.
11.3. (*a*) 270 ft·pf, (*b*) 6.00 ft/sec, (*c*) 45.0 ft·pf/sec.
11.5. (*a*) 4.70 × 10³ ft·pf, (*b*) 0.855 hp.
11.7. 117 pf.
11.9. 1.25 ft·pf.

11.11. (*a*) 2.57×10^6 ergs, (*b*) 1.43×10^6 ergs, (*c*) 220 cm.
11.13. (*a*) 999 ft·pf, (*b*) 0.605 hp.
11.15. 78.8 ft·pf.
11.17. 10.0 rad/sec.
11.19. 36.6 mi/hr.
11.21. 70.0 hp.
11.23. 60.0 tf.
11.25. 2.45×10^4 nt.
11.27. (*a*) (*1*) 3.32×10^{-14} joules, (*2*) 5.34×10^{-14} joules, (*3*) 37.8%; (*b*) (*1*) 625 joules, (*2*) 625 joules, (*3*) negligible.
11.29. (*a*) 1.90×10^3 joules, (*b*) 745 joules, (*c*) 15.2 m/sec, (*d*) 360 watts.
11.31. 0.200.
11.33. (*a*) 2.95 ft, (*b*) 8.87 ft·pf, (*c*) 5.39 ft/sec.
11.35. 100 hp.
11.37. (*a*) 20.0 in., (*b*) $11/\sqrt{3}$ ft/sec.
11.41. (*a*) 12.5 ft/sec, (*b*) 9.37 ft/sec.
11.43. $(27/10)(R - r) = 13.5$ ft.

Chapter 12

12.1. (*a*) 7.50×10^3 ft·pf, (*b*) 1.26×10^4 ft·pf, (*c*) 35.0, (*d*) 20.8, (*e*) 59.5%.
12.3. 312 pf.
12.5. 7.50 in.
12.11. (*a*) 7, (*b*) $2^n - 1$.
12.13. (*a*) 3, (*b*) 4.
12.19. (*a*) 1.14, (*b*) 65.9%.
12.21. (*a*) 2.92, (*b*) 1.75, (*c*) 54.7 hp.
12.23. (*a*) 452, (*b*) 181, (*c*) 1.81×10^4 pf.
12.25. 21.0%.
12.27. 5.61.

Chapter 13

13.1. (*a*) 11.0×10^3 slug·ft/sec, (*b*) 7.81 slug·ft/sec, (*c*) 15.8×10^{-23} kgm·m/sec.
13.3. 7.50 ft/sec.
13.5. (*a*) 2.93 slug·ft/sec, (*b*) 14.6 pf.
13.7. 625 pf.
13.9. 0.980 nt upward.
13.11. (*a*) 4.00 m/sec, (*b*) 996 joules.
13.13. (*a*) v_A = 5.00 ft/sec eastward and v_B = 20.0 ft/sec eastward, (*b*) 4.69 slug·ft/sec, (*c*) 35.2 ft·pf.
13.17. v_A = 100 m/sec in $-x$ direction, v_B = 25.0 m/sec in x direction.
13.21. v_A = 9.06 ft/sec to the left, v_B = 14.5 ft/sec to the right.
13.23. v_A = 1.09 m/sec northward, v_B = 18.6 m/sec at 49.4° north of west.

13.27. (a) 29.4 m/sec, (b) 10.3 joules, 95.3%.
13.29. 0.126 m.
13.31. (a) 4.95 ft/sec in x direction, (b) 3.83 ft.
13.37. (a) 29.1 ft/sec, (b) 36.1° with the wall's normal.
13.39. (a) $v_A = 0$ and $v_B = 400$ cm/sec, (b) 1.50 joules.
13.41. 23.4 pf.
13.43. (a) 272 pf, (b) 612 pf.
13.45. (a) 22.9 rad/sec, (b) 45.7 ft/sec, (c) 45.7 pf.
13.47. (a) 23.3 rad/sec counterclockwise, (b) 1.22×10^3 joules.
13.49. 40.0 cm.
13.51. 0.588 rad/sec clockwise.
13.53. 5.81 pf increase in load on outer wheel and 5.81 pf decrease in load on inner
        wheel.

Chapter 14

14.1.   (a) 2.44×10^7 nt/m², (b) 2.22×10^{-3}, (c) 2.22×10^{-2} m.
14.3.   (a) yes, (b) 0.13%.
14.5. $E_B/E_A = 8.00$.
14.7.   (a) 9.34 in, (b) 6.56 ft/sec.
14.11. (a) 1.30×10^{-3} pf/in², (b) 0.100, (c) 1.30×10^{-2} pf/in².
14.13. 0.55%.
14.15. 0.31 pf/in².
14.17. 28.4×10^{-6} atm⁻¹.
14.19. 1.14×10^{11} nt/m².
14.21. 2.00.
14.23. (a) 3.2×10^{10} cm·dyne/rad, (b) 3.2×10^8 cm·dyne.
14.29. (a) 1.53×10^{-2} in, (b) 7.73×10^{-6} in.

Chapter 15

15.1.   (a) 58.2 pf/ft, (b) −45.8 ft/sec², (c) ±2.30 ft/sec.
15.3.   (a) 0.397 sec/cycle, (b) 0.790 m/sec, (c) 446 nt.
15.5.   (a) ±15.8 cm/sec, ∓54.8 cm/sec², (b) ±10.8 cm/sec, ∓59.4 cm/sec².
15.9.   23.5 ft/sec.
15.11. (a) 20.0 cm, (b) 0.464 sec/cycle, (c) 271 cm/sec, (d) 262 cm/sec, (e) 1.83×10^3
        cm/sec², (f) 1.90×10^6 ergs, (g) 2.32×10^5 dynes, (h) 1.34×10^5 dynes
        compression, (i) 1.96×10^6 ergs.
15.13. (a) 5.72 pm, (b) 3.18 pf/ft.
15.15. 0.382 cycle/sec.
15.17. (a) 2.45 cycles/sec, (b) 66.8 cm/sec, (c) ±171 cm/sec², (d) fraction potential
        energy = 1/4, fraction kinetic energy = 3/4.
15.19. 977.9 cm/sec².
15.21. (a) 0.419 sec/cycle, (b) 1.07 joules.

15.23. 1.40 sec/cycle.
15.25. 4.81 sec/cycle.
15.29. (*a*) 63.7 pf·ft/rad, (*b*) 4.91 ft·pf, (*c*) 0.660 sec/cycle, (*d*) 7.88 rad/sec.
15.31. 34.0 m·nt/rad, 2.68 kgm·m².
15.33. (*a*) 0.898 sec/cycle, (*b*) 12.1 rad/sec².
15.35. (*a*) 1.56 sec/cycle, (*b*) at the 70.8 cm mark.
15.37. (*a*) 2.28 sec/cycle, (*b*) 2.29 sec/cycle.

Chapter 16

16.1. 1.31×10^{-8} nt.
16.3. 6.20×10^{23} kgm.
16.5. 7.24×10^{4} mi.
16.7. 2.01×10^{30} kgm.
16.11. (*a*) 160 mi., (*b*) 1.74×10^{4} mi/hr.
16.13. 7.84 m/sec².
16.15. (*b*) 6.96 mi/sec.
16.17. 1.47 mi/sec.
16.19. 2.08×10^{-5} dyne in the $-x$ direction.
16.21. -9.17×10^{-6} erg/gm.
16.23. (*a*) 1.87×10^{-6} dyne/gm in a direction normal to and toward the line joining the masses, (*b*) 1.87×10^{-5} erg.

Chapter 17

17.1. 11.3 gm/cm³.
17.3. 11.6 pf/in², 0.800 bar.
17.5. 407 in.
17.7. (*a*) 1.62 pf/in², (*b*) 7.35×10^{4} pf.
17.9. 27.2 ft.
17.11. (*a*) 1.14×10^{6} pf, (*b*) 1.03×10^{7} pf·ft.
17.13. 600 pf.
17.15. 41.1 cm.
17.17. 2.66×10^{5} dynes/cm².
17.19. 0.673 gm/cm³.
17.23. 0.850 gm/cm³.
17.25. (*a*) 4.50, (*b*) 0.875.
17.27. 1.4×10^{8} nt/m².
17.31. 8.62 in.
17.35. 1.24.
17.37. 8.57.
17.39. 0.110.
17.43. 1.67 ft.
17.45. (*a*) 31.9 pf, (*b*) 8.98 ft.
17.47. 5.00×10^{-2} gm.

ANSWERS *{502}*

17.49. Inside diameter = 5.14 cm, outside diameter = 5.29 cm.
17.51. 19.5 dynes away from the ether.
17.53. 1.16 cm.
17.55. 73.9 cm.
17.57. 1.16×10^4 dynes/cm².

Chapter 18

18.1. (*a*) 2.05 in/sec, (*b*) 5.69 in/sec.
18.3. 1.25 ft³/min.
18.5. 0.191 pf/ft².
18.9. 20.1 pf/in².
18.11. 0.77 ft³/min.
18.13. 45.0 ft.
18.17. (*a*) 21.7 ft³/min, (*b*) 14.1 ft.
18.19. 9.00 min.
18.21. 1.54 mm.
18.23. 1.42 poises.
18.25. 1.27.

Chapter 19

19.1. 621°F, 600°K, 1080°R.
19.3. 167°F, −25.6°F, 40.0°F.
19.5. −40.0°.
19.7. (*a*) −125°B, (*b*) $116\frac{2}{3}°$.
19.9. 1.03 mm.
19.11. 28.51 ft.
19.13. 0.176 in.
19.15. 8.25×10^{-5}.
19.19. $\alpha_1 = 22.21 \times 10^{-6}/C°$, $\alpha_2 = 11.50 \times 10^{-9}/(C°)^2$.
19.21. 9.83°C.
19.27. (*a*) $10.9 \times 10^{-6}/C°$, (*b*) 2.03×10^4 nt.
19.29. l_0 (copper) = $5.06 l_0$ (aluminum).
19.33. $7.33 \times 10^{-6}/C°$.
19.37. (*a*) $3.66 \times 10^{-3}/C°$, (*b*) 77.9°C.
19.41. 3.21×10^{-3} gm.
19.43. (*a*) 19.9 gm, (*b*) 3.66 liters.
19.45. $m_H = 3.35 \times 10^{-24}$ gm, $m_N = 4.65 \times 10^{-23}$ gm, $m_O = 5.32 \times 10^{-23}$ gm.

Chapter 20

20.1. 61.4 Btu.
20.3. 5.55×10^3 cal.

20.5. 3.32×10^5 cal.
20.7. $49.1°$C.
20.9. 0.255 Btu/pm·F°.
20.11. $23.5°$C.
20.13. 5.84 cal/gm.
20.15. $5.62°$C.
20.19. 4.20 joules/cal.
20.21. 4.02 m/sec.
20.27. (*a*) 95.7%, (*b*) $10.4°$C.

Chapter 21

21.1. 1.0×10^6 cal/hr.
21.3. 0.719 cal/sec·cm·C°.
21.7. 718 Btu/hr.
21.13. 38 gm.
21.15. 21.0 watts.
21.17. 3.95×10^{26} watts.
21.19. 1.25 watts.

Chapter 22

22.1. 18.4×10^2 m/sec for H_2, 4.62×10^2 m/sec for O_2, 9.23×10^2 m/sec for He,
            2.92×10^2 m/sec for A.
22.3. 399 joules.
22.11. (*a*) 169.2 joules, (*b*) 498.2 cal.
22.13. 711 cal.
22.15. (*a*) 354 cm Hg, (*b*) $193°$C.
22.21. 40.0%.
22.23. 47.3 C°.

Chapter 23

23.1. 1.04 m.
23.3. 1.72×10^4 ft/sec.
23.5. 16.2×10^6 pf/in².
23.7. 0.44 cm, 1.5×10^2 cm/sec², 2.8×10^4 cm/sec².
23.13. $y = A \sin\left[(\pi x/100) - 270°\right]$.
23.15. 4.28×10^{-3} watt/cm².

Chapter 24

24.1. 0.6%.

24.3. 710 vib/sec.

24.5. 10%.

24.7. (*a*) 342 m/sec, (*b*) 0.9 cm.

24.9. 448 vib/sec.

24.11. 3.38 cm.

24.13. 6.34 in.

24.17. 2.89×10^{-4} dyne/cm².

24.19. (*a*) 1.60×10^{-12} watt/cm², (*b*) -7.96 db.

24.21. (*a*) 216 vib/sec, (*b*) 184 vib/sec.

24.23. 660 vib/sec.

Index